Table of Integrals

W9-AKX-019

ELEMENTARY FORMS

1. $\displaystyle\int u\,dv = uv - \int v\,du$

2. $\displaystyle\int u^n\,du = \frac{1}{n+1}u^{n+1} + C \quad \text{if } n \neq -1$

3. $\displaystyle\int \frac{du}{u} = \ln|u| + C$

4. $\displaystyle\int e^u\,du = e^u + C$

5. $\displaystyle\int a^u\,du = \frac{a^u}{\ln a} + C$

6. $\displaystyle\int \sin u\,du = -\cos u + C$

7. $\displaystyle\int \cos u\,du = \sin u + C$

8. $\displaystyle\int \sec^2 u\,du = \tan u + C$

9. $\displaystyle\int \csc^2 u\,du = -\cot u + C$

10. $\displaystyle\int \sec u \tan u\,du = \sec u + C$

11. $\displaystyle\int \csc u \cot u\,du = -\csc u + C$

12. $\displaystyle\int \tan u\,du = \ln|\sec u| + C$

13. $\displaystyle\int \cot u\,du = \ln|\sin u| + C$

14. $\displaystyle\int \sec u\,du = \ln|\sec u + \tan u| + C$

15. $\displaystyle\int \csc u\,du = \ln|\csc u - \cot u| + C$

16. $\displaystyle\int \frac{du}{\sqrt{a^2 - u^2}} = \sin^{-1}\frac{u}{a} + C$

17. $\displaystyle\int \frac{du}{a^2 + u^2} = \frac{1}{a}\tan^{-1}\frac{u}{a} + C$

18. $\displaystyle\int \frac{du}{a^2 - u^2} = \frac{1}{2a}\ln\left|\frac{u+a}{u-a}\right| + C$

TRIGONOMETRIC FORMS

19. $\displaystyle\int \sin^2 u\,du = \frac{1}{2}u - \frac{1}{4}\sin 2u + C$

20. $\displaystyle\int \cos^2 u\,du = \frac{1}{2}u + \frac{1}{4}\sin 2u + C$

21. $\displaystyle\int \tan^2 u\,du = \tan u - u + C$

22. $\displaystyle\int \cot^2 u\,du = -\cot u - u + C$

23. $\displaystyle\int \sin^3 u\,du = -\frac{1}{3}(2 + \sin^2 u)\cos u + C$

24. $\displaystyle\int \cos^3 u\,du = \frac{1}{3}(2 + \cos^2 u)\sin u + C$

25. $\displaystyle\int \tan^3 u\,du = \frac{1}{2}\tan^2 u + \ln|\cos u| + C$

26. $\displaystyle\int \cot^3 u\,du = -\frac{1}{2}\cot^2 u - \ln|\sin u| + C$

27. $\displaystyle\int \sec^3 u\,du = \frac{1}{2}\sec u \tan u + \frac{1}{2}\ln|\sec u + \tan u| + C$

28. $\displaystyle\int \csc^3 u\,du = -\frac{1}{2}\csc u \cot u + \frac{1}{2}\ln|\csc u - \cot u| + C$

29. $\displaystyle\int \sin au \sin bu\,du = \frac{\sin(a-b)u}{2(a-b)} - \frac{\sin(a+b)u}{2(a+b)} + C \quad \text{if } a^2 \neq b^2$

(Continued on Rear Endpaper)

Custom Edition for
the University of Illinois
at Urbana–Champaign

Differential Equations & Boundary Value Problems
Computing and Modeling

C. Henry Edwards
David E. Penney

Taken from:

*Differential Equations and Boundary Value Problems
Computing and Modeling,* Fourth Edition
by C. Henry Edwards and David E. Penney

PEARSON
Custom
Publishing

PEARSON
Prentice
Hall

Taken from:

Differential Equations and Boundary Value Problems: Computing and Modeling, Fourth Edition
by C. Henry Edwards and David E. Penney
Copyright © 2008, 2004, 2000, 1996 by Pearson Education, Inc.
Published by Prentice Hall
Upper Saddle River, NJ 07458

Copyright © 2008 by Pearson Custom Publishing
All rights reserved.

Permission in writing must be obtained from the publisher before any part of this work may be reproduced or
transmitted in any form or by any means, electronic or mechanical, including photocopying and recording, or by
any information storage or retrieval system.

All trademarks, service marks, registered trademarks, and registered service marks are the property of their
respective owners and are used herein for identification purposes only.

Printed in the United States of America

10 9 8 7 6 5 4 3 2 1

ISBN 0-536-50169-6

2007361215

KM

Please visit our web site at *www.pearsoncustom.com*

PEARSON CUSTOM PUBLISHING
501 Boylston Street, Suite 900, Boston, MA 02116
A Pearson Education Company

CONTENTS

A P P L I C A T I O N   M O D U L E S

The modules listed here follow the indicated sections in the text. Most provide computing projects that illustrate the content of the corresponding text sections. *Maple*, *Mathematica*, and MATLAB versions of these investigations are included in the Applications Manual that accompanies this text.

PREFACE

The evolution of the present text in successive editions is based on experience teaching the introductory differential equations course with an emphasis on conceptual ideas and the use of applications and projects to involve students in active problem-solving experiences. Technical computing environments like *Maple*, *Mathematica*, and MATLAB are widely available and are now used extensively by practicing engineers and scientists. This change in professional practice motivates a shift from the traditional concentration on manual symbolic methods to coverage also of qualitative and computer-based methods that employ numerical computation and graphical visualization to develop greater conceptual understanding. A bonus of this more comprehensive approach is accessibility to a wider range of more realistic applications of differential equations.

Principal Features of This Revision

While the successful features of preceding editions have been retained, the exposition has been significantly enhanced in every chapter and in most individual sections of the text. Both new graphics and new text have been inserted where needed for improved student understanding of key concepts. However, the solid class-tested chapter and section structure of the book is unchanged, so class notes and syllabi will not require revision for use of this new edition. The following examples of this revision illustrate the way the local structure of the text has been augmented and polished for this edition.

Chapter 1: New Figures 1.3.9 and 1.3.10 showing direction fields that illustrate failure of existence and uniqueness of solutions (page 24); new Problems 34 and 35 showing that small changes in initial conditions can make big differences in results, but big changes in initial conditions may sometimes make only small differences in results (page 30); new Remarks 1 and 2 clarifying the concept of implicit solutions (page 35); new Remark clarifying the meaning of homogeneity for first-order equations (page 62).

Chapter 2: Additional details inserted in the derivation of the rocket propulsion equation (page 110), and new Problem 5 inserted to investigate the liftoff pause of a rocket on the launch pad sometimes observed before blastoff (page 112).

Chapter 3: New explanation of signs and directions of internal forces in mass-spring systems (page 148); new introduction of differential operators and clarification of the algebra of polynomial operators (page 175); new introduction and illustration of polar exponential forms of complex numbers (page 181); fuller explanation of method of undetermined coefficients in Examples 1 and 3 (page 199); new Remarks 1 and 2 introducing "shooting" terminology, and new Figures 3.8.1 and 3.8.2 illustrating why some endpoint value problems have infinitely many solutions, while others have no solutions at all (page 233); new Figures 3.8.4 and 3.8.5 illustrating different types of eigenfunctions (pages 235–236).

Chapter 4: New discussion with new Figures 4.3.11 and 4.3.12 clarifying the difference between rotating and non-rotating coordinate systems in moonearth orbit problems (page 278).

Chapter 5: New Problems 20–23 for student exploration of three-railway-car systems with different initial velocity conditions (page 329); new Remark illustrating the relation between matrix exponential methods and the generalized eigenvalue methods discussed previously (page 356); new exposition inserted at end of section to explain the connection between matrix variation of parameters here and (scalar) variation of parameters for second-order equations discussed previously in Chapter 3 (page 368).

Chapter 6: New remarks on phase plane portraits, autonomous systems, and critical points (page 373–374); new introduction of linearized systems (page 386); new 3-dimensional Figures 6.5.18 and 6.5.20 illustrating Lorenz and Rössler trajectories (page 439–440).

Chapter 7: New discussion clarifying functions of exponential order and existence of Laplace transforms (page 448); new Remark discussing the mechanics of partial-fraction decomposition (page 455); new much-expanded discussion of the proof of the Laplace-transform existence theorem and its extension to include the jump discontinuities that play an important role in many practical applications (page 461-462).

Chapter 8: New Problem 35 on determination of radii of convergence of power series solutions of differential equations (page 528); new Example 3 just before the subsection on logarithmic cases in the method of Frobenius, to illustrate first the reduction-of-order formula with a simple non-series problem (page 552).

Chapter 9: New considerably expanded explanation of even and odd extensions and their Fourier sine-cosine series (page 599–600); new discussion of periodic and non-periodic particular solutions illustrated by new Figure 9.4.4, together with new Problems 19 and 20 at end of section (pages 611, 615); new example and discussion inserted at end of section to illustrate the effects of damping in mass-spring systems (page 614); new discussion of signs and direction of heat flow in the derivation of the heat equation (page 616).

Chapter 10: Clarification of the effect of internal stretching in deriving the wave equation for longitudinal vibrations of a bar (page 669); new Figures 10.5.15 and 10.5.16 illustrating ocean waves on a small planet (page 720).

Computing Features

The following features highlight the flavor of computing technology that distinguishes much of our exposition.

- Almost 700 *computer-generated figures* show students vivid pictures of direction fields, solution curves, and phase plane portraits that bring symbolic solutions of differential equations to life.

- About 45 *application modules* follow key sections throughout the text. Most of these applications outline "technology neutral" investigations illustrating the use of technical computing systems and seek to actively engage students in the application of new technology.

- A fresh *numerical emphasis* that is afforded by the early introduction of numerical solution techniques in Chapter 2 (on mathematical models and numerical methods). Here and in Chapter 4, where numerical techniques for systems are treated, a concrete and tangible flavor is achieved by the inclusion of numerical algorithms presented in parallel fashion for systems ranging from graphing calculators to MATLAB.

Modeling Features

Mathematical modeling is a goal and constant motivation for the study of differential equations. To sample the range of applications in this text, take a look at the following questions:

- What explains the commonly observed time lag between indoor and outdoor daily temperature oscillations? (Section 1.5)

- What makes the difference between doomsday and extinction in alligator populations? (Section 2.1)

- How do a unicycle and a two-axle car react differently to road bumps? (Sections 3.7 and 5.3)

- How can you predict the time of next perihelion passage of a newly observed comet? (Section 4.3)

- Why might an earthquake demolish one building and leave standing the one next door? (Section 5.3)

- What determines whether two species will live harmoniously together, or whether competition will result in the extinction of one of them and the survival of the other? (Section 6.3)

- Why and when does non-linearity lead to chaos in biological and mechanical systems? (Section 6.5)

- If a mass on a spring is periodically struck with a hammer, how does the behavior of the mass depend on the frequency of the hammer blows? (Section 7.6)

- Why are flagpoles hollow instead of solid? (Section 8.6)

- What explains the difference in the sounds of a guitar, a xylophone, and drum? (Sections 9.6, 10.2, and 10.4)

Organization and Content

We have reshaped the usual approach and sequence of topics to accommodate new technology and new perspectives. For instance:

- After a precis of first-order equations in Chapter 1 (though with the coverage of certain traditional symbolic methods streamlined a bit), Chapter 2 offers an early introduction to mathematical modeling, stability and qualitative properties of differential equations, and numerical methods—a combination of topics that frequently are dispersed later in an introductory course.

- Chapters 4 and 5 provide a flexible treatment of linear systems. Motivated by current trends in science and engineering education and practice, Chapter 4 offers an early, intuitive introduction to first-order systems, models, and numerical approximation techniques. Chapter 5 begins with a self-contained treatment of the linear algebra that is needed, and then presents the eigenvalue approach to linear systems. It includes a wide range of applications (ranging from railway cars to earthquakes) of all the various cases of the eigenvalue method. Section 5.5 includes a fairly extensive treatment of matrix exponentials, which are exploited in Section 5.6 on nonhomogeneous linear systems.

- Chapter 6 on nonlinear systems and phenomena ranges from phase plane analysis to ecological and mechanical systems to a concluding section on chaos and bifurcation in dynamical systems. Section 6.5 presents an elementary introduction to such contemporary topics as period-doubling in biological and mechanical systems, the pitchfork diagram, and the Lorenz strange attractor (all illustrated with vivid computer graphics).

- Laplace transform methods (Chapter 7) and power series methods (Chapter 8) follow the material on linear and nonlinear systems, but can be covered at any earlier point (after Chapter 3) the instructor desires.

- Chapters 9 and 10 treat the applications of Fourier series, separation of variables, and Sturm-Liouville theory to partial differential equations and boundary value problems. After the introduction of Fourier series, the three classical equations—the wave and heat equations and Laplace's equation—are discussed in the last three sections of Chapter 9. The Sturm-Liouville methods of Chapter 10 are developed sufficiently to include some rather significant and realistic applications.

This book includes enough material appropriately arranged for different courses varying in length from one quarter to two semesters. The briefer version **Differential Equations: Computing and Modeling** (0-13-600438-5) ends with Chapter 7 on Laplace transform methods (and thus omits the material on power series methods, Fourier series, separation of variables and partial differential equations).

Applications and Solutions Manuals

The answer section has been expanded considerably to increase its value as a learning aid. It now includes the answers to most odd-numbered problems plus a good many even-numbered ones. The 605-page **Instructor's Solutions Manual** (0-13-156109-X) accompanying this book provides worked-out solutions for most of the problems in the book, and the 345-page **Student Solutions Manual** (0-13-156110-3) contains solutions for most of the odd-numbered problems.

The approximately 45 application modules in the text contain additional problem and project material designed largely to engage students in the exploration and application of computational technology. These investigations are expanded considerably in the 335-page **Applications Manual** (0-13-600679-5) that accompanies the text and supplements it with additional and sometimes more challenging investigations. Each section in this manual has parallel subsections **Using *Maple***, **Using *Mathematica***, and **Using MATLAB** that detail the applicable methods and techniques of each system, and will afford student users an opportunity to compare the merits and styles of different computational systems.

Acknowledgments

In preparing this revision we profited greatly from the advice and assistance of the following very capable and perceptive reviewers:

Raymond A. Claspadle, *University of Memphis*
Semion Gutman, *University of Oklahoma*
Miklos Bona, *University of Florida*
Irfan Ul-Haq, *University of Wisconsin-Platteville*
Carl Lutzer, *Rochester Institute of Technology*
Sigal Gottlieb, *University of Massachusetts, Dartmouth*

It is a pleasure to (once again) credit Dennis Kletzing and his extraordinary TEXpertise for the attractive presentation of both the text and the art in this book. Finally, but far from least, I am especially happy to acknowledge a new contributor to this effort, David Calvis, who assisted in every aspect of this revision and contributed tangibly to the improvement of every chapter in the book.

C. H. E.
h.edwards@mindspring.com

About The Cover

This image illustrates the trajectory of a moving point whose space coordinates satisfy (as functions of time) the *Lorenz system* of differential equations that is discussed on pages 438–439. In its motion along this *Lorenz trajectory* the point may appear to traverse a random number of loops on the left, then a random number of loops on the right, then a random number on the left, and so on. As it wanders back and forth, it typically approaches closer and closer to a mysterious set known as a *Lorenz strange attractor*. The Lorenz equations have a meteorological origin, so one might envision random numbers of rainy days and sunny days alternating in succession (though this is not what the loops actually signify).

The tiniest change in the starting point of the curve can change drastically the resulting back and forth sequence of loops. This illustrates the phenomenon of *chaos*, in which tiny differences in initial conditions can result in enormous differences in the resulting situations some time later. Two points that start at imperceptively different positions may later wind up far apart on different sides of the "Lorenz butterfly". The butterfly shape of the figure calls to mind the so-called "butterfly effect" that in recent years has crept into popular usage. A butterfly flaps its wings and stirs a tiny puff of air that sets in train a sequence of atmospheric events that ultimately results in a tornado somewhere on the opposite side of the earth.

To mark the back and forth progress of the moving point, we can regard its trajectory as a necklace string on which beads are placed to mark its successive positions at fixed increments of time (so the point is moving fastest where the spacing between beads is greatest). The color of the beads changes continuously with the passage of time and motion along the trajectory. This color gradation of the beads in the *Lorenz necklace* effectively displays visually a fourth time dimension in addition to the three space dimensions. If your eye follows the course of the moving point around the trajectory by "going with the flow" of the color and adjusting its speed with the spacing of the beads, then the whole figure can take on a dynamic aspect rather than the merely static aspect of a still picture.

First-Order Differential Equations

1.1 Differential Equations and Mathematical Models

The laws of the universe are written in the language of mathematics. Algebra is sufficient to solve many static problems, but the most interesting natural phenomena involve change and are described by equations that relate changing quantities.

Because the derivative $dx/dt = f'(t)$ of the function f is the rate at which the quantity $x = f(t)$ is changing with respect to the independent variable t, it is natural that equations involving derivatives are frequently used to describe the changing universe. An equation relating an unknown function and one or more of its derivatives is called a **differential equation**.

Example 1 The differential equation

$$\frac{dx}{dt} = x^2 + t^2$$

involves both the unknown function $x(t)$ and its first derivative $x'(t) = dx/dt$. The differential equation

$$\frac{d^2y}{dx^2} + 3\frac{dy}{dx} + 7y = 0$$

involves the unknown function y of the independent variable x and the first two derivatives y' and y'' of y. ∎

The study of differential equations has three principal goals:

1. To discover the differential equation that describes a specified physical situation.
2. To find—either exactly or approximately—the appropriate solution of that equation.
3. To interpret the solution that is found.

1

In algebra, we typically seek the unknown *numbers* that satisfy an equation such as $x^3 + 7x^2 - 11x + 41 = 0$. By contrast, in solving a differential equation, we are challenged to find the unknown *functions* $y = y(x)$ for which an identity such as $y'(x) = 2xy(x)$—that is, the differential equation

$$\frac{dy}{dx} = 2xy$$

—holds on some interval of real numbers. Ordinarily, we will want to find *all* solutions of the differential equation, if possible.

Example 2   If C is a constant and

$$y(x) = Ce^{x^2}, \tag{1}$$

then

$$\frac{dy}{dx} = C\left(2xe^{x^2}\right) = (2x)\left(Ce^{x^2}\right) = 2xy.$$

Thus every function $y(x)$ of the form in Eq. (1) *satisfies*—and thus is a solution of—the differential equation

$$\frac{dy}{dx} = 2xy \tag{2}$$

for all x. In particular, Eq. (1) defines an *infinite* family of different solutions of this differential equation, one for each choice of the arbitrary constant C. By the method of separation of variables (Section 1.4) it can be shown that every solution of the differential equation in (2) is of the form in Eq. (1). ∎

Differential Equations and Mathematical Models

The following three examples illustrate the process of translating scientific laws and principles into differential equations. In each of these examples the independent variable is time t, but we will see numerous examples in which some quantity other than time is the independent variable.

Example 3   Newton's law of cooling may be stated in this way: The *time rate of change* (the rate of change with respect to time t) of the temperature $T(t)$ of a body is proportional to the difference between T and the temperature A of the surrounding medium (Fig. 1.1.1). That is,

$$\frac{dT}{dt} = -k(T - A), \tag{3}$$

where k is a positive constant. Observe that if $T > A$, then $dT/dt < 0$, so the temperature is a decreasing function of t and the body is cooling. But if $T < A$, then $dT/dt > 0$, so that T is increasing.

Thus the physical law is translated into a differential equation. If we are given the values of k and A, we should be able to find an explicit formula for $T(t)$, and then—with the aid of this formula—we can predict the future temperature of the body. ∎

Temperature A

Temperature T

FIGURE 1.1.1. Newton's law of cooling, Eq. (3), describes the cooling of a hot rock in water.

Example 4   Torricelli's law implies that the *time rate of change* of the volume V of water in a draining tank (Fig. 1.1.2) is proportional to the square root of the depth y of water in the tank:

$$\frac{dV}{dt} = -k\sqrt{y}, \tag{4}$$

where k is a constant. If the tank is a cylinder with vertical sides and cross-sectional area A, then $V = Ay$, so $dV/dt = A \cdot (dy/dt)$. In this case Eq. (4) takes the form

$$\frac{dy}{dt} = -h\sqrt{y}, \tag{5}$$

where $h = k/A$ is a constant. ∎

Example 5 The *time rate of change* of a population $P(t)$ with constant birth and death rates is, in many simple cases, proportional to the size of the population. That is,

$$\frac{dP}{dt} = kP, \tag{6}$$

where k is the constant of proportionality. ∎

FIGURE 1.1.2. Torricelli's law of draining, Eq. (4), describes the draining of a water tank.

Volume V

Let us discuss Example 5 further. Note first that each function of the form

$$P(t) = Ce^{kt} \tag{7}$$

is a solution of the differential equation

$$\frac{dP}{dt} = kP$$

in (6). We verify this assertion as follows:

$$P'(t) = Cke^{kt} = k\left(Ce^{kt}\right) = kP(t)$$

for all real numbers t. Because substitution of each function of the form given in (7) into Eq. (6) produces an identity, all such functions are solutions of Eq. (6).

Thus, even if the value of the constant k is known, the differential equation $dP/dt = kP$ has *infinitely many* different solutions of the form $P(t) = Ce^{kt}$, one for each choice of the "arbitrary" constant C. This is typical of differential equations. It is also fortunate, because it may allow us to use additional information to select from among all these solutions a particular one that fits the situation under study.

Example 6 Suppose that $P(t) = Ce^{kt}$ is the population of a colony of bacteria at time t, that the population at time $t = 0$ (hours, h) was 1000, and that the population doubled after 1 h. This additional information about $P(t)$ yields the following equations:

$$1000 = P(0) = Ce^0 = C,$$
$$2000 = P(1) = Ce^k.$$

It follows that $C = 1000$ and that $e^k = 2$, so $k = \ln 2 \approx 0.693147$. With this value of k the differential equation in (6) is

$$\frac{dP}{dt} = (\ln 2)P \approx (0.693147)P.$$

Substitution of $k = \ln 2$ and $C = 1000$ in Eq. (7) yields the p⌐

$$P(t) = 1000e^{(\ln 2)t} = 1000(e^{\ln 2})^t = 1000 \cdot 2^t$$

that satisfies the given conditions. We can use th⌐ future populations of the bacteria colony. For i⌐ bacteria in the population after one and a half hou⌐

$$P(1.5) = 1000 \cdot 2^{3/2} \approx$$

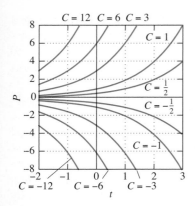

FIGURE 1.1.3. Graphs of $P(t) = Ce^{kt}$ with $k = \ln 2$.

The condition $P(0) = 1000$ in Example 6 is called an **initial condition** because we frequently write differential equations for which $t = 0$ is the "starting time." Figure 1.1.3 shows several different graphs of the form $P(t) = Ce^{kt}$ with $k = \ln 2$. The graphs of all the infinitely many solutions of $dP/dt = kP$ in fact fill the entire two-dimensional plane, and no two intersect. Moreover, the selection of any one point P_0 on the P-axis amounts to a determination of $P(0)$. Because exactly one solution passes through each such point, we see in this case that an initial condition $P(0) = P_0$ determines a unique solution agreeing with the given data.

Mathematical Models

Our brief discussion of population growth in Examples 5 and 6 illustrates the crucial process of *mathematical modeling* (Fig. 1.1.4), which involves the following:

1. The formulation of a real-world problem in mathematical terms; that is, the construction of a mathematical model.
2. The analysis or solution of the resulting mathematical problem.
3. The interpretation of the mathematical results in the context of the original real-world situation—for example, answering the question originally posed.

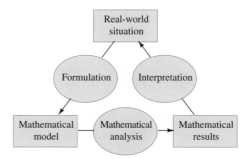

FIGURE 1.1.4. The process of mathematical modeling.

In the population example, the real-world problem is that of determining the population at some future time. A **mathematical model** consists of a list of variables (P and t) that describe the given situation, together with one or more equations relating these variables ($dP/dt = kP$, $P(0) = P_0$) that are known or are assumed to hold. The mathematical analysis consists of solving these equations (here, for P as a function of t). Finally, we apply these mathematical results to attempt to answer the original real-world question.

As an example of this process, think of first formulating the mathematical model consisting of the equations $dP/dt = kP$, $P(0) = 1000$, describing the bacteria population of Example 6. Then our mathematical analysis there consisted of solving for the solution function $P(t) = 1000e^{(\ln 2)t} = 1000 \cdot 2^t$ as our mathematical result. For an interpretation in terms of our real-world situation—the actual bacteria population—we substituted $t = 1.5$ to obtain the predicted population of $P(1.5) \approx 2828$ bacteria after 1.5 hours. If, for instance, the bacteria population is growing under ideal conditions of unlimited space and food supply, our prediction may be quite accurate, in which case we conclude that the mathematical model is quite adequate for studying this particular population.

On the other hand, it may turn out that no solution of the selected differential equation accurately fits the actual population we're studying. For instance, for *no* choice of the constants C and k does the solution $P(t) = Ce^{kt}$ in Eq. (7) accurately describe the actual growth of the human population of the world over the past few centuries. We must conclude that the differential equation $dP/dt = kP$ is inadequate for modeling the world population—which in recent decades has "leveled off" as compared with the steeply climbing graphs in the upper half ($P > 0$) of Fig. 1.1.3. With sufficient insight, we might formulate a new mathematical model including a perhaps more complicated differential equation, one that that takes into account such factors as a limited food supply and the effect of increased population on birth and death rates. With the formulation of this new mathematical model, we may attempt to traverse once again the diagram of Fig. 1.1.4 in a counterclockwise manner. If we can solve the new differential equation, we get new solution functions to compare with the real-world population. Indeed, a successful population analysis may require refining the mathematical model still further as it is repeatedly measured against real-world experience.

But in Example 6 we simply ignored any complicating factors that might affect our bacteria population. This made the mathematical analysis quite simple, perhaps unrealistically so. A satisfactory mathematical model is subject to two contradictory requirements: It must be sufficiently detailed to represent the real-world situation with relative accuracy, yet it must be sufficiently simple to make the mathematical analysis practical. If the model is so detailed that it fully represents the physical situation, then the mathematical analysis may be too difficult to carry out. If the model is too simple, the results may be so inaccurate as to be useless. Thus there is an inevitable tradeoff between what is physically realistic and what is mathematically possible. The construction of a model that adequately bridges this gap between realism and feasibility is therefore the most crucial and delicate step in the process. Ways must be found to simplify the model mathematically without sacrificing essential features of the real-world situation.

Mathematical models are discussed throughout this book. The remainder of this introductory section is devoted to simple examples and to standard terminology used in discussing differential equations and their solutions.

Examples and Terminology

Example 7 If C is a constant and $y(x) = 1/(C - x)$, then

$$\frac{dy}{dx} = \frac{1}{(C - x)^2} = y^2$$

if $x \neq C$. Thus

$$y(x) = \frac{1}{C - x} \tag{8}$$

defines a solution of the differential equation

$$\frac{dy}{dx} = y^2 \tag{9}$$

on any interval of real numbers not containing the point $x = C$. Actually, Eq. (8) defines a *one-parameter family* of solutions of $dy/dx = y^2$, one for each value of the arbitrary constant or "parameter" C. With $C = 1$ we get the particular solution

$$y(x) = \frac{1}{1 - x}$$

that satisfies the initial condition $y(0) = 1$. As indicated in Fig. 1.1.5, this is continuous on the interval $(-\infty, 1)$ but has a vertical asymptote at x

Example 8   Verify that the function $y(x) = 2x^{1/2} - x^{1/2} \ln x$ satisfies the differential equation

$$4x^2 y'' + y = 0 \qquad (10)$$

for all $x > 0$.

Solution   First we compute the derivatives

$$y'(x) = -\tfrac{1}{2}x^{-1/2} \ln x \quad \text{and} \quad y''(x) = \tfrac{1}{4}x^{-3/2} \ln x - \tfrac{1}{2}x^{-3/2}.$$

Then substitution into Eq. (10) yields

$$4x^2 y'' + y = 4x^2 \left(\tfrac{1}{4}x^{-3/2} \ln x - \tfrac{1}{2}x^{-3/2}\right) + 2x^{1/2} - x^{1/2} \ln x = 0$$

if x is positive, so the differential equation is satisfied for all $x > 0$.   ■

The fact that we can write a differential equation is not enough to guarantee that it has a solution. For example, it is clear that the differential equation

$$(y')^2 + y^2 = -1 \qquad (11)$$

has *no* (real-valued) solution, because the sum of nonnegative numbers cannot be negative. For a variation on this theme, note that the equation

$$(y')^2 + y^2 = 0 \qquad (12)$$

obviously has only the (real-valued) solution $y(x) \equiv 0$. In our previous examples any differential equation having at least one solution indeed had infinitely many.

The **order** of a differential equation is the order of the highest derivative that appears in it. The differential equation of Example 8 is of second order, those in Examples 2 through 7 are first-order equations, and

$$y^{(4)} + x^2 y^{(3)} + x^5 y = \sin x$$

is a fourth-order equation. The most general form of an ***n*th-order** differential equation with independent variable x and unknown function or dependent variable $y = y(x)$ is

$$F\left(x, y, y', y'', \ldots, y^{(n)}\right) = 0, \qquad (13)$$

where F is a specific real-valued function of $n + 2$ variables.

Our use of the word *solution* has been until now somewhat informal. To be precise, we say that the continuous function $u = u(x)$ is a **solution** of the differential equation in (13) **on the interval** I provided that the derivatives $u', u'', \ldots, u^{(n)}$ exist on I and

$$F\left(x, u, u', u'', \ldots, u^{(n)}\right) = 0$$

for all x in I. For the sake of brevity, we may say that $u = u(x)$ **satisfies** the differential equation in (13) on I.

Remark: Recall from elementary calculus that a differentiable function on an open interval is necessarily continuous there. This is why only a continuous function can qualify as a (differentiable) solution of a differential equation on an interval.   ■

Example 7

Continued

Figure 1.1.5 shows the two "connected" branches of the graph $y = 1/(1 - x)$. The left-hand branch is the graph of a (continuous) solution of the differential equation $y' = y^2$ that is defined on the interval $(-\infty, 1)$. The right-hand branch is the graph of a *different* solution of the differential equation that is defined (and continuous) on the different interval $(1, \infty)$. So the single formula $y(x) = 1/(1 - x)$ actually defines two different solutions (with different domains of definition) of the same differential equation $y' = y^2$. ∎

Example 9

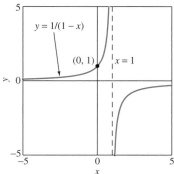

FIGURE 1.1.5. The solution of $y' = y^2$ defined by $y(x) = 1/(1 - x)$.

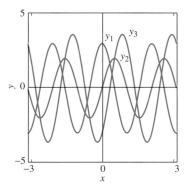

FIGURE 1.1.6. The three solutions $y_1(x) = 3 \cos 3x$, $y_2(x) = 2 \sin 3x$, and $y_3(x) = -3 \cos 3x + 2 \sin 3x$ of the differential equation $y'' + 9y = 0$.

If A and B are constants and

$$y(x) = A \cos 3x + B \sin 3x, \tag{14}$$

then two successive differentiations yield

$$y'(x) = -3A \sin 3x + 3B \cos 3x,$$
$$y''(x) = -9A \cos 3x - 9B \sin 3x = -9y(x)$$

for all x. Consequently, Eq. (14) defines what it is natural to call a *two-parameter family* of solutions of the second-order differential equation

$$y'' + 9y = 0 \tag{15}$$

on the whole real number line. Figure 1.1.6 shows the graphs of several such solutions. ∎

Although the differential equations in (11) and (12) are exceptions to the general rule, we will see that an *n*th-order differential equation ordinarily has an *n*-parameter family of solutions—one involving *n* different arbitrary constants or parameters.

In both Eqs. (11) and (12), the appearance of y' as an implicitly defined function causes complications. For this reason, we will ordinarily assume that any differential equation under study can be solved explicitly for the highest derivative that appears; that is, that the equation can be written in the so-called *normal form*

$$y^{(n)} = G\left(x, y, y', y'', \ldots, y^{(n-1)}\right), \tag{16}$$

where G is a real-valued function of $n + 1$ variables. In addition, we will always seek only real-valued solutions unless we warn the reader otherwise.

All the differential equations we have mentioned so far are **ordinary** differential equations, meaning that the unknown function (dependent variable) depends on only a *single* independent variable. If the dependent variable is a function of two or more independent variables, then partial derivatives are likely to be involved; if they are, the equation is called a **partial** differential equation. For example, the temperature $u = u(x, t)$ of a long thin uniform rod at the point x at time t satisfies (under appropriate simple conditions) the partial differential equation

$$\frac{\partial u}{\partial t} = k \frac{\partial^2 u}{\partial x^2},$$

where k is a constant (called the *thermal diffusivity* of the rod). In Chapters 1 through 8 we will be concerned only with *ordinary* differential equations and will refer to them simply as differential equations.

In this chapter we concentrate on *first-order* differential equations of the form

$$\frac{dy}{dx} = f(x, y). \tag{17}$$

We also will sample the wide range of applications of such equations. A typical mathematical model of an applied situation will be an **initial value problem,** consisting of a differential equation of the form in (17) together with an **initial condition** $y(x_0) = y_0$. Note that we call $y(x_0) = y_0$ an initial condition whether or not $x_0 = 0$. To **solve** the initial value problem

$$\frac{dy}{dx} = f(x, y), \quad y(x_0) = y_0 \tag{18}$$

means to find a differentiable function $y = y(x)$ that satisfies both conditions in Eq. (18) on some interval containing x_0.

Example 10   Given the solution $y(x) = 1/(C - x)$ of the differential equation $dy/dx = y^2$ discussed in Example 7, solve the initial value problem

$$\frac{dy}{dx} = y^2, \quad y(1) = 2.$$

Solution   We need only find a value of C so that the solution $y(x) = 1/(C - x)$ satisfies the initial condition $y(1) = 2$. Substitution of the values $x = 1$ and $y = 2$ in the given solution yields

$$2 = y(1) = \frac{1}{C - 1},$$

so $2C - 2 = 1$, and hence $C = \frac{3}{2}$. With this value of C we obtain the desired solution

$$y(x) = \frac{1}{\frac{3}{2} - x} = \frac{2}{3 - 2x}.$$

Figure 1.1.7 shows the two branches of the graph $y = 2/(3 - 2x)$. The left-hand branch is the graph on $(-\infty, \frac{3}{2})$ of the solution of the given initial value problem $y' = y^2$, $y(1) = 2$. The right-hand branch passes through the point $(2, -2)$ and is therefore the graph on $(\frac{3}{2}, \infty)$ of the solution of the different initial value problem $y' = y^2$, $y(2) = -2$. ∎

The central question of greatest immediate interest to us is this: If we are given a differential equation known to have a solution satisfying a given initial condition, how do we actually *find* or *compute* that solution? And, once found, what can we do with it? We will see that a relatively few simple techniques—separation of variables (Section 1.4), solution of linear equations (Section 1.5), elementary substitution methods (Section 1.6)—are enough to enable us to solve a variety of first-order equations having impressive applications.

FIGURE 1.1.7.   The solutions of $y' = y^2$ defined by $y(x) = 2/(3 - 2x)$.

1.1 Problems

In Problems 1 through 12, verify by substitution that each given function is a solution of the given differential equation. Throughout these problems, primes denote derivatives with respect to x.

1. $y' = 3x^2$; $y = x^3 + 7$

2. $y' + 2y = 0$; $y = 3e^{-2x}$

3. $y'' + 4y = 0$; $y_1 = \cos 2x$, $y_2 = \sin 2x$

4. $y'' = 9y$; $y_1 = e^{3x}$, $y_2 = e^{-3x}$

5. $y' = y + 2e^{-x}$; $y = e^x - e^{-x}$

6. $y'' + 4y' + 4y = 0$; $y_1 = e^{-2x}$, $y_2 = xe^{-2x}$

7. $y'' - 2y' + 2y = 0$; $y_1 = e^x \cos x$, $y_2 = e^x \sin x$

8. $y'' + y = 3\cos 2x$, $y_1 = \cos x - \cos 2x$, $y_2 = \sin x - \cos 2x$

9. $y' + 2xy^2 = 0$; $y = \dfrac{1}{1 + x^2}$

10. $x^2 y'' + xy' - y = \ln x$; $y_1 = x - \ln x$, $y_2 = \dfrac{1}{x} - \ln x$

11. $x^2 y'' + 5x y' + 4y = 0$; $y_1 = \dfrac{1}{x^2}$, $y_2 = \dfrac{\ln x}{x^2}$

12. $x^2 y'' - x y' + 2y = 0$; $y_1 = x \cos(\ln x)$, $y_2 = x \sin(\ln x)$

In Problems 13 through 16, substitute $y = e^{rx}$ into the given differential equation to determine all values of the constant r for which $y = e^{rx}$ is a solution of the equation.

13. $3y' = 2y$

14. $4y'' = y$

15. $y'' + y' - 2y = 0$

16. $3y'' + 3y' - 4y = 0$

In Problems 17 through 26, first verify that $y(x)$ satisfies the given differential equation. Then determine a value of the constant C so that $y(x)$ satisfies the given initial condition. Use a computer or graphing calculator (if desired) to sketch several typical solutions of the given differential equation, and highlight the one that satisfies the given initial condition.

17. $y' + y = 0$; $y(x) = Ce^{-x}$, $y(0) = 2$

18. $y' = 2y$; $y(x) = Ce^{2x}$, $y(0) = 3$

19. $y' = y + 1$; $y(x) = Ce^{x} - 1$, $y(0) = 5$

20. $y' = x - y$; $y(x) = Ce^{-x} + x - 1$, $y(0) = 10$

21. $y' + 3x^2 y = 0$; $y(x) = Ce^{-x^3}$, $y(0) = 7$

22. $e^y y' = 1$; $y(x) = \ln(x + C)$, $y(0) = 0$

23. $x\dfrac{dy}{dx} + 3y = 2x^5$; $y(x) = \frac{1}{4}x^5 + Cx^{-3}$, $y(2) = 1$

24. $x y' - 3y = x^3$; $y(x) = x^3(C + \ln x)$, $y(1) = 17$

25. $y' = 3x^2(y^2 + 1)$; $y(x) = \tan(x^3 + C)$, $y(0) = 1$

26. $y' + y \tan x = \cos x$; $y(x) = (x + C)\cos x$, $y(\pi) = 0$

In Problems 27 through 31, a function $y = g(x)$ is described by some geometric property of its graph. Write a differential equation of the form $dy/dx = f(x, y)$ having the function g as its solution (or as one of its solutions).

27. The slope of the graph of g at the point (x, y) is the sum of x and y.

28. The line tangent to the graph of g at the point (x, y) intersects the x-axis at the point $(x/2, 0)$.

29. Every straight line normal to the graph of g passes through the point $(0, 1)$. Can you *guess* what the graph of such a function g might look like?

30. The graph of g is normal to every curve of the form $y = x^2 + k$ (k is a constant) where they meet.

31. The line tangent to the graph of g at (x, y) passes through the point $(-y, x)$.

In Problems 32 through 36, write—in the manner of Eqs. (3) through (6) of this section—a differential equation that is a mathematical model of the situation described.

32. The time rate of change of a population P is proportional to the square root of P.

33. The time rate of change of the velocity v of a coasting motorboat is proportional to the square of v.

34. The acceleration dv/dt of a Lamborghini is proportional to the difference between 250 km/h and the velocity of the car.

35. In a city having a fixed population of P persons, the time rate of change of the number N of those persons who have heard a certain rumor is proportional to the number of those who have not yet heard the rumor.

36. In a city with a fixed population of P persons, the time rate of change of the number N of those persons infected with a certain contagious disease is proportional to the product of the number who have the disease and the number who do not.

In Problems 37 through 42, determine by inspection at least one solution of the given differential equation. That is, use your knowledge of derivatives to make an intelligent guess. Then test your hypothesis.

37. $y'' = 0$

38. $y' = y$

39. $x y' + y = 3x^2$

40. $(y')^2 + y^2 = 1$

41. $y' + y = e^x$

42. $y'' + y = 0$

43. (a) If k is a constant, show that a general (one-parameter) solution of the differential equation

$$\frac{dx}{dt} = kx^2$$

is given by $x(t) = 1/(C - kt)$, where C is an arbitrary constant.

(b) Determine by inspection a solution of the initial value problem $x' = kx^2$, $x(0) = 0$.

44. (a) Continuing Problem 43, assume that k is positive, and then sketch graphs of solutions of $x' = kx^2$ with several typical positive values of $x(0)$.

(b) How would these solutions differ if the constant k were negative?

45. Suppose a population P of rodents satisfies the differential equation $dP/dt = kP^2$. Initially, there are $P(0) = 2$ rodents, and their number is increasing at the rate of $dP/dt = 1$ rodent per month when there are $P = 10$ rodents. How long will it take for this population to grow to a hundred rodents? To a thousand? What's happening here?

46. Suppose the velocity v of a motorboat coasting in water satisfies the differential equation $dv/dt = kv^2$. The initial speed of the motorboat is $v(0) = 10$ meters per second (m/s), and v is decreasing at the rate of 1 m/s² when $v = 5$ m/s. How long does it take for the velocity of the boat to decrease to 1 m/s? To $\frac{1}{10}$ m/s? When does the boat come to a stop?

47. In Example 7 we saw that $y(x) = 1/(C - x)$ defines a one-parameter family of solutions of the differential equation $dy/dx = y^2$. **(a)** Determine a value of C so that $y(10) = 10$. **(b)** Is there a value of C such that $y(0) = 0$? Can you nevertheless find by inspection a solution of $dy/dx = y^2$ such that $y(0) = 0$? **(c)** Figure 1.1.8 shows typical graphs of solutions of the form $y(x) = 1/(C - x)$. Does it appear that these solution curves fill the entire xy-plane? Can you conclude that, given any point (a, b) in the plane, the differential equation $dy/dx = y^2$ has exactly one solution $y(x)$ satisfying the condition $y(a) = b$?

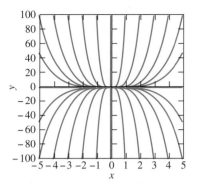

FIGURE 1.1.8. Graphs of solutions of the equation $dy/dx = y^2$.

FIGURE 1.1.9. The graph $y = Cx^4$ for various values of C.

48. (a) Show that $y(x) = Cx^4$ defines a one-parameter family of differentiable solutions of the differential equation $xy' = 4y$ (Fig. 1.1.9). **(b)** Show that

$$y(x) = \begin{cases} -x^4 & \text{if } x < 0, \\ x^4 & \text{if } x \geq 0 \end{cases}$$

defines a differentiable solution of $xy' = 4y$ for all x, but is not of the form $y(x) = Cx^4$. **(c)** Given any two real numbers a and b, explain why—in contrast to the situation in part (c) of Problem 47—there exist infinitely many differentiable solutions of $xy' = 4y$ that all satisfy the condition $y(a) = b$.

1.2 Integrals as General and Particular Solutions

The first-order equation $dy/dx = f(x, y)$ takes an especially simple form if the right-hand-side function f does not actually involve the dependent variable y, so

$$\frac{dy}{dx} = f(x). \tag{1}$$

In this special case we need only integrate both sides of Eq. (1) to obtain

$$y(x) = \int f(x)\, dx + C. \tag{2}$$

This is a **general solution** of Eq. (1), meaning that it involves an arbitrary constant C, and for every choice of C it is a solution of the differential equation in (1). If $G(x)$ is a particular antiderivative of f—that is, if $G'(x) \equiv f(x)$—then

$$y(x) = G(x) + C. \tag{3}$$

The graphs of any two such solutions $y_1(x) = G(x) + C_1$ and $y_2(x) = G(x) + C_2$ on the same interval I are "parallel" in the sense illustrated by Figs. 1.2.1 and 1.2.2. There we see that the constant C is geometrically the vertical distance between the two curves $y(x) = G(x)$ and $y(x) = G(x) + C$.

To satisfy an initial condition $y(x_0) = y_0$, we need only substitute $x = x_0$ and $y = y_0$ into Eq. (3) to obtain $y_0 = G(x_0) + C$, so that $C = y_0 - G(x_0)$. With this choice of C, we obtain the **particular solution** of Eq. (1) satisfying the initial value problem

$$\frac{dy}{dx} = f(x), \quad y(x_0) = y_0.$$

FIGURE 1.2.1. Graphs of $y = \frac{1}{4}x^2 + C$ for various values of C.

FIGURE 1.2.2. Graphs of $y = \sin x + C$ for various values of C.

We will see that this is the typical pattern for solutions of first-order differential equations. Ordinarily, we will first find a *general solution* involving an arbitrary constant C. We can then attempt to obtain, by appropriate choice of C, a *particular solution* satisfying a given initial condition $y(x_0) = y_0$.

Remark: As the term is used in the previous paragraph, a *general solution* of a first-order differential equation is simply a one-parameter family of solutions. A natural question is whether a given general solution contains *every* particular solution of the differential equation. When this is known to be true, we call it **the** general solution of the differential equation. For example, because any two antiderivatives of the same function $f(x)$ can differ only by a constant, it follows that every solution of Eq. (1) is of the form in (2). Thus Eq. (2) serves to define **the** general solution of (1). ∎

Example 1   Solve the initial value problem

$$\frac{dy}{dx} = 2x + 3, \quad y(1) = 2.$$

Solution   Integration of both sides of the differential equation as in Eq. (2) immediately yields the general solution

$$y(x) = \int (2x + 3)\, dx = x^2 + 3x + C.$$

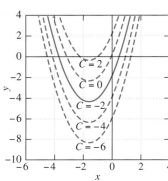

FIGURE 1.2.3. Solution curves for the differential equation in Example 1.

Figure 1.2.3 shows the graph $y = x^2 + 3x + C$ for various values of C. The particular solution we seek corresponds to the curve that passes through the point $(1, 2)$, thereby satisfying the initial condition

$$y(1) = (1)^2 + 3 \cdot (1) + C = 2.$$

It follows that $C = -2$, so the desired particular solution is

$$y(x) = x^2 + 3x - 2. \qquad ∎$$

Second-order equations. The observation that the special first-order equation $dy/dx = f(x)$ is readily solvable (provided that an antiderivative of f can be found) extends to second-order differential equations of the special form

$$\frac{d^2 y}{dx^2} = g(x), \tag{4}$$

in which the function g on the right-hand side involves neither the dependent variable y nor its derivative dy/dx. We simply integrate once to obtain

$$\frac{dy}{dx} = \int y''(x)\, dx = \int g(x)\, dx = G(x) + C_1,$$

where G is an antiderivative of g and C_1 is an arbitrary constant. Then another integration yields

$$y(x) = \int y'(x)\, dx = \int [G(x) + C_1]\, dx = \int G(x)\, dx + C_1 x + C_2,$$

where C_2 is a second arbitrary constant. In effect, the second-order differential equation in (4) is one that can be solved by solving successively the *first-order* equations

$$\frac{dv}{dx} = g(x) \quad \text{and} \quad \frac{dy}{dx} = v(x).$$

Velocity and Acceleration

Direct integration is sufficient to allow us to solve a number of important problems concerning the motion of a particle (or *mass point*) in terms of the forces acting on it. The motion of a particle along a straight line (the x-axis) is described by its **position function**

$$x = f(t) \tag{5}$$

giving its x-coordinate at time t. The **velocity** of the particle is defined to be

$$v(t) = f'(t); \quad \text{that is,} \quad v = \frac{dx}{dt}. \tag{6}$$

Its **acceleration** $a(t)$ is $a(t) = v'(t) = x''(t)$; in Leibniz notation,

$$a = \frac{dv}{dt} = \frac{d^2 x}{dt^2}. \tag{7}$$

Equation (6) is sometimes applied either in the indefinite integral form $x(t) = \int v(t)\, dt$ or in the definite integral form

$$x(t) = x(t_0) + \int_{t_0}^{t} v(s)\, ds,$$

which you should recognize as a statement of the fundamental theorem of calculus (precisely because $dx/dt = v$).

Newton's *second law of motion* says that if a force $F(t)$ acts on the particle and is directed along its line of motion, then

$$ma(t) = F(t); \quad \text{that is,} \quad F = ma, \tag{8}$$

where m is the mass of the particle. If the force F is known, then the equation $x''(t) = F(t)/m$ can be integrated twice to find the position function $x(t)$ in terms of two constants of integration. These two arbitrary constants are frequently determined by the **initial position** $x_0 = x(0)$ and the **initial velocity** $v_0 = v(0)$ of the particle.

Constant acceleration. For instance, suppose that the force F, and therefore the acceleration $a = F/m$, are *constant*. Then we begin with the equation

$$\frac{dv}{dt} = a \quad (a \text{ is a constant}) \tag{9}$$

and integrate both sides to obtain

$$v(t) = \int a\, dt = at + C_1.$$

We know that $v = v_0$ when $t = 0$, and substitution of this information into the preceding equation yields the fact that $C_1 = v_0$. So

$$v(t) = \frac{dx}{dt} = at + v_0. \tag{10}$$

A second integration gives

$$x(t) = \int v(t)\, dt = \int (at + v_0)\, dt = \tfrac{1}{2}at^2 + v_0 t + C_2,$$

and the substitution $t = 0$, $x = x_0$ gives $C_2 = x_0$. Therefore,

$$x(t) = \tfrac{1}{2}at^2 + v_0 t + x_0. \tag{11}$$

Thus, with Eq. (10) we can find the velocity, and with Eq. (11) the position, of the particle at any time t in terms of its *constant* acceleration a, its initial velocity v_0, and its initial position x_0.

Example 2   A lunar lander is falling freely toward the surface of the moon at a speed of 450 meters per second (m/s). Its retrorockets, when fired, provide a constant deceleration of 2.5 meters per second per second (m/s^2) (the gravitational acceleration produced by the moon is assumed to be included in the given deceleration). At what height above the lunar surface should the retrorockets be activated to ensure a "soft touchdown" ($v = 0$ at impact)?

Solution   We denote by $x(t)$ the height of the lunar lander above the surface, as indicated in Fig. 1.2.4. We let $t = 0$ denote the time at which the retrorockets should be fired. Then $v_0 = -450$ (m/s, negative because the height $x(t)$ is decreasing), and $a = +2.5$, because an upward thrust increases the velocity v (although it decreases the *speed* $|v|$). Then Eqs. (10) and (11) become

$$v(t) = 2.5t - 450 \tag{12}$$

and

$$x(t) = 1.25t^2 - 450t + x_0, \tag{13}$$

FIGURE 1.2.4. The lunar lander of Example 2.

where x_0 is the height of the lander above the lunar surface at the time $t = 0$ when the retrorockets should be activated.

From Eq. (12) we see that $v = 0$ (soft touchdown) occurs when $t = 450/2.5 = 180$ s (that is, 3 minutes); then substitution of $t = 180$, $x = 0$ into Eq. (13) yields

$$x_0 = 0 - (1.25)(180)^2 + 450(180) = 40{,}500$$

meters—that is, $x_0 = 40.5$ km $\approx 25\frac{1}{6}$ miles. Thus the retrorockets should be activated when the lunar lander is 40.5 kilometers above the surface of the moon, and it will touch down softly on the lunar surface after 3 minutes of decelerating descent. ■

Physical Units

Numerical work requires units for the measurement of physical quantities such as distance and time. We sometimes use ad hoc units—such as distance in miles or kilometers and time in hours—in special situations (such as in a problem involving an auto trip). However, the foot-pound-second (fps) and meter-kilogram-second (mks) unit systems are used more generally in scientific and engineering problems. In fact, fps units are commonly used only in the United States (and a few other countries), while mks units constitute the standard international system of scientific units.

	fps units	mks units
Force	pound (lb)	newton (N)
Mass	slug	kilogram (kg)
Distance	foot (ft)	meter (m)
Time	second (s)	second (s)
g	32 ft/s^2	9.8 m/s^2

The last line of this table gives values for the gravitational acceleration g at the surface of the earth. Although these approximate values will suffice for most examples and problems, more precise values are 9.7805 m/s^2 and 32.088 ft/s^2 (at sea level at the equator).

Both systems are compatible with Newton's second law $F = ma$. Thus 1 N is (by definition) the force required to impart an acceleration of 1 m/s^2 to a mass of 1 kg. Similarly, 1 slug is (by definition) the mass that experiences an acceleration of 1 ft/s^2 under a force of 1 lb. (We will use mks units in all problems requiring mass units and thus will rarely need slugs to measure mass.)

Inches and centimeters (as well as miles and kilometers) also are commonly used in describing distances. For conversions between fps and mks units it helps to remember that

$$1 \text{ in.} = 2.54 \text{ cm (exactly)} \quad \text{and} \quad 1 \text{ lb} \approx 4.448 \text{ N.}$$

For instance,

$$1 \text{ ft} = 12 \text{ in.} \times 2.54 \frac{\text{cm}}{\text{in.}} = 30.48 \text{ cm,}$$

and it follows that

$$1 \text{ mi} = 5280 \text{ ft} \times 30.48 \frac{\text{cm}}{\text{ft}} = 160934.4 \text{ cm} \approx 1.609 \text{ km.}$$

Thus a posted U.S. speed limit of 50 mi/h means that—in international terms—the legal speed limit is about $50 \times 1.609 \approx 80.45$ km/h.

Vertical Motion with Gravitational Acceleration

The **weight** W of a body is the force exerted on the body by gravity. Substitution of $a = g$ and $F = W$ in Newton's second law $F = ma$ gives

$$W = mg \tag{14}$$

for the weight W of the mass m at the surface of the earth (where $g \approx 32$ ft/s$^2 \approx 9.8$ m/s^2). For instance, a mass of $m = 20$ kg has a weight of $W = (20 \text{ kg})(9.8 \text{ m/s}^2) = 196$ N. Similarly, a mass m weighing 100 pounds has mks weight

$$W = (100 \text{ lb})(4.448 \text{ N/lb}) = 444.8 \text{ N,}$$

so its mass is

$$m = \frac{W}{g} = \frac{444.8 \text{ N}}{9.8 \text{ m/s}^2} \approx 45.4 \text{ kg.}$$

To discuss vertical motion it is natural to choose the y-axis as the coordinate system for position, frequently with $y = 0$ corresponding to "ground level." If we choose the *upward* direction as the positive direction, then the effect of gravity on a vertically moving body is to decrease its height and also to decrease its velocity $v = dy/dt$. Consequently, if we ignore air resistance, then the acceleration $a = dv/dt$ of the body is given by

$$\frac{dv}{dt} = -g. \tag{15}$$

This acceleration equation provides a starting point in many problems involving vertical motion. Successive integrations (as in Eqs. (10) and (11)) yield the velocity and height formulas

$$v(t) = -gt + v_0 \tag{16}$$

and

$$y(t) = -\tfrac{1}{2}gt^2 + v_0 t + y_0. \tag{17}$$

Here, y_0 denotes the initial ($t = 0$) height of the body and v_0 its initial velocity.

Example 3

(a) Suppose that a ball is thrown straight upward from the ground ($y_0 = 0$) with initial velocity $v_0 = 96$ (ft/s, so we use $g = 32$ ft/s^2 in fps units). Then it reaches its maximum height when its velocity (Eq. (16)) is zero,

$$v(t) = -32t + 96 = 0,$$

and thus when $t = 3$ s. Hence the maximum height that the ball attains is

$$y(3) = -\tfrac{1}{2} \cdot 32 \cdot 3^2 + 96 \cdot 3 + 0 = 144 \text{ (ft)}$$

(with the aid of Eq. (17)).

(b) If an arrow is shot straight upward from the ground with initial velocity $v_0 = 49$ (m/s, so we use $g = 9.8$ m/s^2 in mks units), then it returns to the ground when

$$y(t) = -\tfrac{1}{2} \cdot (9.8)t^2 + 49t = (4.9)t(-t + 10) = 0,$$

and thus after 10 s in the air.   ∎

A Swimmer's Problem

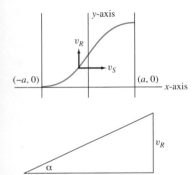

FIGURE 1.2.5. A swimmer's problem (Example 4).

Figure 1.2.5 shows a northward-flowing river of width $w = 2a$. The lines $x = \pm a$ represent the banks of the river and the y-axis its center. Suppose that the velocity v_R at which the water flows increases as one approaches the center of the river, and indeed is given in terms of distance x from the center by

$$v_R = v_0 \left(1 - \frac{x^2}{a^2} \right). \tag{18}$$

You can use Eq. (18) to verify that the water does flow the fastest at the center, where $v_R = v_0$, and that $v_R = 0$ at each riverbank.

Suppose that a swimmer starts at the point $(-a, 0)$ on the west bank and swims due east (relative to the water) with constant speed v_S. As indicated in Fig. 1.2.5, his velocity vector (relative to the riverbed) has horizontal component v_S and vertical component v_R. Hence the swimmer's direction angle α is given by

$$\tan \alpha = \frac{v_R}{v_S}.$$

Because $\tan \alpha = dy/dx$, substitution using (18) gives the differential equation

$$\frac{dy}{dx} = \frac{v_0}{v_S} \left(1 - \frac{x^2}{a^2} \right) \tag{19}$$

for the swimmer's trajectory $y = y(x)$ as he crosses the river.

Example 4

Suppose that the river is 1 mile wide and that its midstream velocity is $v_0 = 9$ mi/h. If the swimmer's velocity is $v_S = 3$ mi/h, then Eq. (19) takes the form

$$\frac{dy}{dx} = 3(1 - 4x^2).$$

Integration yields

$$y(x) = \int (3 - 12x^2)\, dx = 3x - 4x^3 + C$$

for the swimmer's trajectory. The initial condition $y\left(-\frac{1}{2}\right) = 0$ yields $C = 1$, so

$$y(x) = 3x - 4x^3 + 1.$$

Then

$$y\left(\tfrac{1}{2}\right) = 3\left(\tfrac{1}{2}\right) - 4\left(\tfrac{1}{2}\right)^3 + 1 = 2,$$

so the swimmer drifts 2 miles downstream while he swims 1 mile across the river. ∎

1.2 Problems

In Problems 1 through 10, find a function $y = f(x)$ satisfying the given differential equation and the prescribed initial condition.

1. $\dfrac{dy}{dx} = 2x + 1;\; y(0) = 3$

2. $\dfrac{dy}{dx} = (x - 2)^2;\; y(2) = 1$

3. $\dfrac{dy}{dx} = \sqrt{x};\; y(4) = 0$

4. $\dfrac{dy}{dx} = \dfrac{1}{x^2};\; y(1) = 5$

5. $\dfrac{dy}{dx} = \dfrac{1}{\sqrt{x + 2}};\; y(2) = -1$

6. $\dfrac{dy}{dx} = x\sqrt{x^2 + 9};\; y(-4) = 0$

7. $\dfrac{dy}{dx} = \dfrac{10}{x^2 + 1};\; y(0) = 0$ **8.** $\dfrac{dy}{dx} = \cos 2x;\; y(0) = 1$

9. $\dfrac{dy}{dx} = \dfrac{1}{\sqrt{1 - x^2}};\; y(0) = 0$ **10.** $\dfrac{dy}{dx} = xe^{-x};\; y(0) = 1$

In Problems 11 through 18, find the position function $x(t)$ of a moving particle with the given acceleration $a(t)$, initial position $x_0 = x(0)$, and initial velocity $v_0 = v(0)$.

11. $a(t) = 50,\; v_0 = 10,\; x_0 = 20$

12. $a(t) = -20,\; v_0 = -15,\; x_0 = 5$

13. $a(t) = 3t,\; v_0 = 5,\; x_0 = 0$

14. $a(t) = 2t + 1,\; v_0 = -7,\; x_0 = 4$

15. $a(t) = 4(t + 3)^2,\; v_0 = -1,\; x_0 = 1$

16. $a(t) = \dfrac{1}{\sqrt{t + 4}},\; v_0 = -1,\; x_0 = 1$

17. $a(t) = \dfrac{1}{(t + 1)^3},\; v_0 = 0,\; x_0 = 0$

18. $a(t) = 50\sin 5t,\; v_0 = -10,\; x_0 = 8$

In Problems 19 through 22, a particle starts at the origin and travels along the x-axis with the velocity function $v(t)$ whose graph is shown in Figs. 1.2.6 through 1.2.9. Sketch the graph of the resulting position function $x(t)$ for $0 \leqq t \leqq 10$.

19.

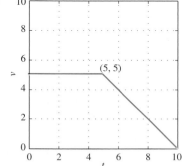

FIGURE 1.2.6. Graph of the velocity function $v(t)$ of Problem 19.

20.

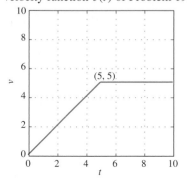

FIGURE 1.2.7. Graph of the velocity function $v(t)$ of Problem 20.

21.

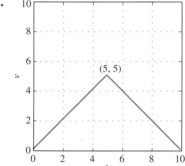

FIGURE 1.2.8. Graph of the velocity function $v(t)$ of Problem 21.

22.

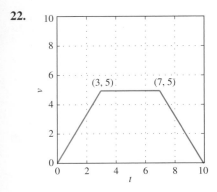

FIGURE 1.2.9. Graph of the velocity function $v(t)$ of Problem 22.

23. What is the maximum height attained by the arrow of part (b) of Example 3?

24. A ball is dropped from the top of a building 400 ft high. How long does it take to reach the ground? With what speed does the ball strike the ground?

25. The brakes of a car are applied when it is moving at 100 km/h and provide a constant deceleration of 10 meters per second per second (m/s^2). How far does the car travel before coming to a stop?

26. A projectile is fired straight upward with an initial velocity of 100 m/s from the top of a building 20 m high and falls to the ground at the base of the building. Find (a) its maximum height above the ground; (b) when it passes the top of the building; (c) its total time in the air.

27. A ball is thrown straight downward from the top of a tall building. The initial speed of the ball is 10 m/s. It strikes the ground with a speed of 60 m/s. How tall is the building?

28. A baseball is thrown straight downward with an initial speed of 40 ft/s from the top of the Washington Monument (555 ft high). How long does it take to reach the ground, and with what speed does the baseball strike the ground?

29. A diesel car gradually speeds up so that for the first 10 s its acceleration is given by

$$\frac{dv}{dt} = (0.12)t^2 + (0.6)t \quad (ft/s^2).$$

If the car starts from rest ($x_0 = 0$, $v_0 = 0$), find the distance it has traveled at the end of the first 10 s and its velocity at that time.

30. A car traveling at 60 mi/h (88 ft/s) skids 176 ft after its brakes are suddenly applied. Under the assumption that the braking system provides constant deceleration, what is that deceleration? For how long does the skid continue?

31. The skid marks made by an automobile indicated that its brakes were fully applied for a distance of 75 m before it came to a stop. The car in question is known to have a constant deceleration of 20 m/s^2 under these conditions. How fast—in km/h—was the car traveling when the brakes were first applied?

32. Suppose that a car skids 15 m if it is moving at 50 km/h when the brakes are applied. Assuming that the car has the same constant deceleration, how far will it skid if it is moving at 100 km/h when the brakes are applied?

33. On the planet Gzyx, a ball dropped from a height of 20 ft hits the ground in 2 s. If a ball is dropped from the top of a 200-ft-tall building on Gzyx, how long will it take to hit the ground? With what speed will it hit?

34. A person can throw a ball straight upward from the surface of the earth to a maximum height of 144 ft. How high could this person throw the ball on the planet Gzyx of Problem 29?

35. A stone is dropped from rest at an initial height h above the surface of the earth. Show that the speed with which it strikes the ground is $v = \sqrt{2gh}$.

36. Suppose a woman has enough "spring" in her legs to jump (on earth) from the ground to a height of 2.25 feet. If she jumps straight upward with the same initial velocity on the moon—where the surface gravitational acceleration is (approximately) 5.3 ft/s^2—how high above the surface will she rise?

37. At noon a car starts from rest at point A and proceeds at constant acceleration along a straight road toward point B. If the car reaches B at 12:50 P.M. with a velocity of 60 mi/h, what is the distance from A to B?

38. At noon a car starts from rest at point A and proceeds with constant acceleration along a straight road toward point C, 35 miles away. If the constantly accelerated car arrives at C with a velocity of 60 mi/h, at what time does it arrive at C?

39. If $a = 0.5$ mi and $v_0 = 9$ mi/h as in Example 4, what must the swimmer's speed v_S be in order that he drifts only 1 mile downstream as he crosses the river?

40. Suppose that $a = 0.5$ mi, $v_0 = 9$ mi/h, and $v_S = 3$ mi/h as in Example 4, but that the velocity of the river is given by the fourth-degree function

$$v_R = v_0 \left(1 - \frac{x^4}{a^4} \right)$$

rather than the quadratic function in Eq. (18). Now find how far downstream the swimmer drifts as he crosses the river.

41. A bomb is dropped from a helicopter hovering at an altitude of 800 feet above the ground. From the ground directly beneath the helicopter, a projectile is fired straight upward toward the bomb, exactly 2 seconds after the bomb is released. With what initial velocity should the projectile be fired, in order to hit the bomb at an altitude of exactly 400 feet?

42. A spacecraft is in free fall toward the surface of the moon at a speed of 1000 mph (mi/h). Its retrorockets, when fired, provide a constant deceleration of 20,000 mi/h^2. At what height above the lunar surface should the astronauts fire the retrorockets to insure a soft touchdown? (As in Example 2, ignore the moon's gravitational field.)

43. Arthur Clarke's *The Wind from the Sun* (1963) describes Diana, a spacecraft propelled by the solar wind. Its aluminized sail provides it with a constant acceleration of $0.001g = 0.0098$ m/s^2. Suppose this spacecraft starts from rest at time $t = 0$ and simultaneously fires a projectile (straight ahead in the same direction) that travels at one-tenth of the speed $c = 3 \times 10^8$ m/s of light. How long will it take the spacecraft to catch up with the projectile,

and how far will it have traveled by then?

44. A driver involved in an accident claims he was going only 25 mph. When police tested his car, they found that when its brakes were applied at 25 mph, the car skidded only 45 feet before coming to a stop. But the driver's skid marks at the accident scene measured 210 feet. Assuming the same (constant) deceleration, determine the speed he was actually traveling just prior to the accident.

1.3 Slope Fields and Solution Curves

Consider a differential equation of the form

$$\frac{dy}{dx} = f(x, y) \tag{1}$$

where the right-hand function $f(x, y)$ involves both the independent variable x and the dependent variable y. We might think of integrating both sides in (1) with respect to x, and hence write $y(x) = \int f(x, y(x))\,dx + C$. However, this approach does not lead to a solution of the differential equation, because the indicated integral involves the *unknown* function $y(x)$ itself, and therefore cannot be evaluated explicitly. Actually, there exists *no* straightforward procedure by which a general differential equation can be solved explicitly. Indeed, the solutions of such a simple-looking differential equation as $y' = x^2 + y^2$ cannot be expressed in terms of the ordinary elementary functions studied in calculus textbooks. Nevertheless, the graphical and numerical methods of this and later sections can be used to construct *approximate* solutions of differential equations that suffice for many practical purposes.

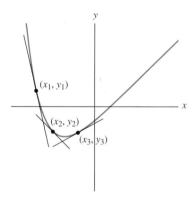

FIGURE 1.3.1. A solution curve for the differential equation $y' = x - y$ together with tangent lines having

- slope $m_1 = x_1 - y_1$ at the point (x_1, y_1);
- slope $m_2 = x_2 - y_2$ at the point (x_2, y_2); and
- slope $m_3 = x_3 - y_3$ at the point (x_3, y_3).

Slope Fields and Graphical Solutions

There is a simple geometric way to think about solutions of a given differential equation $y' = f(x, y)$. At each point (x, y) of the xy-plane, the value of $f(x, y)$ determines a slope $m = f(x, y)$. A solution of the differential equation is simply a differentiable function whose graph $y = y(x)$ has this "correct slope" at each point $(x, y(x))$ through which it passes—that is, $y'(x) = f(x, y(x))$. Thus a **solution curve** of the differential equation $y' = f(x, y)$—the graph of a solution of the equation—is simply a curve in the xy-plane whose tangent line at each point (x, y) has slope $m = f(x, y)$. For instance, Fig. 1.3.1 shows a solution curve of the differential equation $y' = x - y$ together with its tangent lines at three typical points.

This geometric viewpoint suggests a *graphical method* for constructing *approximate* solutions of the differential equation $y' = f(x, y)$. Through each of a representative collection of points (x, y) in the plane we draw a short line segment having the proper slope $m = f(x, y)$. All these line segments constitute a **slope field** (or a **direction field**) for the equation $y' = f(x, y)$.

Example 1 Figures 1.3.2 (a)–(d) show slope fields and solution curves for the differential equation

$$\frac{dy}{dx} = ky \tag{2}$$

with the values $k = 2, 0.5, -1$, and -3 of the parameter k in Eq. (2). Note that each slope field yields important qualitative information about the set of all solutions

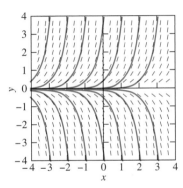

FIGURE 1.3.2(a) Slope field and solution curves for $y' = 2y$.

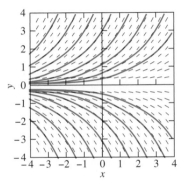

FIGURE 1.3.2(b) Slope field and solution curves for $y' = (0.5)y$.

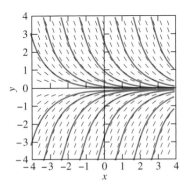

FIGURE 1.3.2(c) Slope field and solution curves for $y' = -y$.

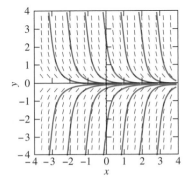

FIGURE 1.3.2(d) Slope field and solution curves for $y' = -3y$.

of the differential equation. For instance, Figs. 1.3.2(a) and (b) suggest that each solution $y(x)$ approaches $\pm\infty$ as $x \to +\infty$ if $k > 0$, whereas Figs. 1.3.2(c) and (d) suggest that $y(x) \to 0$ as $x \to +\infty$ if $k < 0$. Moreover, although the sign of k determines the *direction* of increase or decrease of $y(x)$, its absolute value $|k|$ appears to determine the *rate of change* of $y(x)$. All this is apparent from slope fields like those in Fig. 1.3.2, even without knowing that the general solution of Eq. (2) is given explicitly by $y(x) = Ce^{kx}$. ■

A slope field suggests visually the general shapes of solution curves of the differential equation. Through each point a solution curve should proceed in such a direction that its tangent line is nearly parallel to the nearby line segments of the slope field. Starting at any initial point (a, b), we can attempt to sketch freehand an approximate solution curve that threads its way through the slope field, following the visible line segments as closely as possible.

Example 2

Construct a slope field for the differential equation $y' = x - y$ and use it to sketch an approximate solution curve that passes through the point $(-4, 4)$.

Solution

Solution Fig. 1.3.3 shows a table of slopes for the given equation. The numerical slope $m = x - y$ appears at the intersection of the horizontal x-row and the vertical y-column of the table. If you inspect the pattern of upper-left to lower-right diagonals in this table, you can see that it was easily and quickly constructed. (Of

$x \backslash y$	−4	−3	−2	−1	0	1	2	3	4
−4	0	−1	−2	−3	−4	−5	−6	−7	−8
−3	1	0	−1	−2	−3	−4	−5	−6	−7
−2	2	1	0	−1	−2	−3	−4	−5	−6
−1	3	2	1	0	−1	−2	−3	−4	−5
0	4	3	2	1	0	−1	−2	−3	−4
1	5	4	3	2	1	0	−1	−2	−3
2	6	5	4	3	2	1	0	−1	−2
3	7	6	5	4	3	2	1	0	−1
4	8	7	6	5	4	3	2	1	0

FIGURE 1.3.3. Values of the slope $y' = x - y$ for $-4 \leqq x,\ y \leqq 4$.

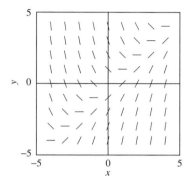

FIGURE 1.3.4. Slope field for $y' = x - y$ corresponding to the table of slopes in Fig. 1.3.3.

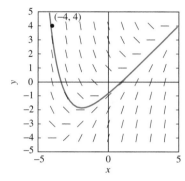

FIGURE 1.3.5. The solution curve through $(-4, 4)$.

course, a more complicated function $f(x, y)$ on the right-hand side of the differential equation would necessitate more complicated calculations.) Figure 1.3.4 shows the corresponding slope field, and Fig. 1.3.5 shows an approximate solution curve sketched through the point $(-4, 4)$ so as to follow as this slope field as closely as possible. At each point it appears to proceed in the direction indicated by the nearby line segments of the slope field. ∎

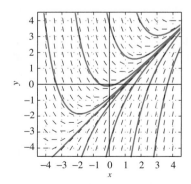

FIGURE 1.3.6. Slope field and typical solution curves for $y' = x - y$.

Although a spreadsheet program (for instance) readily constructs a table of slopes as in Fig. 1.3.3, it can be quite tedious to plot by hand a sufficient number of slope segments as in Fig. 1.3.4. However, most computer algebra systems include commands for quick and ready construction of slope fields with as many line segments as desired; such commands are illustrated in the application material for this section. The more line segments are constructed, the more accurately solution curves can be visualized and sketched. Figure 1.3.6 shows a "finer" slope field for the differential equation $y' = x - y$ of Example 2, together with typical solution curves treading through this slope field.

If you look closely at Fig. 1.3.6, you may spot a solution curve that appears to be a straight line! Indeed, you can verify that the linear function $y = x - 1$ is a solution of the equation $y' = x - y$, and it appears likely that the other solution curves approach this straight line as an asymptote as $x \to +\infty$. This inference illustrates the fact that a slope field can suggest tangible information about solutions that is not at all evident from the differential equation itself. Can you, by tracing the appropriate solution curve in this figure, infer that $y(3) \approx 2$ for the solution $y(x)$ of the initial value problem $y' = x - y$, $y(-4) = 4$?

Applications of Slope fields

The next two examples illustrate the use of slope fields to glean useful information in physical situations that are modeled by differential equations. Example 3 is based on the fact that a baseball moving through the air at a moderate speed v (less than about 300 ft/s) encounters air resistance that is approximately proportional to v. If the baseball is thrown straight downward from the top of a tall building or from a hovering helicopter, then it experiences both the downward acceleration of gravity and an upward acceleration of air resistance. If the y-axis is directed *downward*, then the ball's velocity $v = dy/dt$ and its gravitational acceleration $g = 32$ ft/s^2 are both positive, while its acceleration due to air resistance is negative. Hence its total acceleration is of the form

$$\frac{dv}{dt} = g - kv. \tag{3}$$

A typical value of the air resistance proportionality constant might be $k = 0.16$.

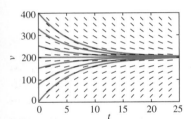

FIGURE 1.3.7. Slope field and typical solution curves for $v' = 32 - 0.16v$.

| Example 3 | Suppose you throw a baseball straight downward from a helicopter hovering at an altitude of 3000 feet. You wonder whether someone standing on the ground below could conceivably catch it. In order to estimate the speed with which the ball will land, you can use your laptop's computer algebra system to construct a slope field for the differential equation |

$$\frac{dv}{dt} = 32 - 0.16v. \tag{4}$$

The result is shown in Fig. 1.3.7, together with a number of solution curves corresponding to different values of the initial velocity $v(0)$ with which you might throw the baseball downward. Note that all these solution curves appear to approach the horizontal line $v = 200$ as an asymptote. This implies that—however you throw it—the baseball should approach the *limiting velocity* $v = 200$ ft/s instead of accelerating indefinitely (as it would in the absence of any air resistance). The handy fact that 60 mi/h = 88 ft/s yields

$$v = 200\frac{\text{ft}}{\text{s}} \times \frac{60 \text{ mi/h}}{88 \text{ ft/s}} \approx 136.36 \frac{\text{mi}}{\text{h}}.$$

Perhaps a catcher accustomed to 100 mi/h fastballs would have some chance of fielding this speeding ball. ∎

Comment If the ball's initial velocity is $v(0) = 200$, then Eq. (4) gives $v'(0) = 32 - (0.16)(200) = 0$, so the ball experiences *no* initial acceleration. Its velocity therefore remains unchanged, and hence $v(t) \equiv 200$ is a constant "equilibrium solution" of the differential equation. If the initial velocity is greater than 200, then the initial acceleration given by Eq. (4) is negative, so the ball slows down as it falls. But if the initial velocity is less than 200, then the initial acceleration given by (4) is positive, so the ball speeds up as it falls. It therefore seems quite reasonable that, because of air resistance, the baseball will approach a limiting velocity of 200 ft/s—whatever initial velocity it starts with. You might like to verify that—in the absence of air resistance—this ball would hit the ground at over 300 mi/h. ∎

In Section 2.1 we will discuss in detail the logistic differential equation

$$\frac{dP}{dt} = kP(M - P) \tag{5}$$

that often is used to model a population $P(t)$ that inhabits an environment with *carrying capacity* M. This means that M is the maximum population that this environment can sustain on a long-term basis (in terms of the maximum available food, for instance).

Example 4 If we take $k = 0.0004$ and $M = 150$, then the logistic equation in (5) takes the form

$$\frac{dP}{dt} = 0.0004P(150 - P) = 0.06P - 0.0004P^2. \tag{6}$$

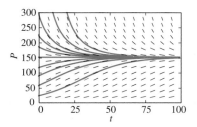

FIGURE 1.3.8. Slope field and typical solution curves for $P' = 0.06P - 0.0004P^2$.

The positive term $0.06P$ on the right in (6) corresponds to natural growth at a 6% annual rate (with time t measured in years). The negative term $-0.0004P^2$ represents the inhibition of growth due to limited resources in the environment.

Figure 1.3.8 shows a slope field for Eq. (6), together with a number of solution curves corresponding to possible different values of the initial population $P(0)$. Note that all these solution curves appear to approach the horizontal line $P = 150$ as an asymptote. This implies that—whatever the initial population—the population $P(t)$ approaches the *limiting population* $P = 150$ as $t \to \infty$. ■

Comment   If the initial population is $P(0) = 150$, then Eq. (6) gives

$$P'(0) = 0.0004(150)(150 - 150) = 0,$$

so the population experiences *no* initial (instantaneous) change. It therefore remains unchanged, and hence $P(t) \equiv 150$ is a constant "equilibrium solution" of the differential equation. If the initial population is greater than 150, then the initial rate of change given by (6) is negative, so the population immediately begins to decrease. But if the initial population is less than 150, then the initial rate of change given by (6) is positive, so the population immediately begins to increase. It therefore seems quite reasonable to conclude that the population will approach a limiting value of 150—whatever the (positive) initial population. ■

Existence and Uniqueness of Solutions

Before one spends much time attempting to solve a given differential equation, it is wise to know that solutions actually *exist*. We may also want to know whether there is only one solution of the equation satisfying a given initial condition—that is, whether its solutions are *unique*.

Example 5 **(a)** [Failure of existence] The initial value problem

$$y' = \frac{1}{x}, \quad y(0) = 0 \tag{7}$$

has *no* solution, because no solution $y(x) = \int (1/x)\, dx = \ln|x| + C$ of the differential equation is defined at $x = 0$. We see this graphically in Fig. 1.3.9, which shows a direction field and some typical solution curves for the equation $y' = 1/x$. It is apparent that the indicated direction field "forces" all solution curves near the y-axis to plunge downward so that none can pass through the point $(0, 0)$.

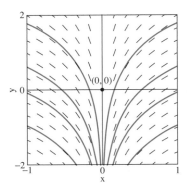

FIGURE 1.3.9. Direction field and typical solution curves for the equation $y' = 1/x$.

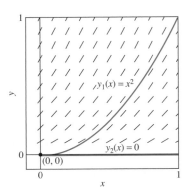

FIGURE 1.3.10. Direction field and two different solution curves for the initial value problem $y' = 2\sqrt{y}$, $y(0) = 0$.

(b) [Failure of uniqueness] On the other hand, you can readily verify that the initial value problem

$$y' = 2\sqrt{y}, \quad y(0) = 0 \tag{8}$$

has the *two* different solutions $y_1(x) = x^2$ and $y_2(x) \equiv 0$ (see Problem 27). Figure 1.3.10 shows a direction field and these two different solution curves for the initial value problem in (8). We see that the curve $y_1(x) = x^2$ threads its way through the indicated direction field, whereas the differential equation $y' = 2\sqrt{y}$ specifies slope $y' = 0$ along the x-axis $y_2(x) = 0$. ∎

Example 5 illustrates the fact that, before we can speak of "the" solution of an initial value problem, we need to know that it has *one and only one* solution. Questions of existence and uniqueness of solutions also bear on the process of mathematical modeling. Suppose that we are studying a physical system whose behavior is completely determined by certain initial conditions, but that our proposed mathematical model involves a differential equation *not* having a unique solution satisfying those conditions. This raises an immediate question as to whether the mathematical model adequately represents the physical system.

The theorem stated below implies that the initial value problem $y' = f(x, y)$, $y(a) = b$ has one and only one solution defined near the point $x = a$ on the x-axis, provided that both the function f and its partial derivative $\partial f/\partial y$ are continuous near the point (a, b) in the xy-plane. Methods of proving existence and uniqueness theorems are discussed in the Appendix.

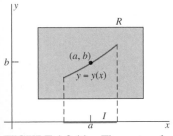

FIGURE 1.3.11. The rectangle R and x-interval I of Theorem 1, and the solution curve $y = y(x)$ through the point (a, b).

THEOREM 1 Existence and Uniqueness of Solutions

Suppose that both the function $f(x, y)$ and its partial derivative $D_y f(x, y)$ are continuous on some rectangle R in the xy-plane that contains the point (a, b) in its interior. Then, for some open interval I containing the point a, the initial value problem

$$\frac{dy}{dx} = f(x, y), \quad y(a) = b \tag{9}$$

has one and only one solution that is defined on the interval I. (As illustrated in Fig. 1.3.11, the solution interval I may not be as "wide" as the original rectangle R of continuity; see Remark 3 below.)

Remark 1: In the case of the differential equation $dy/dx = -y$ of Example 1 and Fig. 1.3.2(c), both the function $f(x, y) = -y$ and the partial derivative $\partial f/\partial y = -1$ are continuous everywhere, so Theorem 1 implies the existence of a unique solution for any initial data (a, b). Although the theorem ensures existence only on some open interval containing $x = a$, each solution $y(x) = Ce^{-x}$ actually is defined for all x.

Remark 2: In the case of the differential equation $dy/dx = -2\sqrt{y}$ of Example 5(b) and Eq. (8), the function $f(x, y) = -2\sqrt{y}$ is continuous wherever $y > 0$, but the partial derivative $\partial f/\partial y = 1/\sqrt{y}$ is discontinuous when $y = 0$, and hence at the point $(0, 0)$. This is why it is possible for there to exist two different solutions $y_1(x) = x^2$ and $y_2(x) \equiv 0$, each of which satisfies the initial condition $y(0) = 0$.

Remark 3: In Example 7 of Section 1.1 we examined the especially simple differential equation $dy/dx = y^2$. Here we have $f(x, y) = y^2$ and $\partial f/\partial y = 2y$. Both of these functions are continuous everywhere in the xy-plane, and in particular on the rectangle $-2 < x < 2, 0 < y < 2$. Because the point $(0, 1)$ lies in the interior of this rectangle, Theorem 1 guarantees a unique solution—necessarily a continuous function—of the initial value problem

$$\frac{dy}{dx} = y^2, \quad y(0) = 1 \tag{10}$$

on some open x-interval containing $a = 0$. Indeed this is the solution

$$y(x) = \frac{1}{1 - x}$$

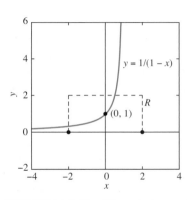

FIGURE 1.3.12. The solution curve through the initial point $(0, 1)$ leaves the rectangle R before it reaches the right side of R.

that we discussed in Example 7. But $y(x) = 1/(1 - x)$ is discontinuous at $x = 1$, so our unique continuous solution does not exist on the entire interval $-2 < x < 2$. Thus the solution interval I of Theorem 1 may not be as wide as the rectangle R where f and $\partial f/\partial y$ are continuous. Geometrically, the reason is that the solution curve provided by the theorem may leave the rectangle—wherein solutions of the differential equation are guaranteed to exist—before it reaches the one or both ends of the interval (see Fig. 1.3.12). ∎

The following example shows that, if the function $f(x, y)$ and/or its partial derivative $\partial f/\partial y$ fail to satisfy the continuity hypothesis of Theorem 1, then the initial value problem in (9) may have *either* no solution *or* many—even infinitely many—solutions.

Example 6   Consider the first-order differential equation

$$x\frac{dy}{dx} = 2y. \tag{11}$$

Applying Theorem 1 with $f(x, y) = 2y/x$ and $\partial f/\partial y = 2/x$, we conclude that Eq. (11) must have a unique solution near any point in the xy-plane where $x \neq 0$. Indeed, we see immediately by substitution in (11) that

$$y(x) = Cx^2 \tag{12}$$

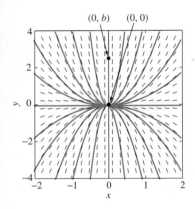

FIGURE 1.3.13. There are infinitely many solution curves through the point $(0, 0)$, but no solution curves through the point $(0, b)$ if $b \neq 0$.

satisfies Eq. (11) for any value of the constant C and for all values of the variable x. In particular, the initial value problem

$$x\frac{dy}{dx} = 2y, \quad y(0) = 0 \tag{13}$$

has infinitely many different solutions, whose solution curves are the parabolas $y = Cx^2$ illustrated in Fig. 1.3.13. (In case $C = 0$ the "parabola" is actually the x-axis $y = 0$.)

Observe that all these parabolas pass through the origin $(0, 0)$, but none of them passes through any other point on the y-axis. It follows that the initial value problem in (13) has infinitely many solutions, but the initial value problem

$$x\frac{dy}{dx} = 2y, \quad y(0) = b \tag{14}$$

has no solution if $b \neq 0$.

Finally, note that through any point off the y-axis there passes only one of the parabolas $y = Cx^2$. Hence, if $a \neq 0$, then the initial value problem

$$x\frac{dy}{dx} = 2y, \quad y(a) = b \tag{15}$$

has a unique solution on any interval that contains the point $x = a$ but not the origin $x = 0$ In summary, the initial value problem in (15) has

- a unique solution near (a, b) if $a \neq 0$;
- no solution if $a = 0$ but $b \neq 0$;
- infinitely many solutions if $a = b = 0$. ∎

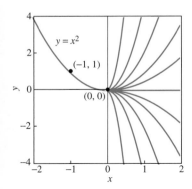

FIGURE 1.3.14. There are infinitely many solution curves through the point $(1, -1)$.

Still more can be said about the initial value problem in (15). Consider a typical initial point off the y-axis—for instance the point $(-1, 1)$ indicated in Fig. 1.3.14. Then for any value of the constant C the function defined by

$$y(x) = \begin{cases} x^2 & \text{if } x \leq 0, \\ Cx^2 & \text{if } x > 0 \end{cases} \tag{16}$$

is continuous and satisfies the initial value problem

$$x\frac{dy}{dx} = 2y, \quad y(-1) = 1. \tag{17}$$

For a particular value of C, the solution curve defined by (16) consists of the left half of the parabola $y = x^2$ and the right half of the parabola $y = Cx^2$. Thus the unique solution curve near $(-1, 1)$ branches at the origin into the infinitely many solution curves illustrated in Fig. 1.3.14.

We therefore see that Theorem 1 (if its hypotheses are satisfied) guarantees uniqueness of the solution near the initial point (a, b), but a solution curve through (a, b) may eventually branch elsewhere so that uniqueness is lost. Thus a solution may exist on a larger interval than one on which the solution is unique. For instance, the solution $y(x) = x^2$ of the initial value problem in (17) exists on the whole x-axis, but this solution is unique only on the negative x-axis $-\infty < x < 0$.

1.3 Problems

In Problems 1 through 10, we have provided the slope field of the indicated differential equation, together with one or more solution curves. Sketch likely solution curves through the additional points marked in each slope field.

1. $\dfrac{dy}{dx} = -y - \sin x$

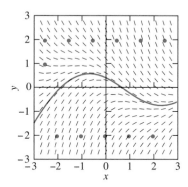

FIGURE 1.3.15.

2. $\dfrac{dy}{dx} = x + y$

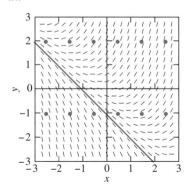

FIGURE 1.3.16.

3. $\dfrac{dy}{dx} = y - \sin x$

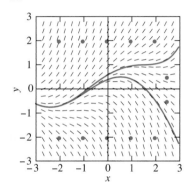

FIGURE 1.3.17.

4. $\dfrac{dy}{dx} = x - y$

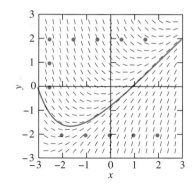

FIGURE 1.3.18.

5. $\dfrac{dy}{dx} = y - x + 1$

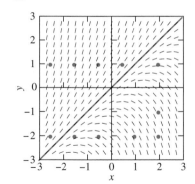

FIGURE 1.3.19.

6. $\dfrac{dy}{dx} = x - y + 1$

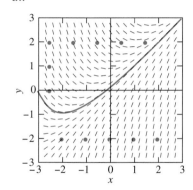

FIGURE 1.3.20.

7. $\dfrac{dy}{dx} = \sin x + \sin y$

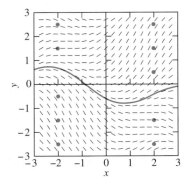

FIGURE 1.3.21.

8. $\dfrac{dy}{dx} = x^2 - y$

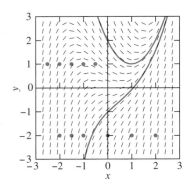

FIGURE 1.3.22.

9. $\dfrac{dy}{dx} = x^2 - y - 2$

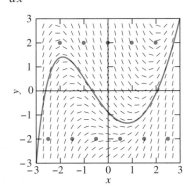

FIGURE 1.3.23.

10. $\dfrac{dy}{dx} = -x^2 + \sin y$

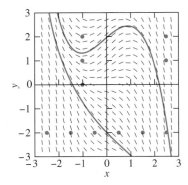

FIGURE 1.3.24.

In Problems 11 through 20, determine whether Theorem 1 does or does not guarantee existence of a solution of the given initial value problem. If existence is guaranteed, determine whether Theorem 1 does or does not guarantee uniqueness of that solution.

11. $\dfrac{dy}{dx} = 2x^2 y^2; \quad y(1) = -1$

12. $\dfrac{dy}{dx} = x \ln y; \quad y(1) = 1$

13. $\dfrac{dy}{dx} = \sqrt[3]{y}; \quad y(0) = 1$

14. $\dfrac{dy}{dx} = \sqrt[3]{y}; \quad y(0) = 0$

15. $\dfrac{dy}{dx} = \sqrt{x - y}; \quad y(2) = 2$

16. $\dfrac{dy}{dx} = \sqrt{x - y}; \quad y(2) = 1$

17. $y\dfrac{dy}{dx} = x - 1; \quad y(0) = 1$

18. $y\dfrac{dy}{dx} = x - 1; \quad y(1) = 0$

19. $\dfrac{dy}{dx} = \ln(1 + y^2); \quad y(0) = 0$

20. $\dfrac{dy}{dx} = x^2 - y^2; \quad y(0) = 1$

In Problems 21 and 22, first use the method of Example 2 to construct a slope field for the given differential equation. Then sketch the solution curve corresponding to the given initial condition. Finally, use this solution curve to estimate the desired value of the solution $y(x)$.

21. $y' = x + y, \quad y(0) = 0; \quad y(-4) = ?$

22. $y' = y - x, \quad y(4) = 0; \quad y(-4) = ?$

Problems 23 and 24 are like Problems 21 and 22, but now use a computer algebra system to plot and print out a slope field for the given differential equation. If you wish (and know how), you can check your manually sketched solution curve by plotting it with the computer.

23. $y' = x^2 + y^2 - 1$, $y(0) = 0$; $y(2) = ?$

24. $y' = x + \frac{1}{2}y^2$, $y(-2) = 0$; $y(2) = ?$

25. You bail out of the helicopter of Example 3 and pull the ripcord of your parachute. Now $k = 1.6$ in Eq. (3), so your downward velocity satisfies the initial value problem

$$\frac{dv}{dt} = 32 - 1.6v, \quad v(0) = 0.$$

In order to investigate your chances of survival, construct a slope field for this differential equation and sketch the appropriate solution curve. What will your limiting velocity be? Will a strategically located haystack do any good? How long will it take you to reach 95% of your limiting velocity?

26. Suppose the deer population $P(t)$ in a small forest satisfies the logistic equation

$$\frac{dP}{dt} = 0.0225 P - 0.0003 P^2.$$

Construct a slope field and appropriate solution curve to answer the following questions: If there are 25 deer at time $t = 0$ and t is measured in months, how long will it take the number of deer to double? What will be the limiting deer population?

The next seven problems illustrate the fact that, if the hypotheses of Theorem 1 are not satisfied, then the initial value problem $y' = f(x, y)$, $y(a) = b$ may have either no solutions, finitely many solutions, or infinitely many solutions.

27. (a) Verify that if c is a constant, then the function defined piecewise by

$$y(x) = \begin{cases} 0 & \text{for } x \leq c, \\ (x - c)^2 & \text{for } x > c \end{cases}$$

satisfies the differential equation $y' = 2\sqrt{y}$ for all x (including the point $x = c$). Construct a figure illustrating the fact that the initial value problem $y' = 2\sqrt{y}$, $y(0) = 0$ has infinitely many different solutions. **(b)** For what values of b does the initial value problem $y' = 2\sqrt{y}$, $y(0) = b$ have (i) no solution, (ii) a unique solution that is defined for all x?

28. Verify that if k is a constant, then the function $y(x) \equiv kx$ satisfies the differential equation $xy' = y$ for all x. Construct a slope field and several of these straight line solution curves. Then determine (in terms of a and b) how many different solutions the initial value problem $xy' = y$, $y(a) = b$ has—one, none, or infinitely many.

29. Verify that if c is a constant, then the function defined piecewise by

$$y(x) = \begin{cases} 0 & \text{for } x \leq c, \\ (x - c)^3 & \text{for } x > c \end{cases}$$

satisfies the differential equation $y' = 3y^{2/3}$ for all x. Can you also use the "left half" of the cubic $y = (x - c)^3$ in piecing together a solution curve of the differential equation? (See Fig. 1.3.25.) Sketch a variety of such solution curves. Is there a point (a, b) of the xy-plane such that the initial value problem $y' = 3y^{2/3}$, $y(a) = b$ has either no solution or a unique solution that is defined for all x? Reconcile your answer with Theorem 1.

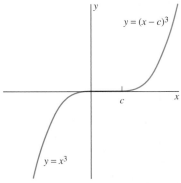

FIGURE 1.3.25. A suggestion for Problem 29.

30. Verify that if c is a constant, then the function defined piecewise by

$$y(x) = \begin{cases} +1 & \text{if } x \leq c, \\ \cos(x - c) & \text{if } c < x < c + \pi, \\ -1 & \text{if } x \geq c + \pi \end{cases}$$

satisfies the differential equation $y' = -\sqrt{1 - y^2}$ for all x. (Perhaps a preliminary sketch with $c = 0$ will be helpful.) Sketch a variety of such solution curves. Then determine (in terms of a and b) how many different solutions the initial value problem $y' = -\sqrt{1 - y^2}$, $y(a) = b$ has.

31. Carry out an investigation similar to that in Problem 30, except with the differential equation $y' = +\sqrt{1 - y^2}$. Does it suffice simply to replace $\cos(x - c)$ with $\sin(x - c)$ in piecing together a solution that is defined for all x?

32. Verify that if $c > 0$, then the function defined piecewise by

$$y(x) = \begin{cases} 0 & \text{if } x^2 \leq c, \\ (x^2 - c)^2 & \text{if } x^2 > c \end{cases}$$

satisfies the differential equation $y' = 4x\sqrt{y}$ for all x. Sketch a variety of such solution curves for different values of c. Then determine (in terms of a and b) how many different solutions the initial value problem $y' = 4x\sqrt{y}$, $y(a) = b$ has.

33. If $c \neq 0$, verify that the function defined by $y(x) = x/(cx - 1)$ (with graph illustrated in Fig. 1.3.26) satisfies the differential equation $x^2 y' + y^2 = 0$ if $x \neq 1/c$. Sketch a variety of such solution curves for different values of c. Also, note the constant-valued function $y(x) \equiv 0$ that does not result from any choice of the constant c. Finally, determine (in terms of a and b) how many different solutions the initial value problem $x^2 y' + y^2 = 0$, $y(a) = b$ has.

FIGURE 1.3.26. Slope field for $x^2 y' + y^2 = 0$ and graph of a solution $y(x) = x/(cx - 1)$.

34. (a) Use the direction field of Problem 5 to estimate the values at $x = 1$ of the two solutions of the differential equation $y' = y - x + 1$ with initial values $y(-1) = -1.2$ and $y(-1) = -0.8$.

(b) Use a computer algebra system to estimate the values at $x = 3$ of the two solutions of this differential equation with initial values $y(-3) = -3.01$ and $y(-3) = -2.99$.

The lesson of this problem is that small changes in initial conditions can make big differences in results.

35. (a) Use the direction field of Problem 6 to estimate the values at $x = 2$ of the two solutions of the differential equation $y' = x - y + 1$ with initial values $y(-3) = -0.2$ and $y(-3) = +0.2$.

(b) Use a computer algebra system to estimate the values at $x = 3$ of the two solutions of this differential equation with initial values $y(-3) = -0.5$ and $y(-3) = +0.5$.

The lesson of this problem is that big changes in initial conditions may make only small differences in results.

1.3 Application   Computer-Generated Slope Fields and Solution Curves

Widely available computer algebra systems and technical computing environments include facilities to automate the construction of slope fields and solution curves, as do some graphing calculators (see Fig. 1.3.27).

FIGURE 1.3.27. Slope field and solution curves for the differential equation

$$\frac{dy}{dx} = \sin(x - y)$$

with initial points $(0, b)$, $b = -3, -1, -2, 0, 2, 4$ and window $-5 \leq x, y \leq 5$ on a TI-89 graphing calculator.

The applications manual accompanying this textbook includes discussion of *Maple*™, *Mathematica*™, and MATLAB™ resources for the investigation of differential equations. For instance, the *Maple* command

```
with(DEtools):
DEplot(diff(y(x),x)=sin(x-y(x)), y(x), x=-5..5, y=-5..5);
```

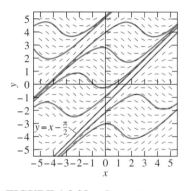

FIGURE 1.3.28. Computer-generated slope field and solution curves for the differential equation $y' = \sin(x - y)$.

and the *Mathematica* command

```
<< Graphics\PlotField.m
PlotVectorField[{1, Sin[x-y]}, {x, -5, 5}, {y, -5, 5}]
```

produce slope fields similar to the one shown in Fig. 1.3.28. Figure 1.3.28 itself was generated with the MATLAB program **dfield** [John Polking and David Arnold, *Ordinary Differential Equations Using* MATLAB, 2nd edition, Upper Saddle River, NJ: Prentice Hall, 1999] that is freely available for educational use (**math.rice.edu/~dfield**). When a differential equation is entered in the **dfield** setup menu (Fig. 1.3.29), you can (with mouse button clicks) plot both a slope field and the solution curve (or curves) through any desired point (or points). Another freely available and user-friendly MATLAB-based ODE package with impressive graphical capabilities is **Iode** (**www.math.uiuc.edu/iode**).

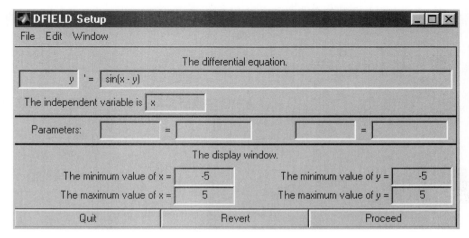

FIGURE 1.3.29. MATLAB **dfield** setup to construct slope field and solution curves for $y' = \sin(x - y)$.

Use a graphing calculator or computer system in the following investigations. You might warm up by generating the slope fields and some solution curves for Problems 1 through 10 in this section.

INVESTIGATION A: Plot a slope field and typical solution curves for the differential equation $dy/dx = \sin(x - y)$, but with a larger window than that of Fig. 1.3.28. With $-10 \le x \le 10$, $-10 \le y \le 10$, for instance, a number of apparent straight line solution curves should be visible.

(a) Substitute $y = ax + b$ in the differential equation to determine what the coefficients a and b must be in order to get a solution.

(b) A computer algebra system gives the general solution

$$y(x) = x - 2 \tan^{-1}\left(\frac{x - 2 - C}{x - C}\right).$$

Plot this solution with selected values of the constant C to compare the resulting solution curves with those indicated in Fig. 1.3.28. Can you see that *no* value of C yields the linear solution $y = x - \pi/2$ corresponding to the initial condition $y(\pi/2) = 0$? Are there any values of C for which the corresponding solution curves lie close to this straight line solution curve?

INVESTIGATION B: For your own personal investigation, let n be the *smallest* digit in your student ID number that is greater than 1, and consider the differential equation

$$\frac{dy}{dx} = \frac{1}{n}\cos(x - ny).$$

(a) First investigate (as in part (a) of Investigation A) the possibility of straight line solutions.

(b) Then generate a slope field for this differential equation, with the viewing window chosen so that you can picture some of these straight lines, plus a sufficient number of nonlinear solution curves that you can formulate a conjecture about what happens to $y(x)$ as $x \to +\infty$. State your inference as plainly as you can. Given the initial value $y(0) = y_0$, try to predict (perhaps in terms of y_0) how $y(x)$ behaves as $x \to +\infty$.

(c) A computer algebra system gives the general solution

$$y(x) = \frac{1}{n}\left[x + 2\tan^{-1}\left(\frac{1}{x - C}\right)\right].$$

Can you make a connection between this symbolic solution and your graphically generated solution curves (straight lines or otherwise)?

1.4 Separable Equations and Applications

The first-order differential equation

$$\frac{dy}{dx} = H(x, y) \tag{1}$$

is called **separable** provided that $H(x, y)$ can be written as the product of a function of x and a function of y:

$$\frac{dy}{dx} = g(x)h(y) = \frac{g(x)}{f(y)},$$

where $h(y) = 1/f(y)$. In this case the variables x and y can be *separated*—isolated on opposite sides of an equation—by writing informally the equation

$$f(y)\,dy = g(x)\,dx,$$

which we understand to be concise notation for the differential equation

$$f(y)\frac{dy}{dx} = g(x). \tag{2}$$

It is easy to solve this special type of differential equation simply by integrating both sides with respect to x:

$$\int f(y(x))\frac{dy}{dx}\,dx = \int g(x)\,dx + C;$$

equivalently,

$$\int f(y)\,dy = \int g(x)\,dx + C. \tag{3}$$

All that is required is that the antiderivatives

$$F(y) = \int f(y)\,dy \quad \text{and} \quad G(x) = \int g(x)\,dx$$

can be found. To see that Eqs. (2) and (3) are equivalent, note the following consequence of the chain rule:

$$D_x[F(y(x))] = F'(y(x))y'(x) = f(y)\frac{dy}{dx} = g(x) = D_x[G(x)],$$

which in turn is equivalent to

$$F(y(x)) = G(x) + C, \tag{4}$$

because two functions have the same derivative on an interval if and only if they differ by a constant on that interval.

Example 1   Solve the initial value problem

$$\frac{dy}{dx} = -6xy, \quad y(0) = 7.$$

Solution   Informally, we divide both sides of the differential equation by y and multiply each side by dx to get

$$\frac{dy}{y} = -6x\,dx.$$

Hence

$$\int \frac{dy}{y} = \int (-6x)\,dx;$$

$$\ln|y| = -3x^2 + C.$$

We see from the initial condition $y(0) = 7$ that $y(x)$ is positive near $x = 0$, so we may delete the absolute value symbols:

$$\ln y = -3x^2 + C,$$

and hence

$$y(x) = e^{-3x^2 + C} = e^{-3x^2}e^C = Ae^{-3x^2},$$

where $A = e^C$. The condition $y(0) = 7$ yields $A = 7$, so the desired solution is

$$y(x) = 7e^{-3x^2}.$$

This is the upper emphasized solution curve shown in Fig. 1.4.1.

FIGURE 1.4.1.   Slope field and solution curves for $y' = -6xy$ in Example 1.

■

Remark: Suppose, instead, that the initial condition in Example 1 had been $y(0) = -4$. Then it would follow that $y(x)$ is *negative* near $x = 0$. We should therefore replace $|y|$ with $-y$ in the integrated equation $\ln|y| = -3x^2 + C$ to obtain

$$\ln(-y) = -3x^2 + C.$$

The initial condition then yields $C = \ln 4$, so $\ln(-y) = -3x^2 + \ln 4$, and hence

$$y(x) = -4e^{-3x^2}.$$

This is the lower emphasized solution curve in Fig. 1.4.1.   ∎

Example 2   Solve the differential equation

$$\frac{dy}{dx} = \frac{4 - 2x}{3y^2 - 5}. \tag{5}$$

Solution   When we separate the variables and integrate both sides, we get

$$\int (3y^2 - 5)\,dy = \int (4 - 2x)\,dx;$$
$$y^3 - 5y = 4x - x^2 + C. \tag{6}$$

This equation is not readily solved for y as an explicit function of x.   ∎

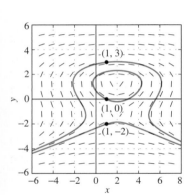

FIGURE 1.4.2. Slope field and solution curves for $y' = (4 - 2x)/(3y^2 - 5)$ in Example 2.

As Example 2 illustrates, it may or may not be possible or practical to solve Eq. (4) explicitly for y in terms of x. If not, then we call (4) an *implicit solution* of the differential equation in (2). Thus Eq. (6) gives an implicit solution of the differential equation in (5). Although it is not convenient to solve Eq. (6) explicitly in terms of x, we see that each solution curve $y = y(x)$ lies on a contour (or level) curve where the function

$$H(x, y) = x^2 - 4x + y^3 - 5y$$

is constant. Figure 1.4.2 shows several of these contour curves.

Example 3   To solve the initial value problem

$$\frac{dy}{dx} = \frac{4 - 2x}{3y^2 - 5}, \quad y(1) = 3, \tag{7}$$

we substitute $x = 1$ and $y = 3$ in Eq. (6) and get $C = 9$. Thus the desired particular solution $y(x)$ is defined implicitly by the equation

$$y^3 - 5y = 4x - x^2 + 9. \tag{8}$$

The corresponding solution curve $y = y(x)$ lies on the upper contour curve in Fig. 1.4.2—the one passing through $(1, 3)$. Because the graph of a differentiable solution cannot have a vertical tangent line anywhere, it appears from the figure that this particular solution is defined on the interval $(-1, 5)$ but not on the interval $(-3, 7)$.   ∎

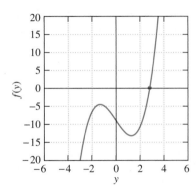

FIGURE 1.4.3. Graph of $f(y) = y^3 - 5y - 9$.

Remark 1: When a specific value of x is substituted in Eq. (8), we can attempt to solve numerically for y. For instance, $x = 4$ yields the equation

$$f(y) = y^3 - 5y - 9 = 0.$$

Figure 1.4.3 shows the graph of f. With a graphing calculator we can solve for the single real root $y \approx 2.8552$. This yields the value $y(4) \approx 2.8552$ of the particular solution in Example 3.

Remark 2: If the initial condition in (7) is replaced with the condition $y(1) = 0$, then the resulting particular solution of the differential equation in (5) lies on the lower "half" of the oval contour curve in Fig. 1.4.2. It appears that this particular solution through $(1, 0)$ is defined on the interval $(0, 4)$ but not on the interval $(-1, 5)$. On the other hand, with the initial condition $y(1) = -2$ we get the lower contour curve in Fig. 1.4.2. This particular solution is defined for all x. Thus the initial condition can determine whether a particular solution is defined on the whole real line or only on some bounded interval. With a computer algebra system one can readily calculate a table of values of the y-solutions of Eq. (8) for x-values at desired increments from $x = -1$ to $x = 5$ (for instance). Such a table of values serves effectively as a "numerical solution" of the initial value problem in (7). ■

Implicit, General, and Singular Solutions

The equation $K(x, y) = 0$ is commonly called an **implicit solution** of a differential equation if it is satisfied (on some interval) by some solution $y = y(x)$ of the differential equation. But note that a particular solution $y = y(x)$ of $K(x, y) = 0$ may or may not satisfy a given initial condition. For example, differentiation of $x^2 + y^2 = 4$ yields

$$x + y\frac{dy}{dx} = 0,$$

so $x^2 + y^2 = 4$ is an implicit solution of the differential equation $x + yy' = 0$. But only the first of the two explicit solutions

$$y(x) = +\sqrt{4 - x^2} \quad \text{and} \quad y(x) = -\sqrt{4 - x^2}$$

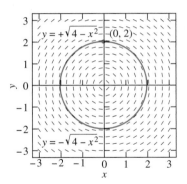

FIGURE 1.4.4. Slope field and solution curves for $y' = -x/y$.

satisfies the initial condition $y(0) = 2$ (Fig. 1.4.4).

Remark 1: You should not assume that every possible algebraic solution $y = y(x)$ of an implicit solution satisfies the same differential equation. For instance, if we multiply the implicit solution $x^2 + y^2 - 4 = 0$ by the factor $(y - 2x)$, then we get the new implicit solution

$$(y - 2x)(x^2 + y^2 - 4) = 0$$

that yields (or "contains") not only the previously noted explicit solutions $y = +\sqrt{4 - x^2}$ and $y = -\sqrt{4 - x^2}$ of the differential equation $x + yy' = 0$, but also the additional function $y = 2x$ that does *not* satisfy this differential equation.

Remark 2: Similarly, solutions of a given differential equation can be either gained or lost when it is multiplied or divided by an algebraic factor. For instance, consider the differential equation

$$(y - 2x)y\frac{dy}{dx} = -x(y - 2x) \tag{9}$$

having the obvious solution $y = 2x$. But if we divide both sides by the common factor $(y - 2x)$, then we get the previously discussed differential equation

$$y\frac{dy}{dx} = -x, \quad \text{or} \quad x + y\frac{dy}{dx} = 0, \tag{10}$$

of which $y = 2x$ is *not* a solution. Thus we "lose" the solution $y = 2x$ of Eq. (9) upon its division by the factor $(y - 2x)$; alternatively, we "gain" this new solution when we multiply Eq. (10) by $(y - 2x)$. Such elementary algebraic operations to simplify a given differential equation before attempting to solve it are common in practice, but the possibility of loss or gain of such "extraneous solutions" should be kept in mind. ∎

A solution of a differential equation that contains an "arbitrary constant" (like the constant C in the solution of Examples 1 and 2) is commonly called a **general solution** of the differential equation; any particular choice of a specific value for C yields a single particular solution of the equation.

The argument preceding Example 1 actually suffices to show that *every* particular solution of the differential equation $f(y)y' = g(x)$ in (2) satisfies the equation $F(y(x)) = G(x) + C$ in (4). Consequently, it is appropriate to call (4) not merely *a* general solution of (2), but *the* general solution of (2).

In Section 1.5 we shall see that every particular solution of a *linear* first-order differential equation is contained in its general solution. By contrast, it is common for a nonlinear first-order differential equation to have both a general solution involving an arbitrary constant C and one or several particular solutions that cannot be obtained by selecting a value for C. These exceptional solutions are frequently called **singular solutions**. In Problem 30 we ask you to show that the general solution of the differential equation $(y')^2 = 4y$ yields the family of parabolas $y = (x - C)^2$ illustrated in Fig. 1.4.5, and to observe that the constant-valued function $y(x) \equiv 0$ is a singular solution that cannot be obtained from the general solution by any choice of the arbitrary constant C.

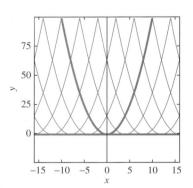

FIGURE 1.4.5. The general solution curves $y = (x - C)^2$ and the singular solution curve $y = 0$ of the differential equation $(y')^2 = 4y$.

Example 4 Find all solutions of the differential equation

$$\frac{dy}{dx} = 6x(y - 1)^{2/3}.$$

Solution Separation of variables gives

$$\int \frac{1}{3(y - 1)^{2/3}} \, dy = \int 2x \, dx;$$

$$(y - 1)^{1/3} = x^2 + C;$$

$$y(x) = 1 + (x^2 + C)^3.$$

Positive values of the arbitrary constant C give the solution curves in Fig. 1.4.6 that lie above the line $y = 1$, whereas negative values yield those that dip below it. The value $C = 0$ gives the solution $y(x) = 1 + x^6$, but *no* value of C gives the singular solution $y(x) \equiv 1$ that was lost when the variables were separated. Note that the two different solutions $y(x) \equiv 1$ and $y(x) = 1 + (x^2 - 1)^3$ both satisfy the initial condition $y(1) = 1$. Indeed, the whole singular solution curve $y = 1$ consists of points where the solution is not unique and where the function $f(x, y) = 6x(y - 1)^{2/3}$ is not differentiable. ∎

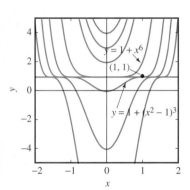

FIGURE 1.4.6. General and singular solution curves for $y' = 6x(y - 1)^{2/3}$.

Natural Growth and Decay

The differential equation

$$\frac{dx}{dt} = kx \quad (k \text{ a constant}) \tag{11}$$

serves as a mathematical model for a remarkably wide range of natural phenomena—any involving a quantity whose time rate of change is proportional to its current size. Here are some examples.

POPULATION GROWTH: Suppose that $P(t)$ is the number of individuals in a population (of humans, or insects, or bacteria) having *constant* birth and death rates β and δ (in births or deaths per individual per unit of time). Then, during a short time interval Δt, approximately $\beta P(t)\,\Delta t$ births and $\delta P(t)\,\Delta t$ deaths occur, so the change in $P(t)$ is given approximately by

$$\Delta P \approx (\beta - \delta)P(t)\,\Delta t,$$

and therefore

$$\frac{dP}{dt} = \lim_{\Delta t \to 0} \frac{\Delta P}{\Delta t} = kP, \tag{12}$$

where $k = \beta - \delta$.

COMPOUND INTEREST: Let $A(t)$ be the number of dollars in a savings account at time t (in years), and suppose that the interest is *compounded continuously* at an annual interest rate r. (Note that 10% annual interest means that $r = 0.10$.) Continuous compounding means that during a short time interval Δt, the amount of interest added to the account is approximately $\Delta A = rA(t)\,\Delta t$, so that

$$\frac{dA}{dt} = \lim_{\Delta t \to 0} \frac{\Delta A}{\Delta t} = rA. \tag{13}$$

RADIOACTIVE DECAY: Consider a sample of material that contains $N(t)$ atoms of a certain radioactive isotope at time t. It has been observed that a constant fraction of those radioactive atoms will spontaneously decay (into atoms of another element or into another isotope of the same element) during each unit of time. Consequently, the sample behaves exactly like a population with a constant death rate and no births. To write a model for $N(t)$, we use Eq. (12) with N in place of P, with $k > 0$ in place of δ, and with $\beta = 0$. We thus get the differential equation

$$\frac{dN}{dt} = -kN. \tag{14}$$

The value of k depends on the particular radioactive isotope.

The key to the method of *radiocarbon dating* is that a constant proportion of the carbon atoms in any living creature is made up of the radioactive isotope ^{14}C of carbon. This proportion remains constant because the fraction of ^{14}C in the atmosphere remains almost constant, and living matter is continuously taking up carbon from the air or is consuming other living matter containing the same constant ratio of ^{14}C atoms to ordinary ^{12}C atoms. This same ratio permeates all life, because organic processes seem to make no distinction between the two isotopes.

The ratio of ^{14}C to normal carbon remains constant in the atmosphere because, although ^{14}C is radioactive and slowly decays, the amount is continuously replenished through the conversion of ^{14}N (ordinary nitrogen) to ^{14}C by cosmic rays bombarding the upper atmosphere. Over the long history of the planet, this decay and replenishment process has come into nearly steady state.

Of course, when a living organism dies, it ceases its metabolism of carbon and the process of radioactive decay begins to deplete its ^{14}C content. There is no replenishment of this ^{14}C, and consequently the ratio of ^{14}C to normal carbon begins to drop. By measuring this ratio, the amount of time elapsed since the death of the organism can be estimated. For such purposes it is necessary to measure the **decay constant** k. For ^{14}C, it is known that $k \approx 0.0001216$ if t is measured in years.

(Matters are not as simple as we have made them appear. In applying the technique of radiocarbon dating, extreme care must be taken to avoid contaminating the sample with organic matter or even with ordinary fresh air. In addition, the cosmic ray levels apparently have not been constant, so the ratio of ^{14}C in the atmosphere has varied over the past centuries. By using independent methods of dating samples, researchers in this area have compiled tables of correction factors to enhance the accuracy of this process.)

DRUG ELIMINATION: In many cases the amount $A(t)$ of a certain drug in the bloodstream, measured by the excess over the natural level of the drug, will decline at a rate proportional to the current excess amount. That is,

$$\frac{dA}{dt} = -\lambda A, \tag{15}$$

where $\lambda > 0$. The parameter λ is called the **elimination constant** of the drug.

The Natural Growth Equation

The prototype differential equation $dx/dt = kx$ with $x(t) > 0$ and k a constant (either negative or positive) is readily solved by separating the variables and integrating:

$$\int \frac{1}{x} dx = \int k \, dt;$$

$$\ln x = kt + C.$$

Then we solve for x:

$$e^{\ln x} = e^{kt+C}; \quad x = x(t) = e^C e^{kt} = A e^{kt}.$$

Because C is a constant, so is $A = e^C$. It is also clear that $A = x(0) = x_0$, so the particular solution of Eq. (11) with the initial condition $x(0) = x_0$ is simply

$$x(t) = x_0 e^{kt}. \tag{16}$$

Because of the presence of the natural exponential function in its solution, the differential equation

$$\frac{dx}{dt} = kx \tag{17}$$

is often called the **exponential** or **natural growth equation**. Figure 1.4.7 shows a typical graph of $x(t)$ in the case $k > 0$; the case $k < 0$ is illustrated in Fig. 1.4.8.

FIGURE 1.4.7. Natural growth.

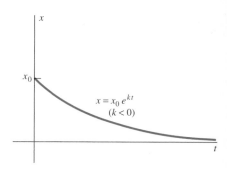

FIGURE 1.4.8. Natural decay.

Example 5

According to data listed at **www.census.gov**, the world's total population reached 6 billion persons in mid-1999, and was then increasing at the rate of about 212 thousand persons each day. Assuming that natural population growth at this rate continues, we want to answer these questions:

(a) What is the annual growth rate k?

(b) What will be the world population at the middle of the 21st century?

(c) How long will it take the world population to increase tenfold—thereby reaching the 60 billion that some demographers believe to be the maximum for which the planet can provide adequate food supplies?

Solution

(a) We measure the world population $P(t)$ in billions and measure time in years. We take $t = 0$ to correspond to (mid) 1999, so $P_0 = 6$. The fact that P is increasing by 212,000, or 0.000212 billion, persons per day at time $t = 0$ means that

$$P'(0) = (0.000212)(365.25) \approx 0.07743$$

billion per year. From the natural growth equation $P' = kP$ with $t = 0$ we now obtain

$$k = \frac{P'(0)}{P(0)} \approx \frac{0.07743}{6} \approx 0.0129.$$

Thus the world population was growing at the rate of about 1.29% annually in 1999. This value of k gives the world population function

$$P(t) = 6e^{0.0129t}.$$

(b) With $t = 51$ we obtain the prediction

$$P(51) = 6e^{(0.0129)(51)} \approx 11.58 \text{ (billion)}$$

for the world population in mid-2050 (so the population will almost have doubled in the just over a half-century since 1999).

(c) The world population should reach 60 billion when

$$60 = 6e^{0.0129t}; \quad \text{that is, when } t = \frac{\ln 10}{0.0129} \approx 178;$$

and thus in the year 2177. ∎

Note: Actually, the rate of growth of the world population is expected to slow somewhat during the next half-century, and the best current prediction for the 2050 population is "only" 9.1 billion. A simple mathematical model cannot be expected to mirror precisely the complexity of the real world.

The decay constant of a radioactive isotope is often specified in terms of another empirical constant, the *half-life* of the isotope, because this parameter is more convenient. The **half-life** τ of a radioactive isotope is the time required for *half* of it to decay. To find the relationship between k and τ, we set $t = \tau$ and $N = \frac{1}{2}N_0$ in the equation $N(t) = N_0 e^{kt}$, so that $\frac{1}{2}N_0 = N_0 e^{k\tau}$. When we solve for τ, we find that

$$\tau = \frac{\ln 2}{k}. \tag{18}$$

For example, the half-life of ^{14}C is $\tau \approx (\ln 2)/(0.0001216)$, approximately 5700 years.

Example 6   A specimen of charcoal found at Stonehenge turns out to contain 63% as much ^{14}C as a sample of present-day charcoal of equal mass. What is the age of the sample?

Solution   We take $t = 0$ as the time of the death of the tree from which the Stonehenge charcoal was made and N_0 as the number of ^{14}C atoms that the Stonehenge sample contained then. We are given that $N = (0.63)N_0$ now, so we solve the equation $(0.63)N_0 = N_0 e^{-kt}$ with the value $k = 0.0001216$. Thus we find that

$$t = -\frac{\ln(0.63)}{0.0001216} \approx 3800 \text{ (years)}.$$

Thus the sample is about 3800 years old. If it has any connection with the builders of Stonehenge, our computations suggest that this observatory, monument, or temple—whichever it may be—dates from 1800 B.C. or earlier. ∎

Cooling and Heating

According to Newton's law of cooling (Eq. (3) of Section 1.1), the time rate of change of the temperature $T(t)$ of a body immersed in a medium of constant temperature A is proportional to the difference $A - T$. That is,

$$\frac{dT}{dt} = k(A - T), \tag{19}$$

where k is a positive constant. This is an instance of the linear first-order differential equation with constant coefficients:

$$\frac{dx}{dt} = ax + b. \tag{20}$$

It includes the exponential equation as a special case ($b = 0$) and is also easy to solve by separation of variables.

Example 7   A 4-lb roast, initially at 50°F, is placed in a 375°F oven at 5:00 P.M. After 75 minutes it is found that the temperature $T(t)$ of the roast is 125°F. When will the roast be 150°F (medium rare)?

Solution   We take time t in minutes, with $t = 0$ corresponding to 5:00 P.M. We also assume (somewhat unrealistically) that at any instant the temperature $T(t)$ of the roast is uniform throughout. We have $T(t) < A = 375$, $T(0) = 50$, and $T(75) = 125$. Hence

$$\frac{dT}{dt} = k(375 - T);$$

$$\int \frac{1}{375 - T} \, dT = \int k \, dt;$$

$$-\ln(375 - T) = kt + C;$$

$$375 - T = Be^{-kt}.$$

Now $T(0) = 50$ implies that $B = 325$, so $T(t) = 375 - 325e^{-kt}$. We also know that $T = 125$ when $t = 75$. Substitution of these values in the preceding equation yields

$$k = -\tfrac{1}{75} \ln \left(\tfrac{250}{325} \right) \approx 0.0035.$$

Hence we finally solve the equation

$$150 = 375 - 325e^{(-0.0035)t}$$

for $t = -[\ln(225/325)]/(0.0035) \approx 105$ (min), the total cooking time required. Because the roast was placed in the oven at 5:00 P.M., it should be removed at about 6:45 P.M.   ∎

Torricelli's Law

Suppose that a water tank has a hole with area a at its bottom, from which water is leaking. Denote by $y(t)$ the depth of water in the tank at time t, and by $V(t)$ the volume of water in the tank then. It is plausible—and true, under ideal conditions—that the velocity of water exiting through the hole is

$$v = \sqrt{2gy}, \tag{21}$$

which is the velocity a drop of water would acquire in falling freely from the surface of the water to the hole (see Problem 35 of Section 1.2). One can derive this formula beginning with the assumption that the sum of the kinetic and potential energy of the system remains constant. Under real conditions, taking into account the constriction of a water jet from an orifice, $v = c\sqrt{2gy}$, where c is an empirical constant between 0 and 1 (usually about 0.6 for a small continuous stream of water). For simplicity we take $c = 1$ in the following discussion.

As a consequence of Eq. (21), we have

$$\frac{dV}{dt} = -av = -a\sqrt{2gy}; \tag{22a}$$

equivalently,

$$\frac{dV}{dt} = -k\sqrt{y} \quad \text{where} \quad k = a\sqrt{2g}. \tag{22b}$$

This is a statement of Torricelli's law for a draining tank. Let $A(y)$ denote the horizontal cross-sectional area of the tank at height y. Then, applied to a thin horizontal slice of water at height $\overline{y}$ with area $A(\overline{y})$ and thickness $d\overline{y}$, the integral calculus method of cross sections gives

$$V(y) = \int_0^y A(\overline{y})\, d\overline{y}.$$

The fundamental theorem of calculus therefore implies that $dV/dy = A(y)$ and hence that

$$\frac{dV}{dt} = \frac{dV}{dy} \cdot \frac{dy}{dt} = A(y)\frac{dy}{dt}. \tag{23}$$

From Eqs. (22) and (23) we finally obtain

$$A(y)\frac{dy}{dt} = -a\sqrt{2gy} = -k\sqrt{y}, \tag{24}$$

an alternative form of Torricelli's law. ∎

Example 8   A hemispherical bowl has top radius 4 ft and at time $t = 0$ is full of water. At that moment a circular hole with diameter 1 in. is opened in the bottom of the tank. How long will it take for all the water to drain from the tank?

Solution   From the right triangle in Fig. 1.4.9, we see that

$$A(y) = \pi r^2 = \pi \left[16 - (4 - y)^2\right] = \pi(8y - y^2).$$

With $g = 32$ ft/s^2, Eq. (24) becomes

$$\pi(8y - y^2)\frac{dy}{dt} = -\pi \left(\tfrac{1}{24}\right)^2 \sqrt{2 \cdot 32y}\,;$$

$$\int (8y^{1/2} - y^{3/2})\, dy = -\int \tfrac{1}{72}\, dt;$$

$$\tfrac{16}{3} y^{3/2} - \tfrac{2}{5} y^{5/2} = -\tfrac{1}{72}t + C.$$

Now $y(0) = 4$, so

$$C = \tfrac{16}{3} \cdot 4^{3/2} - \tfrac{2}{5} \cdot 4^{5/2} = \tfrac{448}{15}.$$

The tank is empty when $y = 0$, thus when

$$t = 72 \cdot \tfrac{448}{15} \approx 2150 \text{ (s)};$$

that is, about 35 min 50 s. So it takes slightly less than 36 min for the tank to drain. ∎

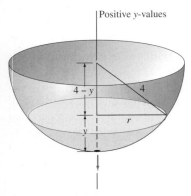

FIGURE 1.4.9. Draining a hemispherical tank.

Positive y-values

$4 - y$ 4

r

1.4 Problems

Find general solutions (implicit if necessary, explicit if convenient) of the differential equations in Problems 1 through 18. Primes denote derivatives with respect to x.

1. $\dfrac{dy}{dx} + 2xy = 0$

2. $\dfrac{dy}{dx} + 2xy^2 = 0$

3. $\dfrac{dy}{dx} = y \sin x$

4. $(1+x)\dfrac{dy}{dx} = 4y$

5. $2\sqrt{x}\dfrac{dy}{dx} = \sqrt{1-y^2}$

6. $\dfrac{dy}{dx} = 3\sqrt{xy}$

7. $\dfrac{dy}{dx} = (64xy)^{1/3}$

8. $\dfrac{dy}{dx} = 2x \sec y$

9. $(1-x^2)\dfrac{dy}{dx} = 2y$

10. $(1+x)^2\dfrac{dy}{dx} = (1+y)^2$

11. $y' = xy^3$

12. $yy' = x(y^2+1)$

13. $y^3\dfrac{dy}{dx} = (y^4+1)\cos x$

14. $\dfrac{dy}{dx} = \dfrac{1+\sqrt{x}}{1+\sqrt{y}}$

15. $\dfrac{dy}{dx} = \dfrac{(x-1)y^5}{x^2(2y^3-y)}$

16. $(x^2+1)(\tan y)y' = x$

17. $y' = 1+x+y+xy$ (*Suggestion*: Factor the right-hand side.)

18. $x^2y' = 1 - x^2 + y^2 - x^2y^2$

Find explicit particular solutions of the initial value problems in Problems 19 through 28.

19. $\dfrac{dy}{dx} = ye^x, \quad y(0) = 2e$

20. $\dfrac{dy}{dx} = 3x^2(y^2+1), \quad y(0) = 1$

21. $2y\dfrac{dy}{dx} = \dfrac{x}{\sqrt{x^2-16}}, \quad y(5) = 2$

22. $\dfrac{dy}{dx} = 4x^3y - y, \quad y(1) = -3$

23. $\dfrac{dy}{dx} + 1 = 2y, \quad y(1) = 1$

24. $(\tan x)\dfrac{dy}{dx} = y, \quad y\left(\tfrac{1}{2}\pi\right) = \tfrac{1}{2}\pi$

25. $x\dfrac{dy}{dx} - y = 2x^2y, \quad y(1) = 1$

26. $\dfrac{dy}{dx} = 2xy^2 + 3x^2y^2, \quad y(1) = -1$

27. $\dfrac{dy}{dx} = 6e^{2x-y}, \quad y(0) = 0$

28. $2\sqrt{x}\dfrac{dy}{dx} = \cos^2 y, \quad y(4) = \pi/4$

29. **(a)** Find a general solution of the differential equation $dy/dx = y^2$. **(b)** Find a singular solution that is not included in the general solution. **(c)** Inspect a sketch of typical solution curves to determine the points (a,b) for which the initial value problem $y' = y^2$, $y(a) = b$ has a unique solution.

30. Solve the differential equation $(dy/dx)^2 = 4y$ to verify the general solution curves and singular solution curve that are illustrated in Fig. 1.4.5. Then determine the points (a,b) in the plane for which the initial value problem $(y')^2 = 4y$, $y(a) = b$ has **(a)** no solution, **(b)** infinitely many solutions that are defined for all x, **(c)** on some neighborhood of the point $x = a$, only finitely many solutions.

31. Discuss the difference between the differential equations $(dy/dx)^2 = 4y$ and $dy/dx = 2\sqrt{y}$. Do they have the same solution curves? Why or why not? Determine the points (a,b) in the plane for which the initial value problem $y' = 2\sqrt{y}$, $y(a) = b$ has **(a)** no solution, **(b)** a unique solution, **(c)** infinitely many solutions.

32. Find a general solution and any singular solutions of the differential equation $dy\,myslashdx = y\sqrt{y^2-1}$. Determine the points (a,b) in the plane for which the initial value problem $y' = y\sqrt{y^2-1}$, $y(a) = b$ has **(a)** no solution, **(b)** a unique solution, **(c)** infinitely many solutions.

33. (Population growth) A certain city had a population of 25000 in 1960 and a population of 30000 in 1970. Assume that its population will continue to grow exponentially at a constant rate. What population can its city planners expect in the year 2000?

34. (Population growth) In a certain culture of bacteria, the number of bacteria increased sixfold in 10 h. How long did it take for the population to double?

35. (Radiocarbon dating) Carbon extracted from an ancient skull contained only one-sixth as much ^{14}C as carbon extracted from present-day bone. How old is the skull?

36. (Radiocarbon dating) Carbon taken from a purported relic of the time of Christ contained 4.6×10^{10} atoms of ^{14}C per gram. Carbon extracted from a present-day specimen of the same substance contained 5.0×10^{10} atoms of ^{14}C per gram. Compute the approximate age of the relic. What is your opinion as to its authenticity?

37. (Continuously compounded interest) Upon the birth of their first child, a couple deposited $5000 in an account that pays 8% interest compounded continuously. The interest payments are allowed to accumulate. How much will the account contain on the child's eighteenth birthday?

38. (Continuously compounded interest) Suppose that you discover in your attic an overdue library book on which your grandfather owed a fine of 30 cents 100 years ago. If an overdue fine grows exponentially at a 5% annual rate compounded continuously, how much would you have to pay if you returned the book today?

39. (Drug elimination) Suppose that sodium pentobarbital is used to anesthetize a dog. The dog is anesthetized when its bloodstream contains at least 45 milligrams (mg) of sodium pentobarbitol per kilogram of the dog's body weight. Suppose also that sodium pentobarbitol is eliminated exponentially from the dog's bloodstream, with a half-life of 5 h. What single dose should be administered in order to anesthetize a 50-kg dog for 1 h?

40. The half-life of radioactive cobalt is 5.27 years. Suppose that a nuclear accident has left the level of cobalt radiation in a certain region at 100 times the level acceptable for human habitation. How long will it be until the region is again habitable? (Ignore the probable presence of other radioactive isotopes.)

41. Suppose that a mineral body formed in an ancient cataclysm—perhaps the formation of the earth itself—originally contained the uranium isotope ^{238}U (which has a half-life of 4.51×10^9 years) but no lead, the end product of the radioactive decay of ^{238}U. If today the ratio of ^{238}U atoms to lead atoms in the mineral body is 0.9, when did the cataclysm occur?

42. A certain moon rock was found to contain equal numbers of potassium and argon atoms. Assume that all the argon is the result of radioactive decay of potassium (its half-life is about 1.28×10^9 years) and that one of every nine potassium atom disintegrations yields an argon atom. What is the age of the rock, measured from the time it contained only potassium?

43. A pitcher of buttermilk initially at $25°C$ is to be cooled by setting it on the front porch, where the temperature is $0°C$. Suppose that the temperature of the buttermilk has dropped to $15°C$ after 20 min. When will it be at $5°C$?

44. When sugar is dissolved in water, the amount A that remains undissolved after t minutes satisfies the differential equation $dA/dt = -kA$ $(k > 0)$. If 25% of the sugar dissolves after 1 min, how long does it take for half of the sugar to dissolve?

45. The intensity I of light at a depth of x meters below the surface of a lake satisfies the differential equation $dI/dx = (-1.4)I$. **(a)** At what depth is the intensity half the intensity I_0 at the surface (where $x = 0$)? **(b)** What is the intensity at a depth of 10 m (as a fraction of I_0)? **(c)** At what depth will the intensity be 1% of that at the surface?

46. The barometric pressure p (in inches of mercury) at an altitude x miles above sea level satisfies the initial value problem $dp/dx = (-0.2)p$, $p(0) = 29.92$. **(a)** Calculate the barometric pressure at 10,000 ft and again at 30,000 ft. **(b)** Without prior conditioning, few people can survive when the pressure drops to less than 15 in. of mercury. How high is that?

47. A certain piece of dubious information about phenylethylamine in the drinking water began to spread one day in a city with a population of 100,000. Within a week, 10,000 people had heard this rumor. Assume that the rate of increase of the number who have heard the rumor is proportional to the number who have not yet heard it. How long will it be until half the population of the city has heard the rumor?

48. According to one cosmological theory, there were equal amounts of the two uranium isotopes ^{235}U and ^{238}U at the creation of the universe in the "big bang." At present there are 137.7 atoms of ^{238}U for each atom of ^{235}U. Using the half-lives 4.51×10^9 years for ^{238}U and 7.10×10^8 years for ^{235}U, calculate the age of the universe.

49. A cake is removed from an oven at $210°F$ and left to cool at room temperature, which is $70°F$. After 30 min the temperature of the cake is $140°F$. When will it be $100°F$?

50. The amount $A(t)$ of atmospheric pollutants in a certain mountain valley grows naturally and is tripling every 7.5 years.

(a) If the initial amount is 10 pu (pollutant units), write a formula for $A(t)$ giving the amount (in pu) present after t years.

(b) What will be the amount (in pu) of pollutants present in the valley atmosphere after 5 years?

(c) If it will be dangerous to stay in the valley when the amount of pollutants reaches 100 pu, how long will this take?

51. An accident at a nuclear power plant has left the surrounding area polluted with radioactive material that decays naturally. The initial amount of radioactive material present is 15 su (safe units), and 5 months later it is still 10 su.

(a) Write a formula giving the amount $A(t)$ of radioactive material (in su) remaining after t months.

(b) What amount of radioactive material will remain after 8 months?

(c) How long—total number of months or fraction thereof—will it be until $A = 1$ su, so it is safe for people to return to the area?

52. There are now about 3300 different human "language families" in the whole world. Assume that all these are derived from a single original language, and that a language family develops into 1.5 language families every 6 thousand years. About how long ago was the single original human language spoken?

53. Thousands of years ago ancestors of the Native Americans crossed the Bering Strait from Asia and entered the western hemisphere. Since then, they have fanned out across North and South America. The single language that the original Native Americans spoke has since split into many Indian "language families." Assume (as in Problem 52) that the number of these language families has been multiplied by 1.5 every 6000 years. There are now 150 Native American language families in the western hemisphere. About when did the ancestors of today's Native Americans arrive?

54. A tank is shaped like a vertical cylinder; it initially contains water to a depth of 9 ft, and a bottom plug is removed at time $t = 0$ (hours). After 1 h the depth of the water has dropped to 4 ft. How long does it take for all the water to drain from the tank?

55. Suppose that the tank of Problem 48 has a radius of 3 ft and that its bottom hole is circular with radius 1 in. How long will it take the water (initially 9 ft deep) to drain completely?

56. At time $t = 0$ the bottom plug (at the vertex) of a full conical water tank 16 ft high is removed. After 1 h the water in the tank is 9 ft deep. When will the tank be empty?

57. Suppose that a cylindrical tank initially containing V_0 gallons of water drains (through a bottom hole) in T minutes. Use Torricelli's law to show that the volume of water in the tank after $t \leq T$ minutes is $V = V_0 [1 - (t/T)]^2$.

58. A water tank has the shape obtained by revolving the curve $y = x^{4/3}$ around the y-axis. A plug at the bottom is removed at 12 noon, when the depth of water in the tank is 12 ft. At 1 P.M. the depth of the water is 6 ft. When will the tank be empty?

59. A water tank has the shape obtained by revolving the parabola $x^2 = by$ around the y-axis. The water depth is 4 ft at 12 noon, when a circular plug in the bottom of the tank is removed. At 1 P.M. the depth of the water is 1 ft. **(a)** Find the depth $y(t)$ of water remaining after t hours. **(b)** When will the tank be empty? **(c)** If the initial radius of the top surface of the water is 2 ft, what is the radius of the circular hole in the bottom?

60. A cylindrical tank with length 5 ft and radius 3 ft is situated with its axis horizontal. If a circular bottom hole with a radius of 1 in. is opened and the tank is initially half full of xylene, how long will it take for the liquid to drain completely?

61. A spherical tank of radius 4 ft is full of gasoline when a circular bottom hole with radius 1 in. is opened. How long will be required for all the gasoline to drain from the tank?

62. Suppose that an initially full hemispherical water tank of radius 1 m has its flat side as its bottom. It has a bottom hole of radius 1 cm. If this bottom hole is opened at 1 P.M., when will the tank be empty?

63. Consider the initially full hemispherical water tank of Example 8, except that the radius r of its circular bottom hole is now unknown. At 1 P.M. the bottom hole is opened and at 1:30 P.M. the depth of water in the tank is 2 ft. **(a)** Use Torricelli's law in the form $dV/dt = -(0.6)\pi r^2 \sqrt{2gy}$ (taking constriction into account) to determine when the tank will be empty. **(b)** What is the radius of the bottom hole?

64. (The *clepsydra*, or water clock) A 12-h water clock is to be designed with the dimensions shown in Fig. 1.4.10, shaped like the surface obtained by revolving the curve $y = f(x)$ around the y-axis. What should be this curve, and what should be the radius of the circular bottom hole, in order that the water level will fall at the *constant* rate of 4 inches per hour (in./h)?

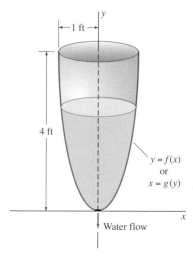

FIGURE 1.4.10. The clepsydra.

65. Just before midday the body of an apparent homicide victim is found in a room that is kept at a constant temperature of $70°$F. At 12 noon the temperature of the body is $80°$F and at 1 P.M. it is $75°$F. Assume that the temperature of the body at the time of death was $98.6°$F and that it has cooled in accord with Newton's law. What was the time of death?

66. Early one morning it began to snow at a constant rate. At 7 A.M. a snowplow set off to clear a road. By 8 A.M. it had traveled 2 miles, but it took two more hours (until 10 A.M.) for the snowplow to go an additional 2 miles. **(a)** Let $t = 0$ when it began to snow and let x denote the distance traveled by the snowplow at time t. Assuming that the snowplow clears snow from the road at a constant rate (in cubic feet per hour, say), show that

$$k \frac{dx}{dt} = \frac{1}{t}$$

where k is a constant. **(b)** What time did it start snowing? (*Answer*: 6 A.M.)

67. A snowplow sets off at 7 A.M. as in Problem 66. Suppose now that by 8 A.M. it had traveled 4 miles and that by 9 A.M. it had moved an additional 3 miles. What time did it start snowing? This is a more difficult snowplow problem because now a transcendental equation must be solved numerically to find the value of k. (*Answer*: 4:27 A.M.)

68. Figure 1.4.11 shows a bead sliding down a frictionless wire from point P to point Q. The *brachistochrone problem* asks what shape the wire should be in order to minimize the bead's time of descent from P to Q. In June of 1696, John Bernoulli proposed this problem as a public challenge, with a 6-month deadline (later extended to Easter 1697 at George Leibniz's request). Isaac Newton, then retired from academic life and serving as Warden of the Mint in London, received Bernoulli's challenge on January 29, 1697. The very next day he communicated his own solution—the curve of minimal descent time is an arc of an inverted cycloid—to the Royal Society of London. For a modern derivation of this result, suppose the bead starts from rest at the origin P and let $y = y(x)$ be the equation of the desired curve in a coordinate system with the y-axis pointing downward. Then a mechanical analogue of Snell's law in optics implies that

$$\frac{\sin \alpha}{v} = \text{constant}, \qquad \text{(i)}$$

where α denotes the angle of deflection (from the vertical) of the tangent line to the curve—so $\cot \alpha = y'(x)$ (why?)—and $v = \sqrt{2gy}$ is the bead's velocity when it has descended a distance y vertically (from KE $= \frac{1}{2}mv^2 = mgy = -\text{PE}$).

FIGURE 1.4.11. A bead sliding down a wire—the brachistochrone problem.

(a) First derive from Eq. (i) the differential equation

$$\frac{dy}{dx} = \sqrt{\frac{2a - y}{y}} \qquad \text{(ii)}$$

where a is an appropriate positive constant.

(b) Substitute $y = 2a \sin^2 t$, $dy = 4a \sin t \cos t \, dt$ in (ii) to derive the solution

$$x = a(2t - \sin 2t), \quad y = a(1 - \cos 2t) \qquad \text{(iii)}$$

for which $t = y = 0$ when $x = 0$. Finally, the substitution of $\theta = 2a$ in (iii) yields the standard parametric equations $x = a(\theta - \sin \theta)$, $y = a(1 - \cos \theta)$

of the cycloid that is generated by a point on the rim of a circular wheel of radius a as it rolls along the x-axis. [See Example 5 in Section 9.4 of Edwards and Penney, *Calculus: Early Transcendentals*, 7th edition (Upper Saddle River, NJ: Prentice Hall, 2008).]

69. Suppose a uniform flexible cable is suspended between two points $(\pm L, H)$ at equal heights located symmetrically on either side of the x-axis (Fig. 1.4.12). Principles of physics can be used to show that the shape $y = y(x)$ of the hanging cable satisfies the differential equation

$$a\frac{d^2y}{dx^2} = \sqrt{1 + \left(\frac{dy}{dx}\right)^2},$$

where the constant $a = T/\rho$ is the ratio of the cable's tension T at its lowest point $x = 0$ (where $y'(0) = 0$) and its (constant) linear density ρ. If we substitute $v = dy/dx$, $dv/dx = d^2y/dx^2$ in this second-order differential equation, we get the first-order equation

$$a\frac{dv}{dx} = \sqrt{1 + v^2}.$$

Solve this differential equation for $y'(x) = v(x) = \sinh(x/a)$. Then integrate to get the shape function

$$y(x) = a \cosh\left(\frac{x}{a}\right) + C$$

of the hanging cable. This curve is called a *catenary*, from the Latin word for *chain*.

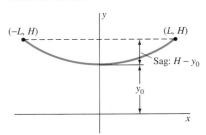

FIGURE 1.4.12. The catenary.

1.4 Application   The Logistic Equation

As in Eq. (3) of this section, the solution of a separable differential equation reduces to the evaluation of two indefinite integrals. It is tempting to use a symbolic algebra system for this purpose. We illustrate this approach using the *logistic differential equation*

$$\frac{dx}{dt} = ax - bx^2 \qquad \text{(1)}$$

that models a population $x(t)$ with births (per unit time) proportional to x and deaths proportional to x^2. Here we concentrate on the solution of Eq. (1) and defer discussion of population applications to Section 2.1.

If $a = 0.01$ and $b = 0.0001$, for instance, Eq. (1) is

$$\frac{dx}{dt} = (0.01)x - (0.0001)x^2 = \frac{x}{10000}(100 - x). \tag{2}$$

Separation of variables leads to

$$\int \frac{1}{x(100 - x)} dx = \int \frac{1}{10000} dt = \frac{t}{10000} + C. \tag{3}$$

We can evaluate the integral on the left by using the *Maple* command

```
int(1/(x*(100 - x)), x);
```

the *Mathematica* command

```
Integrate[ 1/(x*(100 - x)), x ]
```

or the MATLAB command

```
syms x;    int(1/(x*(100 - x)))
```

Any computer algebra system gives a result of the form

$$\frac{1}{100} \ln x - \frac{1}{100} \ln(x - 100) = \frac{t}{10000} + C \tag{4}$$

FIGURE 1.4.13. TI-89 screen showing the integral in Eq. (3).

equivalent to the graphing calculator result shown in Fig. 1.4.13.

You can now apply the initial condition $x(0) = x_0$, combine logarithms, and finally exponentiate to solve Eq. (4) for the particular solution

$$x(t) = \frac{100x_0 e^{t/100}}{100 - x_0 + x_0 e^{t/100}} \tag{5}$$

of Eq. (2). The slope field and solution curves shown in Fig. 1.4.14 suggest that, whatever is the initial value x_0, the solution $x(t)$ approaches 100 as $t \to +\infty$. Can you use Eq. (5) to verify this conjecture?

INVESTIGATION: For your own personal logistic equation, take $a = m/n$ and $b = 1/n$ in Eq. (1), with m and n being the *largest* two distinct digits (in either order) in your student ID number.

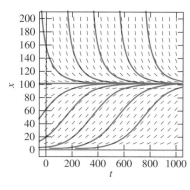

FIGURE 1.4.14. Slope field and solution curves for $x' = (0.01)x - (0.0001)x^2$.

(a) First generate a slope field for your differential equation and include a sufficient number of solution curves that you can see what happens to the population as $t \to +\infty$. State your inference plainly.

(b) Next use a computer algebra system to solve the differential equation symbolically; then use the symbolic solution to find the limit of $x(t)$ as $t \to +\infty$. Was your graphically-based inference correct?

(c) Finally, state and solve a numerical problem using the symbolic solution. For instance, how long does it take x to grow from a selected initial value x_0 to a given target value x_1?

1.5 Linear First-Order Equations

In Section 1.4 we saw how to solve a separable differential equation by integrating *after* multiplying both sides by an appropriate factor. For instance, to solve the equation

$$\frac{dy}{dx} = 2xy \quad (y > 0),$$

(1)

we multiply both sides by the factor $1/y$ to get

$$\frac{1}{y} \cdot \frac{dy}{dx} = 2x; \quad \text{that is,} \quad D_x(\ln y) = D_x(x^2).$$

(2)

Because each side of the equation in (2) is recognizable as a *derivative* (with respect to the independent variable x), all that remains are two simple integrations, which yield $\ln y = x^2 + C$. For this reason, the function $\rho(y) = 1/y$ is called an *integrating factor* for the original equation in (1). An **integrating factor** for a differential equation is a function $\rho(x, y)$ such that the multiplication of each side of the differential equation by $\rho(x, y)$ yields an equation in which each side is recognizable as a derivative.

With the aid of the appropriate integrating factor, there is a standard technique for solving the **linear first-order equation**

➤ $$\frac{dy}{dx} + P(x)y = Q(x)$$

(3)

on an interval on which the coefficient functions $P(x)$ and $Q(x)$ are continuous. We multiply each side in Eq. (3) by the integrating factor

➤ $$\rho(x) = e^{\int P(x)\,dx}.$$

(4)

The result is

$$e^{\int P(x)\,dx} \frac{dy}{dx} + P(x)e^{\int P(x)\,dx}y = Q(x)e^{\int P(x)\,dx}.$$

(5)

Because

$$D_x\left[\int P(x)\,dx\right] = P(x),$$

the left-hand side is the derivative of the *product* $y(x) \cdot e^{\int P(x)\,dx}$, so Eq. (5) is equivalent to

$$D_x\left[y(x) \cdot e^{\int P(x)\,dx}\right] = Q(x)e^{\int P(x)\,dx}.$$

Integration of both sides of this equation gives

$$y(x)e^{\int P(x)\,dx} = \int \left(Q(x)e^{\int P(x)\,dx}\right)dx + C.$$

Finally, solving for y, we obtain the general solution of the linear first-order equation in (3):

$$y(x) = e^{-\int P(x)\,dx}\left[\int \left(Q(x)e^{\int P(x)\,dx}\right)dx + C\right].$$

(6)

This formula should **not** be memorized. In a specific problem it generally is simpler to use the *method* by which we developed the formula. That is, in order to solve an equation that can be written in the form in Eq. (3) with the coefficient functions $P(x)$ and $Q(x)$ displayed explicitly, you should attempt to carry out the following steps.

METHOD: SOLUTION OF FIRST-ORDER EQUATIONS

1. Begin by calculating the integrating factor $\rho(x) = e^{\int P(x)\,dx}$.
2. Then multiply both sides of the differential equation by $\rho(x)$.
3. Next, recognize the left-hand side of the resulting equation as the derivative of a product:

$$D_x\left[\rho(x)y(x)\right] = \rho(x)Q(x).$$

4. Finally, integrate this equation,

$$\rho(x)y(x) = \int \rho(x)Q(x)\,dx + C,$$

then solve for y to obtain the general solution of the original differential equation.

Remark 1: Given an initial condition $y(x_0) = y_0$, you can (as usual) substitute $x = x_0$ and $y = y_0$ into the general solution and solve for the value of C yielding the particular solution that satisfies this initial condition.

Remark 2: You need not supply explicitly a constant of integration when you find the integrating factor $\rho(x)$. For if we replace

$$\int P(x)\,dx \quad \text{with} \quad \int P(x)\,dx + K$$

in Eq. (4), the result is

$$\rho(x) = e^{K + \int P(x)\,dx} = e^K e^{\int P(x)\,dx}.$$

But the constant factor e^K does not affect materially the result of multiplying both sides of the differential equation in (3) by $\rho(x)$, so we might as well take $K = 0$. You may therefore choose for $\int P(x)\,dx$ *any* convenient antiderivative of $P(x)$, without bothering to add a constant of integration. ∎

Example 1 Solve the initial value problem

$$\frac{dy}{dx} - y = \tfrac{11}{8}e^{-x/3}, \quad y(0) = -1.$$

Solution Here we have $P(x) \equiv -1$ and $Q(x) = \tfrac{11}{8}e^{-x/3}$, so the integrating factor is

$$\rho(x) = e^{\int(-1)\,dx} = e^{-x}.$$

Multiplication of both sides of the given equation by e^{-x} yields

$$e^{-x}\frac{dy}{dx} - e^{-x}y = \tfrac{11}{8}e^{-4x/3}, \tag{7}$$

which we recognize as

$$\frac{d}{dx}\left(e^{-x}y\right) = \tfrac{11}{8}e^{-4x/3}.$$

Hence integration with respect to x gives

$$e^{-x}y = \int \tfrac{11}{8}e^{-4x/3}\,dx = -\tfrac{33}{32}e^{-4x/3} + C,$$

and multiplication by e^x gives the general solution

$$y(x) = Ce^x - \tfrac{33}{32}e^{-x/3}. \tag{8}$$

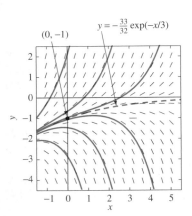

$y = -\tfrac{33}{32}\exp(-x/3)$

$(0, -1)$

FIGURE 1.5.1. Slope field and solution curves for $y' = y + \tfrac{11}{8}e^{-x/3}$.

Substitution of $x = 0$ and $y = -1$ now gives $C = \tfrac{1}{32}$, so the desired particular solution is

$$y(x) = \tfrac{1}{32}e^x - \tfrac{33}{32}e^{-x/3} = \tfrac{1}{32}\left(e^x - 33e^{-x/3}\right). \qquad \blacksquare$$

Remark: Figure 1.5.1 shows a slope field and typical solution curves for Eq. (7), including the one passing through the point $(0, -1)$. Note that some solutions grow rapidly in the positive direction as x increases, while others grow rapidly in the negative direction. The behavior of a given solution curve is determined by its initial condition $y(0) = y_0$. The two types of behavior are separated by the particular solution $y(x) = -\tfrac{33}{32}e^{-x/3}$ for which $C = 0$ in Eq. (8), so $y_0 = -\tfrac{33}{32}$ for the solution curve that is dashed in Fig. 1.5.1. If $y_0 > -\tfrac{33}{32}$, then $C > 0$ in Eq. (8), so the term e^x eventually dominates the behavior of $y(x)$, and hence $y(x) \to +\infty$ as $x \to +\infty$. But if $y_0 < -\tfrac{33}{32}$, then $C < 0$, so both terms in $y(x)$ are negative and therefore $y(x) \to -\infty$ as $x \to +\infty$. Thus the initial condition $y_0 = -\tfrac{33}{32}$ is *critical* in the sense that solutions that start above $-\tfrac{33}{32}$ on the y-axis grow in the positive direction, while solutions that start lower than $-\tfrac{33}{32}$ grow in the negative direction as $x \to +\infty$. The interpretation of a mathematical model often hinges on finding such a critical condition that separates one kind of behavior of a solution from a different kind of behavior. $\blacksquare$

Example 2 Find a general solution of

$$(x^2 + 1)\frac{dy}{dx} + 3xy = 6x. \tag{9}$$

Solution After division of both sides of the equation by $x^2 + 1$, we recognize the result

$$\frac{dy}{dx} + \frac{3x}{x^2 + 1}y = \frac{6x}{x^2 + 1}$$

as a first-order linear equation with $P(x) = 3x/(x^2 + 1)$ and $Q(x) = 6x/(x^2 + 1)$. Multiplication by

$$\rho(x) = \exp\left(\int \frac{3x}{x^2 + 1}\,dx\right) = \exp\left(\tfrac{3}{2}\ln(x^2 + 1)\right) = (x^2 + 1)^{3/2}$$

yields

$$(x^2 + 1)^{3/2}\frac{dy}{dx} + 3x(x^2 + 1)^{1/2}y = 6x(x^2 + 1)^{1/2},$$

and thus

$$D_x\left[(x^2 + 1)^{3/2}y\right] = 6x(x^2 + 1)^{1/2}.$$

Integration then yields

$$(x^2+1)^{3/2}y = \int 6x(x^2+1)^{1/2}\,dx = 2(x^2+1)^{3/2} + C.$$

Multiplication of both sides by $(x^2+1)^{-3/2}$ gives the general solution

$$y(x) = 2 + C(x^2+1)^{-3/2}. \qquad (10)$$

∎

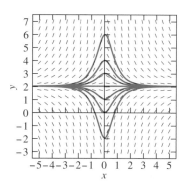

FIGURE 1.5.2. Slope field and solution curves for the differential equation in Eq. (9).

Remark: Figure 1.5.2 shows a slope field and typical solution curves for Eq. (9). Note that, as $x \to +\infty$, all other solution curves approach the constant solution curve $y(x) \equiv 2$ that corresponds to $C = 0$ in Eq. (10). This constant solution can be described as an *equilibrium solution* of the differential equation, because $y(0) = 2$ implies that $y(x) = 2$ for all x (and thus the value of the solution remains forever where it starts). More generally, the word "equilibrium" connotes "unchanging," so by an equilibrium solution of a differential equation is meant a constant solution $y(x) \equiv c$, for which it follows that $y'(x) \equiv 0$. Note that substitution of $y' = 0$ in the differential equation (9) yields $3xy = 6x$, so it follows that $y = 2$ if $x \neq 0$. Hence we see that $y(x) \equiv 2$ is the only equilibrium solution of this differential equation, as seems visually obvious in Fig. 1.5.2. ∎

A Closer Look at the Method

The preceding derivation of the solution in Eq. (6) of the linear first-order equation $y' + Py = Q$ bears closer examination. Suppose that the coefficient functions $P(x)$ and $Q(x)$ are continuous on the (possibly unbounded) open interval I. Then the antiderivatives

$$\int P(x)\,dx \quad \text{and} \quad \int \left(Q(x)e^{\int P(x)\,dx} \right) dx$$

exist on I. Our derivation of Eq. (6) shows that *if* $y = y(x)$ is a solution of Eq. (3) on I, *then* $y(x)$ is given by the formula in Eq. (6) for some choice of the constant C. Conversely, you may verify by direct substitution (Problem 31) that the function $y(x)$ given in Eq. (6) satisfies Eq. (3). Finally, given a point x_0 of I and any number y_0, there is—as previously noted—a unique value of C such that $y(x_0) = y_0$. Consequently, we have proved the following existence-uniqueness theorem.

THEOREM 1   The Linear First-Order Equation

If the functions $P(x)$ and $Q(x)$ are continuous on the open interval I containing the point x_0, then the initial value problem

$$\frac{dy}{dx} + P(x)y = Q(x), \quad y(x_0) = y_0 \qquad (11)$$

has a unique solution $y(x)$ on I, given by the formula in Eq. (6) with an appropriate value of C.

Remark 1:   Theorem 1 gives a solution on the *entire* interval I for a *linear* differential equation, in contrast with Theorem 1 of Section 1.3, which guarantees only a solution on a possibly smaller interval.

Remark 2: Theorem 1 tells us that every solution of Eq. (3) is included in the general solution given in Eq. (6). Thus a *linear* first-order differential equation has *no* singular solutions.

Remark 3: The appropriate value of the constant C in Eq. (6)—as needed to solve the initial value problem in Eq. (11)—can be selected "automatically" by writing

$$\rho(x) = \exp\left(\int_{x_0}^{x} P(t)\, dt\right),$$
$$y(x) = \frac{1}{\rho(x)}\left[y_0 + \int_{x_0}^{x} \rho(t) Q(t)\, dt\right].$$

(12)

The indicated limits x_0 and x effect a choice of indefinite integrals in Eq. (6) that guarantees in advance that $\rho(x_0) = 1$ and that $y(x_0) = y_0$ (as you can verify directly by substituting $x = x_0$ in Eqs. (12)). ∎

Example 3 Solve the initial value problem

$$x^2 \frac{dy}{dx} + xy = \sin x, \quad y(1) = y_0.$$

(13)

Solution Division by x^2 gives the linear first-order equation

$$\frac{dy}{dx} + \frac{1}{x} y = \frac{\sin x}{x^2}$$

with $P(x) = 1/x$ and $Q(x) = (\sin x)/x^2$. With $x_0 = 1$ the integrating factor in (12) is

$$\rho(x) = \exp\left(\int_1^x \frac{1}{t}\, dt\right) = \exp(\ln x) = x,$$

so the desired particular solution is given by

$$y(x) = \frac{1}{x}\left[y_0 + \int_1^x \frac{\sin t}{t}\, dt\right].$$

(14)

In accord with Theorem 1, this solution is defined on the whole positive x-axis. ∎

Comment: In general, an integral such as the one in Eq. (14) would (for given x) need to be approximated numerically—using Simpson's rule, for instance—to find the value $y(x)$ of the solution at x. In this case, however, we have the sine integral function

$$\text{Si}(x) = \int_0^x \frac{\sin t}{t}\, dt,$$

which appears with sufficient frequency in applications that its values have been tabulated. A good set of tables of special functions is Abramowitz and Stegun, *Handbook of Mathematical Functions* (New York: Dover, 1965). Then the particular solution in Eq. (14) reduces to

$$y(x) = \frac{1}{x}\left[y_0 + \int_0^x \frac{\sin t}{t}\, dt - \int_0^1 \frac{\sin t}{t}\, dt\right] = \frac{1}{x}[y_0 + \text{Si}(x) - \text{Si}(1)]. \quad (15)$$

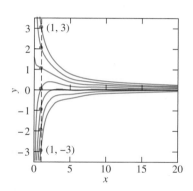

FIGURE 1.5.3. Typical solution curves defined by Eq. (15).

The sine integral function is available in most scientific computing systems and can be used to plot typical solution curves defined by Eq. (15). Figure 1.5.3 shows a selection of solution curves with initial values $y(1) = y_0$ ranging from $y_0 = -3$ to $y_0 = 3$. It appears that on each solution curve, $y(x) \to 0$ as $x \to +\infty$, and this is in fact true because the sine integral function is bounded. ∎

In the sequel we will see that it is the exception—rather than the rule—when a solution of a differential equation can be expressed in terms of elementary functions. We will study various devices for obtaining good approximations to the values of the nonelementary functions we encounter. In Chapter 2 we will discuss numerical integration of differential equations in some detail.

Mixture Problems

As a first application of linear first-order equations, we consider a tank containing a solution—a mixture of solute and solvent—such as salt dissolved in water. There is both inflow and outflow, and we want to compute the *amount* $x(t)$ of solute in the tank at time t, given the amount $x(0) = x_0$ at time $t = 0$. Suppose that solution with a concentration of c_i grams of solute per liter of solution flows into the tank at the constant rate of r_i liters per second, and that the solution in the tank—kept thoroughly mixed by stirring—flows out at the constant rate of r_o liters per second.

To set up a differential equation for $x(t)$, we estimate the change Δx in x during the brief time interval $[t, t + \Delta t]$. The amount of solute that flows into the tank during Δt seconds is $r_i c_i \, \Delta t$ grams. To check this, note how the cancellation of dimensions checks our computations:

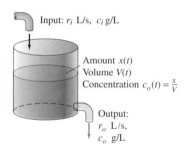

Input: r_i L/s, c_i g/L

Amount $x(t)$
Volume $V(t)$
Concentration $c_o(t) = \frac{x}{V}$

Output:
r_o L/s,
c_o g/L

FIGURE 1.5.4. The single-tank mixture problem.

$$\left(r_i \, \frac{\text{liters}}{\text{second}}\right)\left(c_i \, \frac{\text{grams}}{\text{liter}}\right)(\Delta t \text{ seconds})$$

yields a quantity measured in grams.

The amount of solute that flows out of the tank during the same time interval depends on the concentration $c_o(t)$ of solute in the solution at time t. But as noted in Fig. 1.5.4, $c_o(t) = x(t)/V(t)$, where $V(t)$ denotes the volume (not constant unless $r_i = r_o$) of solution in the tank at time t. Then

$$\Delta x = \{\text{grams input}\} - \{\text{grams output}\} \approx r_i c_i \, \Delta t - r_o c_o \, \Delta t.$$

We now divide by Δt:

$$\frac{\Delta x}{\Delta t} \approx r_i c_i - r_o c_o.$$

Finally, we take the limit as $\Delta t \to 0$; if all the functions involved are continuous and $x(t)$ is differentiable, then the error in this approximation also approaches zero, and we obtain the differential equation

$$\frac{dx}{dt} = r_i c_i - r_o c_o, \tag{16}$$

in which r_i, c_i, and r_o are constants, but c_o denotes the variable concentration

$$c_o(t) = \frac{x(t)}{V(t)} \tag{17}$$

of solute in the tank at time t. Thus the amount $x(t)$ of solute in the tank satisfies the differential equation

$$\frac{dx}{dt} = r_i c_i - \frac{r_o}{V} x. \tag{18}$$

If $V_0 = V(0)$, then $V(t) = V_0 + (r_i - r_o)t$, so Eq. (18) is a linear first-order differential equation for the amount $x(t)$ of solute in the tank at time t.

Important: Equation (18) need not be committed to memory. It is the *process* we used to obtain that equation—examination of the behavior of the system over a short time interval $[t, t + \Delta t]$—that you should strive to understand, because it is a very useful tool for obtaining all sorts of differential equations.

Remark: It was convenient for us to use g/L mass/volume units in deriving Eq. (18). But any other consistent system of units can be used to measure amounts of solute and volumes of solution. In the following example we measure both in cubic kilometers. ∎

Example 4 Assume that Lake Erie has a volume of 480 km³ and that its rate of inflow (from Lake Huron) and outflow (to Lake Ontario) are both 350 km³ per year. Suppose that at the time $t = 0$ (years), the pollutant concentration of Lake Erie—caused by past industrial pollution that has now been ordered to cease—is five times that of Lake Huron. If the outflow henceforth is perfectly mixed lake water, how long will it take to reduce the pollution concentration in Lake Erie to twice that of Lake Huron?

Solution Here we have

$$V = 480 \ (\text{km}^3),$$

$$r_i = r_o = r = 350 \ (\text{km}^3/\text{yr}),$$

$$c_i = c \ (\text{the pollutant concentration of Lake Huron), and}$$

$$x_0 = x(0) = 5cV,$$

and the question is this: When is $x(t) = 2cV$? With this notation, Eq. (18) is the separable equation

$$\frac{dx}{dt} = rc - \frac{r}{V} x, \tag{19}$$

which we rewrite in the linear first-order form

$$\frac{dx}{dt} + px = q \tag{20}$$

with constant coefficients $p = r/V$, $q = rc$, and integrating factor $\rho = e^{pt}$. You can either solve this equation directly or apply the formula in (12). The latter gives

$$x(t) = e^{-pt} \left[x_0 + \int_0^t q e^{pt} \, dt \right] = e^{-pt} \left[x_0 + \frac{q}{p} \left(e^{pt} - 1 \right) \right]$$

$$= e^{-rt/V} \left[5cV + \frac{rc}{r/V} \left(e^{rt/V} - 1 \right) \right];$$

$$x(t) = cV + 4cV e^{-rt/V}. \tag{21}$$

To find when $x(t) = 2cV$, we therefore need only solve the equation

$$cV + 4cVe^{-rt/V} = 2cV \quad \text{for} \quad t = \frac{V}{r}\ln 4 = \frac{480}{350}\ln 4 \approx 1.901 \text{ (years).}\quad \blacksquare$$

Example 5 | A 120-gallon (gal) tank initially contains 90 lb of salt dissolved in 90 gal of water. Brine containing 2 lb/gal of salt flows into the tank at the rate of 4 gal/min, and the well-stirred mixture flows out of the tank at the rate of 3 gal/min. How much salt does the tank contain when it is full?

Solution | The interesting feature of this example is that, due to the differing rates of inflow and outflow, the volume of brine in the tank increases steadily with $V(t) = 90 + t$ gallons. The change Δx in the amount x of salt in the tank from time t to time $t + \Delta t$ (minutes) is given by

$$\Delta x \approx (4)(2)\,\Delta t - 3\left(\frac{x}{90+t}\right)\Delta t,$$

so our differential equation is

$$\frac{dx}{dt} + \frac{3}{90+t}x = 8.$$

An integrating factor is

$$\rho(x) = \exp\left(\int \frac{3}{90+t}\,dt\right) = e^{3\ln(90+t)} = (90+t)^3,$$

which gives

$$D_t\left[(90+t)^3 x\right] = 8(90+t)^3;$$
$$(90+t)^3 x = 2(90+t)^4 + C.$$

Substitution of $x(0) = 90$ gives $C = -(90)^4$, so the amount of salt in the tank at time t is

$$x(t) = 2(90+t) - \frac{90^4}{(90+t)^3}.$$

The tank is full after 30 min, and when $t = 30$, we have

$$x(30) = 2(90+30) - \frac{90^4}{120^3} \approx 202 \text{ (lb)}$$

of salt in the tank. $\blacksquare$

1.5 Problems

Find general solutions of the differential equations in Problems 1 through 25. If an initial condition is given, find the corresponding particular solution. Throughout, primes denote derivatives with respect to x.

1. $y' + y = 2$, $y(0) = 0$ **2.** $y' - 2y = 3e^{2x}$, $y(0) = 0$
3. $y' + 3y = 2xe^{-3x}$ **4.** $y' - 2xy = e^{x^2}$
5. $xy' + 2y = 3x$, $y(1) = 5$
6. $xy' + 5y = 7x^2$, $y(2) = 5$
7. $2xy' + y = 10\sqrt{x}$ **8.** $3xy' + y = 12x$
9. $xy' - y = x$, $y(1) = 7$ **10.** $2xy' - 3y = 9x^3$
11. $xy' + y = 3xy$, $y(1) = 0$
12. $xy' + 3y = 2x^5$, $y(2) = 1$
13. $y' + y = e^x$, $y(0) = 1$
14. $xy' - 3y = x^3$, $y(1) = 10$
15. $y' + 2xy = x$, $y(0) = -2$
16. $y' = (1 - y)\cos x$, $y(\pi) = 2$
17. $(1 + x)y' + y = \cos x$, $y(0) = 1$
18. $xy' = 2y + x^3 \cos x$
19. $y' + y \cot x = \cos x$
20. $y' = 1 + x + y + xy$, $y(0) = 0$
21. $xy' = 3y + x^4 \cos x$, $y(2\pi) = 0$
22. $y' = 2xy + 3x^2 \exp(x^2)$, $y(0) = 5$
23. $xy' + (2x - 3)y = 4x^4$
24. $(x^2 + 4)y' + 3xy = x$, $y(0) = 1$
25. $(x^2 + 1)\dfrac{dy}{dx} + 3x^3y = 6x \exp\left(-\tfrac{3}{2}x^2\right)$, $y(0) = 1$

Solve the differential equations in Problems 26 through 28 by regarding y as the independent variable rather than x.

26. $(1 - 4xy^2)\dfrac{dy}{dx} = y^3$ **27.** $(x + ye^y)\dfrac{dy}{dx} = 1$

28. $(1 + 2xy)\dfrac{dy}{dx} = 1 + y^2$

29. Express the general solution of $dy/dx = 1 + 2xy$ in terms of the **error function**

$$\text{erf}(x) = \frac{2}{\sqrt{\pi}} \int_0^x e^{-t^2} \, dt.$$

30. Express the solution of the initial value problem

$$2x\frac{dy}{dx} = y + 2x \cos x, \quad y(1) = 0$$

as an integral as in Example 3 of this section.

Problems 31 and 32 illustrate—for the special case of first-order linear equations—techniques that will be important when we study higher-order linear equations in Chapter 3.

31. (a) Show that
$$y_c(x) = Ce^{-\int P(x)\,dx}$$
is a general solution of $dy/dx + P(x)y = 0$.   **(b)** Show that
$$y_p(x) = e^{-\int P(x)\,dx}\left[\int \left(Q(x)e^{\int P(x)\,dx}\right)dx\right]$$

is a particular solution of $dy/dx + P(x)y = Q(x)$.
(c) Suppose that $y_c(x)$ is any general solution of $dy/dx + P(x)y = 0$ and that $y_p(x)$ is any particular solution of $dy/dx + P(x)y = Q(x)$. Show that $y(x) = y_c(x) + y_p(x)$ is a general solution of $dy/dx + P(x)y = Q(x)$.

32. (a) Find constants A and B such that $y_p(x) = A \sin x + B \cos x$ is a solution of $dy/dx + y = 2 \sin x$.   **(b)** Use the result of part (a) and the method of Problem 31 to find the general solution of $dy/dx + y = 2 \sin x$.   **(c)** Solve the initial value problem $dy/dx + y = 2 \sin x$, $y(0) = 1$.

33. A tank contains 1000 liters (L) of a solution consisting of 100 kg of salt dissolved in water. Pure water is pumped into the tank at the rate of 5 L/s, and the mixture—kept uniform by stirring— is pumped out at the same rate. How long will it be until only 10 kg of salt remains in the tank?

34. Consider a reservoir with a volume of 8 billion cubic feet (ft^3) and an initial pollutant concentration of 0.25%. There is a daily inflow of 500 million ft^3 of water with a pollutant concentration of 0.05% and an equal daily outflow of the well-mixed water in the reservoir. How long will it take to reduce the pollutant concentration in the reservoir to 0.10%?

35. Rework Example 4 for the case of Lake Ontario, which empties into the St. Lawrence River and receives inflow from Lake Erie (via the Niagara River). The only differences are that this lake has a volume of 1640 km^3 and an inflow-outflow rate of 410 km^3/year.

36. A tank initially contains 60 gal of pure water. Brine containing 1 lb of salt per gallon enters the tank at 2 gal/min, and the (perfectly mixed) solution leaves the tank at 3 gal/min; thus the tank is empty after exactly 1 h. **(a)** Find the amount of salt in the tank after t minutes. **(b)** What is the maximum amount of salt ever in the tank?

37. A 400-gal tank initially contains 100 gal of brine containing 50 lb of salt. Brine containing 1 lb of salt per gallon enters the tank at the rate of 5 gal/s, and the well-mixed brine in the tank flows out at the rate of 3 gal/s. How much salt will the tank contain when it is full of brine?

38. Consider the *cascade* of two tanks shown in Fig. 1.5.5, with $V_1 = 100$ (gal) and $V_2 = 200$ (gal) the volumes of brine in the two tanks. Each tank also initially contains 50 lb of salt. The three flow rates indicated in the figure are each 5 gal/min, with pure water flowing into tank 1. **(a)** Find the amount $x(t)$ of salt in tank 1 at time t. **(b)** Suppose that $y(t)$ is the amount of salt in tank 2 at time t. Show first that

$$\frac{dy}{dt} = \frac{5x}{100} - \frac{5y}{200},$$

and then solve for $y(t)$, using the function $x(t)$ found in part (a). **(c)** Finally, find the maximum amount of salt ever in tank 2.

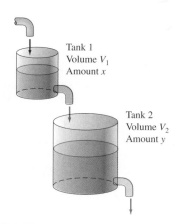

FIGURE 1.5.5. A cascade of two tanks.

39. Suppose that in the cascade shown in Fig. 1.5.5, tank 1 initially contains 100 gal of pure ethanol and tank 2 initially contains 100 gal of pure water. Pure water flows into tank 1 at 10 gal/min, and the other two flow rates are also 10 gal/min. **(a)** Find the amounts $x(t)$ and $y(t)$ of ethanol in the two tanks at time $t \geq 0$. **(b)** Find the maximum amount of ethanol ever in tank 2.

40. A multiple cascade is shown in Fig. 1.5.6. At time $t = 0$, tank 0 contains 1 gal of ethanol and 1 gal of water; all the remaining tanks contain 2 gal of pure water each. Pure water is pumped into tank 0 at 1 gal/min, and the varying mixture in each tank is pumped into the one below it at the same rate. Assume, as usual, that the mixtures are kept perfectly uniform by stirring. Let $x_n(t)$ denote the amount of ethanol in tank n at time t.

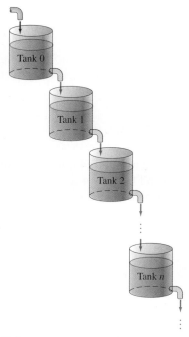

FIGURE 1.5.6. A multiple cascade.

(a) Show that $x_0(t) = e^{-t/2}$. **(b)** Show by induction on n

that

$$x_n(t) = \frac{t^n e^{-t/2}}{n! \, 2^n} \quad \text{for } n > 0.$$

(c) Show that the maximum value of $x_n(t)$ for $n > 0$ is $M_n = x_n(2n) = n^n e^{-n}/n!$. **(d)** Conclude from **Stirling's approximation** $n! \approx n^n e^{-n} \sqrt{2\pi n}$ that $M_n \approx (2\pi n)^{-1/2}$.

41. A 30-year-old woman accepts an engineering position with a starting salary of \$30,000 per year. Her salary $S(t)$ increases exponentially, with $S(t) = 30 e^{t/20}$ thousand dollars after t years. Meanwhile, 12% of her salary is deposited continuously in a retirement account, which accumulates interest at a continuous annual rate of 6%. **(a)** Estimate ΔA in terms of Δt to derive the differential equation satisfied by the amount $A(t)$ in her retirement account after t years. **(b)** Compute $A(40)$, the amount available for her retirement at age 70.

42. Suppose that a falling hailstone with density $\delta = 1$ starts from rest with negligible radius $r = 0$. Thereafter its radius is $r = kt$ (k is a constant) as it grows by accretion during its fall. Use Newton's second law—according to which the net force F acting on a possibly variable mass m equals the time rate of change dp/dt of its momentum $p = mv$—to set up and solve the initial value problem

$$\frac{d}{dt}(mv) = mg, \quad v(0) = 0,$$

where m is the variable mass of the hailstone, $v = dy/dt$ is its velocity, and the positive y-axis points downward. Then show that $dv/dt = g/4$. Thus the hailstone falls as though it were under *one-fourth* the influence of gravity.

43. Figure 1.5.7 shows a slope field and typical solution curves for the equation $y' = x - y$. **(a)** Show that every solution curve approaches the straight line $y = x - 1$ as $x \to +\infty$. **(b)** For each of the five values $y_1 = 3.998$, 3.999, 4.000, 4.001, and 4.002, determine the initial value y_0 (accurate to four decimal places) such that $y(5) = y_1$ for the solution satisfying the initial condition $y(-5) = y_0$.

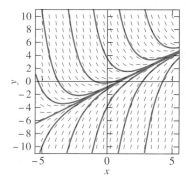

FIGURE 1.5.7. Slope field and solution curves for $y' = x - y$.

44. Figure 1.5.8 shows a slope field and typical solution curves for the equation $y' = x + y$. **(a)** Show that every solution curve approaches the straight line $y = -x - 1$ as $x \to -\infty$. **(b)** For each of the five values $y_1 = -10$, $-5, 0, 5$, and 10, determine the initial value y_0 (accurate to five decimal places) such that $y(5) = y_1$ for the solution satisfying the initial condition $y(-5) = y_0$.

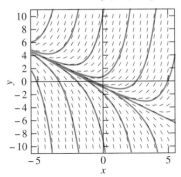

FIGURE 1.5.8. Slope field and solution curves for $y' = x + y$.

Problems 45 and 46 deal with a shallow reservoir that has a one square kilometer water surface and an average water depth of 2 meters. Initially it is filled with fresh water, but at time $t = 0$ water contaminated with a liquid pollutant begins flowing into the reservoir at the rate of 200 thousand cubic meters per month. The well-mixed water in the reservoir flows out at the same rate. Your first task is to find the amount $x(t)$ of pollutant (in millions of liters) in the reservoir after t months.

45. The incoming water has a pollutant concentration of $c(t) = 10$ liters per cubic meter (L/m^3). Verify that the graph of $x(t)$ resembles the steadily rising curve in Fig. 1.5.9, which approaches asymptotically the graph of the equilibrium solution $x(t) \equiv 20$ that corresponds to the reservoir's long-term pollutant content. How long does it take the pollutant concentration in the reservoir to reach $5 \, L/m^3$?

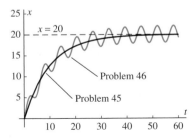

FIGURE 1.5.9. Graphs of solutions in Problems 45 and 46.

46. The incoming water has pollutant concentration $c(t) = 10(1 + \cos t) \, L/m^3$ that varies between 0 and 20, with an average concentration of $10 \, L/m^3$ and a period of oscillation of slightly over $6\frac{1}{4}$ months. Does it seem predictable that the lake's polutant content should ultimately oscillate periodically about an average level of 20 million liters? Verify that the graph of $x(t)$ does, indeed, resemble the oscillatory curve shown in Fig. 1.5.9. How long does it take the pollutant concentration in the reservoir to reach $5 \, L/m^3$?

1.5 Application Indoor Temperature Oscillations

For an interesting applied problem that involves the solution of a linear differential equation, consider indoor temperature oscillations that are driven by outdoor temperature oscillations of the form

$$A(t) = a_0 + a_1 \cos \omega t + b_1 \sin \omega t. \tag{1}$$

If $\omega = \pi/12$, then these oscillations have a period of 24 hours (so that the cycle of outdoor temperatures repeats itself daily) and Eq. (1) provides a realistic model for the temperature outside a house on a day when no change in the overall day-to-day weather pattern is occurring. For instance, for a typical July day in Athens, GA with a minimum temperature of $70°F$ when $t = 4$ (4 A.M.) and a maximum of $90°F$ when $t = 16$ (4 P.M.), we would take

$$A(t) = 80 - 10 \cos \omega (t - 4) = 80 - 5 \cos \omega t - 5\sqrt{3} \sin \omega t. \tag{2}$$

We derived Eq. (2) by using the identity $\cos(\alpha - \beta) = \cos \alpha \cos \beta + \sin \alpha \sin \beta$ to get $a_0 = 80$, $a_1 = -5$, and $b_1 = -5\sqrt{3}$ in Eq. (1).

If we write Newton's law of cooling (Eq. (3) of Section 1.1) for the corresponding indoor temperature $u(t)$ at time t, but with the outside temperature $A(t)$

given by Eq. (1) instead of a constant ambient temperature A, we get the linear first-order differential equation

$$\frac{du}{dt} = -k(u - A(t));$$

that is,

$$\frac{du}{dt} + ku = k(a_0 + a_1 \cos \omega t + b_1 \sin \omega t) \tag{3}$$

with coefficient functions $P(t) \equiv k$ and $Q(t) = kA(t)$. Typical values of the proportionality constant k range from 0.2 to 0.5 (although k might be greater than 0.5 for a poorly insulated building with open windows, or less than 0.2 for a well-insulated building with tightly sealed windows).

SCENARIO: Suppose that our air conditioner fails at time $t_0 = 0$ one midnight, and we cannot afford to have it repaired until payday at the end of the month. We therefore want to investigate the resulting indoor temperatures that we must endure for the next several days.

Begin your investigation by solving Eq. (3) with the initial condition $u(0) = u_0$ (the indoor temperature at the time of the failure of the air conditioner). You may want to use the integral formulas in 49 and 50 of the endpapers, or possibly a computer algebra system. You should get the solution

$$u(t) = a_0 + c_0 e^{-kt} + c_1 \cos \omega t + d_1 \sin \omega t, \tag{4}$$

where

$$c_0 = u_0 - a_0 - \frac{k^2 a_1 - k\omega b_1}{k^2 + \omega^2},$$

$$c_1 = \frac{k^2 a_1 - k\omega b_1}{k^2 + \omega^2}, \quad d_1 = \frac{k\omega a_1 + k^2 b_1}{k^2 + \omega^2}$$

with $\omega = \pi/12$.

With $a_0 = 80$, $a_1 = -5$, $b_1 = -5\sqrt{3}$ (as in Eq. (2)), $\omega = \pi/12$, and $k = 0.2$ (for instance), this solution reduces (approximately) to

$$u(t) = 80 + e^{-t/5}(u_0 - 82.3351) + (2.3351) \cos \frac{\pi t}{12} - (5.6036) \sin \frac{\pi t}{12}. \tag{5}$$

Observe first that the "damped" exponential term in Eq. (5) approaches zero as $t \to +\infty$, leaving the long-term "steady periodic" solution

$$u_{\text{sp}}(t) = 80 + (2.3351) \cos \frac{\pi t}{12} - (5.6036) \sin \frac{\pi t}{12}. \tag{6}$$

Consequently, the long-term indoor temperatures oscillate every 24 hours around the same average temperature $80°F$ as the average outdoor temperature.

Figure 1.5.10 shows a number of solution curves corresponding to possible initial temperatures u_0 ranging from $65°F$ to $95°F$. Observe that—whatever the initial temperature—the indoor temperature "settles down" within about 18 hours to a periodic daily oscillation. But the amplitude of temperature variation is less

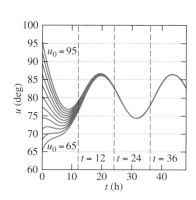

FIGURE 1.5.10. Solution curves given by Eq. (5) with $u_0 = 65, 68, 71, \ldots, 92, 95$.

indoors than outdoors. Indeed, using the trigonometric identity mentioned earlier, Eq. (6) can be rewritten (verify this!) as

$$u(t) = 80 - (6.0707) \cos\left(\frac{\pi t}{12} - 1.9656\right)$$

$$= 80 - (6.0707) \cos\frac{\pi}{12}(t - 7.5082). \tag{7}$$

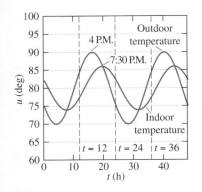

FIGURE 1.5.11. Comparison of indoor and outdoor temperature oscillations.

Do you see that this implies that the indoor temperature varies between a minimum of about $74°F$ and a maximum of about $86°F$?

Finally, comparison of Eqs. (2) and (7) indicates that the indoor temperature lags behind the outdoor temperature by about $7.5082 - 4 \approx 3.5$ hours, as illustrated in Fig. 1.5.11. Thus the temperature inside the house continues to rise until about 7:30 P.M. each evening, so the hottest part of the day inside is early evening rather than late afternoon (as outside).

For a personal problem to investigate, carry out a similar analysis using average July daily maximum/minimum figures for your own locale and a value of k appropriate to your own home. You might also consider a winter day instead of a summer day. (What is the winter-summer difference for the indoor temperature problem?) You may wish to explore the use of available technology both to solve the differential equation and to graph its solution for the indoor temperature in comparison with the outdoor temperature.

1.6 Substitution Methods and Exact Equations

The first-order differential equations we have solved in the previous sections have all been either separable or linear. But many applications involve differential equations that are neither separable nor linear. In this section we illustrate (mainly with examples) substitution methods that sometimes can be used to transform a given differential equation into one that we already know how to solve.

For instance, the differential equation

$$\frac{dy}{dx} = f(x, y), \tag{1}$$

with dependent variable y and independent variable x, may contain a conspicuous combination

$$v = \alpha(x, y) \tag{2}$$

of x and y that suggests itself as a new independent variable v. Thus the differential equation

$$\frac{dy}{dx} = (x + y + 3)^2$$

practically demands the substitution $v = x + y + 3$ of the form in Eq. (2).

If the substitution relation in Eq. (2) can be solved for

$$y = \beta(x, v), \tag{3}$$

then application of the chain rule—regarding v as an (unknown) function of x—yields

$$\frac{dy}{dx} = \frac{\partial\beta}{\partial x}\frac{dx}{dx} + \frac{\partial\beta}{\partial v}\frac{dv}{dx} = \beta_x + \beta_v\frac{dv}{dx},\tag{4}$$

where the partial derivatives $\partial\beta/\partial x = \beta_x(x, v)$ and $\partial\beta/\partial v = \beta_v(x, v)$ are *known* functions of x and v. If we substitute the right-hand side in (4) for dy/dx in Eq. (1) and then solve for dv/dx, the result is a *new* differential equation of the form

$$\frac{dv}{dx} = g(x, v)\tag{5}$$

with *new* dependent variable v. If this new equation is either separable or linear, then we can apply the methods of preceding sections to solve it.

If $v = v(x)$ is a solution of Eq. (5), then $y = \beta(x, v(x))$ will be a solution of the original Eq. (1). The trick is to select a substitution such that the transformed Eq. (5) is one we can solve. Even when possible, this is not always easy; it may require a fair amount of ingenuity or trial and error.

Example 1   Solve the differential equation

$$\frac{dy}{dx} = (x + y + 3)^2.$$

Solution   As indicated earlier, let's try the substitution

$$v = x + y + 3; \quad\text{that is,}\quad y = v - x - 3.$$

Then

$$\frac{dy}{dx} = \frac{dv}{dx} - 1,$$

so the transformed equation is

$$\frac{dv}{dx} = 1 + v^2.$$

This is a separable equation, and we have no difficulty in obtaining its solution

$$x = \int\frac{dv}{1 + v^2} = \tan^{-1} v + C.$$

So $v = \tan(x - C)$. Because $v = x + y + 3$, the general solution of the original equation $dy/dx = (x + y + 3)^2$ is $x + y + 3 = \tan(x - C)$; that is,

$$y(x) = \tan(x - C) - x - 3. \quad\blacksquare$$

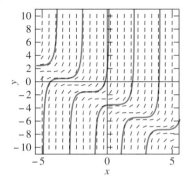

FIGURE 1.6.1. Slope field and solution curves for $y' = (x + y + 3)^2$.

Remark: Figure 1.6.1 shows a slope field and typical solution curves for the differential equation of Example 1. We see that, although the function $f(x, y) = (x+y+3)^2$ is continuously differentiable for all x and y, each solution is continuous only on a bounded interval. In particular, because the tangent function is continuous on the open interval $(-\pi/2, \pi/2)$, the particular solution with arbitrary constant value C is continuous on the interval where $-\pi/2 < x-C < \pi/2$; that is, $C-\pi/2 < x < C + \pi/2$. This situation is fairly typical of nonlinear differential equations, in contrast with linear differential equations, whose solutions are continuous wherever the coefficient functions in the equation are continuous. $\quad\blacksquare$

Example 1 illustrates the fact that any differential equation of the form

$$\frac{dy}{dx} = F(ax + by + c) \tag{6}$$

can be transformed into a separable equation by use of the substitution $v = ax + by + c$ (see Problem 55). The paragraphs that follow deal with other classes of first-order equations for which there are standard substitutions that are known to succeed.

Homogeneous Equations

A **homogeneous** first-order differential equation is one that can be written in the form

$$\frac{dy}{dx} = F\left(\frac{y}{x}\right). \tag{7}$$

If we make the substitutions

$$v = \frac{y}{x}, \quad y = vx, \quad \frac{dy}{dx} = v + x\frac{dv}{dx}, \tag{8}$$

then Eq. (7) is transformed into the *separable* equation

$$x\frac{dv}{dx} = F(v) - v.$$

Thus every homogeneous first-order differential equation can be reduced to an integration problem by means of the substitutions in (8).

    Remark: A dictionary definition of "homogeneous" is "of a similar kind or nature." Consider a differential equation of the form

$$Ax^m y^n \frac{dy}{dx} = Bx^p y^q + Cx^r y^s \tag{$*$}$$

whose polynomial coefficient functions are "homogeneous" in the sense that each of their terms has the same total degree, $m + n = p + q = r + s = K$. If we divide each side of ($*$) by x^K, then the result—because $x^m y^n / x^{m+n} = (y/x)^n$, and so forth—is the equation

$$A\left(\frac{y}{x}\right)^n \frac{dy}{dx} = B\left(\frac{y}{x}\right)^q + C\left(\frac{y}{x}\right)^s$$

which evidently can be written (by another division) in the form of Eq. (7). More generally, a differential equation of the form $P(x, y)y' = Q(x, y)$ with polynomial coefficients P and Q is homogeneous if the terms in these polynomials all have the same total degree K. The differential equation in the following example is of this form with $K = 2$.

Example 2   Solve the differential equation

$$2xy\frac{dy}{dx} = 4x^2 + 3y^2.$$

Solution This equation is neither separable nor linear, but we recognize it as a homogeneous equation by writing it in the form

$$\frac{dy}{dx} = \frac{4x^2 + 3y^2}{2xy} = 2\left(\frac{x}{y}\right) + \frac{3}{2}\left(\frac{y}{x}\right).$$

The substitutions in (8) then take the form

$$y = vx, \quad \frac{dy}{dx} = v + x\frac{dv}{dx}, \quad v = \frac{y}{x}, \quad \text{and} \quad \frac{1}{v} = \frac{x}{y}.$$

These yield

$$v + x\frac{dv}{dx} = \frac{2}{v} + \frac{3}{2}v,$$

and hence

$$x\frac{dv}{dx} = \frac{2}{v} + \frac{v}{2} = \frac{v^2 + 4}{2v};$$

$$\int \frac{2v}{v^2 + 4}\,dv = \int \frac{1}{x}\,dx;$$

$$\ln(v^2 + 4) = \ln|x| + \ln C.$$

We apply the exponential function to both sides of the last equation to obtain

$$v^2 + 4 = C|x|;$$

$$\frac{y^2}{x^2} + 4 = C|x|;$$

$$y^2 + 4x^2 = kx^3.$$

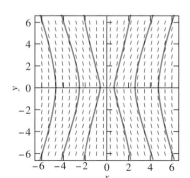

FIGURE 1.6.2. Slope field and solution curves for $2xyy' = 4x^2 + 3y^2$.

Note that the left-hand side of this equation is necessarily nonnegative. It follows that $k > 0$ in the case of solutions that are defined for $x > 0$, while $k < 0$ for solutions where $x < 0$. Indeed, the family of solution curves illustrated in Fig. 1.6.2 exhibits symmetry about both coordinate axes. Actually, there are positive-valued and negative-valued solutions of the forms $y(x) = \pm\sqrt{kx^3 - 4x^2}$ that are defined for $x > 4/k$ if the constant k is positive, and for $x < 4/k$ if k is negative. ∎

Example 3 Solve the initial value problem

$$x\frac{dy}{dx} = y + \sqrt{x^2 - y^2}, \quad y(x_0) = 0,$$

where $x_0 > 0$.

Solution We divide both sides by x and find that

$$\frac{dy}{dx} = \frac{y}{x} + \sqrt{1 - \left(\frac{y}{x}\right)^2},$$

so we make the substitutions in (8); we get

$$v + x\frac{dv}{dx} = v + \sqrt{1 - v^2};$$

$$\int \frac{1}{\sqrt{1 - v^2}}\, dv = \int \frac{1}{x}\, dx;$$

$$\sin^{-1} v = \ln x + C.$$

We need not write $\ln |x|$ because $x > 0$ near $x = x_0 > 0$. Now note that $v(x_0) = y(x_0)/x_0 = 0$, so $C = \sin^{-1} 0 - \ln x_0 = -\ln x_0$. Hence

$$v = \frac{y}{x} = \sin(\ln x - \ln x_0) = \sin\left(\ln \frac{x}{x_0}\right),$$

and therefore

$$y(x) = x\sin\left(\ln \frac{x}{x_0}\right)$$

is the desired particular solution. Figure 1.6.3 shows some typical solution curves. Because of the radical in the differential equation, these solution curves are confined to the indicated triangular region $x \geq |y|$. You can check that the boundary lines $y = x$ and $y = -x$ (for $x > 0$) are singular solution curves that consist of points of tangency with the solution curves found earlier. ∎

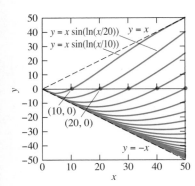

FIGURE 1.6.3. Solution curves for $xy' = y + \sqrt{x^2 - y^2}$.

Bernoulli Equations

A first-order differential equation of the form

$$\frac{dy}{dx} + P(x)y = Q(x)y^n \tag{9}$$

is called a **Bernoulli equation.** If either $n = 0$ or $n = 1$, then Eq. (9) is linear. Otherwise, as we ask you to show in Problem 56, the substitution

$$v = y^{1-n} \tag{10}$$

transforms Eq. (9) into the linear equation

$$\frac{dv}{dx} + (1 - n)P(x)v = (1 - n)Q(x).$$

Rather than memorizing the form of this transformed equation, it is more efficient to make the substitution in Eq. (10) explicitly, as in the following examples.

Example 4 If we rewrite the homogeneous equation $2xyy' = 4x^2 + 3y^2$ of Example 2 in the form

$$\frac{dy}{dx} - \frac{3}{2x}y = \frac{2x}{y},$$

we see that it is also a Bernoulli equation with $P(x) = -3/(2x)$, $Q(x) = 2x$, $n = -1$, and $1 - n = 2$. Hence we substitute

$$v = y^2, \quad y = v^{1/2}, \quad \text{and} \quad \frac{dy}{dx} = \frac{dy}{dv}\frac{dv}{dx} = \frac{1}{2}v^{-1/2}\frac{dv}{dx}.$$

This gives

$$\frac{1}{2}v^{-1/2}\frac{dv}{dx} - \frac{3}{2x}v^{1/2} = 2xv^{-1/2}.$$

Then multiplication by $2v^{1/2}$ produces the linear equation

$$\frac{dv}{dx} - \frac{3}{x}v = 4x$$

with integrating factor $\rho = e^{\int(-3/x)\,dx} = x^{-3}$. So we obtain

$$D_x(x^{-3}v) = \frac{4}{x^2};$$

$$x^{-3}v = -\frac{4}{x} + C;$$

$$x^{-3}y^2 = -\frac{4}{x} + C;$$

$$y^2 = -4x^2 + Cx^3.$$ ∎

| **Example 5** | The equation |

$$x\frac{dy}{dx} + 6y = 3xy^{4/3}$$

is neither separable nor linear nor homogeneous, but it is a Bernoulli equation with $n = \frac{4}{3}$, $1 - n = -\frac{1}{3}$. The substitutions

$$v = y^{-1/3}, \quad y = v^{-3}, \quad \text{and} \quad \frac{dy}{dx} = \frac{dy}{dv}\frac{dv}{dx} = -3v^{-4}\frac{dv}{dx}$$

transform it into

$$-3xv^{-4}\frac{dv}{dx} + 6v^{-3} = 3xv^{-4}.$$

Division by $-3xv^{-4}$ yields the linear equation

$$\frac{dv}{dx} - \frac{2}{x}v = -1$$

with integrating factor $\rho = e^{\int(-2/x)\,dx} = x^{-2}$. This gives

$$D_x(x^{-2}v) = -\frac{1}{x^2}; \quad x^{-2}v = \frac{1}{x} + C; \quad v = x + Cx^2;$$

and finally,

$$y(x) = \frac{1}{(x + Cx^2)^3}.$$ ∎

Example 6   The equation

$$2xe^{2y}\frac{dy}{dx} = 3x^4 + e^{2y} \tag{11}$$

is neither separable, nor linear, nor homogeneous, nor is it a Bernoulli equation. But we observe that y appears only in the combinations e^{2y} and $D_x(e^{2y}) = 2e^{2y}y'$. This prompts the substitution

$$v = e^{2y}, \quad \frac{dv}{dx} = 2e^{2y}\frac{dy}{dx}$$

that transforms Eq. (11) into the linear equation $xv'(x) = 3x^4 + v(x)$; that is,

$$\frac{dv}{dx} - \frac{1}{x}v = 3x^3.$$

After multiplying by the integrating factor $\rho = 1/x$, we find that

$$\frac{1}{x}v = \int 3x^2\,dx = x^3 + C, \quad \text{so} \quad e^{2y} = v = x^4 + Cx,$$

and hence

$$y(x) = \tfrac{1}{2}\ln\left|x^4 + Cx\right|. \qquad \blacksquare$$

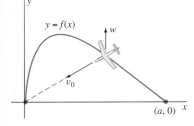

FIGURE 1.6.4. The airplane headed for the origin.

Flight Trajectories

Suppose that an airplane departs from the point $(a, 0)$ located due east of its intended destination—an airport located at the origin $(0, 0)$. The plane travels with constant speed v_0 relative to the wind, which is blowing due north with constant speed w. As indicated in Fig. 1.6.4, we assume that the plane's pilot maintains its heading directly toward the origin.

Figure 1.6.5 helps us derive the plane's velocity components relative to the ground. They are

$$\frac{dx}{dt} = -v_0\cos\theta = -\frac{v_0 x}{\sqrt{x^2 + y^2}},$$

$$\frac{dy}{dt} = -v_0\sin\theta + w = -\frac{v_0 y}{\sqrt{x^2 + y^2}} + w.$$

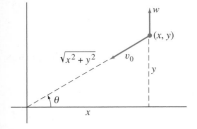

FIGURE 1.6.5. The components of the velocity vector of the airplane.

Hence the trajectory $y = f(x)$ of the plane satisfies the differential equation

$$\frac{dy}{dx} = \frac{dy/dt}{dx/dt} = \frac{1}{v_0 x}\left(v_0 y - w\sqrt{x^2 + y^2}\right). \tag{12}$$

If we set

$$k = \frac{w}{v_0}, \tag{13}$$

the ratio of the windspeed to the plane's airspeed, then Eq. (12) takes the homogeneous form

$$\frac{dy}{dx} = \frac{y}{x} - k\left[1 + \left(\frac{y}{x}\right)^2\right]^{1/2}. \tag{14}$$

The substitution $y = xv$, $y' = v + xv'$ then leads routinely to

$$\int \frac{dv}{\sqrt{1 + v^2}} = -\int \frac{k}{x}\,dx. \tag{15}$$

By trigonometric substitution, or by consulting a table for the integral on the left, we find that

$$\ln\left(v + \sqrt{1 + v^2}\right) = -k\ln x + C, \tag{16}$$

and the initial condition $v(a) = y(a)/a = 0$ yields

$$C = k\ln a. \tag{17}$$

As we ask you to show in Problem 68, the result of substituting (17) in Eq. (16) and then solving for v is

$$v = \frac{1}{2}\left[\left(\frac{x}{a}\right)^{-k} - \left(\frac{x}{a}\right)^{k}\right]. \tag{18}$$

Because $y = xv$, we finally obtain

$$y(x) = \frac{a}{2}\left[\left(\frac{x}{a}\right)^{1-k} - \left(\frac{x}{a}\right)^{1+k}\right] \tag{19}$$

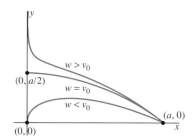

FIGURE 1.6.6. The three cases $w < v_0$ (plane velocity exceeds wind velocity), $w = v_0$ (equal velocities), and $w > v_0$ (wind is greater).

for the equation of the plane's trajectory.

Note that only in the case $k < 1$ (that is, $w < v_0$) does the curve in Eq. (19) pass through the origin, so that the plane reaches its destination. If $w = v_0$ (so that $k = 1$), then Eq. (19) takes the form $y(x) = \frac{1}{2}a(1 - x^2/a^2)$, so the plane's trajectory approaches the point $(0, a/2)$ rather than $(0, 0)$. The situation is even worse if $w > v_0$ (so $k > 1$)—in this case it follows from Eq. (19) that $y \to +\infty$ as $x \to 0$. The three cases are illustrated in Fig. 1.6.6.

Example 7 If $a = 200$ mi, $v_0 = 500$ mi/h, and $w = 100$ mi/h, then $k = w/v_0 = \frac{1}{5}$, so the plane will succeed in reaching the airport at $(0, 0)$. With these values, Eq. (19) yields

$$y(x) = 100\left[\left(\frac{x}{200}\right)^{4/5} - \left(\frac{x}{200}\right)^{6/5}\right]. \tag{20}$$

Now suppose that we want to find the maximum amount by which the plane is blown off course during its trip. That is, what is the maximum value of $y(x)$ for $0 \le x \le 200$?

Solution Differentiation of the function in Eq. (20) yields

$$\frac{dy}{dx} = \frac{1}{2}\left[\frac{4}{5}\left(\frac{x}{200}\right)^{-1/5} - \frac{6}{5}\left(\frac{x}{200}\right)^{1/5}\right],$$

and we readily solve the equation $y'(x) = 0$ to obtain $(x/200)^{2/5} = \frac{2}{3}$. Hence

$$y_{max} = 100 \left[\left(\frac{2}{3} \right)^2 - \left(\frac{2}{3} \right)^3 \right] = \frac{400}{27} \approx 14.81.$$

Thus the plane is blown almost 15 mi north at one point during its westward journey. (The graph of the function in Eq. (20) is the one used to construct Fig. 1.6.4. The vertical scale there is exaggerated by a factor of 4.) ■

Exact Differential Equations

We have seen that a general solution $y(x)$ of a first-order differential equation is often defined implicitly by an equation of the form

$$F(x, y(x)) = C, \tag{21}$$

where C is a constant. On the other hand, given the identity in (21), we can recover the original differential equation by differentiating each side with respect to x. Provided that Eq. (21) implicitly defines y as a differentiable function of x, this gives the original differential equation in the form

$$\frac{\partial F}{\partial x} + \frac{\partial F}{\partial y} \frac{dy}{dx} = 0;$$

that is,

$$M(x, y) + N(x, y) \frac{dy}{dx} = 0, \tag{22}$$

where $M(x, y) = F_x(x, y)$ and $N(x, y) = F_y(x, y)$.

It is sometimes convenient to rewrite Eq. (22) in the more symmetric form

➤ $$M(x, y) \, dx + N(x, y) \, dy = 0, \tag{23}$$

called its **differential** form. The general first-order differential equation $y' = f(x, y)$ can be written in this form with $M = f(x, y)$ and $N \equiv -1$. The preceding discussion shows that, *if* there exists a function $F(x, y)$ such that

$$\frac{\partial F}{\partial x} = M \quad \text{and} \quad \frac{\partial F}{\partial y} = N,$$

then the equation

➤ $$F(x, y) = C$$

implicitly defines a general solution of Eq. (23). In this case, Eq. (23) is called an **exact differential equation**—the differential

$$dF = F_x \, dx + F_y \, dy$$

of $F(x, y)$ is exactly $M \, dx + N \, dy$.

Natural questions are these: How can we determine whether the differential equation in (23) is exact? And if it is exact, how can we find the function F such that $F_x = M$ and $F_y = N$? To answer the first question, let us recall that if the mixed second-order partial derivatives F_{xy} and F_{yx} are continuous on an open set in the xy-plane, then they are equal: $F_{xy} = F_{yx}$. If Eq. (23) is exact and M and N have continuous partial derivatives, it then follows that

$$\frac{\partial M}{\partial y} = F_{xy} = F_{yx} = \frac{\partial N}{\partial x}.$$

Thus the equation

$$\frac{\partial M}{\partial y} = \frac{\partial N}{\partial x} \tag{24}$$

is a *necessary condition* that the differential equation $M\,dx + N\,dy = 0$ be exact. That is, if $M_y \neq N_x$, then the differential equation in question is not exact, so we need not attempt to find a function $F(x, y)$ such that $F_x = M$ and $F_y = N$—there is no such function.

Example 8

The differential equation

$$y^3\,dx + 3xy^2\,dy = 0 \tag{25}$$

is exact because we can immediately see that the function $F(x, y) = xy^3$ has the property that $F_x = y^3$ and $F_y = 3xy^2$. Thus a general solution of Eq. (25) is

$$xy^3 = C;$$

if you prefer, $y(x) = kx^{-1/3}$. ∎

But suppose that we divide each term of the differential equation in Example 8 by y^2 to obtain

$$y\,dx + 3x\,dy = 0. \tag{26}$$

This equation is not exact because, with $M = y$ and $N = 3x$, we have

$$\frac{\partial M}{\partial y} = 1 \neq 3 = \frac{\partial N}{\partial x}.$$

Hence the necessary condition in Eq. (24) is not satisfied.

We are confronted with a curious situation here. The differential equations in (25) and (26) are essentially equivalent, and they have exactly the same solutions, yet one is exact and the other is not. In brief, whether a given differential equation is exact or not is related to the precise form $M\,dx + N\,dy = 0$ in which it is written.

Theorem 1 tells us that (subject to differentiability conditions usually satisfied in practice) the necessary condition in (24) is also a *sufficient* condition for exactness. In other words, if $M_y = N_x$, then the differential equation $M\,dx + N\,dy = 0$ is exact.

THEOREM 1 Criterion for Exactness

Suppose that the functions $M(x, y)$ and $N(x, y)$ are continuous and have continuous first-order partial derivatives in the open rectangle $R: a < x < b$, $c < y < d$. Then the differential equation

$$M(x, y)\, dx + N(x, y)\, dy = 0 \tag{23}$$

is exact in R if and only if

$$\frac{\partial M}{\partial y} = \frac{\partial N}{\partial x} \tag{24}$$

at each point of R. That is, there exists a function $F(x, y)$ defined on R with $\partial F/\partial x = M$ and $\partial F/\partial y = N$ if and only if Eq. (24) holds on R.

Proof: We have seen already that it is necessary for Eq. (24) to hold if Eq. (23) is to be exact. To prove the converse, we must show that if Eq. (24) holds, then we can construct a function $F(x, y)$ such that $\partial F/\partial x = M$ and $\partial F/\partial y = N$. Note first that, for *any* function $g(y)$, the function

$$F(x, y) = \int M(x, y)\, dx + g(y) \tag{27}$$

satisfies the condition $\partial F/\partial x = M$. (In Eq. (27), the notation $\int M(x, y)\, dx$ denotes an antiderivative of $M(x, y)$ with respect to x.) We plan to choose $g(y)$ so that

$$N = \frac{\partial F}{\partial y} = \left(\frac{\partial}{\partial y} \int M(x, y)\, dx \right) + g'(y)$$

as well; that is, so that

$$g'(y) = N - \frac{\partial}{\partial y} \int M(x, y)\, dx. \tag{28}$$

To see that there *is* such a function of y, it suffices to show that the right-hand side in Eq. (28) is a function of y alone. We can then find $g(y)$ by integrating with respect to y. Because the right-hand side in Eq. (28) is defined on a rectangle, and hence on an interval as a function of x, it suffices to show that its derivative with respect to x is identically zero. But

$$\frac{\partial}{\partial x} \left(N - \frac{\partial}{\partial y} \int M(x, y)\, dx \right) = \frac{\partial N}{\partial x} - \frac{\partial}{\partial x} \frac{\partial}{\partial y} \int M(x, y)\, dx$$

$$= \frac{\partial N}{\partial x} - \frac{\partial}{\partial y} \frac{\partial}{\partial x} \int M(x, y)\, dx$$

$$= \frac{\partial N}{\partial x} - \frac{\partial M}{\partial y} = 0$$

by hypothesis. So we can, indeed, find the desired function $g(y)$ by integrating Eq. (28). We substitute this result in Eq. (27) to obtain

$$F(x, y) = \int M(x, y)\, dx + \int \left(N(x, y) - \frac{\partial}{\partial y} \int M(x, y)\, dx \right) dy \tag{29}$$

as the desired function with $F_x = M$ and $F_y = N$. ▲

Instead of memorizing Eq. (29), it is usually better to solve an exact equation $M\,dx + N\,dy = 0$ by carrying out the process indicated by Eqs. (27) and (28). First we integrate $M(x, y)$ with respect to x and write

$$F(x, y) = \int M(x, y)\,dx + g(y),$$

thinking of the function $g(y)$ as an "arbitrary constant of integration" as far as the variable x is concerned. Then we determine $g(y)$ by imposing the condition that $\partial F/\partial y = N(x, y)$. This yields a general solution in the implicit form $F(x, y) = C$.

Example 9   Solve the differential equation

$$(6xy - y^3)\,dx + (4y + 3x^2 - 3xy^2)\,dy = 0. \tag{30}$$

Solution   Let $M(x, y) = 6xy - y^3$ and $N(x, y) = 4y + 3x^2 - 3xy^2$. The given equation is exact because

$$\frac{\partial M}{\partial y} = 6x - 3y^2 = \frac{\partial N}{\partial x}.$$

Integrating $\partial F/\partial x = M(x, y)$ with respect to x, we get

$$F(x, y) = \int (6xy - y^3)\,dx = 3x^2y - xy^3 + g(y).$$

Then we differentiate with respect to y and set $\partial F/\partial y = N(x, y)$. This yields

$$\frac{\partial F}{\partial y} = 3x^2 - 3xy^2 + g'(y) = 4y + 3x^2 - 3xy^2,$$

and it follows that $g'(y) = 4y$. Hence $g(y) = 2y^2 + C_1$, and thus

$$F(x, y) = 3x^2y - xy^3 + 2y^2 + C_1.$$

Therefore, a general solution of the differential equation is defined implicitly by the equation

$$3x^2y - xy^3 + 2y^2 = C \tag{31}$$

(we have absorbed the constant C_1 into the constant C). ∎

FIGURE 1.6.7. Slope field and solution curves for the exact equation in Example 9.

Remark: Figure 1.6.7 shows a rather complicated structure of solution curves for the differential equation of Example 9. The solution satisfying a given initial condition $y(x_0) = y_0$ is defined implicitly by Eq. (31), with C determined by substituting $x = x_0$ and $y = y_0$ in the equation. For instance, the particular solution satisfying $y(0) = 1$ is defined implicitly by the equation $3x^2y - xy^3 + 2y^2 = 2$. The other two special points in the figure—at $(0, 0)$ and near $(0.75, 2.12)$—are ones where both coefficient functions in Eq. (30) vanish, so the theorem of Section 1.3 does not guarantee a unique solution. ∎

Reducible Second-Order Equations

A *second-order differential equation* involves the second derivative of the unknown function $y(x)$, and thus has the general form

$$F(x, y, y', y'') = 0. \tag{32}$$

If *either* the dependent variable y *or* the independent variable x is missing from a second-order equation, then it is easily reduced by a simple substitution to a first-order equation that may be solvable by the methods of this chapter.

Dependent variable y missing. If y is missing, then Eq. (32) takes the form

➤ $$F(x, y', y'') = 0. \tag{33}$$

Then the substitution

➤ $$p = y' = \frac{dy}{dx}, \quad y'' = \frac{dp}{dx} \tag{34}$$

results in the *first-order* differential equation

$$F(x, p, p') = 0.$$

If we can solve this equation for a general solution $p(x, C_1)$ involving an arbitrary constant C_1, then we need only write

$$y(x) = \int y'(x)\,dx = \int p(x, C_1)\,dx + C_2$$

to get a solution of Eq. (33) that involves two arbitrary constants C_1 and C_2 (as is to be expected in the case of a second-order differential equation).

| Example 10 | Solve the equation $xy'' + 2y' = 6x$ in which the dependent variable y is missing.

Solution The substitution defined in (34) gives the first-order equation

$$x\frac{dp}{dx} + 2p = 6x; \quad \text{that is,} \quad \frac{dp}{dx} + \frac{2}{x}p = 6.$$

Observing that the equation on the right here is linear, we multiply by its integrating factor $\rho = \exp\left(\int (2/x)\,dx\right) = e^{2\ln x} = x^2$ and get

$$D_x(x^2 p) = 6x^2,$$
$$x^2 p = 2x^3 + C_1,$$
$$p = \frac{dy}{dx} = 2x + \frac{C_1}{x^2}.$$

A final integration with respect to x yields the general solution

$$y(x) = x^2 + \frac{C_1}{x} + C_2$$

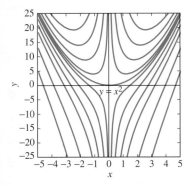

FIGURE 1.6.8. Solution curves of the form $y = x^2 + \dfrac{C_1}{x}$ for $C_1 = 0, \pm 3, \pm 10, \pm 20, \pm 35, \pm 60, \pm 100$.

of the second-order equation $xy'' + 2y' = 6x$. Solution curves with $C_1 = 0$ but $C_2 \neq 0$ are simply vertical translates of the parabola $y = x^2$ (for which $C_1 = C_2 = 0$). Figure 1.6.8 shows this parabola and some typical solution curves with $C_2 = 0$ but $C_1 \neq 0$. Solution curves with C_1 and C_2 both nonzero are vertical translates of those (other than the parabola) shown in Fig. 1.6.8. ∎

Independent variable x missing.   If x is missing, then Eq. (32) takes the form

$$F(y, y', y'') = 0. \qquad (35)$$

Then the substitution

$$p = y' = \frac{dy}{dx}, \quad y'' = \frac{dp}{dx} = \frac{dp}{dy}\frac{dy}{dx} = p\frac{dp}{dy} \qquad (36)$$

results in the *first-order* differential equation

$$F\left(y, p, p\frac{dp}{dy}\right) = 0$$

for p as a function of y. If we can solve this equation for a general solution $p(y, C_1)$ involving an arbitrary constant C_1, then (assuming that $y' \neq 0$) we need only write

$$x(y) = \int \frac{dx}{dy}\, dy = \int \frac{1}{dy/dx}\, dy = \int \frac{1}{p}\, dy = \int \frac{dy}{p(y, C_1)} + C_2.$$

If the final integral $P = \int (1/p)\, dy$ can be evaluated, the result is an implicit solution $x(y) = P(y, C_1) + C_2$ of our second-order differential equation.

Example 11   Solve the equation $yy'' = (y')^2$ in which the independent variable x is missing.

Solution   We assume temporarily that y and y' are both nonnegative, and then point out at the end that this restriction is unnecessary. The substitution defined in (36) gives the first-order equation

$$yp\frac{dp}{dy} = p^2.$$

Then separation of variables gives

$$\int \frac{dp}{p} = \int \frac{dy}{y},$$

$$\ln p = \ln y + C \quad \text{(because } y > 0 \text{ and } p = y' > 0\text{)},$$

$$p = C_1 y$$

where $C_1 = e^C$. Hence

$$\frac{dx}{dy} = \frac{1}{p} = \frac{1}{C_1 y},$$

$$C_1 x = \int \frac{dy}{y} = \ln y + C_1.$$

The resulting general solution of the second-order equation $yy'' = (y')^2$ is

$$y(x) = \exp(C_1 x - C_2) = Ae^{Bx},$$

where $A = e^{-C_2}$ and $B = C_1$. Despite our temporary assumptions, which imply that the constants A and B are both positive, we readily verify that $y(x) = Ae^{Bx}$ satisfies $yy'' = (y')^2$ for *all* real values of A and B. With $B = 0$ and different values of A, we get all horizontal lines in the plane as solution curves. The upper half of Fig. 1.6.9 shows the solution curves obtained with $A = 1$ (for instance) and different positive values of B. With $A = -1$ these solution curves are reflected in the x-axis, and with negative values of B they are reflected in the y-axis. In particular, we see that we get solutions of $yy'' = (y')^2$, allowing both positive and negative possibilities for both y and y'. ∎

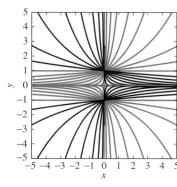

FIGURE 1.6.9. The solution curves $y = Ae^{Bx}$ with $B = 0$ and $A = 0, \pm 1$ are the horizontal lines $y = 0, \pm 1$. The exponential curves with $B > 0$ and $A = \pm 1$ are in color, those with $B < 0$ and $A = \pm 1$ are black.

1.6 Problems

Find general solutions of the differential equations in Problems 1 through 30. Primes denote derivatives with respect to x throughout.

1. $(x + y)y' = x - y$

2. $2xyy' = x^2 + 2y^2$

3. $xy' = y + 2\sqrt{xy}$

4. $(x - y)y' = x + y$

5. $x(x + y)y' = y(x - y)$

6. $(x + 2y)y' = y$

7. $xy^2y' = x^3 + y^3$

8. $x^2y' = xy + x^2e^{y/x}$

9. $x^2y' = xy + y^2$

10. $xyy' = x^2 + 3y^2$

11. $(x^2 - y^2)y' = 2xy$

12. $xyy' = y^2 + x\sqrt{4x^2 + y^2}$

13. $xy' = y + \sqrt{x^2 + y^2}$

14. $yy' + x = \sqrt{x^2 + y^2}$

15. $x(x + y)y' + y(3x + y) = 0$

16. $y' = \sqrt{x + y + 1}$

17. $y' = (4x + y)^2$

18. $(x + y)y' = 1$

19. $x^2y' + 2xy = 5y^3$

20. $y^2y' + 2xy^3 = 6x$

21. $y' = y + y^3$

22. $x^2y' + 2xy = 5y^4$

23. $xy' + 6y = 3xy^{4/3}$

24. $2xy' + y^3e^{-2x} = 2xy$

25. $y^2(xy' + y)(1 + x^4)^{1/2} = x$

26. $3y^2y' + y^3 = e^{-x}$

27. $3xy^2y' = 3x^4 + y^3$

28. $xe^yy' = 2(e^y + x^3e^{2x})$

29. $(2x \sin y \cos y)y' = 4x^2 + \sin^2 y$

30. $(x + e^y)y' = xe^{-y} - 1$

In Problems 31 through 42, verify that the given differential equation is exact; then solve it.

31. $(2x + 3y)\,dx + (3x + 2y)\,dy = 0$

32. $(4x - y)\,dx + (6y - x)\,dy = 0$

33. $(3x^2 + 2y^2)\,dx + (4xy + 6y^2)\,dy = 0$

34. $(2xy^2 + 3x^2)\,dx + (2x^2y + 4y^3)\,dy = 0$

35. $\left(x^3 + \dfrac{y}{x}\right)dx + (y^2 + \ln x)\,dy = 0$

36. $(1 + ye^{xy})\,dx + (2y + xe^{xy})\,dy = 0$

37. $(\cos x + \ln y)\,dx + \left(\dfrac{x}{y} + e^y\right)dy = 0$

38. $(x + \tan^{-1} y)\,dx + \dfrac{x + y}{1 + y^2}\,dy = 0$

39. $(3x^2y^3 + y^4)\,dx + (3x^3y^2 + y^4 + 4xy^3)\,dy = 0$

40. $(e^x \sin y + \tan y)\,dx + (e^x \cos y + x \sec^2 y)\,dy = 0$

41. $\left(\dfrac{2x}{y} - \dfrac{3y^2}{x^4}\right)dx + \left(\dfrac{2y}{x^3} - \dfrac{x^2}{y^2} + \dfrac{1}{\sqrt{y}}\right)dy = 0$

42. $\dfrac{2x^{5/2} - 3y^{5/3}}{2x^{5/2}y^{2/3}}\,dx + \dfrac{3y^{5/3} - 2x^{5/2}}{3x^{3/2}y^{5/3}}\,dy = 0$

Find a general solution of each reducible second-order differential equation in Problems 43–54. Assume x, y and/or y' positive where helpful (as in Example 11).

43. $xy'' = y'$

44. $yy'' + (y')^2 = 0$

45. $y'' + 4y = 0$

46. $xy'' + y' = 4x$

47. $y'' = (y')^2$

48. $x^2y'' + 3xy' = 2$

49. $yy'' + (y')^2 = yy'$

50. $y'' = (x + y')^2$

51. $y'' = 2y(y')^3$

52. $y^3y'' = 1$

53. $y'' = 2yy'$

54. $yy'' = 3(y')^2$

55. Show that the substitution $v = ax + by + c$ transforms the differential equation $dy/dx = F(ax + by + c)$ into a separable equation.

56. Suppose that $n \neq 0$ and $n \neq 1$. Show that the substitution $v = y^{1-n}$ transforms the Bernoulli equation $dy/dx + P(x)y = Q(x)y^n$ into the linear equation

$$\frac{dv}{dx} + (1 - n)P(x)v(x) = (1 - n)Q(x).$$

57. Show that the substitution $v = \ln y$ transforms the differential equation $dy/dx + P(x)y = Q(x)(y \ln y)$ into the linear equation $dv/dx + P(x) = Q(x)v(x)$.

58. Use the idea in Problem 57 to solve the equation

$$x\frac{dy}{dx} - 4x^2y + 2y \ln y = 0.$$

59. Solve the differential equation

$$\frac{dy}{dx} = \frac{x - y - 1}{x + y + 3}$$

by finding h and k so that the substitutions $x = u + h$, $y = v + k$ transform it into the homogeneous equation

$$\frac{dv}{du} = \frac{u - v}{u + v}.$$

60. Use the method in Problem 59 to solve the differential equation

$$\frac{dy}{dx} = \frac{2y - x + 7}{4x - 3y - 18}.$$

61. Make an appropriate substitution to find a solution of the equation $dy/dx = \sin(x - y)$. Does this general solution contain the linear solution $y(x) = x - \pi/2$ that is readily verified by substitution in the differential equation?

62. Show that the solution curves of the differential equation

$$\frac{dy}{dx} = -\frac{y(2x^3 - y^3)}{x(2y^3 - x^3)}$$

are of the form $x^3 + y^3 = 3Cxy$.

63. The equation $dy/dx = A(x)y^2 + B(x)y + C(x)$ is called a **Riccati equation.** Suppose that one particular solution $y_1(x)$ of this equation is known. Show that the substitution

$$y = y_1 + \frac{1}{v}$$

transforms the Riccati equation into the *linear* equation

$$\frac{dv}{dx} + (B + 2Ay_1)v = -A.$$

Use the method of Problem 63 to solve the equations in Problems 64 and 65, given that $y_1(x) = x$ is a solution of each.

64. $\dfrac{dy}{dx} + y^2 = 1 + x^2$

65. $\dfrac{dy}{dx} + 2xy = 1 + x^2 + y^2$

66. An equation of the form

$$y = xy' + g(y') \qquad (37)$$

is called a **Clairaut equation**. Show that the one-parameter family of straight lines described by

$$y(x) = Cx + g(C) \qquad (38)$$

is a general solution of Eq. (37).

67. Consider the Clairaut equation

$$y = xy' - \tfrac{1}{4}(y')^2$$

for which $g(y') = -\tfrac{1}{4}(y')^2$ in Eq. (37). Show that the line

$$y = Cx - \tfrac{1}{4}C^2$$

is tangent to the parabola $y = x^2$ at the point $\left(\tfrac{1}{2}C, \tfrac{1}{4}C^2\right)$. Explain why this implies that $y = x^2$ is a singular solution of the given Clairaut equation. This singular solution and the one-parameter family of straight line solutions are illustrated in Fig. 1.6.10.

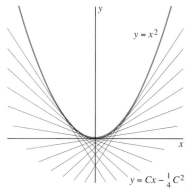

FIGURE 1.6.10. Solutions of the Clairaut equation of Problem 67. The "typical" straight line with equation $y = Cx - \tfrac{1}{4}C^2$ is tangent to the parabola at the point $\left(\tfrac{1}{2}C, \tfrac{1}{4}C^2\right)$.

68. Derive Eq. (18) in this section from Eqs. (16) and (17).

69. In the situation of Example 7, suppose that $a = 100$ mi, $v_0 = 400$ mi/h, and $w = 40$ mi/h. Now how far northward does the wind blow the airplane?

70. As in the text discussion, suppose that an airplane maintains a heading toward an airport at the origin. If $v_0 = 500$ mi/h and $w = 50$ mi/h (with the wind blowing due north), and the plane begins at the point (200, 150), show that its trajectory is described by

$$y + \sqrt{x^2 + y^2} = 2(200x^9)^{1/10}.$$

71. A river 100 ft wide is flowing north at w feet per second. A dog starts at (100, 0) and swims at $v_0 = 4$ ft/s, always heading toward a tree at (0, 0) on the west bank directly across from the dog's starting point. **(a)** If $w = 2$ ft/s, show that the dog reaches the tree. **(b)** If $w = 4$ ft/s, show that the dog reaches instead the point on the west bank 50 ft north of the tree. **(c)** If $w = 6$ ft/s, show that the dog never reaches the west bank.

72. In the calculus of plane curves, one learns that the *curvature* κ of the curve $y = y(x)$ at the point (x, y) is given by

$$\kappa = \frac{|y''(x)|}{[1 + y'(x)^2]^{3/2}},$$

and that the curvature of a circle of radius r is $\kappa = 1/r$. [See Example 3 in Section 11.6 of Edwards and Penney, *Calculus: Early Transcendentals*, 7th edition (Upper Saddle River, NJ: Prentice Hall, 2008).] Conversely, substitute $\rho = y'$ to derive a general solution of the second-order differential equation

$$ry'' = [1 + (y')^2]^{3/2}$$

(with r constant) in the form

$$(x - a)^2 + (y - b)^2 = r^2.$$

Thus a circle of radius r (or a part thereof) is the *only* plane curve with constant curvature $1/r$.

1.6 Application Computer Algebra Solutions

Computer algebra systems typically include commands for the "automatic" solution of differential equations. But two different such systems often give different results whose equivalence is not clear, and a single system may give the solution in an overly complicated form. Consequently, computer algebra solutions of differential equations often require considerable "processing" or simplification by a human user in order to yield concrete and applicable information. Here we illustrate these issues using the interesting differential equation

$$\frac{dy}{dx} = \sin(x - y) \tag{1}$$

that appeared in the Section 1.3 Application. The *Maple* command

```
dsolve( D(y)(x) = sin(x - y(x)), y(x));
```

yields the simple and attractive result

$$y(x) = x - 2\tan^{-1}\left(\frac{x - 2 - C1}{x - C1}\right) \tag{2}$$

that was cited there. But the supposedly equivalent *Mathematica* command

```
DSolve[ y'[x] == Sin[x - y[x]], y[x], x]
```

yields a considerably more complicated result from which—with a fair amount of effort in simplification—one can extract the quite different looking solution

$$y(x) = 2\cos^{-1}\left(\frac{2\cos\frac{x}{2} + (x - c)\left(\cos\frac{x}{2} + \sin\frac{x}{2}\right)}{\sqrt{2 + 2(x - c + 1)^2}}\right). \tag{3}$$

This apparent disparity is not unusual; different symbolic algebra systems, or even different versions of the same system, often yield different forms of a solution of the same differential equation. As an alternative to attempted reconciliation of such seemingly disparate results as in Eqs. (2) and (3), a common tactic is simplification of the differential equation before submitting it to a computer algebra system.

EXERCISE 1: Show that the plausible substitution $v = x - y$ in Eq. (1) yields the separable equation

$$\frac{dv}{dx} = 1 - \sin v. \tag{4}$$

Now the *Maple* command `int(1/(1-sin(v)),v)` yields

$$\int \frac{dv}{1 - v} = \frac{2}{1 - \tan\frac{v}{2}} \tag{5}$$

(omitting the constant of integration, as symbolic computer algebra systems often do).

EXERCISE 2: Use simple algebra to deduce from Eq. (5) the integral formula

$$\int \frac{dv}{1 - v} = \frac{1 + \tan\frac{v}{2}}{1 - \tan\frac{v}{2}} + C. \tag{6}$$

EXERCISE 3:   Deduce from (6) that Eq. (4) has the general solution

$$v(x) = 2\tan^{-1}\left(\frac{x - 1 + C}{x + 1 + C}\right),$$

and hence that Eq. (1) has the general solution

$$y(x) = x - 2\tan^{-1}\left(\frac{x - 1 + C}{x + 1 + C}\right). \tag{7}$$

EXERCISE 4:   Finally, reconcile the forms in Eq. (2) and Eq. (7). What is the relation between the constants C and $C1$?

EXERCISE 5:   Show that the integral in Eq. (5) yields immediately the graphing calculator implicit solution shown in Fig. 1.6.11.

FIGURE 1.6.11. Implicit solution of $y' = \sin(x - y)$ generated by a TI-89 graphing calculator.

INVESTIGATION: For your own personal differential equation, let p and q be two distinct nonzero digits in your student ID number, and consider the differential equation

$$\frac{dy}{dx} = \frac{1}{p}\cos(x - qy). \tag{8}$$

(a) Find a symbolic general solution using a computer algebra system and/or some combination of the techniques listed in this project.

(b) Determine the symbolic particular solution corresponding to several typical initial conditions of the form $y(x_0) = y_0$.

(c) Determine the possible values of a and b such that the straight line $y = ax + b$ is a solution curve of Eq. (8).

(d) Plot a direction field and some typical solution curves. Can you make a connection between the symbolic solution and your (linear and nonlinear) solution curves?

Chapter 1 Summary

In this chapter we have discussed applications of and solution methods for several important types of first-order differential equations, including those that are separable (Section 1.4), linear (Section 1.5), or exact (Section 1.6). In Section 1.6 we also discussed substitution techniques that can sometimes be used to transform a given first-order differential equation into one that is either separable, linear, or exact.

Lest it appear that these methods constitute a "grab bag" of special and unrelated techniques, it is important to note that they are all versions of a single idea. Given a differential equation

$$f(x, y, y') = 0, \tag{1}$$

we attempt to write it in the form

$$\frac{d}{dx}[G(x, y)] = 0. \tag{2}$$

It is precisely to obtain the form in Eq. (2) that we multiply the terms in Eq. (1) by an appropriate integrating factor (even if all we are doing is separating the variables).

But once we have found a function $G(x, y)$ such that Eqs. (1) and (2) are equivalent, a general solution is defined implicitly by means of the equation

$$G(x, y) = C \tag{3}$$

that one obtains by integrating Eq. (2).

Given a specific first-order differential equation to be solved, we can attack it by means of the following steps:

- Is it *separable*? If so, separate the variables and integrate (Section 1.4).
- Is it *linear*? That is, can it be written in the form

$$\frac{dy}{dx} + P(x)y = Q(x)?$$

  If so, multiply by the integrating factor $\rho = \exp\left(\int P\, dx\right)$ of Section 1.5.
- Is it *exact*? That is, when the equation is written in the form $M\, dx + N\, dy = 0$, is $\partial M / \partial y = \partial N / \partial x$ (Section 1.6)?
- If the equation as it stands is not separable, linear, or exact, is there a plausible substitution that will make it so? For instance, is it homogeneous (Section 1.6)?

Many first-order differential equations succumb to the line of attack outlined here. Nevertheless, many more do not. Because of the wide availability of computers, numerical techniques are commonly used to *approximate* the solutions of differential equations that cannot be solved readily or explicitly by the methods of this chapter. Indeed, most of the solution curves shown in figures in this chapter were plotted using numerical approximations rather than exact solutions. Several numerical methods for the appropriate solution of differential equations will be discussed in Chapter 2.

Chapter 1 Review Problems

Find general solutions of the differential equations in Problems 1 through 30. Primes denote derivatives with respect to x.

1. $x^3 + 3y - xy' = 0$
2. $xy^2 + 3y^2 - x^2y' = 0$
3. $xy + y^2 - x^2y' = 0$
4. $2xy^3 + e^x + (3x^2y^2 + \sin y)y' = 0$
5. $3y + x^4y' = 2xy$
6. $2xy^3 + x^2y' = y^2$
7. $2x^2y + x^3y' = 1$
8. $2xy + x^2y' = y^2$
9. $xy' + 2y = 6x^2\sqrt{y}$
10. $y' = 1 + x^2 + y^2 + x^2y^2$
11. $x^2y' = xy + 3y^2$
12. $6xy^3 + 2y^4 + (9x^2y^2 + 8xy^3)y' = 0$
13. $4xy^2 + y' = 5x^4y^2$
14. $x^3y' = x^2y - y^3$
15. $y' + 3y = 3x^2e^{-3x}$
16. $y' = x^2 - 2xy + y^2$
17. $e^x + ye^{xy} + (e^y + xe^{yx})y' = 0$
18. $2x^2y - x^3y' = y^3$
19. $3x^5y^2 + x^3y' = 2y^2$
20. $xy' + 3y = 3x^{-3/2}$
21. $(x^2 - 1)y' + (x - 1)y = 1$
22. $xy' = 6y + 12x^4y^{2/3}$
23. $e^y + y\cos x + (xe^y + \sin x)y' = 0$
24. $9x^2y^2 + x^{3/2}y' = y^2$
25. $2y + (x + 1)y' = 3x + 3$

26. $9x^{1/2}y^{4/3} - 12x^{1/5}y^{3/2} + (8x^{3/2}y^{1/3} - 15x^{6/5}y^{1/2})y' = 0$
27. $3y + x^3y^4 + 3xy' = 0$
28. $y + xy' = 2e^{2x}$
29. $(2x + 1)y' + y = (2x + 1)^{3/2}$
30. $y' = \sqrt{x + y}$

Each of the differential equations in Problems 31 through 36 is of two different types considered in this chapter—separable, linear, homogeneous, Bernoulli, exact, etc. Hence, derive general solutions for each of these equations in two different ways; then reconcile your results.

31. $\dfrac{dy}{dx} = 3(y + 7)x^2$
32. $\dfrac{dy}{dx} = xy^3 - xy$
33. $\dfrac{dy}{dx} = -\dfrac{3x^2 + 2y^2}{4xy}$
34. $\dfrac{dy}{dx} = \dfrac{x + 3y}{y - 3x}$
35. $\dfrac{dy}{dx} = \dfrac{2xy + 2x}{x^2 + 1}$
36. $\dfrac{dy}{dx} = \dfrac{\sqrt{y} - y}{\tan x}$

Mathematical Models and Numerical Methods

Population Models

In Section 1.4 we introduced the exponential differential equation $dP/dt = kP$, with solution $P(t) = P_0e^{kt}$, as a mathematical model for natural population growth that occurs as a result of constant birth and death rates. Here we present a more general population model that accommodates birth and death rates that are not necessarily constant. As before, however, our population function $P(t)$ will be a *continuous* approximation to the actual population, which of course changes only by integral increments—that is, by one birth or death at a time.

Suppose that the population changes only by the occurrence of births and deaths—there is no immigration or emigration from outside the country or environment under consideration. It is customary to track the growth or decline of a population in terms of its *birth rate* and *death rate* functions defined as follows:

- $\beta(t)$ is the number of births per unit of population per unit of time at time t;
- $\delta(t)$ is the number of deaths per unit of population per unit of time at time t.

Then the numbers of births and deaths that occur during the time interval $[t, t + \Delta t]$ is given (approximately) by

$$\text{births: } \beta(t) \cdot P(t) \cdot \Delta t, \qquad \text{deaths: } \delta(t) \cdot P(t) \cdot \Delta t.$$

Hence the change ΔP in the population during the time interval $[t, t + \Delta t]$ of length Δt is

$$\Delta P = \{\text{births}\} - \{\text{deaths}\} \approx \beta(t) \cdot P(t) \cdot \Delta t - \delta(t) \cdot P(t) \cdot \Delta t,$$

so

$$\frac{\Delta P}{\Delta t} \approx [\beta(t) - \delta(t)] \, P(t).$$

The error in this approximation should approach zero as $\Delta t \to 0$, so—taking the limit—we get the differential equation

➤
$$\frac{dP}{dt} = (\beta - \delta)P, \tag{1}$$

in which we write $\beta = \beta(t)$, $\delta = \delta(t)$, and $P = P(t)$ for brevity. Equation (1) is the **general population equation.** If β and δ are constant, Eq. (1) reduces to the natural growth equation with $k = \beta - \delta$. But it also includes the possibility that β and δ are variable functions of t. The birth and death rates need not be known in advance; they may well depend on the unknown function $P(t)$.

Example 1 Suppose that an alligator population numbers 100 initially, and that its death rate is $\delta = 0$ (so none of the alligators is dying). If the birth rate is $\beta = (0.0005)P$—and thus increases as the population does—then Eq. (1) gives the initial value problem

$$\frac{dP}{dt} = (0.0005)P^2, \quad P(0) = 100$$

(with t in years). Then upon separating the variables we get

$$\int \frac{1}{P^2}\, dP = \int (0.0005)\, dt;$$

$$-\frac{1}{P} = (0.0005)t + C.$$

Substitution of $t = 0$, $P = 100$ gives $C = -1/100$, and then we readily solve for

$$P(t) = \frac{2000}{20 - t}.$$

For instance, $P(10) = 2000/10 = 200$, so after 10 years the alligator population has doubled. But we see that $P \to +\infty$ as $t \to 20$, so a real "population explosion" occurs in 20 years. Indeed, the direction field and solution curves shown in Fig. 2.1.1 indicate that a population explosion always occurs, whatever the size of the (positive) initial population $P(0) = P_0$. In particular, it appears that the population always becomes unbounded in a *finite* period of time. ∎

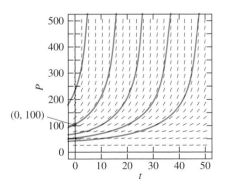

FIGURE 2.1.1. Slope field and solution curves for the equation $dP/dt = (0.0005)P^2$ in Example 1.

Bounded Populations and the Logistic Equation

In situations as diverse as the human population of a nation and a fruit fly population in a closed container, it is often observed that the birth rate decreases as the population itself increases. The reasons may range from increased scientific or cultural sophistication to a limited food supply. Suppose, for example, that the birth rate β is a *linear* decreasing function of the population size P, so that $\beta = \beta_0 - \beta_1 P$, where β_0 and β_1 are positive constants. If the death rate $\delta = \delta_0$ remains constant, then Eq. (1) takes the form

$$\frac{dP}{dt} = (\beta_0 - \beta_1 P - \delta_0)P;$$

that is,

$$\frac{dP}{dt} = aP - bP^2, \tag{2}$$

where $a = \beta_0 - \delta_0$ and $b = \beta_1$.

If the coefficients a and b are both positive, then Eq. (2) is called the **logistic equation.** For the purpose of relating the behavior of the population $P(t)$ to the values of the parameters in the equation, it is useful to rewrite the logistic equation in the form

$$\frac{dP}{dt} = kP(M - P), \tag{3}$$

where $k = b$ and $M = a/b$ are constants.

Example 2   In Example 4 of Section 1.3 we explored graphically a population that is modeled by the logistic equation

$$\frac{dP}{dt} = 0.0004P(150 - P) = 0.06P - 0.0004P^2. \tag{4}$$

To solve this differential equation symbolically, we separate the variables and integrate. We get

$$\int \frac{dP}{P(150 - P)} = \int 0.0004 \, dt,$$

$$\frac{1}{150} \int \left(\frac{1}{P} + \frac{1}{150 - P} \right) dP = \int 0.0004 \, dt \qquad \text{[partial fractions]},$$

$$\ln|P| - \ln|150 - P| = 0.06t + C,$$

$$\frac{P}{150 - P} = \pm e^C e^{0.06t} = Be^{0.06t} \quad \text{[where } B = \pm e^C\text{]}.$$

If we substitute $t = 0$ and $P = P_0 \neq 150$ into this last equation, we find that $B = P_0/(150 - P_0)$. Hence

$$\frac{P}{150 - P} = \frac{P_0 e^{0.06t}}{150 - P_0}.$$

Finally, this equation is easy to solve for the population

$$P(t) = \frac{150 P_0}{P_0 + (150 - P_0)e^{-0.06t}} \tag{5}$$

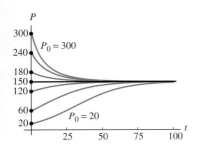

FIGURE 2.1.2. Typical solution curves for the logistic equation $P' = 0.06P - 0.0004P^2$.

at time t in terms of the initial population $P_0 = P(0)$. Figure 2.1.2 shows a number of solution curves corresponding to different values of the initial population ranging from $P_0 = 20$ to $P_0 = 300$. Note that all these solution curves appear to approach the horizontal line $P = 150$ as an asymptote. Indeed, you should be able to see directly from Eq. (5) that $\lim_{t \to \infty} P(t) = 150$, whatever the initial value $P_0 > 0$. ∎

Limiting Populations and Carrying Capacity

The finite limiting population noted in Example 2 is characteristic of logistic populations. In Problem 32 we ask you to use the method of solution of Example 2 to show that the solution of the logistic initial value problem

$$\frac{dP}{dt} = kP(M - P), \quad P(0) = P_0 \tag{6}$$

is

$$P(t) = \frac{MP_0}{P_0 + (M - P_0)e^{-kMt}}. \tag{7}$$

Actual animal populations are positive valued. If $P_0 = M$, then (7) reduces to the unchanging (constant-valued) "equilibrium population" $P(t) \equiv M$. Otherwise, the behavior of a logistic population depends on whether $0 < P_0 < M$ or $P_0 > M$. If $0 < P_0 < M$, then we see from (6) and (7) that $P' > 0$ and

$$P(t) = \frac{MP_0}{P_0 + (M - P_0)e^{-kMt}} = \frac{MP_0}{P_0 + \{\text{pos. number}\}} < \frac{MP_0}{P_0} = M.$$

However, if $P_0 > M$, then we see from (6) and (7) that $P' < 0$ and

$$P(t) = \frac{MP_0}{P_0 + (M - P_0)e^{-kMt}} = \frac{MP_0}{P_0 + \{\text{neg. number}\}} > \frac{MP_0}{P_0} = M.$$

In either case, the "positive number" or "negative number" in the denominator has absolute value less than P_0 and—because of the exponential factor—approaches 0 as $t \to +\infty$. It follows that

$$\lim_{t \to +\infty} P(t) = \frac{MP_0}{P_0 + 0} = M. \tag{8}$$

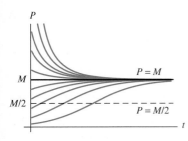

FIGURE 2.1.3. Typical solution curves for the logistic equation $P' = kP(M - P)$. Each solution curve that starts below the line $P = M/2$ has an inflection point on this line. (See Problem 34.)

Thus a population that satisfies the logistic equation does *not* grow without bound like a naturally growing population modeled by the exponential equation $P' = kP$. Instead, it approaches the finite **limiting population** M as $t \to +\infty$. As illustrated by the typical logistic solution curves in Fig. 2.1.3, the population $P(t)$ steadily increases and approaches M from below if $0 < P_0 < M$, but steadily decreases and approaches M from above if $P_0 > M$. Sometimes M is called the **carrying capacity** of the environment, considering it to be the maximum population that the environment can support on a long-term basis.

Example 3 Suppose that in 1885 the population of a certain country was 50 million and was growing at the rate of 750,000 people per year at that time. Suppose also that in 1940 its population was 100 million and was then growing at the rate of 1 million per year. Assume that this population satisfies the logistic equation. Determine both the limiting population M and the predicted population for the year 2000.

Solution We substitute the two given pairs of data in Eq. (3) and find that

$$0.75 = 50k(M - 50), \quad 1.00 = 100k(M - 100).$$

We solve simultaneously for $M = 200$ and $k = 0.0001$. Thus the limiting population of the country in question is 200 million. With these values of M and k, and with $t = 0$ corresponding to the year 1940 (in which $P_0 = 100$), we find that—according to Eq. (7)—the population in the year 2000 will be

$$P(60) = \frac{100 \cdot 200}{100 + (200 - 100)e^{-(0.0001)(200)(60)}},$$

about 153.7 million people. ∎

Historical Note

The logistic equation was introduced (around 1840) by the Belgian mathematician and demographer P. F. Verhulst as a possible model for human population growth. In the next two examples we compare natural growth and logistic model fits to the 19th-century U.S. population census data, then compare projections for the 20th century.

Example 4 The U.S. population in 1800 was 5.308 million and in 1900 was 76.212 million. If we take $P_0 = 5.308$ (with $t = 0$ in 1800) in the natural growth model $P(t) = P_0 e^{rt}$ and substitute $t = 100$, $P = 76.212$, we find that

$$76.212 = 5.308e^{100r}, \quad \text{so} \quad r = \frac{1}{100} \ln \frac{76.212}{5.308} \approx 0.026643.$$

Thus our natural growth model for the U.S. population during the 19th century is

$$P(t) = (5.308)e^{(0.026643)t} \tag{9}$$

(with t in years and P in millions). Because $e^{0.026643} \approx 1.02700$, the average population growth between 1800 and 1900 was about 2.7% per year. ∎

Example 5 The U.S. population in 1850 was 23.192 million. If we take $P_0 = 5.308$ and substitute the data pairs $t = 50$, $P = 23.192$ (for 1850) and $t = 100$, $P = 76.212$ (for 1900) in the logistic model formula in Eq. (7), we get the two equations

$$\frac{(5.308)M}{5.308 + (M - 5.308)e^{-50kM}} = 23.192,$$

$$\frac{(5.308)M}{5.308 + (M - 5.308)e^{-100kM}} = 76.212 \tag{10}$$

in the two unknowns k and M. Nonlinear systems like this ordinarily are solved numerically using an appropriate computer system. But with the right algebraic trick (Problem 36 in this section) the equations in (10) can be solved manually for $k = 0.000167716$, $M = 188.121$. Substitution of these values in Eq. (7) yields the logistic model

$$P(t) = \frac{998.546}{5.308 + (182.813)e^{-(0.031551)t}}. \tag{11}$$

The table in Fig. 2.1.4 compares the actual 1800–1990 U.S. census population figures with those predicted by the exponential growth model in (9) and the logistic model in (11). Both agree well with the 19th-century figures. But the exponential model diverges appreciably from the census data in the early decades of the 20th century, whereas the logistic model remains accurate until 1940. By the end of the 20th century the exponential model vastly overestimates the actual U.S. population—predicting over a billion in the year 2000—whereas the logistic model somewhat underestimates it.

Year	Actual U.S. Pop.	Exponential Model	Exponential Error	Logistic Model	Logistic Error
1800	5.308	5.308	0.000	5.308	0.000
1810	7.240	6.929	0.311	7.202	0.038
1820	9.638	9.044	0.594	9.735	−0.097
1830	12.861	11.805	1.056	13.095	−0.234
1840	17.064	15.409	1.655	17.501	−0.437
1850	23.192	20.113	3.079	23.192	0.000
1860	31.443	26.253	5.190	30.405	1.038
1870	38.558	34.268	4.290	39.326	−0.768
1880	50.189	44.730	5.459	50.034	0.155
1890	62.980	58.387	4.593	62.435	0.545
1900	76.212	76.212	0.000	76.213	−0.001
1910	92.228	99.479	−7.251	90.834	1.394
1920	106.022	129.849	−23.827	105.612	0.410
1930	123.203	169.492	−46.289	119.834	3.369
1940	132.165	221.237	−89.072	132.886	−0.721
1950	151.326	288.780	−137.454	144.354	6.972
1960	179.323	376.943	−197.620	154.052	25.271
1970	203.302	492.023	−288.721	161.990	41.312
1980	226.542	642.236	−415.694	168.316	58.226
1990	248.710	838.308	−589.598	173.252	76.458
2000	281.422	1094.240	−812.818	177.038	104.384

FIGURE 2.1.4. Comparison of exponential growth and logistic models with U.S. census populations (in millions).

FIGURE 2.1.5. Percentage errors in the exponential and logistic population models for 1800–1950.

The two models are compared in Fig. 2.1.5, where plots of their respective errors—as a *percentage* of the actual population—are shown for the 1800–1950 period. We see that the logistic model tracks the actual population reasonably well throughout this 150-year period. However, the exponential error is considerably larger during the 19th century and literally goes off the chart during the first half of the 20th century.

In order to measure the extent to which a given model fits actual data, it is customary to define the **average error** (in the model) as *the square root of the average of the squares of the individual errors* (the latter appearing in the fourth and sixth columns of the table in Fig. 2.1.4). Using only the 1800–1900 data, this definition gives 3.162 for the average error in the exponential model, while the average error in the logistic model is only 0.452. Consequently, even in 1900 we might well have anticipated that the logistic model would predict the U.S. population growth during the 20th century more accurately than the exponential model. ∎

The moral of Examples 4 and 5 is simply that one should not expect too much of models that are based on severely limited information (such as just a pair of data points). Much of the science of *statistics* is devoted to the analysis of large "data sets" to formulate useful (and perhaps reliable) mathematical models.

More Applications of the Logistic Equation

We next describe some situations that illustrate the varied circumstances in which the logistic equation is a satisfactory mathematical model.

1. *Limited environment situation.* A certain environment can support a population of at most M individuals. It is then reasonable to expect the growth rate $\beta - \delta$ (the combined birth and death rates) to be proportional to $M - P$, because we may think of $M - P$ as the potential for further expansion. Then $\beta - \delta = k(M - P)$, so that

$$\frac{dP}{dt} = (\beta - \delta)P = kP(M - P).$$

The classic example of a limited environment situation is a fruit fly population in a closed container.

2. *Competition situation.* If the birth rate β is constant but the death rate δ is proportional to P, so that $\delta = \alpha P$, then

$$\frac{dP}{dt} = (\beta - \alpha P)P = kP(M - P).$$

This might be a reasonable working hypothesis in a study of a cannibalistic population, in which all deaths result from chance encounters between individuals. Of course, competition between individuals is not usually so deadly, nor its effects so immediate and decisive.

3. *Joint proportion situation.* Let $P(t)$ denote the number of individuals in a constant-size susceptible population M who are infected with a certain contagious and incurable disease. The disease is spread by chance encounters. Then $P'(t)$ should be proportional to the product of the number P of individuals having the disease and the number $M - P$ of those not having it, and therefore $dP/dt = kP(M - P)$. Again we discover that the mathematical model is the logistic equation. The mathematical description of the spread of a rumor in a population of M individuals is identical.

Example 6 Suppose that at time $t = 0$, 10 thousand people in a city with population $M = 100$ thousand people have heard a certain rumor. After 1 week the number $P(t)$ of those who have heard it has increased to $P(1) = 20$ thousand. Assuming that $P(t)$ satisfies a logistic equation, when will 80% of the city's population have heard the rumor?

Solution Substituting $P_0 = 10$ and $M = 100$ (thousand) in Eq. (7), we get

$$P(t) = \frac{1000}{10 + 90e^{-100kt}}. \tag{12}$$

Then substitution of $t = 1$, $P = 20$ gives the equation

$$20 = \frac{1000}{10 + 90e^{-100k}}$$

that is readily solved for

$$e^{-100k} = \tfrac{4}{9}, \quad \text{so} \quad k = \tfrac{1}{100} \ln \tfrac{9}{4} \approx 0.008109.$$

With $P(t) = 80$, Eq. (12) takes the form

$$80 = \frac{1000}{10 + 90e^{-100kt}},$$

which we solve for $e^{-100kt} = \tfrac{1}{36}$. It follows that 80% of the population has heard the rumor when

$$t = \frac{\ln 36}{100k} = \frac{\ln 36}{\ln \tfrac{9}{4}} \approx 4.42,$$

thus after about 4 weeks and 3 days. ■

Doomsday versus Extinction

Consider a population $P(t)$ of unsophisticated animals in which females rely solely on chance encounters to meet males for reproductive purposes. It is reasonable to expect such encounters to occur at a rate that is proportional to the product of the number $P/2$ of males and the number $P/2$ of females, hence at a rate proportional to P^2. We therefore assume that births occur at the rate kP^2 (per unit time, with k constant). The birth rate (births/time/population) is then given by $\beta = kP$. If the death rate δ is constant, then the general population equation in (1) yields the differential equation

➤ $$\frac{dP}{dt} = kP^2 - \delta P = kP(P - M) \tag{13}$$

(where $M = \delta/k > 0$) as a mathematical model of the population.

Note that the right-hand side in Eq. (13) is the *negative* of the right-hand side in the logistic equation in (3). We will see that the constant M is now a **threshold population**, with the way the population behaves in the future depending critically on whether the initial population P_0 is less than or greater than M.

Example 7 Consider an animal population $P(t)$ that is modeled by the equation

$$\frac{dP}{dt} = 0.0004P(P - 150) = 0.0004P^2 - 0.06P. \tag{14}$$

We want to find $P(t)$ if (a) $P(0) = 200$; (b) $P(0) = 100$.

Solution To solve the equation in (14), we separate the variables and integrate. We get

$$\int \frac{dP}{P(P-150)} = \int 0.0004 \, dt,$$

$$-\frac{1}{150} \int \left(\frac{1}{P} - \frac{1}{P-150}\right) dP = \int 0.0004 \, dt \quad \text{[partial fractions]},$$

$$\ln|P| - \ln|P-150| = -0.06t + C,$$

$$\frac{P}{P-150} = \pm e^C e^{-0.06t} = Be^{-0.06t} \qquad \text{[where } B = \pm e^C]. \qquad (15)$$

(a) Substitution of $t = 0$ and $P = 200$ into (15) gives $B = 4$. With this value of B we solve Eq. (15) for

$$P(t) = \frac{600e^{-0.06t}}{4e^{-0.06t} - 1}. \qquad (16)$$

Note that, as t increases and approaches $T = \ln(4)/0.06 \approx 23.105$, the positive denominator on the right in (16) decreases and approaches 0. Consequently $P(t) \to +\infty$ as $t \to T^-$. This is a *doomsday* situation—a real population *explosion*.

(b) Substitution of $t = 0$ and $P = 100$ into (15) gives $B = -2$. With this value of B we solve Eq. (15) for

$$P(t) = \frac{300e^{-0.06t}}{2e^{-0.06t} + 1} = \frac{300}{2 + e^{0.06t}}. \qquad (17)$$

Note that, as t increases without bound, the positive denominator on the right in (16) approaches $+\infty$. Consequently, $P(t) \to 0$ as $t \to +\infty$. This is an (eventual) *extinction* situation. ∎

Thus the population in Example 7 either explodes or is an endangered species threatened with extinction, depending on whether or not its initial size exceeds the threshold population $M = 150$. An approximation to this phenomenon is sometimes observed with animal populations, such as the alligator population in certain areas of the southern United States.

Figure 2.1.6 shows typical solution curves that illustrate the two possibilities for a population $P(t)$ satisfying Eq. (13). If $P_0 = M$ (exactly!), then the population remains constant. However, this equilibrium situation is very unstable. If P_0 exceeds M (even slightly), then $P(t)$ rapidly increases without bound, whereas if the initial (positive) population is less than M (however slightly), then it decreases (more gradually) toward zero as $t \to +\infty$. See Problem 33.

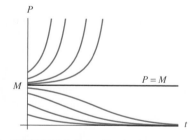

FIGURE 2.1.6. Typical solution curves for the explosion/extinction equation $P' = kP(P - M)$.

2.1 Problems

Separate variables and use partial fractions to solve the initial value problems in Problems 1–8. Use either the exact solution or a computer-generated slope field to sketch the graphs of several solutions of the given differential equation, and highlight the indicated particular solution.

1. $\dfrac{dx}{dt} = x - x^2, \, x(0) = 2$ **2.** $\dfrac{dx}{dt} = 10x - x^2, \, x(0) = 1$

3. $\dfrac{dx}{dt} = 1 - x^2, \, x(0) = 3$ **4.** $\dfrac{dx}{dt} = 9 - 4x^2, \, x(0) = 0$

5. $\dfrac{dx}{dt} = 3x(5 - x)$, $x(0) = 8$

6. $\dfrac{dx}{dt} = 3x(x - 5)$, $x(0) = 2$

7. $\dfrac{dx}{dt} = 4x(7 - x)$, $x(0) = 11$

8. $\dfrac{dx}{dt} = 7x(x - 13)$, $x(0) = 17$

9. The time rate of change of a rabbit population P is proportional to the square root of P. At time $t = 0$ (months) the population numbers 100 rabbits and is increasing at the rate of 20 rabbits per month. How many rabbits will there be one year later?

10. Suppose that the fish population $P(t)$ in a lake is attacked by a disease at time $t = 0$, with the result that the fish cease to reproduce (so that the birth rate is $\beta = 0$) and the death rate δ (deaths per week per fish) is thereafter proportional to $1/\sqrt{P}$. If there were initially 900 fish in the lake and 441 were left after 6 weeks, how long did it take all the fish in the lake to die?

11. Suppose that when a certain lake is stocked with fish, the birth and death rates β and δ are both inversely proportional to $\sqrt{P}$. **(a)** Show that

$$P(t) = \left(\tfrac{1}{2}kt + \sqrt{P_0}\right)^2,$$

where k is a constant. **(b)** If $P_0 = 100$ and after 6 months there are 169 fish in the lake, how many will there be after 1 year?

12. The time rate of change of an alligator population P in a swamp is proportional to the square of P. The swamp contained a dozen alligators in 1988, two dozen in 1998. When will there be four dozen alligators in the swamp? What happens thereafter?

13. Consider a prolific breed of rabbits whose birth and death rates, β and δ, are each proportional to the rabbit population $P = P(t)$, with $\beta > \delta$. **(a)** Show that

$$P(t) = \dfrac{P_0}{1 - kP_0 t}, \quad k \text{ constant}.$$

Note that $P(t) \to +\infty$ as $t \to 1/(kP_0)$. This is doomsday. **(b)** Suppose that $P_0 = 6$ and that there are nine rabbits after ten months. When does doomsday occur?

14. Repeat part (a) of Problem 13 in the case $\beta < \delta$. What now happens to the rabbit population in the long run?

15. Consider a population $P(t)$ satisfying the logistic equation $dP/dt = aP - bP^2$, where $B = aP$ is the time rate at which births occur and $D = bP^2$ is the rate at which deaths occur. If the initial population is $P(0) = P_0$, and B_0 births per month and D_0 deaths per month are occurring at time $t = 0$, show that the limiting population is $M = B_0 P_0 / D_0$.

16. Consider a rabbit population $P(t)$ satisfying the logistic equation as in Problem 15. If the initial population is 120 rabbits and there are 8 births per month and 6 deaths per month occurring at time $t = 0$, how many months does it take for $P(t)$ to reach 95% of the limiting population M?

17. Consider a rabbit population $P(t)$ satisfying the logistic equation as in Problem 15. If the initial population is 240 rabbits and there are 9 births per month and 12 deaths per month occurring at time $t = 0$, how many months does it take for $P(t)$ to reach 105% of the limiting population M?

18. Consider a population $P(t)$ satisfying the extinction-explosion equation $dP/dt = aP^2 - bP$, where $B = aP^2$ is the time rate at which births occur and $D = bP$ is the rate at which deaths occur. If the initial population is $P(0) = P_0$ and B_0 births per month and D_0 deaths per month are occurring at time $t = 0$, show that the threshold population is $M = D_0 P_0 / B_0$.

19. Consider an alligator population $P(t)$ satisfying the extinction/explosion equation as in Problem 18. If the initial population is 100 alligators and there are 10 births per month and 9 deaths per months occurring at time $t = 0$, how many months does it take for $P(t)$ to reach 10 times the threshold population M?

20. Consider an alligator population $P(t)$ satisfying the extinction/explosion equation as in Problem 18. If the initial population is 110 alligators and there are 11 births per month and 12 deaths per month occurring at time $t = 0$, how many months does it take for $P(t)$ to reach 10% of the threshold population M?

21. Suppose that the population $P(t)$ of a country satisfies the differential equation $dP/dt = kP(200 - P)$ with k constant. Its population in 1940 was 100 million and was then growing at the rate of 1 million per year. Predict this country's population for the year 2000.

22. Suppose that at time $t = 0$, half of a "logistic" population of 100,000 persons have heard a certain rumor, and that the number of those who have heard it is then increasing at the rate of 1000 persons per day. How long will it take for this rumor to spread to 80% of the population? (*Suggestion*: Find the value of k by substituting $P(0)$ and $P'(0)$ in the logistic equation, Eq. (3).)

23. As the salt KNO_3 dissolves in methanol, the number $x(t)$ of grams of the salt in a solution after t seconds satisfies the differential equation $dx/dt = 0.8x - 0.004x^2$.

    (a) What is the maximum amount of the salt that will ever dissolve in the methanol?

    (b) If $x = 50$ when $t = 0$, how long will it take for an additional 50 g of salt to dissolve?

24. Suppose that a community contains 15,000 people who are susceptible to Michaud's syndrome, a contagious disease. At time $t = 0$ the number $N(t)$ of people who have developed Michaud's syndrome is 5000 and is increasing at the rate of 500 per day. Assume that $N'(t)$ is proportional to the product of the numbers of those who have caught the disease and of those who have not. How long will it take for another 5000 people to develop Michaud's syndrome?

25. The data in the table in Fig. 2.1.7 are given for a certain population $P(t)$ that satisfies the logistic equation in (3). **(a)** What is the limiting population M? (*Suggestion*: Use the approximation

$$P'(t) \approx \frac{P(t+h) - P(t-h)}{2h}$$

with $h = 1$ to estimate the values of $P'(t)$ when $P = 25.00$ and when $P = 47.54$. Then substitute these values in the logistic equation and solve for k and M.) **(b)** Use the values of k and M found in part (a) to determine when $P = 75$. (*Suggestion*: Take $t = 0$ to correspond to the year 1925.)

Year	P (millions)
1924	24.63
1925	25.00
1926	25.38
⋮	⋮
1974	47.04
1975	47.54
1976	48.04

FIGURE 2.1.7. Population data for Problem 25.

26. A population $P(t)$ of small rodents has birth rate $\beta = (0.001)P$ (births per month per rodent) and *constant* death rate δ. If $P(0) = 100$ and $P'(0) = 8$, how long (in months) will it take this population to double to 200 rodents? (*Suggestion*: First find the value of δ.)

27. Consider an animal population $P(t)$ with constant death rate $\delta = 0.01$ (deaths per animal per month) and with birth rate β proportional to P. Suppose that $P(0) = 200$ and $P'(0) = 2$. **(a)** When is $P = 1000$? **(b)** When does doomsday occur?

28. Suppose that the number $x(t)$ (with t in months) of alligators in a swamp satisfies the differential equation $dx/dt = 0.0001x^2 - 0.01x$.

(a) If initially there are 25 alligators in the swamp, solve this differential equation to determine what happens to the alligator population in the long run.

(b) Repeat part (a), except with 150 alligators initially.

29. During the period from 1790 to 1930, the U.S. population $P(t)$ (t in years) grew from 3.9 million to 123.2 million. Throughout this period, $P(t)$ remained close to the solution of the initial value problem

$$\frac{dP}{dt} = 0.03135P - 0.0001489P^2, \quad P(0) = 3.9.$$

(a) What 1930 population does this logistic equation predict?

(b) What limiting population does it predict?

(c) Has this logistic equation continued since 1930 to accurately model the U.S. population?

[This problem is based on a computation by Verhulst, who in 1845 used the 1790–1840 U.S. population data to predict accurately the U.S. population through the year 1930 (long after his own death, of course).]

30. A tumor may be regarded as a population of multiplying cells. It is found empirically that the "birth rate" of the cells in a tumor decreases exponentially with time, so that $\beta(t) = \beta_0 e^{-\alpha t}$ (where α and β_0 are positive constants), and hence

$$\frac{dP}{dt} = \beta_0 e^{-\alpha t} P, \quad P(0) = P_0.$$

Solve this initial value problem for

$$P(t) = P_0 \exp\left(\frac{\beta_0}{\alpha}(1 - e^{-\alpha t})\right).$$

Observe that $P(t)$ approaches the finite limiting population $P_0 \exp(\beta_0/\alpha)$ as $t \to +\infty$.

31. For the tumor of Problem 30, suppose that at time $t = 0$ there are $P_0 = 10^6$ cells and that $P(t)$ is then increasing at the rate of 3×10^5 cells per month. After 6 months the tumor has doubled (in size and in number of cells). Solve numerically for α, and then find the limiting population of the tumor.

32. Derive the solution

$$P(t) = \frac{MP_0}{P_0 + (M - P_0)e^{-kMt}}$$

of the logistic initial value problem $P' = kP(M - P)$, $P(0) = P_0$. Make it clear how your derivation depends on whether $0 < P_0 < M$ or $P_0 > M$.

33. (a) Derive the solution

$$P(t) = \frac{MP_0}{P_0 + (M - P_0)e^{kMt}}$$

of the extinction-explosion initial value problem $P' = kP(P - M)$, $P(0) = P_0$.

(b) How does the behavior of $P(t)$ as t increases depend on whether $0 < P_0 < M$ or $P_0 > M$?

34. If $P(t)$ satisfies the logistic equation in (3), use the chain rule to show that

$$P''(t) = 2k^2 P(P - \tfrac{1}{2}M)(P - M).$$

Conclude that $P'' > 0$ if $0 < P < \tfrac{1}{2}M$; $P'' = 0$ if $P = \tfrac{1}{2}M$; $P'' < 0$ if $\tfrac{1}{2}M < P < M$; and $P'' > 0$ if $P > M$. In particular, it follows that any solution curve that crosses the line $P = \tfrac{1}{2}M$ has an inflection point where it crosses that line, and therefore resembles one of the lower S-shaped curves in Fig. 2.1.3.

35. Consider two population functions $P_1(t)$ and $P_2(t)$, both of which satisfy the logistic equation with the same limiting population M but with different values k_1 and k_2 of the constant k in Eq. (3). Assume that $k_1 < k_2$. Which population approaches M the most rapidly? You can reason *geometrically* by examining slope fields (especially if appropriate software is available), *symbolically* by analyzing the solution given in Eq. (7), or *numerically* by substituting successive values of t.

36. To solve the two equations in (10) for the values of k and M, begin by solving the first equation for the quantity $x = e^{-50kM}$ and the second equation for $x^2 = e^{-100kM}$. Upon equating the two resulting expressions for x^2 in terms of M, you get an equation that is readily solved for M. With M now known, either of the original equations is readily solved for k. This technique can be used to "fit" the logistic equation to any three population values P_0, P_1, and P_2 corresponding to *equally spaced* times $t_0 = 0$, t_1, and $t_2 = 2t_1$.

37. Use the method of Problem 36 to fit the logistic equation to the actual U.S. population data (Fig. 2.1.4) for the years 1850, 1900, and 1950. Solve the resulting logistic equation and compare the predicted and actual populations for the years 1990 and 2000.

38. Fit the logistic equation to the actual U.S. population data (Fig. 2.1.4) for the years 1900, 1930, and 1960. Solve the resulting logistic equation, then compare the predicted and actual populations for the years 1980, 1990, and 2000.

39. Birth and death rates of animal populations typically are not constant; instead, they vary periodically with the passage of seasons. Find $P(t)$ if the population P satisfies the differential equation

$$\frac{dP}{dt} = (k + b\cos 2\pi t)P,$$

where t is in years and k and b are positive constants. Thus the growth-rate function $r(t) = k + b\cos 2\pi t$ varies periodically about its mean value k. Construct a graph that contrasts the growth of this population with one that has the same initial value P_0 but satisfies the natural growth equation $P' = kP$ (same constant k). How would the two populations compare after the passage of many years?

2.1 Application Logistic Modeling of Population Data

These investigations deal with the problem of fitting a logistic model to given population data. Thus we want to determine the numerical constants a and b so that the solution $P(t)$ of the initial value problem

$$\frac{dP}{dt} = aP + bP^2, \quad P(0) = P_0 \tag{1}$$

approximates the given values P_0, P_1, ..., P_n of the population at the times $t_0 = 0$, t_1, ..., t_n. If we rewrite Eq. (1) (the logistic equation with $kM = a$ and $k = -b$) in the form

$$\frac{1}{P}\frac{dP}{dt} = a + bP, \tag{2}$$

then we see that the points

$$\left(P(t_i), \frac{P'(t_i)}{P(t_i)}\right), \quad i = 0, 1, 2, \ldots, n,$$

should all lie on the straight line with y-intercept a and slope b (as determined by the function of P on the right-hand side in Eq. (2)).

This observation provides a way to find a and b. If we can determine the approximate values of the derivatives P_1', P_2', ... corresponding to the given population data, then we can proceed with the following agenda:

- First plot the points $(P_1, P_1'/P_1)$, $(P_2, P_2'/P_2)$, ... on a sheet of graph paper with horizontal P-axis.
- Then use a ruler to draw a straight line that appears to approximate these points well.

- Finally, measure this straight line's y-intercept a and slope b.

But where are we to find the needed values of the derivative $P'(t)$ of the (as yet) unknown function P? It is easiest to use the approximation

$$P'_i = \frac{P_{i+1} - P_{i-1}}{t_{i+1} - t_{i-1}} \tag{3}$$

suggested by Fig. 2.1.8. For instance, if we take $i = 0$ corresponding to the year 1790, then the U.S. population data in Fig. 2.1.9 give

$$P'_1 = \frac{P_2 - P_0}{t_2 - t_0} = \frac{7.240 - 3.929}{20} \approx 0.166$$

for the slope at (t_1, P_1) corresponding to the year 1800.

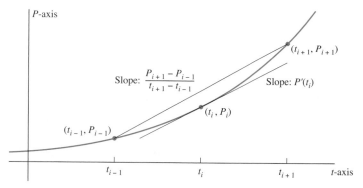

FIGURE 2.1.8. The symmetric difference approximation $\dfrac{P_{i+1} - P_{i-1}}{t_{i+1} - t_{i-1}}$ to the derivative $P'(t_i)$.

INVESTIGATION A: Use Eq. (3) to verify the slope figures shown in the final column of the table in Fig. 2.1.9, then plot the points $(P_1, P'_1/P_1), \ldots, (P_{11}, P'_{11}/P_{11})$ indicated by the dots in Fig. 2.1.10. If an appropriate graphing calculator, spreadsheet, or computer program is available, use it to find the straight line $y = a + bP$ as in (2) that best fits these points. If not, draw your own straight line approximating these points, and then measure its intercept a and slope b as accurately as you can. Next, solve the logistic equation in (1) with these numerical parameters, taking $t = 0$ corresponding to the year 1800. Finally, compare the predicted 20th-century U.S. population figures with the actual data listed in Fig. 2.1.4.

INVESTIGATION B: Repeat Investigation A, but take $t = 0$ in 1900 and use only 20th-century population data. Do you get a better approximation for the U.S. population during the final decades of the 20th century?

INVESTIGATION C: Model similarly the world population data shown in Fig. 2.1.11. The Population Division of the United Nations predicts a world population of 8.177 billion in the year 2025. What do you predict?

Year	i	t_i	Population P_i	Slope P_i'
1790	0	−10	3.929	
1800	1	0	5.308	0.166
1810	2	10	7.240	0.217
1820	3	20	9.638	0.281
1830	4	30	12.861	0.371
1840	5	40	17.064	0.517
1850	6	50	23.192	0.719
1860	7	60	31.443	0.768
1870	8	70	38.558	0.937
1880	9	80	50.189	1.221
1890	10	90	62.980	1.301
1900	11	100	76.212	1.462
1910	12	110	92.228	

FIGURE 2.1.9. U.S. population data (in millions) and approximate slopes.

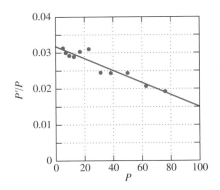

FIGURE 2.1.10. Points and approximating straight line for U.S. population data from 1800 to 1900.

Year	World Population (billions)
1960	3.049
1965	3.358
1970	3.721
1975	4.103
1980	4.473
1985	4.882
1990	5.249
1995	5.679
2000	6.127

FIGURE 2.1.11. World population data.

2.2 Equilibrium Solutions and Stability

In previous sections we have often used explicit solutions of differential equations to answer specific numerical questions. But even when a given differential equation is difficult or impossible to solve explicitly, it often is possible to extract *qualitative* information about general properties of its solutions. For example, we may be able to establish that every solution $x(t)$ grows without bound as $t \to +\infty$, or approaches a finite limit, or is a periodic function of t. In this section we introduce—mainly by consideration of simple differential equations that *can* be solved explicitly—some of the more important qualitative questions that can sometimes be answered for equations that are difficult or impossible to solve.

Example 1

Let $x(t)$ denote the temperature of a body with initial temperature $x(0) = x_0$. At time $t = 0$ this body is immersed in a medium with constant temperature A. Assuming Newton's law of cooling,

$$\frac{dx}{dt} = -k(x - A) \qquad (k > 0 \quad \text{constant}), \tag{1}$$

we readily solve (by separation of variables) for the explicit solution

$$x(t) = A + (x_0 - A)e^{-kt}.$$

It follows immediately that

$$\lim_{t \to \infty} x(t) = A, \tag{2}$$

so the temperature of the body approaches that of the surrounding medium (as is evident to one's intuition). Note that the constant function $x(t) \equiv A$ is a solution of Eq. (1); it corresponds to the temperature of the body when it is in thermal equilibrium with the surrounding medium. In Fig. 2.2.1 the limit in (2) means that every other solution curve approaches the equilibrium solution curve $x = A$ asymptotically as $t \to +\infty$. ∎

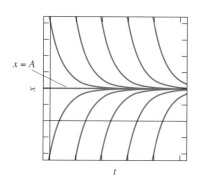

FIGURE 2.2.1. Typical solution curves for the equation of Newton's law of cooling, $dx/dt = -k(x - A)$.

FIGURE 2.2.2. Phase diagram for the equation $dx/dt = f(x) = k(A - x)$.

Remark: The behavior of solutions of Eq. (1) is summarized briefly by the **phase diagram** in Fig. 2.2.2—which indicates the direction (or "phase") of change in x as a function of x itself. The right-hand side $f(x) = -k(x - A) = k(A - x)$ is positive if $x < A$, negative if $x > A$. This observation corresponds to the fact that solutions starting above the line $x = A$ and those starting below it both approach the limiting solution $x(t) \equiv A$ as t increases (as indicated by the arrows). ∎

In Section 2.1 we introduced the general population equation

$$\frac{dx}{dt} = (\beta - \delta)x, \tag{3}$$

where β and δ are the birth and death rates, respectively, in births or deaths per individual per unit of time. The question of whether a population $x(t)$ is bounded or unbounded as $t \to +\infty$ is of evident interest. In many situations—like the logistic and explosion/extinction populations of Section 2.1—the birth and death rates are known functions of x. Then Eq. (3) takes the form

$$\frac{dx}{dt} = f(x). \tag{4}$$

This is an **autonomous** first-order differential equation—one in which the independent variable t does not appear explicitly (the terminology here stemming from the Greek word *autonomos* for "independent," e.g., of the time t). As in Example 1, the solutions of the equation $f(x) = 0$ play an important role and are called **critical points** of the autonomous differential equation $dx/dt = f(x)$.

If $x = c$ is a critical point of Eq. (4), then the differential equation has the constant solution $x(t) \equiv c$. A constant solution of a differential equation is sometimes called an **equilibrium solution** (one may think of a population that remains constant because it is in "equilibrium" with its environment). Thus the critical point $x = c$, a number, corresponds to the equilibrium solution $x(t) \equiv c$, a constant-valued function.

Example 2 illustrates the fact that the qualitative behavior (as t increases) of the solutions of an autonomous first-order equation can be described in terms of its critical points.

| **Example 2** | Consider the logistic differential equation |

$$\frac{dx}{dt} = kx(M - x) \tag{5}$$

(with $k > 0$ and $M > 0$). It has two critical points—the solutions $x = 0$ and $x = M$ of the equation

$$f(x) = kx(M - x) = 0.$$

In Section 2.1 we discussed the logistic-equation solution

$$x(t) = \frac{Mx_0}{x_0 + (M - x_0)e^{-kMt}} \tag{6}$$

satisfying the initial condition $x(0) = x_0$. Note that the initial values $x_0 = 0$ and $x_0 = M$ yield the equilibrium solutions $x(t) \equiv 0$ and $x(t) \equiv M$ of Eq. (5).

We observed in Section 2.1 that if $x_0 > 0$, then $x(t) \to M$ as $t \to +\infty$. But if $x_0 < 0$, then the denominator in Eq. (6) initially is positive, but vanishes when

$$t = t_1 = \frac{1}{kM} \ln \frac{M - x_0}{-x_0} > 0.$$

Because the numerator in (6) is negative in this case, it follows that

$$\lim_{t \to t_1^-} x(t) = -\infty \quad \text{if} \quad x_0 < 0.$$

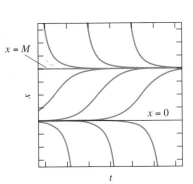

FIGURE 2.2.3. Typical solution curves for the logistic equation $dx/dt = kx(M - x)$.

It follows that the solution curves of the logistic equation in (5) look as illustrated in Fig. 2.2.3. Here we see graphically that every solution either approaches the equilibrium solution $x(t) \equiv M$ as t increases, or (in a visually obvious sense) diverges away from the other equilibrium solution $x(t) \equiv 0$. ∎

Stability of Critical Points

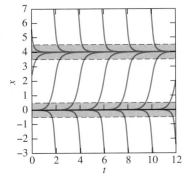

FIGURE 2.2.4. Solution curves, funnel, and spout for $dx/dt = 4x - x^2$.

Figure 2.2.3 illustrates the concept of *stability*. A critical point $x = c$ of an autonomous first-order equation is said to be *stable* provided that, if the initial value x_0 is sufficiently close to c, then $x(t)$ remains close to c for all $t > 0$. More precisely, the critical point c is **stable** if, for each $\epsilon > 0$, there exists $\delta > 0$ such that

$$|x_0 - c| < \delta \quad \text{implies that} \quad |x(t) - c| < \epsilon \tag{7}$$

for all $t > 0$. The critical point $x = c$ is **unstable** if it is not stable.

Figure 2.2.4 shows a "wider view" of the solution curves of a logistic equation with $k = 1$ and $M = 4$. Note that the strip $3.5 < x < 4.5$ enclosing the stable equilibrium curve $x = 4$ acts like a *funnel*—solution curves (moving from left to right) enter this strip and thereafter remain within it. By contrast, the strip $-0.5 < x < 0.5$ enclosing the unstable solution curve $x = 0$ acts like a *spout*—solution curves leave this strip and thereafter remain outside it. Thus the critical point $x = M$ is stable, whereas the critical point $x = 0$ is unstable.

Remark 1: We can summarize the behavior of solutions of the logistic equation in (5)—in terms of their initial values—by means of the phase diagram shown in Fig. 2.2.5. It indicates that $x(t) \to M$ as $t \to +\infty$ if either $x_0 > M$ or $0 < x_0 < M$, whereas $x(t) \to -\infty$ as t increases if $x_0 < 0$. The fact that M is a stable critical point would be important, for instance, if we wished to conduct an experiment with a population of M bacteria. It is impossible to count precisely M bacteria for M large, but any initially positive population will approach M as t increases.

FIGURE 2.2.5. Phase diagram for the logistic equation $dx/dt = f(x) = kx(M - x)$.

Remark 2: Related to the stability of the limiting solution $M = a/b$ of the logistic equation

$$\frac{dx}{dt} = ax - bx^2 \qquad (8)$$

is the "predictability" of M for an actual population. The coefficients a and b are unlikely to be known precisely for an actual population. But if they are replaced with close approximations $a^\star$ and $b^\star$—derived perhaps from empirical measurements—then the approximate limiting population $M^\star = a^\star/b^\star$ will be close to the actual limiting population $M = a/b$. We may therefore say that the value M of the limiting population predicted by a logistic equation not only is a stable critical point of the differential equation; this value also is "stable" with respect to small perturbations of the constant coefficients in the equation. (Note that one of these two statements involves changes in the initial value x_0; the other involves changes in the coefficients a and b.) ■

| **Example 3** | Consider now the explosion/extinction equation |

$$\frac{dx}{dt} = kx(x - M) \qquad (9)$$

of Eq. (10) in Section 2.1. Like the logistic equation, it has the two critical points $x = 0$ and $x = M$ corresponding to the equilibrium solutions $x(t) \equiv 0$ and $x(t) \equiv M$. According to Problem 33 in Section 2.1, its solution with $x(0) = x_0$ is given by

$$x(t) = \frac{Mx_0}{x_0 + (M - x_0)e^{kMt}} \qquad (10)$$

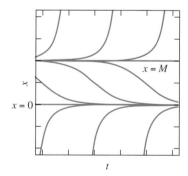

FIGURE 2.2.6. Typical solution curves for the explosion/extinction equation $dx/dt = kx(x - M)$.

(with only a single difference in sign from the logistic solution in (6)). If $x_0 < M$, then (because the coefficient of the exponential in the denominator is positive) it follows immediately from Eq. (10) that $x(t) \to 0$ as $t \to +\infty$. But if $x_0 > M$, then the denominator in (10) initially is positive, but vanishes when

$$t = t_1 = \frac{1}{kM} \ln \frac{x_0}{x_0 - M} > 0.$$

Because the numerator in (10) is positive in this case, it follows that

$$\lim_{t \to t_1^-} x(t) = +\infty \quad \text{if} \quad x_0 > M.$$

Therefore, the solution curves of the explosion/extinction equation in (9) look as illustrated in Fig. 2.2.6. A narrow band along the equilibrium curve $x = 0$ (as in Fig. 2.2.4) would serve as a funnel, while a band along the solution curve $x = M$ would serve as a spout for solutions. The behavior of the solutions of Eq. (9) is summarized by the phase diagram in Fig. 2.2.7, where we see that the critical point $x = 0$ is stable and the critical point $x = M$ is unstable. ■

$x' > 0$ $x' < 0$ $x' > 0$

$x = 0$ $x = M$

Stable   Unstable

FIGURE 2.2.7. Phase diagram for the explosion/extinction equation $dx/dt = f(x) = kx(x - M)$.

Harvesting a Logistic Population

The autonomous differential equation

$$\frac{dx}{dt} = ax - bx^2 - h \tag{11}$$

(with a, b, and h all positive) may be considered to describe a logistic population *with harvesting*. For instance, we might think of the population of fish in a lake from which h fish per year are removed by fishing.

Example 4   Let us rewrite Eq. (11) in the form

$$\frac{dx}{dt} = kx(M - x) - h, \tag{12}$$

which exhibits the limiting population M in the case $h = 0$ of no harvesting. Assuming hereafter that $h > 0$, we can solve the quadratic equation $-kx^2 + kMx - h = 0$ for the two critical points

$$H, N = \frac{kM \pm \sqrt{(kM)^2 - 4hk}}{2k} = \frac{1}{2}\left(M \pm \sqrt{M^2 - 4h/k}\right), \tag{13}$$

assuming that the harvesting rate h is sufficiently small that $4h < kM^2$, so both roots H and N are real with $0 < H < N < M$. Then we can rewrite Eq. (12) in the form

$$\frac{dx}{dt} = k(N - x)(x - H). \tag{14}$$

For instance, the number of critical points of the equation may change abruptly as the value of a parameter is changed. In Problem 24 we ask you to solve this equation for the solution

$$x(t) = \frac{N(x_0 - H) - H(x_0 - N)e^{-k(N-H)t}}{(x_0 - H) - (x_0 - N)e^{-k(N-H)t}} \tag{15}$$

in terms of the initial value $x(0) = x_0$.

Note that the exponent $-k(N - H)t$ is negative for $t > 0$. If $x_0 > N$, then each of the coefficients within parentheses in Eq. (15) is positive; it follows that

$$\text{If} \quad x_0 > N \quad \text{then} \quad x(t) \rightarrow N \quad \text{as} \quad t \rightarrow +\infty. \tag{16}$$

In Problem 25 we ask you to deduce also from Eq. (15) that

$$\text{If} \quad H < x_0 < N \quad \text{then} \quad x(t) \rightarrow N \quad \text{as} \quad t \rightarrow +\infty, \quad \text{whereas} \tag{17}$$

$$\text{if} \quad x_0 < H \quad \text{then} \quad x(t) \rightarrow -\infty \quad \text{as} \quad t \rightarrow t_1 \tag{18}$$

for a positive value t_1 that depends on x_0. It follows that the solution curves of Eq. (12)—still assuming that $4h < kM^2$—look as illustrated in Fig. 2.2.8. (Can you visualize a funnel along the line $x = N$ and a spout along the line $x = H$?) Thus the constant solution $x(t) \equiv N$ is an equilibrium *limiting solution*, whereas $x(t) \equiv H$ is a *threshold solution* that separates different behaviors—the population approaches N if $x_0 > H$, while it becomes extinct because of harvesting if $x_0 < H$. Finally, the stable critical point $x = N$ and the unstable critical point $x = H$ are illustrated in the phase diagram in Fig. 2.2.9. ■

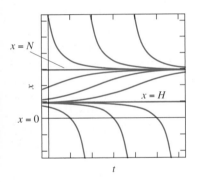

FIGURE 2.2.8. Typical solution curves for the logistic harvesting equation $dx/dt = k(N - x)(x - H)$.

$$\underset{\substack{x = H \\ \text{Unstable}}}{\xleftarrow{\hspace{1em} x' < 0 \hspace{1em}}} \quad \underset{\substack{x = N \\ \text{Stable}}}{\xrightarrow{\hspace{1em} x' > 0 \hspace{1em}}} \xleftarrow{\hspace{1em} x' < 0 \hspace{1em}}$$

FIGURE 2.2.9. Phase diagram for the logistic harvesting equation $dx/dt = f(x) = k(N - x)(x - H)$.

| **Example 5** | For a concrete application of our stability conclusions in Example 4, suppose that $k = 1$ and $M = 4$ for a logistic population $x(t)$ of fish in a lake, measured in hundreds after t years. Without any fishing at all, the lake would eventually contain nearly 400 fish, whatever the initial population. Now suppose that $h = 3$, so that 300 fish are "harvested" annually (at a constant rate throughout the year). Equation (12) is then $dx/dt = x(4 - x) - 3$, and the quadratic equation |

$$-x^2 + 4x - 3 = (3 - x)(x - 1) = 0$$

has solutions $H = 1$ and $N = 3$. Thus the threshold population is 100 fish and the (new) limiting population is 300 fish. In short, if the lake is stocked initially with more than 100 fish, then as t increases, the fish population will approach a limiting value of 300 fish. But if the lake is stocked initially with fewer than 100 fish, then the lake will be "fished out" and the fish will disappear entirely within a finite period of time.   ■

Bifurcation and Dependence on Parameters

A biological or physical system that is modeled by a differential equation may depend crucially on the numerical values of certain coefficients or parameters that appear in the equation. For instance, the number of critical points of the equation may change abruptly as the value of a parameter is changed.

| **Example 6** | The differential equation |

$$\frac{dx}{dt} = x(4 - x) - h \tag{19}$$

(with x in hundreds) models the harvesting of a logistic population with $k = 1$ and limiting population $M = 4$ (hundred). In Example 5 we considered the case of harvesting level $h = 3$, and found that the new limiting population is $N = 3$ hundred and the threshold population is $H = 1$ hundred. Typical solution curves, including the equilibrium solutions $x(t) \equiv 3$ and $x(t) \equiv 1$, then look like those pictured in Fig. 2.2.8.

Now let's investigate the dependence of this picture upon the harvesting level h. According to Eq. (13) with $k = 1$ and $M = 4$, the limiting and threshold populations N and H are given by

$$H, N = \frac{1}{2} \left(4 \pm \sqrt{16 - 4h} \right) = 2 \pm \sqrt{4 - h}. \tag{20}$$

If $h < 4$—we can consider negative values of h to describe stocking rather than harvesting the fish—then there are distinct equilibrium solutions $x(t) \equiv N$ and $x(t) \equiv H$ with $N > H$ as in Fig. 2.2.8.

But if $h = 4$, then Eq. (20) gives $N = H = 2$, so the differential equation has only the single equilibrium solution $x(t) \equiv 2$. In this case the solution curves of the equation look like those illustrated in Fig. 2.2.10. If the initial number x_0 (in hundreds) of fish exceeds 2, then the population approaches a limiting population of 2 (hundred fish). However, any initial population $x_0 < 2$ (hundred) results in extinction with the fish dying out as a consequence of the harvesting of 4 hundred fish annually. The critical point $x = 2$ might therefore be described as "semistable"—it looks stable on the side $x > 2$ where solution curves approach the equilibrium solution $x(t) \equiv 2$ as t increases, but unstable on the side $x < 2$ where solution curves instead diverge away from the equilibrium solution.

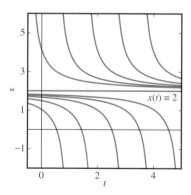

FIGURE 2.2.10. Solution curves of the equation $x' = x(4 - x) - h$ with critical harvesting $h = 4$.

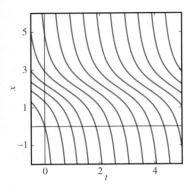

FIGURE 2.2.11. Solution curves of the equation $x' = x(4 - x) - h$ with excessive harvesting $h = 5$.

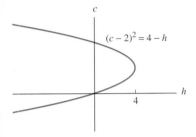

FIGURE 2.2.12. The parabola $(c - 2)^2 = 4 - h$ is the bifurcation diagram for the differential equation $x' = x(4 - x) - h$.

If, finally, $h > 4$, then the quadratic equation corresponding to (20) has no real solutions and the differential equation in (19) has no equilibrium solutions. The solution curves then look like those illustrated in Fig. 2.2.11, and (whatever the initial number of fish) the population dies out as a result of the excessive harvesting. ∎

If we imagine turning a dial to gradually increase the value of the parameter h in Eq. (19), then the picture of the solution curves changes from one like Fig. 2.2.8 with $h < 4$, to Fig. 2.2.10 with $h = 4$, to one like Fig. 2.2.11 with $h > 4$. Thus the differential equation has

- two critical points if $h < 4$;
- one critical point if $h = 4$;
- no critical point if $h > 4$.

The value $h = 4$—for which the qualitative nature of the solutions changes as h increases—is called a **bifurcation point** for the differential equation containing the parameter h. A common way to visualize the corresponding "bifurcation" in the solutions is to plot the **bifurcation diagram** consisting of all points (h, c), where c is a critical point of the equation $x' = x(4 - x) + h$. For instance, if we rewrite Eq. (20) as

$$c = 2 \pm \sqrt{4 - h},$$
$$(c - 2)^2 = 4 - h,$$

where either $c = N$ or $c = H$, then we get the equation of the parabola that is shown in Fig. 2.2.12. This parabola is then the bifurcation diagram for our differential equation that models a logistic fish population with harvesting at the level specified by the parameter h.

2.2 Problems

In Problems 1 through 12 first solve the equation $f(x) = 0$ to find the critical points of the given autonomous differential equation $dx/dt = f(x)$. Then analyze the sign of $f(x)$ to determine whether each critical point is stable or unstable, and construct the corresponding phase diagram for the differential equation. Next, solve the differential equation explicitly for $x(t)$ in terms of t. Finally, use either the exact solution or a computer-generated slope field to sketch typical solution curves for the given differential equation, and verify visually the stability of each critical point.

1. $\dfrac{dx}{dt} = x - 4$

2. $\dfrac{dx}{dt} = 3 - x$

3. $\dfrac{dx}{dt} = x^2 - 4x$

4. $\dfrac{dx}{dt} = 3x - x^2$

5. $\dfrac{dx}{dt} = x^2 - 4$

6. $\dfrac{dx}{dt} = 9 - x^2$

7. $\dfrac{dx}{dt} = (x - 2)^2$

8. $\dfrac{dx}{dt} = -(3 - x)^2$

9. $\dfrac{dx}{dt} = x^2 - 5x + 4$

10. $\dfrac{dx}{dt} = 7x - x^2 - 10$

11. $\dfrac{dx}{dt} = (x - 1)^3$

12. $\dfrac{dx}{dt} = (2 - x)^3$

In Problems 13 through 18, use a computer system or graphing calculator to plot a slope field and/or enough solution curves to indicate the stability or instability of each critical point of the given differential equation. (Some of these critical points may be semistable in the sense mentioned in Example 6.)

13. $\dfrac{dx}{dt} = (x + 2)(x - 2)^2$

14. $\dfrac{dx}{dt} = x(x^2 - 4)$

15. $\dfrac{dx}{dt} = (x^2 - 4)^2$

16. $\dfrac{dx}{dt} = (x^2 - 4)^3$

17. $\dfrac{dx}{dt} = x^2(x^2 - 4)$

18. $\dfrac{dx}{dt} = x^3(x^2 - 4)$

19. The differential equation $dx/dt = \frac{1}{10}x(10 - x) - h$ models a logistic population with harvesting at rate h. Determine (as in Example 6) the dependence of the number of critical points on the parameter h, and then construct a bifurcation diagram like Fig. 2.2.12.

20. The differential equation $dx/dt = \frac{1}{100}x(x - 5) + s$ models a population with stocking at rate s. Determine the depen-

dence of the number of critical points c on the parameter s, and then construct the corresponding bifurcation diagram in the sc-plane.

21. Consider the differential equation $dx/dt = kx - x^3$. **(a)** If $k \leq 0$, show that the only critical value $c = 0$ of x is stable. **(b)** If $k > 0$, show that the critical point $c = 0$ is now unstable, but that the critical points $c = \pm\sqrt{k}$ are stable. Thus the qualitative nature of the solutions changes at $k = 0$ as the parameter k increases, and so $k = 0$ is a bifurcation point for the differential equation with parameter k. The plot of all points of the form (k, c) where c is a critical point of the equation $x' = kx - x^3$ is the "pitchfork diagram" shown in Fig. 2.2.13.

22. Consider the differential equation $dx/dt = x + kx^3$ containing the parameter k. Analyze (as in Problem 21) the dependence of the number and nature of the critical points on the value of k, and construct the corresponding bifurcation diagram.

23. Suppose that the logistic equation $dx/dt = kx(M - x)$ models a population $x(t)$ of fish in a lake after t months during which no fishing occurs. Now suppose that, because of fishing, fish are removed from the lake at the rate of hx fish per month (with h a positive constant). Thus fish are "harvested" at a rate proportional to the existing fish population, rather than at the constant rate of Example 4. **(a)** If $0 < h < kM$, show that the population is still logistic. What is the new limiting population? **(b)** If $h \geq kM$, show that $x(t) \to 0$ are $t \to +\infty$, so the lake is eventually fished out.

24. Separate variables in the logistic harvesting equation $dx/dt = k(N - x)(x - H)$ and then use partial fractions to derive the solution given in Eq. (15).

25. Use the alternative forms

$$x(t) = \frac{N(x_0 - H) + H(N - x_0)e^{-k(N-H)t}}{(x_0 - H) + (N - x_0)e^{-k(N-H)t}}$$

$$= \frac{H(N - x_0)e^{-k(N-H)t} - N(H - x_0)}{(N - x_0)e^{-k(N-H)t} - (H - x_0)}$$

of the solution in (15) to establish the conclusions stated in (17) and (18).

Example 4 dealt with the case $4h > kM^2$ in the equation $dx/dt = kx(M - x) - h$ that describes constant-rate harvesting of a logistic population. Problems 26 and 27 deal with the other cases.

26. If $4h = kM^2$, show that typical solution curves look as illustrated in Fig. 2.2.14. Thus if $x_0 \geq M/2$, then $x(t) \to M/2$ as $t \to +\infty$. But if $x_0 < M/2$, then $x(t) = 0$ after a finite period of time, so the lake is fished out. The critical point $x = M/2$ might be called *semistable,* because it looks stable from one side, unstable from the other.

27. If $4h > kM^2$, show that $x(t) = 0$ after a finite period of time, so the lake is fished out (whatever the initial population). [*Suggestion:* Complete the square to rewrite the differential equation in the form $dx/dt = -k[(x - a)^2 + b^2]$. Then solve explicitly by separation of variables.] The results of this and the previous problem (together with Example 4) show that $h = \frac{1}{4}kM^2$ is a critical harvesting rate for a logistic population. At any lesser harvesting rate the population approaches a limiting population N that is less than M (why?), whereas at any greater harvesting rate the population reaches extinction.

28. This problem deals with the differential equation $dx/dt = kx(x - M) - h$ that models the harvesting of an unsophisticated population (such as alligators). Show that this equation can be rewritten in the form $dx/dt = k(x - H)(x - K)$, where

$$H = \tfrac{1}{2}\left(M + \sqrt{M^2 + 4h/k}\right) > 0,$$

$$K = \tfrac{1}{2}\left(M - \sqrt{M^2 + 4h/k}\right) < 0.$$

Show that typical solution curves look as illustrated in Fig. 2.2.15.

29. Consider the two differential equations

$$\frac{dx}{dt} = (x - a)(x - b)(x - c) \tag{21}$$

and

$$\frac{dx}{dt} = (a - x)(b - x)(c - x), \tag{22}$$

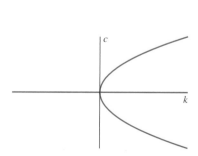

FIGURE 2.2.13. Bifurcation diagram for $dx/dt = kx - x^3$.

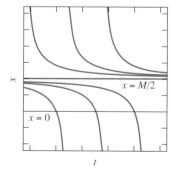

FIGURE 2.2.14. Solution curves for harvesting a logistic population with $4h = kM^2$.

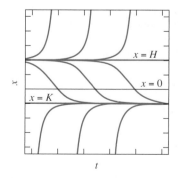

FIGURE 2.2.15. Solution curves for harvesting a population of alligators.

each having the critical points a, b, and c; suppose that $a < b < c$. For one of these equations, only the critical point b is stable; for the other equation, b is the only unstable critical point. Construct phase diagrams for the two equations to determine which is which. Without attempting to solve either equation explicitly, make rough sketches of typical solution curves for each. You should see two funnels and a spout in one case, two spouts and a funnel in the other.

2.3 Acceleration–Velocity Models

In Section 1.2 we discussed vertical motion of a mass m near the surface of the earth under the influence of constant gravitational acceleration. If we neglect any effects of air resistance, then Newton's second law ($F = ma$) implies that the velocity v of the mass m satisfies the equation

$$m\frac{dv}{dt} = F_G, \tag{1}$$

where $F_G = -mg$ is the (downward-directed) force of gravity, where the gravitational acceleration is $g \approx 9.8$ m/s^2 (in mks units; $g \approx 32$ ft/s^2 in fps units).

Example 1 Suppose that a crossbow bolt is shot straight upward from the ground ($y_0 = 0$) with initial velocity $v_0 = 49$ (m/s). Then Eq. (1) with $g = 9.8$ gives

$$\frac{dv}{dt} = -9.8, \quad \text{so} \quad v(t) = -(9.8)t + v_0 = -(9.8)t + 49.$$

Hence the bolt's height function $y(t)$ is given by

$$y(t) = \int [-(9.8)t + 49]\, dt = -(4.9)t^2 + 49t + y_0 = -(4.9)t^2 + 49t.$$

The bolt reaches its maximum height when $v = -(9.8)t + 49 = 0$, hence when $t = 5$ (s). Thus its maximum height is

$$y_{max} = y(5) = -(4.9)(5^2) + (49)(5) = 122.5 \text{ (m)}.$$

The bolt returns to the ground when $y = -(4.9)t(t - 10) = 0$, and thus after 10 seconds aloft. ∎

Now we want to take account of air resistance in a problem like Example 1. The force F_R exerted by air resistance on the moving mass m must be added in Eq. (1), so now

$$m\frac{dv}{dt} = F_G + F_R. \tag{2}$$

Newton showed in his *Principia Mathematica* that certain simple physical assumptions imply that F_R is proportional to the *square* of the velocity: $F_R = kv^2$. But empirical investigations indicate that the actual dependence of air resistance on velocity can be quite complicated. For many purposes it suffices to assume that

$$F_R = kv^p,$$

where $1 \leqq p \leqq 2$ and the value of k depends on the size and shape of the body, as well as the density and viscosity of the air. Generally speaking, $p = 1$ for relatively low speeds and $p = 2$ for high speeds, whereas $1 < p < 2$ for intermediate speeds. But how slow "low speed" and how fast "high speed" are depend on the same factors that determine the value of the coefficient k.

Thus air resistance is a complicated physical phenomenon. But the simplifying assumption that F_R is exactly of the form given here, with either $p = 1$ or $p = 2$, yields a tractable mathematical model that exhibits the most important qualitative features of motion with resistance.

Resistance Proportional to Velocity

Let us first consider the vertical motion of a body with mass m near the surface of the earth, subject to two forces: a downward gravitational force F_G and a force F_R of air resistance that is proportional to velocity (so that $p = 1$) and of course directed opposite the direction of motion of the body. If we set up a coordinate system with the positive y-direction upward and with $y = 0$ at ground level, then $F_G = -mg$ and

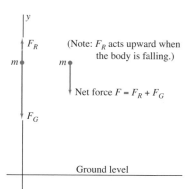

$$F_R = -kv, \tag{3}$$

where k is a positive constant and $v = dy/dt$ is the velocity of the body. Note that the minus sign in Eq. (3) makes F_R positive (an upward force) if the body is falling (v is negative) and makes F_R negative (a downward force) if the body is rising (v is positive). As indicated in Fig. 2.3.1, the net force acting on the body is then

$$F = F_R + F_G = -kv - mg,$$

and Newton's law of motion $F = m(dv/dt)$ yields the equation

$$m\frac{dv}{dt} = -kv - mg.$$

Thus

$$\frac{dv}{dt} = -\rho v - g, \tag{4}$$

where $\rho = k/m > 0$. You should verify for yourself that if the positive y-axis were directed downward, then Eq. (4) would take the form $dv/dt = -\rho v + g$.

Equation (4) is a separable first-order differential equation, and its solution is

$$v(t) = \left(v_0 + \frac{g}{\rho}\right)e^{-\rho t} - \frac{g}{\rho}. \tag{5}$$

Here, $v_0 = v(0)$ is the initial velocity of the body. Note that

$$v_\tau = \lim_{t \to \infty} v(t) = -\frac{g}{\rho}. \tag{6}$$

Thus the speed of a body falling with air resistance does *not* increase indefinitely; instead, it approaches a *finite* limiting speed, or **terminal speed,**

$$|v_\tau| = \frac{g}{\rho} = \frac{mg}{k}. \tag{7}$$

FIGURE 2.3.1. Vertical motion with air resistance.

This fact is what makes a parachute a practical invention; it even helps explain the occasional survival of people who fall without parachutes from high-flying airplanes.

We now rewrite Eq. (5) in the form

$$\frac{dy}{dt} = (v_0 - v_\tau)e^{-\rho t} + v_\tau. \tag{8}$$

Integration gives

$$y(t) = -\frac{1}{\rho}(v_0 - v_\tau)e^{-\rho t} + v_\tau t + C.$$

We substitute 0 for t and let $y_0 = y(0)$ denote the initial height of the body. Thus we find that $C = y_0 + (v_0 - v_\tau)/\rho$, and so

$$y(t) = y_0 + v_\tau t + \frac{1}{\rho}(v_0 - v_\tau)(1 - e^{-\rho t}). \tag{9}$$

Equations (8) and (9) give the velocity v and height y of a body moving vertically under the influence of gravity and air resistance. The formulas depend on the initial height y_0 of the body, its initial velocity v_0, and the *drag coefficient* ρ, the constant such that the acceleration due to air resistance is $a_R = -\rho v$. The two equations also involve the terminal velocity v_τ defined in Eq. (6).

For a person descending with the aid of a parachute, a typical value of ρ is 1.5, which corresponds to a terminal speed of $|v_\tau| \approx 21.3$ ft/s, or about 14.5 mi/h. With an unbuttoned overcoat flapping in the wind in place of a parachute, an unlucky skydiver might increase ρ to perhaps as much as 0.5, which gives a terminal speed of $|v_\tau| \approx 65$ ft/s, about 44 mi/h. See Problems 10 and 11 for some parachute-jump computations.

Example 2   We again consider a bolt shot straight upward with initial velocity $v_0 = 49$ m/s from a crossbow at ground level. But now we take air resistance into account, with $\rho = 0.04$ in Eq. (4). We ask how the resulting maximum height and time aloft compare with the values found in Example 1.

Solution   We substitute $y_0 = 0$, $v_0 = 49$, and $v_\tau = -g/\rho = -245$ in Eqs. (5) and (9), and obtain

$$v(t) = 294e^{-t/25} - 245,$$
$$y(t) = 7350 - 245t - 7350e^{-t/25}.$$

To find the time required for the bolt to reach its maximum height (when $v = 0$), we solve the equation
$$v(t) = 294e^{-t/25} - 245 = 0$$

for $t_m = 25\ln(294/245) \approx 4.558$ (s). Its maximum height is then $y_{max} = v(t_m) \approx 108.280$ meters (as opposed to 122.5 meters without air resistance). To find when the bolt strikes the ground, we must solve the equation

$$y(t) = 7350 - 245t - 7350e^{-t/25} = 0.$$

Using Newton's method, we can begin with the initial guess $t_0 = 10$ and carry out the iteration $t_{n+1} = t_n - y(t_n)/y'(t_n)$ to generate successive approximations to the root. Or we can simply use the **Solve** command on a calculator or computer. We find that the bolt is in the air for $t_f \approx 9.411$ seconds (as opposed to 10 seconds without air resistance). It hits the ground with a reduced speed of $|v(t_f)| \approx 43.227$ m/s (as opposed to its initial velocity of 49 m/s).

Thus the effect of air resistance is to decrease the bolt's maximum height, the total time spent aloft, and its final impact speed. Note also that the bolt now spends more time in descent ($t_f - t_m \approx 4.853$ s) than in ascent ($t_m \approx 4.558$ s). ∎

Resistance Proportional to Square of Velocity

Now we assume that the force of air resistance is proportional to the *square* of the velocity:

➤
$$F_R = \pm k v^2, \tag{10}$$

with $k > 0$. The choice of signs here depends on the direction of motion, which the force of resistance always opposes. Taking the positive y-direction as upward, $F_R < 0$ for upward motion (when $v > 0$) while $F_R > 0$ for downward motion (when $v < 0$). Thus the sign of F_R is always opposite that of v, so we can rewrite Eq. (10) as

$$F_R = -kv|v|. \tag{10'}$$

Then Newton's second law gives

$$m\frac{dv}{dt} = F_G + F_R = -mg - kv|v|;$$

that is,

$$\frac{dv}{dt} = -g - \rho v|v|, \tag{11}$$

where $\rho = k/m > 0$. We must discuss the cases of upward and downward motion separately.

UPWARD MOTION: Suppose that a projectile is launched straight upward from the initial position y_0 with initial velocity $v_0 > 0$. Then Eq. (11) with $v > 0$ gives the differential equation

$$\frac{dv}{dt} = -g - \rho v^2 = -g\left(1 + \frac{\rho}{g}v^2\right). \tag{12}$$

In Problem 13 we ask you to make the substitution $u = v\sqrt{\rho/g}$ and apply the familiar integral

$$\int \frac{1}{1 + u^2}\,du = \tan^{-1} u + C$$

to derive the projectile's velocity function

$$v(t) = \sqrt{\frac{g}{\rho}} \tan\left(C_1 - t\sqrt{\rho g}\right) \quad \text{with} \quad C_1 = \tan^{-1}\left(v_0\sqrt{\frac{\rho}{g}}\right). \tag{13}$$

Because $\int \tan u\,du = -\ln|\cos u| + C$, a second integration (see Problem 14) yields the position function

$$y(t) = y_0 + \frac{1}{\rho} \ln\left|\frac{\cos\left(C_1 - t\sqrt{\rho g}\right)}{\cos C_1}\right|. \tag{14}$$

DOWNWARD MOTION: Suppose that a projectile is launched (or dropped) straight downward from the initial position y_0 with initial velocity $v_0 \leq 0$. Then Eq. (11) with $v < 0$ gives the differential equation

$$\frac{dv}{dt} = -g + \rho v^2 = -g\left(1 - \frac{\rho}{g}v^2\right). \tag{15}$$

In Problem 15 we ask you to make the substitution $u = v\sqrt{\rho/g}$ and apply the integral

$$\int \frac{1}{1 - u^2}\, du = \tanh^{-1} u + C$$

to derive the projectile's velocity function

$$v(t) = \sqrt{\frac{g}{\rho}} \tanh\left(C_2 - t\sqrt{\rho g}\right) \quad \text{with} \quad C_2 = \tanh^{-1}\left(v_0\sqrt{\frac{\rho}{g}}\right). \tag{16}$$

Because $\int \tanh u\, du = \ln|\cosh u| + C$, another integration (Problem 16) yields the position function

$$y(t) = y_0 - \frac{1}{\rho} \ln\left|\frac{\cosh\left(C_2 - t\sqrt{\rho g}\right)}{\cosh C_2}\right|. \tag{17}$$

(Note the analogy between Eqs. (16) and (17) and Eqs. (13) and (14) for upward motion.)

If $v_0 = 0$, then $C_2 = 0$, so $v(t) = -\sqrt{g/\rho} \tanh\left(t\sqrt{\rho g}\right)$. Because

$$\lim_{x\to\infty} \tanh x = \lim_{x\to\infty} \frac{\sinh x}{\cosh x} = \lim_{x\to\infty} \frac{\frac{1}{2}(e^x - e^{-x})}{\frac{1}{2}(e^x + e^{-x})} = 1,$$

it follows that in the case of downward motion the body approaches the terminal speed

$$|v_\tau| = \sqrt{\frac{g}{\rho}} \tag{18}$$

(as compared with $|v_\tau| = g/\rho$ in the case of downward motion with linear resistance described by Eq. (4)).

Example 3

We consider once more a bolt shot straight upward with initial velocity $v_0 = 49$ m/s from a crossbow at ground level, as in Example 2. But now we assume air resistance proportional to the square of the velocity, with $\rho = 0.0011$ in Eqs. (12) and (15). In Problems 17 and 18 we ask you to verify the entries in the last line of the following table.

Air Resistance	Maximum Height (ft)	Time Aloft (s)	Ascent Time (s)	Descent Time (s)	Impact Speed (ft/s)
0.0	122.5	10	5	5	49
$(0.04)v$	108.28	9.41	4.56	4.85	43.23
$(0.0011)v^2$	108.47	9.41	4.61	4.80	43.49

Comparison of the last two lines of data here indicates little difference—for the motion of our crossbow bolt—between linear air resistance and air resistance proportional to the square of the velocity. And in Fig. 2.3.2, where the corresponding

FIGURE 2.3.2. The height functions in Example 1 (without air resistance), Example 2 (with linear air resistance), and Example 3 (with air resistance proportional to the square of the velocity) are all plotted. The graphs of the latter two are visually indistinguishable.

height functions are graphed, the difference is hardly visible. However, the difference between linear and nonlinear resistance can be significant in more complex situations—such as, for instance, the atmospheric reentry and descent of a space vehicle. ■

Variable Gravitational Acceleration

Unless a projectile in vertical motion remains in the immediate vicinity of the earth's surface, the gravitational acceleration acting on it is not constant. According to Newton's law of gravitation, the gravitational force of attraction between two point masses M and m located at a distance r apart is given by

$$F = \frac{GMm}{r^2}, \tag{19}$$

where G is a certain empirical constant ($G \approx 6.6726 \times 10^{-11}$ N·(m/kg)^2 in mks units). The formula is also valid if either or both of the two masses are homogeneous spheres; in this case, the distance r is measured between the centers of the spheres.

The following example is similar to Example 2 in Section 1.2, but now we take account of lunar gravity.

Example 4   A lunar lander is free-falling toward the moon, and at an altitude of 53 kilometers above the lunar surface its downward velocity is measured at 1477 km/h. Its retrorockets, when fired in free space, provide a deceleration of $T = 4$ m/s^2. At what height above the lunar surface should the retrorockets be activated to ensure a "soft touchdown" ($v = 0$ at impact)?

Solution   Let $r(t)$ denote the lander's distance from the center of the moon at time t (Fig. 2.3.3). When we combine the (constant) thrust acceleration T and the (negative) lunar acceleration $F/m = GM/r^2$ of Eq. (19), we get the (acceleration) differential equation

$$\frac{d^2r}{dt^2} = T - \frac{GM}{r^2}, \tag{20}$$

where $M = 7.35 \times 10^{22}$ (kg) is the mass of the moon, which has a radius of $R = 1.74 \times 10^6$ meters (or 1740 km, a little over a quarter of the earth's radius).

Noting that this second-order differential equation does not involve the independent variable t, we substitute

$$v = \frac{dr}{dt}, \quad \frac{d^2r}{dt^2} = \frac{dv}{dt} = \frac{dv}{dr} \cdot \frac{dr}{dt} = v\frac{dv}{dr}$$

(as in Eq. (36) of Section 1.6) and obtain the first-order equation

$$v\frac{dv}{dr} = T - \frac{GM}{r^2}$$

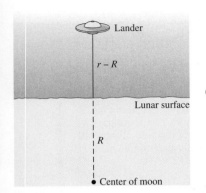

FIGURE 2.3.3. The lunar lander descending to the surface of the moon.

with the new independent variable r. Integration with respect to r now yields the equation

$$\frac{1}{2}v^2 = Tr + \frac{GM}{r} + C \tag{21}$$

that we can apply both before ignition ($T = 0$) and after ignition ($T = 4$).

Before ignition: Substitution of $T = 0$ in (21) gives the equation

$$\frac{1}{2}v^2 = \frac{GM}{r} + C_1 \tag{21a}$$

where the constant is given by $C_1 = v_0^2/2 - GM/r_0$ with

$$v_0 = -1477\,\frac{\text{km}}{\text{h}} \times 1000\,\frac{\text{m}}{\text{km}} \times \frac{1\ \text{h}}{3600\ \text{s}} = -\frac{14770}{36}\,\frac{\text{m}}{\text{s}}$$

and $r_0 = (1.74 \times 10^6) + 53{,}000 = 1.793 \times 10^6$ m (from the initial velocity–position measurement).

After ignition: Substitution of $T = 4$ and $v = 0$, $r = R$ (at touchdown) into (21) gives

$$\frac{1}{2}v^2 = 4r + \frac{GM}{r} + C_2 \tag{21b}$$

where the constant $C_2 = -4R - GM/R$ is obtained by substituting the values $v = 0$, $r = R$ at touchdown.

At the instant of ignition the lunar lander's position and velocity satisfy both (21a) and (21b). Therefore we can find its desired height h above the lunar surface at ignition by equating the right-hand sides in (21a) and (21b). This gives $r = \frac{1}{4}(C_1 - C_2) = 1.78187 \times 10^6$ and finally $h = r - R = 41{,}870$ meters (that is, 41.87 kilometers—just over 26 miles). Moreover, substitution of this value of r in (21a) gives the velocity $v = -450$ m/s at the instant of ignition. ∎

Escape Velocity

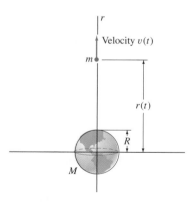

FIGURE 2.3.4. A mass m at a great distance from the earth.

In his novel *From the Earth to the Moon* (1865), Jules Verne raised the question of the initial velocity necesary for a projectile fired from the surface of the earth to reach the moon. Similarly, we can ask what initial velocity v_0 is necessary for the projectile to escape from the earth altogether. This will be so if its velocity $v = dr/dt$ remains *positive* for all $t > 0$, so it continues forever to move away from the earth. With $r(t)$ denoting the projectile's distance from the earth's center at time t (Fig. 2.3.4), we have the equation

$$\frac{dv}{dt} = \frac{d^2r}{dt^2} = -\frac{GM}{r^2}, \tag{22}$$

similar to Eq. (20), but with $T = 0$ (no thrust) and with $M = 5.975 \times 10^{24}$ (kg) denoting the mass of the earth, which has an equatorial radius of $R = 6.378 \times 10^6$ (m). Substitution of the chain rule expression $dv/dt = v(dv/dr)$ as in Example 4 gives

$$v\frac{dv}{dr} = -\frac{GM}{r^2}.$$

Then integration of both sides with respect to r yields

$$\frac{1}{2}v^2 = \frac{GM}{r} + C.$$

Now $v = v_0$ and $r = R$ when $t = 0$, so $C = \frac{1}{2}v_0^2 - GM/R$, and hence solution for v^2 gives

$$v^2 = v_0^2 + 2GM\left(\frac{1}{r} - \frac{1}{R}\right). \tag{23}$$

This implicit solution of Eq. (22) determines the projectile's velocity v as a function of its distance r from the earth's center. In particular,

$$v^2 > v_0^2 - \frac{2GM}{R},$$

so v will remain positive provided that $v_0^2 \geqq 2GM/R$. Therefore, the **escape velocity** from the earth is given by

$$v_0 = \sqrt{\frac{2GM}{R}}. \tag{24}$$

In Problem 27 we ask you to show that, if the projectile's initial velocity exceeds $\sqrt{2GM/R}$, then $r(t) \to \infty$ as $t \to \infty$, so it does, indeed, "escape" from the earth. With the given values of G and the earth's mass M and radius R, this gives $v_0 \approx 11{,}180$ (m/s) (about 36,680 ft/s, about 6.95 mi/s, about 25,000 mi/h).

Remark: Equation (24) gives the escape velocity for any other (spherical) planetary body when we use *its* mass and radius. For instance, when we use the mass M and radius R for the moon given in Example 4, we find that escape velocity from the lunar surface is $v_0 \approx 2375$ m/s. This is just over one-fifth of the escape velocity from the earth's surface, a fact that greatly facilitates the return trip ("From the Moon to the Earth"). ∎

2.3 Problems

1. The acceleration of a Maserati is proportional to the difference between 250 km/h and the velocity of this sports car. If this machine can accelerate from rest to 100 km/h in 10 s, how long will it take for the car to accelerate from rest to 200 km/h?

2. Suppose that a body moves through a resisting medium with resistance proportional to its velocity v, so that $dv/dt = -kv$. (a) Show that its velocity and position at time t are given by

$$v(t) = v_0 e^{-kt}$$

and

$$x(t) = x_0 + \left(\frac{v_0}{k}\right)(1 - e^{-kt}).$$

(b) Conclude that the body travels only a finite distance, and find that distance.

3. Suppose that a motorboat is moving at 40 ft/s when its motor suddenly quits, and that 10 s later the boat has slowed to 20 ft/s. Assume, as in Problem 2, that the resistance it encounters while coasting is proportional to its velocity. How far will the boat coast in all?

4. Consider a body that moves horizontally through a medium whose resistance is proportional to the *square* of the velocity v, so that $dv/dt = -kv^2$. Show that

$$v(t) = \frac{v_0}{1 + v_0 kt}$$

and that

$$x(t) = x_0 + \frac{1}{k}\ln(1 + v_0 kt).$$

Note that, in contrast with the result of Problem 2, $x(t) \to +\infty$ as $t \to +\infty$. Which offers less resistance when the body is moving fairly slowly—the medium in this problem or the one in Problem 2? Does your answer seem consistent with the observed behaviors of $x(t)$ as $t \to \infty$?

5. Assuming resistance proportional to the square of the velocity (as in Problem 4), how far does the motorboat of Problem 3 coast in the first minute after its motor quits?

6. Assume that a body moving with velocity v encounters resistance of the form $dv/dt = -kv^{3/2}$. Show that

$$v(t) = \frac{4v_0}{\left(kt\sqrt{v_0} + 2\right)^2}$$

and that

$$x(t) = x_0 + \frac{2}{k}\sqrt{v_0}\left(1 - \frac{2}{kt\sqrt{v_0} + 2}\right).$$

Conclude that under a $\frac{3}{2}$-power resistance a body coasts only a finite distance before coming to a stop.

7. Suppose that a car starts from rest, its engine providing an acceleration of 10 ft/s², while air resistance provides 0.1 ft/s² of deceleration for each foot per second of the car's velocity. (a) Find the car's maximum possible (limiting) velocity. (b) Find how long it takes the car to attain 90% of its limiting velocity, and how far it travels while doing so.

8. Rework both parts of Problem 7, with the sole difference that the deceleration due to air resistance now is $(0.001)v^2$ ft/s² when the car's velocity is v feet per second.

9. A motorboat weighs 32,000 lb and its motor provides a thrust of 5000 lb. Assume that the water resistance is 100 pounds for each foot per second of the speed v of the boat. Then

$$1000\frac{dv}{dt} = 5000 - 100v.$$

If the boat starts from rest, what is the maximum velocity that it can attain?

10. A woman bails out of an airplane at an altitude of 10,000 ft, falls freely for 20 s, then opens her parachute. How long will it take her to reach the ground? Assume linear air resistance ρv ft/s², taking $\rho = 0.15$ without the parachute and $\rho = 1.5$ with the parachute. (*Suggestion:* First determine her height above the ground and velocity when the parachute opens.)

11. According to a newspaper account, a paratrooper survived a training jump from 1200 ft when his parachute failed to open but provided some resistance by flapping unopened in the wind. Allegedly he hit the ground at 100 mi/h after falling for 8 s. Test the accuracy of this account. (*Suggestion:* Find ρ in Eq. (4) by assuming a terminal velocity of 100 mi/h. Then calculate the time required to fall 1200 ft.)

12. It is proposed to dispose of nuclear wastes—in drums with weight $W = 640$ lb and volume 8 ft³—by dropping them into the ocean ($v_0 = 0$). The force equation for a drum falling through water is

$$m\frac{dv}{dt} = -W + B + F_R,$$

where the buoyant force B is equal to the weight (at 62.5 lb/ft³) of the volume of water displaced by the drum (Archimedes' principle) and F_R is the force of water resistance, found empirically to be 1 lb for each foot per second of the velocity of a drum. If the drums are likely to burst upon an impact of more than 75 ft/s, what is the maximum depth to which they can be dropped in the ocean without likelihood of bursting?

13. Separate variables in Eq. (12) and substitute $u = v\sqrt{\rho/g}$ to obtain the upward-motion velocity function given in Eq. (13) with initial condition $v(0) = v_0$.

14. Integrate the velocity function in Eq. (13) to obtain the upward-motion position function given in Eq. (14) with initial condition $y(0) = y_0$.

15. Separate variables in Eq. (15) and substitute $u = v\sqrt{\rho/g}$ to obtain the downward-motion velocity function given in Eq. (16) with initial condition $v(0) = v_0$.

16. Integrate the velocity function in Eq. (16) to obtain the downward-motion position function given in Eq. (17) with initial condition $y(0) = y_0$.

17. Consider the crossbow bolt of Example 3, shot straight upward from the ground ($y = 0$) at time $t = 0$ with initial velocity $v_0 = 49$ m/s. Take $g = 9.8$ m/s² and $\rho = 0.0011$ in Eq. (12). Then use Eqs. (13) and (14) to show that the bolt reaches its maximum height of about 108.47 m in about 4.61 s.

18. Continuing Problem 17, suppose that the bolt is now dropped ($v_0 = 0$) from a height of $y_0 = 108.47$ m. Then use Eqs. (16) and (17) to show that it hits the ground about 4.80 s later with an impact speed of about 43.49 m/s.

19. A motorboat starts from rest (initial velocity $v(0) = v_0 = 0$). Its motor provides a constant acceleration of 4 ft/s², but water resistance causes a deceleration of $v^2/400$ ft/s². Find v when $t = 10$ s, and also find the *limiting velocity* as $t \to +\infty$ (that is, the maximum possible speed of the boat).

20. An arrow is shot straight upward from the ground with an initial velocity of 160 ft/s. It experiences both the deceleration of gravity and deceleration $v^2/800$ due to air resistance. How high in the air does it go?

21. If a ball is projected upward from the ground with initial velocity v_0 and resistance proportional to v^2, deduce from Eq. (14) that the maximum height it attains is

$$y_{max} = \frac{1}{2\rho} \ln \left(1 + \frac{\rho v_0^2}{g} \right).$$

22. Suppose that $\rho = 0.075$ (in fps units, with $g = 32$ ft/s²) in Eq. (15) for a paratrooper falling with parachute open. If he jumps from an altitude of 10,000 ft and opens his parachute immediately, what will be his terminal speed? How long will it take him to reach the ground?

23. Suppose that the paratrooper of Problem 22 falls freely for 30 s with $\rho = 0.00075$ before opening his parachute. How long will it now take him to reach the ground?

24. The mass of the sun is 329,320 times that of the earth and its radius is 109 times the radius of the earth. **(a)** To what radius (in meters) would the earth have to be compressed in order for it to become a *black hole*—the escape velocity from its surface equal to the velocity $c = 3 \times 10^8$ m/s of light? **(b)** Repeat part (a) with the sun in place of the earth.

25. **(a)** Show that if a projectile is launched straight upward from the surface of the earth with initial velocity v_0 less than escape velocity $\sqrt{2GM/R}$, then the maximum distance from the center of the earth attained by the projectile is

$$r_{max} = \frac{2GMR}{2GM - Rv_0^2},$$

where M and R are the mass and radius of the earth, respectively. **(b)** With what initial velocity v_0 must such a projectile be launched to yield a maximum altitude of 100 kilometers above the surface of the earth? **(c)** Find the maximum distance from the center of the earth, expressed in terms of earth radii, attained by a projectile launched from the surface of the earth with 90% of escape velocity.

26. Suppose that you are stranded—your rocket engine has failed—on an asteroid of diameter 3 miles, with density equal to that of the earth with radius 3960 miles. If you

have enough spring in your legs to jump 4 feet straight up on earth while wearing your space suit, can you blast off from this asteroid using leg power alone?

27. **(a)** Suppose a projectile is launched vertically from the surface $r = R$ of the earth with initial velocity $v_0 = \sqrt{2GM/R}$ so $v_0^2 = k^2/R$ where $k^2 = 2GM$. Then solve the differential equation $dr/dt = k/\sqrt{r}$ (from Eq. (23) in this section) explicitly to deduce that $r(t) \to \infty$ as $t \to \infty$.

(b) If the projectile is launched vertically with initial velocity $v_0 > \sqrt{2GM/R}$, deduce that

$$\frac{dr}{dt} = \sqrt{\frac{k^2}{r} + \alpha} > \frac{k}{\sqrt{r}}.$$

Why does it again follow that $r(t) \to \infty$ as $t \to \infty$?

28. **(a)** Suppose that a body is dropped ($v_0 = 0$) from a distance $r_0 > R$ from the earth's center, so its acceleration is $dv/dt = -GM/r^2$. Ignoring air resistance, show that it reaches the height $r < r_0$ at time

$$t = \sqrt{\frac{r_0}{2GM}} \left(\sqrt{rr_0 - r^2} + r_0 \cos^{-1} \sqrt{\frac{r}{r_0}} \right).$$

(*Suggestion:* Substitute $r = r_0 \cos^2 \theta$ to evaluate $\int \sqrt{r/(r_0 - r)} \, dr$.) **(b)** If a body is dropped from a height of 1000 km above the earth's surface and air resistance is neglected, how long does it take to fall and with what speed will it strike the earth's surface?

29. Suppose that a projectile is fired straight upward from the surface of the earth with initial velocity $v_0 < \sqrt{2GM/R}$. Then its height $y(t)$ above the surface satisfies the initial value problem

$$\frac{d^2 y}{dt^2} = -\frac{GM}{(y + R)^2}; \quad y(0) = 0, \quad y'(0) = v_0.$$

Substitute $dv/dt = v(dv/dy)$ and then integrate to obtain

$$v^2 = v_0^2 - \frac{2GMy}{R(R + y)}$$

for the velocity v of the projectile at height y. What maximum altitude does it reach if its initial velocity is 1 km/s?

30. In Jules Verne's original problem, the projectile launched from the surface of the earth is attracted by both the earth and the moon, so its distance $r(t)$ from the center of the earth satisfies the initial value problem

$$\frac{d^2 r}{dt^2} = -\frac{GM_e}{r^2} + \frac{GM_m}{(S - r)^2}; \quad r(0) = R, \quad r'(0) = v_0$$

where M_e and M_m denote the masses of the earth and the moon, respectively; R is the radius of the earth and $S = 384,400$ km is the distance between the centers of the earth and the moon. To reach the moon, the projectile must only just pass the point between the moon and earth where its net acceleration vanishes. Thereafter it is "under the control" of the moon, and falls from there to the lunar surface. Find the *minimal* launch velocity v_0 that suffices for the projectile to make it "From the Earth to the Moon."

2.3 Application Rocket Propulsion

FIGURE 2.3.5. An ascending rocket.

Suppose that the rocket of Fig. 2.3.5 blasts off straight upward from the surface of the earth at time $t = 0$. We want to calculate its height y and velocity $v = dy/dt$ at time t. The rocket is propelled by exhaust gases that exit (rearward) with constant speed c (relative to the rocket). Because of the combustion of its fuel, the mass $m = m(t)$ of the rocket is variable.

To derive the equation of motion of the rocket, we use Newton's second law in the form

$$\frac{dP}{dt} = F \tag{1}$$

where P is momentum (the product of mass and velocity) and F denotes net external force (gravity, air resistance, etc.). If the mass m of the rocket is constant so $m'(t) \equiv 0$—when its rockets are turned off or burned out, for instance—then Eq. (1) gives

$$F = \frac{d(mv)}{dt} = m\frac{dv}{dt} + \frac{dm}{dt}v = m\frac{dv}{dt},$$

which (with $dv/dt = a$) is the more familiar form $F = ma$ of Newton's second law.

But here m is not constant. Suppose m changes to $m + \Delta m$ and v to $v + \Delta v$ during the short time interval from t to $t + \Delta t$. Then the change in the momentum *of the rocket itself* is

$$\Delta P \approx (m + \Delta m)(v + \Delta v) - mv = m\,\Delta v + v\,\Delta m + \Delta m\,\Delta v.$$

But the system also includes the exhaust gases expelled during this time interval, with mass $-\Delta m$ and approximate velocity $v - c$. Hence the total change in momentum during the time interval Δt is

$$\Delta P \approx (m\,\Delta v + v\,\Delta m + \Delta m\,\Delta v) + (-\Delta m)(v - c)$$
$$= m\,\Delta v + c\,\Delta m + \Delta m\,\Delta v.$$

Now we divide by Δt and take the limit as $\Delta t \to 0$, so $\Delta m \to 0$, assuming continuity of $m(t)$. The substitution of the resulting expression for dP/dt in (1) yields the **rocket propulsion equation**

$$m\frac{dv}{dt} + c\frac{dm}{dt} = F. \tag{2}$$

If $F = F_G + F_R$, where $F_G = -mg$ is a constant force of gravity and $F_R = -kv$ is a force of air resistance proportional to velocity, then Eq. (2) finally gives

$$m\frac{dv}{dt} + c\frac{dm}{dt} = -mg - kv. \tag{3}$$

Constant Thrust

Now suppose that the rocket fuel is consumed at the constant "burn rate" β during the time interval $[0, t_1]$, during which time the mass of the rocket decreases from m_0 to m_1. Thus

$$m(0) = m_0, \qquad m(t_1) = m_1,$$
$$m(t) = m_0 - \beta t, \qquad \frac{dm}{dt} = -\beta \quad \text{for } t \le t_1, \tag{4}$$

with burnout occurring at time $t = t_1$.

PROBLEM 1 Substitute the expressions in (4) into Eq. (3) to obtain the differential equation

$$(m - \beta t)\frac{dv}{dt} + kv = \beta c - (m_0 - \beta t)g. \tag{5}$$

Solve this linear equation for

$$v(t) = v_0 M^{k/\beta} + \frac{\beta c}{k}(1 - M^{k/\beta}) + \frac{gm_0}{\beta - k}(1 - M^{k/\beta}), \tag{6}$$

where $v_0 = v(0)$ and

$$M = \frac{m(t)}{m_0} = \frac{m_0 - \beta t}{m_0}$$

denotes the rocket's **fractional mass** at time t.

No Resistance

PROBLEM 2 For the case of no air resistance, set $k = 0$ in Eq. (5) and integrate to obtain

$$v(t) = v_0 - gt + c \ln \frac{m_0}{m_0 - \beta t}. \tag{7}$$

Because $m_0 - \beta t_1 = m_1$, it follows that the velocity of the rocket at burnout $(t = t_1)$ is

$$v_1 = v(t_1) = v_0 - gt_1 + c \ln \frac{m_0}{m_1}. \tag{8}$$

PROBLEM 3 Start with Eq. (7) and integrate to obtain

$$y(t) = (v_0 + c)t - \frac{1}{2}gt^2 - \frac{c}{\beta}(m_0 - \beta t) \ln \frac{m_0}{m_0 - \beta t}. \tag{9}$$

It follows that the rocket's altitude at burnout is

$$y_1 = y(t_1) = (v_0 + c)t_1 - \frac{1}{2}gt_1^2 - \frac{cm_1}{\beta} \ln \frac{m_0}{m_1}. \tag{10}$$

PROBLEM 4 The V-2 rocket that was used to attack London in World War II had an initial mass of 12,850 kg, of which 68.5% was fuel. This fuel burned uniformly for 70 seconds with an exhaust velocity of 2 km/s. Assume it encounters air resistance of 1.45 N per m/s of velocity. Then find the velocity and altitude of the V-2 at burnout under the assumption that it is launched vertically upward from rest on the ground.

PROBLEM 5   Actually, our basic differential equation in (3) applies without qualification only when the rocket is already in motion. However, when a rocket is sitting on its launch pad stand and its engines are turned on initially, it is observed that a certain time interval passes before the rocket actually "blasts off" and begins to ascend. The reason is that if $v = 0$ in (3), then the resulting initial acceleration

$$\frac{dv}{dt} = \frac{c}{m}\frac{dm}{dt} - g$$

of the rocket may be *negative*. But the rocket does not descend into the ground; it just "sits there" while (because m is decreasing) this calculated acceleration increases until it reaches 0 and (thereafter) positive values so the rocket can begin to ascend. With the notation introduced to described the constant-thrust case, show that the rocket initially just "sits there" if the exhaust velocity c is less than $m_0 g/\beta$, and that the time t_B which then elapses before actual blastoff is given by

$$t_B = \frac{m_0 g - \beta c}{\beta g}.$$

Free Space

Suppose finally that the rocket is accelerating in free space, where there is neither gravity nor resistance, so $g = k = 0$. With $g = 0$ in Eq. (8) we see that, as the mass of the rocket decreases from m_0 to m_1, its increase in velocity is

$$\Delta v = v_1 - v_0 = c \ln \frac{m_0}{m_1}. \tag{11}$$

Note that Δv depends only on the exhaust gas speed c and the initial-to-final mass ratio m_0/m_1, but does not depend on the burn rate β. For example, if the rocket blasts off from rest ($v_0 = 0$) and $c = 5$ km/s and $m_0/m_1 = 20$, then its velocity at burnout is $v_1 = 5 \ln 20 \approx 15$ km/s. Thus if a rocket initially consists predominantly of fuel, then it can attain velocities significantly greater than the (relative) velocity of its exhaust gases.

2.4 Numerical Approximation: Euler's Method

It is the exception rather than the rule when a differential equation of the general form

$$\frac{dy}{dx} = f(x, y)$$

can be solved exactly and explicitly by elementary methods like those discussed in Chapter 1. For example, consider the simple equation

$$\frac{dy}{dx} = e^{-x^2}. \tag{1}$$

A solution of Eq. (1) is simply an antiderivative of e^{-x^2}. But it is known that every antiderivative of $f(x) = e^{-x^2}$ is a **nonelementary** function—one that cannot be expressed as a finite combination of the familiar functions of elementary calculus. Hence no particular solution of Eq. (1) is finitely expressible in terms of elementary functions. Any attempt to use the symbolic techniques of Chapter 1 to find a simple explicit formula for a solution of (1) is therefore doomed to failure.

As a possible alternative, an old-fashioned computer plotter—one that uses an ink pen to draw curves mechanically—can be programmed to draw a solution curve that starts at the initial point (x_0, y_0) and attempts to thread its way through the slope field of a given differential equation $y' = f(x, y)$. The procedure the plotter carries out can be described as follows.

- The plotter pen starts at the initial point (x_0, y_0) and moves a tiny distance along the slope segment though (x_0, y_0). This takes it to the point (x_1, y_1).
- At (x_1, y_1) the pen changes direction, and now moves a tiny distance along the slope segment through this new starting point (x_1, y_1). This takes it to the next starting point (x_2, y_2).
- At (x_2, y_2) the pen changes direction again, and now moves a tiny distance along the slope segment through (x_2, y_2). This takes it to the next starting point (x_3, y_3).

Figure 2.4.1 illustrates the result of continuing in this fashion—by a sequence of discrete straight-line steps from one starting point to the next. In this figure we see a polygonal curve consisting of line segments that connect the successive points (x_0, y_0), (x_1, y_1), (x_2, y_2), (x_3, y_3), ... However, suppose that each "tiny distance" the pen travels along a slope segment—before the midcourse correction that sends it along a fresh new slope segment—is so very small that the naked eye cannot distinguish the individual line segments constituting the polygonal curve. Then the resulting polygonal curve looks like a smooth, continuously turning solution curve of the differential equation. Indeed, this is (in essence) how most of the solution curves shown in the figures of Chapter 1 were computer generated.

Leonhard Euler—the great 18th-century mathematician for whom so many mathematical concepts, formulas, methods, and results are named—did not have a computer plotter, and his idea was to do all this numerically rather than graphically. In order to approximate the solution of the initial value problem

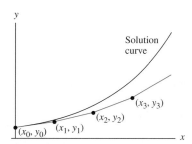

FIGURE 2.4.1. The first few steps in approximating a solution curve.

$$\frac{dy}{dx} = f(x, y), \quad y(x_0) = y_0, \tag{2}$$

we first choose a fixed (horizontal) **step size** h to use in making each step from one point to the next. Suppose we've started at the initial point (x_0, y_0) and after n steps have reached the point (x_n, y_n). Then the step from (x_n, y_n) to the next point (x_{n+1}, y_{n+1}) is illustrated in Fig. 2.4.2. The slope of the direction segment through (x_n, y_n) is $m = f(x_n, y_n)$. Hence a horizontal change of h from x_n to x_{n+1} corresponds to a vertical change of $m \cdot h = h \cdot f(x_n, y_n)$ from y_n to y_{n+1}. Therefore the coordinates of the new point (x_{n+1}, y_{n+1}) are given in terms of the old coordinates by

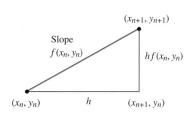

FIGURE 2.4.2. The step from (x_n, y_n) to (x_{n+1}, y_{n+1}).

$$x_{n+1} = x_n + h, \quad y_{n+1} = y_n + h \cdot f(x_n, y_n).$$

Given the initial value problem in (2), **Euler's method** with step size h consists of starting with the initial point (x_0, y_0) and applying the formulas

$$
\begin{aligned}
x_1 &= x_0 + h & y_1 &= y_0 + h \cdot f(x_0, y_0) \\
x_2 &= x_1 + h & y_2 &= y_1 + h \cdot f(x_1, y_1) \\
x_3 &= x_2 + h & y_3 &= y_2 + h \cdot f(x_2, y_2) \\
&\;\;\vdots & &\quad\;\;\vdots
\end{aligned}
$$

to calculate successive points (x_1, y_1), (x_2, y_2), (x_3, y_3), $\ldots$ on an approximate solution curve.

However, we ordinarily do not sketch the corresponding polygonal approximation. Instead, the numerical result of applying Euler's method is the sequence of *approximations*

$$y_1, y_2, y_3, \ldots, y_n, \ldots$$

to the *true values*

$$y(x_1), y(x_2), y(x_3), \ldots, y(x_n), \ldots$$

at the points $x_1, x_2, x_3, \ldots, x_n, \ldots$ of the *exact* (though unknown) solution $y(x)$ of the initial value problem. These results typically are presented in the form of a table of approximate values of the desired solution.

ALGORITHM   The Euler Method

Given the initial value problem

➤
$$\frac{dy}{dx} = f(x, y), \quad y(x_0) = y_0, \tag{2}$$

Euler's method with step size h consists of applying the iterative formula

➤
$$y_{n+1} = y_n + h \cdot f(x_n, y_n) \quad (n \geq 0) \tag{3}$$

to calculate successive approximations $y_1, y_2, y_3, \ldots$ to the [true] values $y(x_1)$, $y(x_2)$, $y(x_3)$, $\ldots$ of the [exact] solution $y = y(x)$ at the points $x_1, x_2, x_3, \ldots$, respectively.

The iterative formula in (3) tells us how to make the typical step from y_n to y_{n+1} and is the heart of Euler's method. Although the most important applications of Euler's method are to nonlinear equations, we first illustrate the method with a simple initial value problem whose exact solution is available, just for the purpose of comparison of approximate and actual solutions.

Example 1   Apply Euler's method to approximate the solution of the initial value problem

$$\frac{dy}{dx} = x + \frac{1}{5}y, \quad y(0) = -3, \tag{4}$$

(a) first with step size $h = 1$ on the interval $[0, 5]$,
(b) then with step size $h = 0.2$ on the interval $[0, 1]$.

Solution   (a) With $x_0 = 0$, $y_0 = -3$, $f(x, y) = x + \frac{1}{5}y$, and $h = 1$ the iterative formula in (3) yields the approximate values

$$y_1 = y_0 + h \cdot [x_0 + \tfrac{1}{5}y_0] = (-3) + (1)[0 + \tfrac{1}{5}(-3)] = -3.6,$$
$$y_2 = y_1 + h \cdot [x_1 + \tfrac{1}{5}y_1] = (-3.6) + (1)[1 + \tfrac{1}{5}(-3.6)] = -3.32,$$
$$y_3 = y_2 + h \cdot [x_2 + \tfrac{1}{5}y_2] = (-3.32) + (1)[2 + \tfrac{1}{5}(-3.32)] = -1.984,$$
$$y_4 = y_3 + h \cdot [x_3 + \tfrac{1}{5}y_3] = (-1.984) + (1)[3 + \tfrac{1}{5}(-1.984)] = 0.6192, \quad \text{and}$$
$$y_5 = y_4 + h \cdot [x_4 + \tfrac{1}{5}y_4] = (0.6912) + (1)[4 + \tfrac{1}{5}(0.6912)] \approx 4.7430$$

at the points $x_1 = 1$, $x_2 = 2$, $x_3 = 3$, $x_4 = 4$, and $x_5 = 5$. Note how the result of each calculation feeds into the next one. The resulting table of approximate values is

x	0	1	2	3	4	5
Approx. y	-3	-3.6	-3.32	-1.984	0.6912	4.7430

Figure 2.4.3 shows the graph of this approximation, together with the graphs of the Euler approximations obtained with step sizes $h = 0.2$ and 0.05, as well as the graph of the exact solution

$$y(x) = 22e^{x/5} - 5x - 25$$

that is readily found using the linear-equation technique of Section 1.5. We see that decreasing the step size increases the accuracy, but with any single approximation, the accuracy decreases with distance from the initial point.

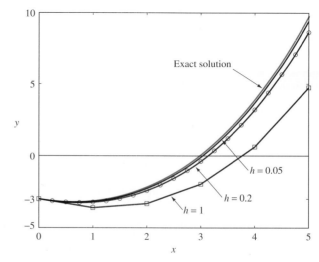

FIGURE 2.4.3. Graphs of Euler approximations with step sizes $h = 1$, $h = 0.2$, and $h = 0.05$.

(b) Starting afresh with $x_0 = 0$, $y_0 = -3$, $f(x, y) = x + \frac{1}{5}y$, and $h = 0.2$, we get the approximate values

$$y_1 = y_0 + h \cdot [x_0 + \tfrac{1}{5}y_0] = (-3) + (0.2)[0 + \tfrac{1}{5}(-3)] = -3.12,$$
$$y_2 = y_1 + h \cdot [x_1 + \tfrac{1}{5}y_1] = (-3.12) + (0.2)[0.2 + \tfrac{1}{5}(-3.12)] \approx -3.205,$$
$$y_3 = y_2 + h \cdot [x_2 + \tfrac{1}{5}y_2] \approx (-3.205) + (0.2)[0.4 + \tfrac{1}{5}(-3.205)] \approx -3.253,$$
$$y_4 = y_3 + h \cdot [x_3 + \tfrac{1}{5}y_3] \approx (-3.253) + (0.2)[0.6 + \tfrac{1}{5}(-3.253)] \approx -3.263,$$
$$y_5 = y_4 + h \cdot [x_4 + \tfrac{1}{5}y_4] \approx (-3.263) + (0.2)[0.8 + \tfrac{1}{5}(-3.263)] \approx -3.234$$

at the points $x_1 = 0.2$, $x_2 = 0.4$, $x_3 = 0.6$, $x_4 = 0.8$, and $x_5 = 1$. The resulting table of approximate values is

x	0	0.2	0.4	0.6	0.8	1
Approx. y	-3	-3.12	-3.205	-3.253	-3.263	-3.234

High accuracy with Euler's method usually requires a very small step size and hence a larger number of steps than can reasonably be carried out by hand. The application material for this section contains calculator and computer programs for automating Euler's method. One of these programs was used to calculate the table entries shown in Fig. 2.4.4. We see that 500 Euler steps (with step size $h = 0.002$) from $x = 0$ to $x = 1$ yield values that are accurate to within 0.001.

x	Approx y with $h = 0.2$	Approx y with $h = 0.02$	Approx y with $h = 0.002$	Actual value of y
0	−3.000	−3.000	−3.000	−3.000
0.2	−3.120	−3.104	−3.102	−3.102
0.4	−3.205	−3.172	−3.168	−3.168
0.6	−3.253	−3.201	−3.196	−3.195
0.8	−3.263	−3.191	−3.184	−3.183
1	−3.234	−3.140	−3.130	−3.129

FIGURE 2.4.4.   Euler approximations with step sizes $h = 0.2$, $h = 0.02$, and $h = 0.002$.

Example 2

Suppose the baseball of Example 3 in Section 1.3 is simply dropped (instead of being thrown downward) from the helicopter. Then its velocity $v(t)$ after t seconds satisfies the initial value problem

$$\frac{dv}{dt} = 32 - 0.16v, \quad v(0) = 0. \tag{5}$$

We use Euler's method with $h = 1$ to track the ball's increasing velocity at 1-second intervals for the first 10 seconds of fall. With $t_0 = 0$, $v_0 = 0$, $F(t, v) = 32 - 0.16v$, and $h = 1$ the iterative formula in (3) yields the approximate values

$$v_1 = v_0 + h \cdot [32 - 0.16v_0] = (0) + (1)[32 - 0.16(0)] = 32,$$
$$v_2 = v_1 + h \cdot [32 - 0.16v_1] = (32) + (1)[32 - 0.16(32)] = 58.88,$$
$$v_3 = v_2 + h \cdot [32 - 0.16v_2] = (58.88) + (1)[32 - 0.16(58.88)] \approx 81.46,$$
$$v_4 = v_3 + h \cdot [32 - 0.16v_3] = (81.46) + (1)[32 - 0.16(81.46)] \approx 100.43, \quad \text{and}$$
$$v_5 = v_4 + h \cdot [32 - 0.16v_4] = (100.43) + (1)[32 - 0.16(100.43)] \approx 116.36.$$

Continuing in this fashion, we complete the $h = 1$ column of v-values shown in the table of Fig. 2.4.5—where we have rounded off velocity entries to the nearest foot per second. The values corresponding to $h = 0.1$ were calculated using a computer, and we see that they are accurate to within about 1 ft/s. Note also that after 10 seconds the falling ball has attained about 80% of its limiting velocity of 200 ft/s. ∎

Local and Cumulative Errors

There are several sources of error in Euler's method that may make the approximation y_n to $y(x_n)$ unreliable for large values of n, those for which x_n is not sufficiently close to x_0. The error in the linear approximation formula

$$y(x_{n+1}) \approx y_n + h \cdot f(x_n, y_n) = y_{n+1} \tag{6}$$

t	Approx v with $h = 1$	Approx v with $h = 0.1$	Actual value of v
1	32	30	30
2	59	55	55
3	81	77	76
4	100	95	95
5	116	111	110
6	130	124	123
7	141	135	135
8	150	145	144
9	158	153	153
10	165	160	160

FIGURE 2.4.5. Euler approximations in Example 2 with step sizes $h = 1$ and $h = 0.1$.

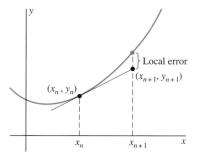

FIGURE 2.4.6. The local error in Euler's method.

is the amount by which the tangent line at (x_n, y_n) departs from the solution curve through (x_n, y_n), as illustrated in Fig. 2.4.6. This error, introduced at each step in the process, is called the **local error** in Euler's method.

The local error indicated in Fig. 2.4.6 *would be* the total error in y_{n+1} *if* the starting point y_n in (6) were an exact value, rather than merely an approximation to the actual value $y(x_n)$. But y_n itself suffers from the accumulated effects of all the local errors introduced at the previous steps. Thus the tangent line in Fig. 2.4.6 is tangent to the "wrong" solution curve—the one through (x_n, y_n) rather than the actual solution curve through the initial point (x_0, y_0). Figure 2.4.7 illustrates this **cumulative error** in Euler's method; it is the amount by which the polygonal stepwise path from (x_0, y_0) departs from the actual solution curve through (x_0, y_0).

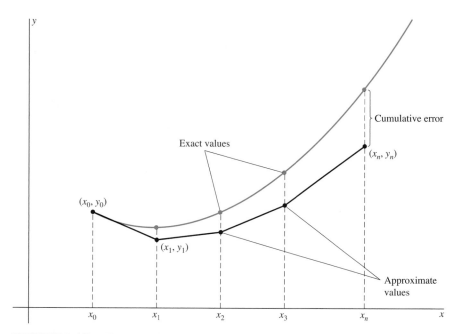

FIGURE 2.4.7. The cumulative error in Euler's method.

x	y with $h = 0.1$	y with $h = 0.02$	y with $h = 0.005$	y with $h = 0.001$	Actual y
0.1	1.1000	1.1082	1.1098	1.1102	1.1103
0.2	1.2200	1.2380	1.2416	1.2426	1.2428
0.3	1.3620	1.3917	1.3977	1.3993	1.3997
0.4	1.5282	1.5719	1.5807	1.5831	1.5836
0.5	1.7210	1.7812	1.7933	1.7966	1.7974
0.6	1.9461	2.0227	2.0388	2.0431	2.0442
0.7	2.1974	2.2998	2.3205	2.3261	2.3275
0.8	2.4872	2.6161	2.6422	2.6493	2.6511
0.9	2.8159	2.9757	3.0082	3.0170	3.0192
1.0	3.1875	3.3832	3.4230	3.4238	3.4266

FIGURE 2.4.8. Approximating the solution of $dy/dx = x + y$, $y(0) = 1$ with successively smaller step sizes.

The usual way of attempting to reduce the cumulative error in Euler's method is to decrease the step size h. The table in Fig. 2.4.8 shows the results obtained in approximating the exact solution $y(x) = 2e^x - x - 1$ of the initial value problem

$$\frac{dy}{dx} = x + y, \quad y(0) = 1,$$

using the successively smaller step sizes $h = 0.1$, $h = 0.02$, $h = 0.005$, and $h = 0.001$. We show computed values only at intervals of $\Delta x = 0.1$. For instance, with $h = 0.001$, the computation required 1000 Euler steps, but the value y_n is shown only when n is a multiple of 100, so that x_n is an integral multiple of 0.1.

By scanning the columns in Fig. 2.4.8 we observe that, for each fixed step size h, the error $y_{\text{actual}} - y_{\text{approx}}$ increases as x gets farther from the starting point $x_0 = 0$. But by scanning the rows of the table we see that for each fixed x, the error decreases as the step size h is reduced. The percentage errors at the final point $x = 1$ range from 7.25% with $h = 0.1$ down to only 0.08% with $h = 0.001$. Thus the smaller the step size, the more slowly does the error grow with increasing distance from the starting point.

The column of data for $h = 0.1$ in Fig. 2.4.8 requires only 10 steps, so Euler's method can be carried out with a hand-held calculator. But 50 steps are required to reach $x = 1$ with $h = 0.02$, 200 steps with $h = 0.005$, and 1000 steps with $h = 0.001$. A computer is almost always used to implement Euler's method when more than 10 or 20 steps are required. Once an appropriate computer program has been written, one step size is—in principle—just as convenient as another; after all, the computer hardly cares how many steps it is asked to carry out.

Why, then, do we not simply choose an exceedingly small step size (such as $h = 10^{-12}$), with the expectation that very great accuracy will result? There are two reasons for not doing so. The first is obvious: the time required for the computation. For example, the data in Fig. 2.4.8 were obtained using a hand-held calculator that carried out nine Euler steps per second. Thus it required slightly over one second to approximate $y(1)$ with $h = 0.1$ and about 1 min 50 s with $h = 0.001$. But with $h = 10^{-12}$ it would require over 3000 years!

The second reason is more subtle. In addition to the local and cumulative errors discussed previously, the computer itself will contribute **roundoff error** at each stage because only finitely many significant digits can be used in each calculation.

An Euler's method computation with $h = 0.0001$ will introduce roundoff errors 1000 times as often as one with $h = 0.1$. Hence with certain differential equations, $h = 0.1$ might actually produce more accurate results than those obtained with $h = 0.0001$, because the cumulative effect of roundoff error in the latter case might exceed combined cumulative and roundoff error in the case $h = 0.1$.

The "best" choice of h is difficult to determine in practice as well as in theory. It depends on the nature of the function $f(x, y)$ in the initial value problem in (2), on the exact code in which the program is written, and on the specific computer used. With a step size that is too large, the approximations inherent in Euler's method may not be sufficiently accurate, whereas if h is too small, then roundoff errors may accumulate to an unacceptable degree or the program may require too much time to be practical. The subject of *error propagation* in numerical algorithms is treated in numerical analysis courses and textbooks.

The computations in Fig. 2.4.8 illustrate the common strategy of applying a numerical algorithm, such as Euler's method, several times in succession, beginning with a selected number n of subintervals for the first application, then doubling n for each succeeding application of the method. Visual comparison of successive results often can provide an "intuitive feel" for their accuracy. In the next two examples we present graphically the results of successive applications of Euler's method.

Example 3 The exact solution of the logistic initial value problem

$$\frac{dy}{dx} = \tfrac{1}{3}y(8 - y), \quad y(0) = 1$$

is $y(x) = 8/(1 + 7e^{-8x/3})$. Figure 2.4.9 shows both the exact solution curve and approximate solution curves obtained by applying Euler's method on the interval $0 \le x \le 5$ with $n = 5$, $n = 10$, and $n = 20$ subintervals. Each of these "curves" actually consists of line segments joining successive points (x_n, y_n) and (x_{n+1}, y_{n+1}). The Euler approximation with 5 subintervals is poor, and the approximation with 10 subintervals also overshoots the limiting value $y = 8$ of the solution before leveling off, but with 20 subintervals we obtain fairly good qualitative agreement with the actual behavior of the solution. ∎

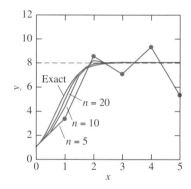

FIGURE 2.4.9. Approximating a logistic solution using Euler's method with $n = 5$, $n = 10$, and $n = 20$ subintervals.

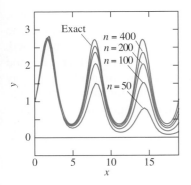

| **Example 4** | The exact solution of the initial value problem |

$$\frac{dy}{dx} = y \cos x, \quad y(0) = 1$$

is the periodic function $y(x) = e^{\sin x}$. Figure 2.4.10 shows both the exact solution curve and approximate solution curves obtained by applying Euler's method on the interval $0 \leq x \leq 6\pi$ with $n = 50$, $n = 100$, $n = 200$, and $n = 400$ subintervals. Even with this many subintervals, Euler's method evidently has considerable difficulty keeping up with the oscillations in the actual solution. Consequently, the more accurate methods discussed in succeeding sections are needed for serious numerical investigations. ■

FIGURE 2.4.10. Approximating the exact solution $y = e^{\sin x}$ using Euler's method with 50, 100, 200, and 400 subintervals.

A Word of Caution

The data shown in Fig. 2.4.8 indicate that Euler's method works well in approximating the solution of $dy/dx = x + y$, $y(0) = 1$ on the interval $[0, 1]$. That is, for each fixed x it appears that the approximate values approach the actual value of $y(x)$ as the step size h is decreased. For instance, the approximate values in the rows corresponding to $x = 0.3$ and $x = 0.5$ suggest that $y(0.3) \approx 1.40$ and $y(0.5) \approx 1.80$, in accord with the actual values shown in the final column of the table.

Example 5, in contrast, shows that some initial value problems are not so well behaved.

| **Example 5** | Use Euler's method to approximate the solution of the initial value problem |

$$\frac{dy}{dx} = x^2 + y^2, \quad y(0) = 1 \tag{7}$$

on the interval $[0, 1]$.

Solution   Here $f(x, y) = x^2 + y^2$, so the iterative formula of Euler's method is

$$y_{n+1} = y_n + h \cdot (x_n^2 + y_n^2). \tag{8}$$

With step size $h = 0.1$ we obtain

$$y_1 = 1 + (0.1) \cdot [(0)^2 + (1)^2] = 1.1,$$
$$y_2 = 1.1 + (0.1) \cdot [(0.1)^2 + (1.1)^2] = 1.222,$$
$$y_3 = 1.222 + (0.1) \cdot [(0.2)^2 + (1.222)^2] \approx 1.3753,$$

and so forth. Rounded to four decimal places, the first ten values obtained in this manner are

$$
\begin{array}{ll}
y_1 = 1.1000 & y_6 = 2.1995 \\
y_2 = 1.2220 & y_7 = 2.7193 \\
y_3 = 1.3753 & y_8 = 3.5078 \\
y_4 = 1.5735 & y_9 = 4.8023 \\
y_5 = 1.8371 & y_{10} = 7.1895
\end{array}
$$

But instead of naively accepting these results as accurate approximations, we decided to use a computer to repeat the computations with smaller values of h. The

x	y with $h = 0.1$	y with $h = 0.02$	y with $h = 0.005$
0.1	1.1000	1.1088	1.1108
0.2	1.2220	1.2458	1.2512
0.3	1.3753	1.4243	1.4357
0.4	1.5735	1.6658	1.6882
0.5	1.8371	2.0074	2.0512
0.6	2.1995	2.5201	2.6104
0.7	2.7193	3.3612	3.5706
0.8	3.5078	4.9601	5.5763
0.9	4.8023	9.0000	12.2061
1.0	7.1895	30.9167	1502.2090

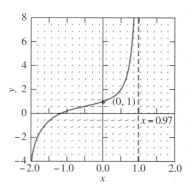

FIGURE 2.4.11. Attempting to approximate the solution of $dy/dx = x^2 + y^2$, $y(0) = 1$.

FIGURE 2.4.12. Solution of $dy/dx = x^2 + y^2$, $y(0) = 1$.

table in Fig. 2.4.11 shows the results obtained with step sizes $h = 0.1$, $h = 0.02$, and $h = 0.005$. Observe that now the "stability" of the procedure in Example 1 is missing. Indeed, it seems obvious that something is going wrong near $x = 1$.

Figure 2.4.12 provides a graphical clue to the difficulty. It shows a slope field for $dy/dx = x^2 + y^2$, together with a solution curve through (0, 1) plotted using one of the more accurate approximation methods of the following two sections. It appears that this solution curve may have a vertical asymptote near $x = 0.97$. Indeed, an exact solution using Bessel functions (see Problem 16 in Section 8.6) can be used to show that $y(x) \to +\infty$ as $x \to 0.969811$ (approximately). Although Euler's method gives values (albeit spurious ones) at $x = 1$, the actual solution does not exist on the entire interval $[0, 1]$. Moreover, Euler's method is unable to "keep up" with the rapid changes in $y(x)$ that occur as x approaches the infinite discontinuity near 0.969811. ∎

The moral of Example 5 is that there are pitfalls in the numerical solution of certain initial value problems. Certainly it's pointless to attempt to approximate a solution on an interval where it doesn't even exist (or where it is not unique, in which case there's no general way to predict which way the numerical approximations will branch at a point of nonuniqueness). One should never accept as accurate the results of applying Euler's method with a single fixed step size h. A second "run" with smaller step size ($h/2$, say, or $h/5$, or $h/10$) may give seemingly consistent results, thereby suggesting their accuracy, or it may—as in Example 5—reveal the presence of some hidden difficulty in the problem. Many problems simply require the more accurate and powerful methods that are discussed in the final two sections of this chapter.

2.4 Problems

In Problems 1 through 10, an initial value problem and its exact solution $y(x)$ are given. Apply Euler's method twice to approximate to this solution on the interval $[0, \frac{1}{2}]$, first with step size $h = 0.25$, then with step size $h = 0.1$. Compare the three-decimal-place values of the two approximations at $x = \frac{1}{2}$ with the value $y(\frac{1}{2})$ of the actual solution.

1. $y' = -y$, $y(0) = 2$; $y(x) = 2e^{-x}$
2. $y' = 2y$, $y(0) = \frac{1}{2}$; $y(x) = \frac{1}{2}e^{2x}$
3. $y' = y + 1$, $y(0) = 1$; $y(x) = 2e^x - 1$
4. $y' = x - y$, $y(0) = 1$; $y(x) = 2e^{-x} + x - 1$
5. $y' = y - x - 1$, $y(0) = 1$; $y(x) = 2 + x - e^x$
6. $y' = -2xy$, $y(0) = 2$; $y(x) = 2e^{-x^2}$

7. $y' = -3x^2 y$, $y(0) = 3$; $y(x) = 3e^{-x^3}$

8. $y' = e^{-y}$, $y(0) = 0$; $y(x) = \ln(x+1)$

9. $y' = \frac{1}{4}(1 + y^2)$, $y(0) = 1$; $y(x) = \tan \frac{1}{4}(x + \pi)$

10. $y' = 2xy^2$, $y(0) = 1$; $y(x) = \dfrac{1}{1 - x^2}$

Note: The application following this problem set lists illustrative calculator/computer programs that can be used in the remaining problems.

A programmable calculator or a computer will be useful for Problems 11 through 16. In each problem find the exact solution of the given initial value problem. Then apply Euler's method twice to approximate (to four decimal places) this solution on the given interval, first with step size $h = 0.01$, then with step size $h = 0.005$. Make a table showing the approximate values and the actual value, together with the percentage error in the more accurate approximation, for x an integral multiple of 0.2. Throughout, primes denote derivatives with respect to x.

11. $y' = y - 2$, $y(0) = 1$; $0 \le x \le 1$

12. $y' = \frac{1}{2}(y - 1)^2$, $y(0) = 2$; $0 \le x \le 1$

13. $yy' = 2x^3$, $y(1) = 3$; $1 \le x \le 2$

14. $xy' = y^2$, $y(1) = 1$; $1 \le x \le 2$

15. $xy' = 3x - 2y$, $y(2) = 3$; $2 \le x \le 3$

16. $y^2 y' = 2x^5$, $y(2) = 3$; $2 \le x \le 3$

A computer with a printer is required for Problems 17 through 24. In these initial value problems, use Euler's method with step sizes $h = 0.1, 0.02, 0.004,$ and 0.0008 to approximate to four decimal places the values of the solution at ten equally spaced points of the given interval. Print the results in tabular form with appropriate headings to make it easy to gauge the effect of varying the step size h. Throughout, primes denote derivatives with respect to x.

17. $y' = x^2 + y^2$, $y(0) = 0$; $0 \le x \le 1$

18. $y' = x^2 - y^2$, $y(0) = 1$; $0 \le x \le 2$

19. $y' = x + \sqrt{y}$, $y(0) = 1$; $0 \le x \le 2$

20. $y' = x + \sqrt[3]{y}$, $y(0) = -1$; $0 \le x \le 2$

21. $y' = \ln y$, $y(1) = 2$; $1 \le x \le 2$

22. $y' = x^{2/3} + y^{2/3}$, $y(0) = 1$; $0 \le x \le 2$

23. $y' = \sin x + \cos y$, $y(0) = 0$; $0 \le x \le 1$

24. $y' = \dfrac{x}{1 + y^2}$, $y(-1) = 1$; $-1 \le x \le 1$

25. You bail out of the helicopter of Example 2 and immediately pull the ripcord of your parachute. Now $k = 1.6$ in Eq. (5), so your downward velocity satisfies the initial value problem

$$\frac{dv}{dt} = 32 - 1.6v, \quad v(0) = 0$$

(with t in seconds and v in ft/sec). Use Euler's method with a programmable calculator or computer to approximate the solution for $0 \le t \le 2$, first with step size $h = 0.01$ and then with $h = 0.005$, rounding off approximate v-values to one decimal place. What percentage of the limiting velocity 20 ft/sec has been attained after 1 second? After 2 seconds?

26. Suppose the deer population $P(t)$ in a small forest initially numbers 25 and satisfies the logistic equation

$$\frac{dP}{dt} = 0.0225P - 0.0003P^2$$

(with t in months). Use Euler's method with a programmable calculator or computer to approximate the solution for 10 years, first with step size $h = 1$ and then with $h = 0.5$, rounding off approximate P-values to integral numbers of deer. What percentage of the limiting population of 75 deer has been attained after 5 years? After 10 years?

Use Euler's method with a computer system to find the desired solution values in Problems 27 and 28. Start with step size $h = 0.1$, and then use successively smaller step sizes until successive approximate solution values at $x = 2$ agree rounded off to two decimal places.

27. $y' = x^2 + y^2 - 1$, $y(0) = 0$; $y(2) = ?$

28. $y' = x + \frac{1}{2}y^2$, $y(-2) = 0$; $y(2) = ?$

29. Consider the initial value problem

$$7x\frac{dy}{dx} + y = 0, \quad y(-1) = 1.$$

(a) Solve this problem for the exact solution

$$y(x) = -\frac{1}{x^{1/7}},$$

which has an infinite discontinuity at $x = 0$. **(b)** Apply Euler's method with step size $h = 0.15$ to approximate this solution on the interval $-1 \le x \le 0.5$. Note that, from these data alone, you might not suspect any difficulty near $x = 0$. The reason is that the numerical approximation "jumps across the discontinuity" to another solution of $7xy' + y = 0$ for $x > 0$. **(c)** Finally, apply Euler's method with step sizes $h = 0.03$ and $h = 0.006$, but still printing results only at the original points $x = -1.00$, $-0.85, -0.70, \ldots, 1.20, 1.35.$ and 1.50. Would you now suspect a discontinuity in the exact solution?

30. Apply Euler's method with successively smaller step sizes on the interval $[0, 2]$ to verify empirically that the solution of the initial value problem

$$\frac{dy}{dx} = x^2 + y^2, \quad y(0) = 0$$

has a vertical asymptote near $x = 2.003147$. (Contrast this with Example 2, in which $y(0) = 1$.)

31. The general solution of the equation

$$\frac{dy}{dx} = (1 + y^2)\cos x$$

is $y(x) = \tan(C + \sin x)$. With the initial condition $y(0) = 0$ the solution $y(x) = \tan(\sin x)$ is well behaved. But with $y(0) = 1$ the solution $y(x) = \tan\left(\frac{1}{4}\pi + \sin x\right)$ has a vertical asymptote at $x = \sin^{-1}(\pi/4) \approx 0.90334$. Use Euler's method to verify this fact empirically.

2.4 Application   Implementing Euler's Method

Construction of a calculator or computer program to implement a numerical algorithm can sharpen one's understanding of the algorithm. Figure 2.4.13 lists TI-85 and BASIC programs implementing Euler's method to approximate the solution of the initial value problem

$$\frac{dy}{dx} = x + y, \quad y(0) = 1$$

considered in this section. The comments provided in the final column should make these programs intelligible even if you have little familiarity with the BASIC and TI calculator programming languages. Indeed, the BASIC language is no longer widely used for programming computers but is still useful (as in Fig. 2.4.13 and subsequent ones in this text) for brief description of mathematical algorithms in a transparent form intermediate between English and higher programming languages. (Appropriately, the name BASIC is an acronym describing the **B**eginner's **A**ll-purpose **S**ymbolic **I**nstruction **C**ode introduced in 1963, intially for instructional use at Dartmouth College.)

TI-85	BASIC	Comment
`PROGRAM:EULER`	`Program EULER`	`Program title`
`:10→N`	`N = 10`	`Number of steps`
`:0→X`	`X = 0`	`Initial x`
`:1→Y`	`Y = 1`	`Initial y`
`:1→X1`	`X1 = 1`	`Final x`
`:(X1-X)/N→H`	`H = (X1-X)/N`	`Step size`
`:For(I,1,N)`	`FOR I=1 TO N`	`Begin loop`
`:X+Y→F`	`F = X + Y`	`Function value`
`:Y+H*F→Y`	`Y = Y + H*F`	`Euler iteration`
`:X+H→X`	`X = X + H`	`New x`
`:Disp X,Y`	`PRINT X,Y`	`Display results`
`:End`	`NEXT I`	`End loop`

FIGURE 2.4.13.   TI-85 and BASIC Euler's method programs.

To increase the number of steps (and thereby decrease the step size) you need only change the value of **N** specified in the first line of the program. To apply Euler's method to a different equation $dy/dx = f(x, y)$, you need change only the single line that calculates the function value **F**.

Any other procedural programming language (such as FORTRAN or Pascal) would follow the pattern illustrated by the parallel lines of TI-85 and BASIC code in Fig. 2.4.13. Some of the modern functional programming languages mirror standard mathematical notation even more closely. Figure 2.4.14 shows a MATLAB implementation of Euler's method. The **euler** function takes as input the initial value **x**, the initial value **y**, the final value **x1** of x, and the desired number **n** of subintervals. For instance, the MATLAB command

```
[X, Y] = euler(0, 1, 1, 10)
```

then generates the x_n- and y_n-data shown in the first two columns of the table of Fig. 2.4.8.

```
function yp = f(x,y)
yp = x + y;                        % yp = y'

function [X,Y] = euler(x,y,x1,n)
h = (x1 - x)/n;                    % step size
X = x;                             % initial x
Y = y;                             % initial y
for i = 1:n                        % begin loop
    y = y + h*f(x,y);             % Euler iteration
    x = x + h;                     % new x
    X = [X;x];                     % update x-column
    Y = [Y;y];                     % update y-column
end                                % end loop
```

FIGURE 2.4.14. MATLAB implementation of Euler's method.

You should begin this project by implementing Euler's method with your own calculator or computer system. Test your program by first applying it to the initial value problem in Example 1, then to some of the problems for this section.

Famous Numbers Investigation

The following problems describe the numbers $e \approx 2.71828$, $\ln 2 \approx 0.69315$, and $\pi \approx 3.14159$ as specific values of solutions of certain initial value problems. In each case, apply Euler's method with $n = 50, 100, 200, \ldots$ subintervals (doubling n each time). How many subintervals are needed to obtain—twice in succession—the correct value of the target number rounded to three decimal places?

1. The number $e = y(1)$, where $y(x)$ is the solution of the initial value problem $dy/dx = y$, $y(0) = 1$.
2. The number $\ln 2 = y(2)$, where $y(x)$ is the solution of the initial value problem $dy/dx = 1/x$, $y(1) = 0$.
3. The number $\pi = y(1)$, where $y(x)$ is the solution of the initial value problem $dy/dx = 4/(1 + x^2)$, $y(0) = 0$.

Also explain in each problem what the point is—why the indicated famous number is the expected numerical result.

2.5 A Closer Look at the Euler Method

The Euler method as presented in Section 2.4 is not often used in practice, mainly because more accurate methods are available. But Euler's method has the advantage of simplicity, and a careful study of this method yields insights into the workings of more accurate methods, because many of the latter are extensions or refinements of the Euler method.

To compare two different methods of numerical approximation, we need some way to measure the accuracy of each. Theorem 1 tells what degree of accuracy we can expect when we use Euler's method.

> **THEOREM 1 The Error in the Euler Method**
>
> Suppose that the initial value problem
>
> $$\frac{dy}{dx} = f(x, y), \quad y(x_0) = y_0 \tag{1}$$
>
> has a unique solution $y(x)$ on the closed interval $[a, b]$ with $a = x_0$, and assume that $y(x)$ has a continuous second derivative on $[a, b]$. (This would follow from the assumption that f, f_x, and f_y are all continuous for $a \leq x \leq b$ and $c \leq y \leq d$, where $c \leq y(x) \leq d$ for all x in $[a, b]$.) Then there exists a constant C such that the following is true: If the approximations $y_1, y_2, y_3, \ldots, y_k$ to the actual values $y(x_1), y(x_2), y(x_3), \ldots, y(x_k)$ at points of $[a, b]$ are computed using Euler's method with step size $h > 0$, then
>
> $$|y_n - y(x_n)| \leq Ch \tag{2}$$
>
> for each $n = 1, 2, 3, \ldots, k$.

Remark: The **error**

$$y_{\text{actual}} - y_{\text{approx}} = y(x_n) - y_n$$

in (2) denotes the [cumulative] error in Euler's method after n steps in the approximation, *exclusive* of roundoff error (as though we were using a perfect machine that made no roundoff errors). The theorem can be summarized by saying that *the error in Euler's method is of order h*; that is, the error is bounded by a [predetermined] constant C multiplied by the step size h. It follows, for instance, that (on a given closed interval) halving the step size cuts the maximum error in half; similarly, with step size $h/10$ we get 10 times the accuracy (that is, $1/10$ the maximum error) as with step size h. Consequently, we can—in principle—get any degree of accuracy we want by choosing h sufficiently small. ∎

We will omit the proof of this theorem, but one can be found in Chapter 7 of G. Birkhoff and G.-C. Rota, *Ordinary Differential Equations,* 4th ed. (New York: John Wiley, 1989). The constant C deserves some comment. Because C tends to increase as the maximum value of $|y''(x)|$ on $[a, b]$ increases, it follows that C must depend in a fairly complicated way on y, and actual computation of a value of C such that the inequality in (2) holds is usually impractical. In practice, the following type of procedure is commonly employed.

1. Apply Euler's method to the initial value problem in (1) with a reasonable value of h.
2. Repeat with $h/2$, $h/4$, and so forth, at each stage halving the step size for the next application of Euler's method.
3. Continue until the results obtained at one stage agree—to an appropriate number of significant digits—with those obtained at the previous stage. Then the approximate values obtained at this stage are considered likely to be accurate to the indicated number of significant digits.

Example 1 Carry out this procedure with the initial value problem

$$\frac{dy}{dx} = -\frac{2xy}{1+x^2}, \quad y(0) = 1 \tag{3}$$

to approximate accurately the value $y(1)$ of the solution at $x = 1$.

Solution Using an Euler method program, perhaps one of those listed in Figs. 2.4.13 and 2.4.14, we begin with a step size $h = 0.04$ requiring $n = 25$ steps to reach $x = 1$. The table in Fig. 2.5.1 shows the approximate values of $y(1)$ obtained with successively smaller values of h. The data suggest that the true value of $y(1)$ is exactly 0.5. Indeed, the exact solution of the initial value problem in (3) is $y(x) = 1/(1 + x^2)$, so the true value of $y(1)$ is exactly $\frac{1}{2}$. ■

h	Approximate $y(1)$	Actual $y(1)$	|Error|/h
0.04	0.50451	0.50000	0.11
0.02	0.50220	0.50000	0.11
0.01	0.50109	0.50000	0.11
0.005	0.50054	0.50000	0.11
0.0025	0.50027	0.50000	0.11
0.00125	0.50013	0.50000	0.10
0.000625	0.50007	0.50000	0.11
0.0003125	0.50003	0.50000	0.10

FIGURE 2.5.1. Table of values in Example 1.

The final column of the table in Fig. 2.5.1 displays the ratio of the magnitude of the error to h; that is, $|y_{\text{actual}} - y_{\text{approx}}|/h$. Observe how the data in this column substantiate Theorem 1—in this computation, the error bound in (2) appears to hold with a value of C slightly larger than 0.1.

An Improvement in Euler's Method

As Fig. 2.5.2 shows, Euler's method is rather unsymmetrical. It uses the predicted slope $k = f(x_n, y_n)$ of the graph of the solution at the left-hand endpoint of the interval $[x_n, x_n + h]$ as if it were the actual slope of the solution over that entire interval. We now turn our attention to a way in which increased accuracy can easily be obtained; it is known as the *improved Euler method*.

Given the initial value problem

$$\frac{dy}{dx} = f(x, y), \quad y(x_0) = y_0, \tag{4}$$

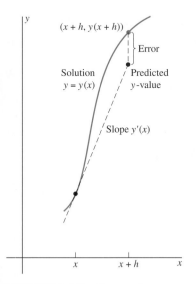

FIGURE 2.5.2. True and predicted values in Euler's method.

suppose that after carrying out n steps with step size h we have computed the approximation y_n to the actual value $y(x_n)$ of the solution at $x_n = x_0 + nh$. We can use the Euler method to obtain a first estimate—which we now call u_{n+1} rather than y_{n+1}—of the value of the solution at $x_{n+1} = x_n + h$. Thus

$$u_{n+1} = y_n + h \cdot f(x_n, y_n) = y_n + h \cdot k_1.$$

Now that $u_{n+1} \approx y(x_{n+1})$ has been computed, we can take

$$k_2 = f(x_{n+1}, u_{n+1})$$

as a second estimate of the slope of the solution curve $y = y(x)$ at $x = x_{n+1}$.

Of course, the approximate slope $k_1 = f(x_n, y_n)$ at $x = x_n$ has already been calculated. Why not *average* these two slopes to obtain a more accurate estimate of the average slope of the solution curve over the entire subinterval $[x_n, x_{n+1}]$? This idea is the essence of the *improved* Euler method. Figure 2.5.3 shows the geometry behind this method.

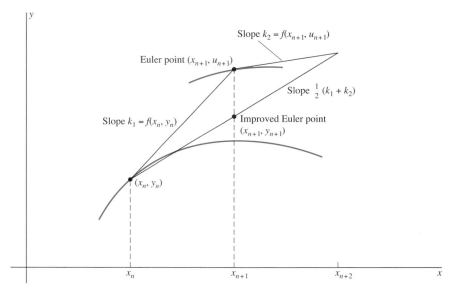

FIGURE 2.5.3.   The improved Euler method: Average the slopes of the tangent lines at (x_n, y_n) and (x_{n+1}, u_{n+1}).

ALGORITHM   The Improved Euler Method

Given the initial value problem

$$\frac{dy}{dx} = f(x, y), \quad y(x_0) = y_0,$$

the **improved Euler method with step size** h consists in applying the iterative formulas

$$
\begin{aligned}
k_1 &= f(x_n, y_n), \\
u_{n+1} &= y_n + h \cdot k_1, \\
k_2 &= f(x_{n+1}, u_{n+1}), \\
y_{n+1} &= y_n + h \cdot \tfrac{1}{2}(k_1 + k_2)
\end{aligned}
\tag{5}
$$

to compute successive approximations y_1, y_2, y_3, ... to the [true] values $y(x_1)$, $y(x_2)$, $y(x_3)$, ... of the [exact] solution $y = y(x)$ at the points x_1, x_2, x_3, ..., respectively.

Remark: The final formula in (5) takes the "Euler form"

$$y_{n+1} = y_n + h \cdot k$$

if we write

$$k = \frac{k_1 + k_2}{2}$$

for the approximate *average slope* on the interval $[x_n, x_{n+1}]$.   ■

The improved Euler method is one of a class of numerical techniques known as **predictor-corrector** methods. First a predictor u_{n+1} of the next y-value is computed; then it is used to correct itself. Thus the **improved Euler method** with step size h consists of using the **predictor**

➤ $$u_{n+1} = y_n + h \cdot f(x_n, y_n) \tag{6}$$

and the **corrector**

➤ $$y_{n+1} = y_n + h \cdot \tfrac{1}{2}\left[f(x_n, y_n) + f(x_{n+1}, u_{n+1})\right] \tag{7}$$

iteratively to compute successive approximations $y_1, y_2, y_2, \ldots$ to the values $y(x_1)$, $y(x_2), y(x_3), \ldots$ of the actual solution of the initial value problem in (4).

Remark: Each improved Euler step requires two evaluations of the function $f(x, y)$, as compared with the single function evaluation required for an ordinary Euler step. We naturally wonder whether this doubled computational labor is worth the trouble.

Answer: Under the assumption that the exact solution $y = y(x)$ of the initial value problem in (4) has a continuous third derivative, it can be proved—see Chapter 7 of Birkhoff and Rota—that the error in the improved Euler method is of order h^2. This means that on a given bounded interval $[a, b]$, each approximate value y_n satisfies the inequality

➤ $$|y(x_n) - y_n| \leq Ch^2, \tag{8}$$

where the constant C does not depend on h. Because h^2 is much smaller than h if h itself is small, this means that the improved Euler method is more accurate than Euler's method itself. This advantage is offset by the fact that about twice as many computations are required. But the factor h^2 in (8) means that halving the step size results in $1/4$ the maximum error, and with step size $h/10$ we get 100 times the accuracy (that is, $1/100$ the maximum error) as with step size h.   ■

Example 2   Figure 2.4.8 shows results of applying Euler's method to the initial value problem

$$\frac{dy}{dx} = x + y, \quad y(0) = 1 \tag{9}$$

with exact solution $y(x) = 2e^x - x - 1$. With $f(x, y) = x + y$ in Eqs. (6) and (7), the predictor-corrector formulas for the improved Euler method are

$$u_{n+1} = y_n + h \cdot (x_n + y_n),$$
$$y_{n+1} = y_n + h \cdot \tfrac{1}{2}\left[(x_n + y_n) + (x_{n+1} + u_{n+1})\right].$$

With step size $h = 0.1$ we calculate

$$u_1 = 1 + (0.1) \cdot (0 + 1) = 1.1,$$
$$y_1 = 1 + (0.05) \cdot [(0 + 1) + (0.1 + 1.1)] = 1.11,$$
$$u_2 = 1.11 + (0.1) \cdot (0.1 + 1.11) = 1.231,$$
$$y_2 = 1.11 + (0.05) \cdot [(0.1 + 1.11) + (0.2 + 1.231)] = 1.24205,$$

and so forth. The table in Fig. 2.5.4 compares the results obtained using the improved Euler method with those obtained previously using the "unimproved" Euler method. When the same step size $h = 0.1$ is used, the error in the Euler approximation to $y(1)$ is 7.25%, but the error in the improved Euler approximation is only 0.24%.

	Euler Method, $h = 0.1$	Euler Method, $h = 0.005$	Improved Euler, $h = 0.1$	Actual
x	Values of y	Values of y	Values of y	y
0.1	1.1000	1.1098	1.1100	1.1103
0.2	1.2200	1.2416	1.2421	1.2428
0.3	1.3620	1.3977	1.3985	1.3997
0.4	1.5282	1.5807	1.5818	1.5836
0.5	1.7210	1.7933	1.7949	1.7974
0.6	1.9431	2.0388	2.0409	2.0442
0.7	2.1974	2.3205	2.3231	2.3275
0.8	2.4872	2.6422	2.6456	2.6511
0.9	2.8159	3.0082	3.0124	3.0192
1.0	3.1875	3.4230	3.4282	3.4366

FIGURE 2.5.4. Euler and improved Euler approximations to the solution of $dy/dx = x + y$, $y(0) = 1$.

Indeed, the improved Euler method with $h = 0.1$ is more accurate (in this example) than the original Euler method with $h = 0.005$. The latter requires 200 evaluations of the function $f(x, y)$, but the former requires only 20 such evaluations, so in this case the improved Euler method yields greater accuracy with only about one-tenth the work.

Figure 2.5.5 shows the results obtained when the improved Euler method is applied to the initial value problem in (9) using step size $h = 0.005$. Accuracy of five significant figures is apparent in the table. This suggests that, in contrast with the original Euler method, the improved Euler method is sufficiently accurate for certain practical applications—such as plotting solution curves. ∎

An improved Euler program (similar to the ones listed in the project material for this section) was used to compute approximations to the exact value $y(1) = 0.5$ of the solution $y(x) = 1/(1 + x^2)$ of the initial value problem

$$\frac{dy}{dx} = -\frac{2xy}{1 + x^2}, \quad y(0) = 1 \tag{3}$$

of Example 1. The results obtained by successively halving the step size appear in the table in Fig. 2.5.6. Note that the final column of this table impressively corroborates the form of the error bound in (8), and that each halving of the step size

	Improved Euler, Approximate	Actual
x	y	y
0.0	1.00000	1.00000
0.1	1.11034	1.11034
0.2	1.24280	1.24281
0.3	1.39971	1.39972
0.4	1.58364	1.58365
0.5	1.79744	1.79744
0.6	2.04423	2.04424
0.7	2.32749	2.32751
0.8	2.65107	2.65108
0.9	3.01919	3.01921
1.0	3.43654	3.43656

FIGURE 2.5.5. Improved Euler approximation to the solution of Eq. (9) with step size $h = 0.005$.

h	Improved Euler Approximation to $y(1)$	Error	$|Error|/h^2$
0.04	0.500195903	−0.000195903	0.12
0.02	0.500049494	−0.000049494	0.12
0.01	0.500012437	−0.000012437	0.12
0.005	0.500003117	−0.000003117	0.12
0.0025	0.500000780	−0.000000780	0.12
0.00125	0.500000195	−0.000000195	0.12
0.000625	0.500000049	−0.000000049	0.12
0.0003125	0.500000012	−0.000000012	0.12

FIGURE 2.5.6. Improved Euler approximation to $y(1)$ for $dy/dx = -2xy/(1+x^2)$, $y(0) = 1$.

reduces the error by a factor of almost exactly 4, as should happen if the error is proportional to h^2.

In the following two examples we exhibit graphical results obtained by employing this strategy of successively halving the step size, and thus doubling the number of subintervals of a fixed interval on which we are approximating a solution.

Example 3   In Example 3 of Section 2.4 we applied Euler's method to the logistic initial value problem

$$\frac{dy}{dx} = \tfrac{1}{3}y(8 - y), \quad y(0) = 1.$$

Figure 2.4.9 shows an obvious difference between the exact solution $y(x) = 8/(1 + 7e^{-8x/3})$ and the Euler approximation on $0 \leqq x \leqq 5$ using $n = 20$ subintervals. Figure 2.5.7 shows approximate solution curves plotted using the improved Euler's method.

The approximation with five subintervals is still bad—perhaps worse! It appears to level off considerably short of the actual limiting population $M = 8$. You should carry out at least the first two improved Euler steps manually to see for yourself how it happens that, after increasing appropriately during the first step, the approximate solution *decreases* in the second step rather than continuing to increase (as it should). In the project for this section we ask you to show empirically that the improved Euler approximate solution with step size $h = 1$ levels off at $y \approx 4.3542$.

In contrast, the approximate solution curve with $n = 20$ subintervals tracks the exact solution curve rather closely, and with $n = 40$ subintervals the exact and approximate solution curves are indistinguishable in Fig. 2.5.7. The table in Fig. 2.5.8 indicates that the improved Euler approximation with $n = 200$ subintervals is accurate rounded to three decimal places (that is, four significant digits) on the interval $0 \leqq x \leqq 5$. Because discrepancies in the fourth significant digit are not visually apparent at the resolution of an ordinary computer screen, the improved Euler method (using several hundred subintervals) is considered adequate for many graphical purposes. ■

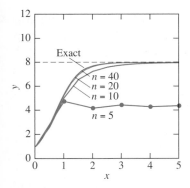

FIGURE 2.5.7. Approximating a logistic solution using the improved Euler method with $n = 5$, $n = 10$, $n = 20$, and $n = 40$ subintervals.

x	Actual $y(x)$	Improved Euler with $n = 200$
0	1.0000	1.0000
1	5.3822	5.3809
2	7.7385	7.7379
3	7.9813	7.9812
4	7.9987	7.9987
5	7.9999	7.9999

FIGURE 2.5.8.   Using the improved Euler method to approximate the actual solution of the initial value problem in Example 3.

Example 4   In Example 4 of Section 2.4 we applied Euler's method to the initial value problem

$$\frac{dy}{dx} = y \cos x, \quad y(0) = 1.$$

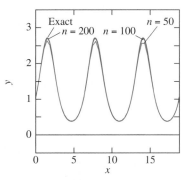

FIGURE 2.5.9.   Approximating the exact solution $y = e^{\sin x}$ using the improved Euler method with $n = 50$, 100, and 200 subintervals.

Figure 2.4.10 shows obvious visual differences between the periodic exact solution $y(x) = e^{\sin x}$ and the Euler approximations on $0 \leq x \leq 6\pi$ with as many as $n = 400$ subintervals.

Figure 2.5.9 shows the exact solution curve and approximate solution curves plotted using the improved Euler method with $n = 50$, $n = 100$, and $n = 200$ subintervals. The approximation obtained with $n = 200$ is indistinguishable from the exact solution curve, and the approximation with $n = 100$ is only barely distinguishable from it. ∎

Although Figs. 2.5.7 and 2.5.9 indicate that the improved Euler method can provide accuracy that suffices for many graphical purposes, it does not provide the higher-precision numerical accuracy that sometimes is needed for more careful investigations. For instance, consider again the initial value problem

$$\frac{dy}{dx} = -\frac{2xy}{1 + x^2}, \quad y(0) = 1$$

of Example 1. The final column of the table in Fig. 2.5.6 suggests that, if the improved Euler method is used on the interval $0 \leq x \leq 1$ with n subintervals and step size $h = 1/n$, then the resulting error E in the final approximation $y_n \approx y(1)$ is given by

$$E = |y(1) - y_n| \approx (0.12)h^2 = \frac{0.12}{n^2}.$$

If so, then 12-place accuracy (for instance) in the value $y(1)$ would require that $(0.12)n^{-2} < 5 \times 10^{-13}$, which means that $n \geq 489,898$. Thus, roughly half a million steps of length $h \approx 0.000002$ would be required. Aside from the possible impracticality of this many steps (using available computational resources), the roundoff error resulting from so many successive steps might well overwhelm the cumulative error predicted by theory (which assumes exact computations in each separate step). Consequently, still more accurate methods than the improved Euler method are needed for such high-precision computations. Such a method is presented in Section 2.6.

2.5 Problems

A hand-held calculator will suffice for Problems 1 through 10, where an initial value problem and its exact solution are given. Apply the improved Euler method to approximate this solution on the interval $[0, 0.5]$ with step size $h = 0.1$. Construct a table showing four-decimal-place values of the approximate solution and actual solution at the points $x = 0.1, 0.2, 0.3, 0.4, 0.5$.

1. $y' = -y$, $y(0) = 2$; $y(x) = 2e^{-x}$
2. $y' = 2y$, $y(0) = \frac{1}{2}$; $y(x) = \frac{1}{2}e^{2x}$
3. $y' = y + 1$, $y(0) = 1$; $y(x) = 2e^x - 1$
4. $y' = x - y$, $y(0) = 1$; $y(x) = 2e^{-x} + x - 1$
5. $y' = y - x - 1$, $y(0) = 1$; $y(x) = 2 + x - e^x$
6. $y' = -2xy$, $y(0) = 2$; $y(x) = 2e^{-x^2}$
7. $y' = -3x^2y$, $y(0) = 3$; $y(x) = 3e^{-x^3}$
8. $y' = e^{-y}$, $y(0) = 0$; $y(x) = \ln(x + 1)$
9. $y' = \frac{1}{4}(1 + y^2)$, $y(0) = 1$; $y(x) = \tan\frac{1}{4}(x + \pi)$
10. $y' = 2xy^2$, $y(0) = 1$; $y(x) = \dfrac{1}{1 - x^2}$

Note: The application following this problem set lists illustrative calculator/computer programs that can be used in Problems 11 through 24.

A programmable calculator or a computer will be useful for Problems 11 through 16. In each problem find the exact solution of the given initial value problem. Then apply the improved Euler method twice to approximate (to five decimal places) this solution on the given interval, first with step size $h = 0.01$, then with step size $h = 0.005$. Make a table showing the approximate values and the actual value, together with the percentage error in the more accurate approximations, for x an integral multiple of 0.2. Throughout, primes denote derivatives with respect to x.

11. $y' = y - 2$, $y(0) = 1$; $0 \le x \le 1$
12. $y' = \frac{1}{2}(y - 1)^2$, $y(0) = 2$; $0 \le x \le 1$
13. $yy' = 2x^3$, $y(1) = 3$; $1 \le x \le 2$
14. $xy' = y^2$, $y(1) = 1$; $1 \le x \le 2$
15. $xy' = 3x - 2y$, $y(2) = 3$; $2 \le x \le 3$
16. $y^2y' = 2x^5$, $y(2) = 3$; $2 \le x \le 3$

A computer with a printer is required for Problems 17 through 24. In these initial value problems, use the improved Euler method with step sizes $h = 0.1, 0.02, 0.004,$ and 0.0008 to approximate to five decimal places the values of the solution at ten equally spaced points of the given interval. Print the results in tabular form with appropriate headings to make it easy to gauge the effect of varying the step size h. Throughout, primes denote derivatives with respect to x.

17. $y' = x^2 + y^2$, $y(0) = 0$; $0 \le x \le 1$
18. $y' = x^2 - y^2$, $y(0) = 1$; $0 \le x \le 2$
19. $y' = x + \sqrt{y}$, $y(0) = 1$; $0 \le x \le 2$
20. $y' = x + \sqrt[3]{y}$, $y(0) = -1$; $0 \le x \le 2$
21. $y' = \ln y$, $y(1) = 2$; $1 \le x \le 2$
22. $y' = x^{2/3} + y^{2/3}$, $y(0) = 1$; $0 \le x \le 2$

23. $y' = \sin x + \cos y$, $y(0) = 0$; $0 \le x \le 1$
24. $y' = \dfrac{x}{1 + y^2}$, $y(-1) = 1$; $-1 \le x \le 1$
25. As in Problem 25 of Section 2.4, you bail out of a helicopter and immediately open your parachute, so your downward velocity satisfies the initial value problem

$$\frac{dv}{dt} = 32 - 1.6v, \quad v(0) = 0$$

(with t in seconds and v in ft/s). Use the improved Euler method with a programmable calculator or computer to approximate the solution for $0 \le t \le 2$, first with step size $h = 0.01$ and then with $h = 0.005$, rounding off approximate v-values to three decimal places. What percentage of the limiting velocity 20 ft/s has been attained after 1 second? After 2 seconds?
26. As in Problem 26 of Section 2.4, suppose the deer population $P(t)$ in a small forest initially numbers 25 and satisfies the logistic equation

$$\frac{dP}{dt} = 0.0225P - 0.0003P^2$$

(with t in months). Use the improved Euler method with a programmable calculator or computer to approximate the solution for 10 years, first with step size $h = 1$ and then with $h = 0.5$, rounding off approximate P-values to three decimal places. What percentage of the limiting population of 75 deer has been attained after 5 years? After 10 years?

Use the improved Euler method with a computer system to find the desired solution values in Problems 27 and 28. Start with step size $h = 0.1$, and then use successively smaller step sizes until successive approximate solution values at $x = 2$ agree rounded off to four decimal places.

27. $y' = x^2 + y^2 - 1$, $y(0) = 0$; $y(2) = ?$
28. $y' = x + \frac{1}{2}y^2$, $y(-2) = 0$; $y(2) = ?$
29. Consider the crossbow bolt of Example 2 in Section 2.3, shot straight upward from the ground with an initial velocity of 49 m/s. Because of linear air resistance, its velocity function $v(t)$ satisfies the initial value problem

$$\frac{dv}{dt} = -(0.04)v - 9.8, \quad v(0) = 49$$

with exact solution $v(t) = 294e^{-t/25} - 245$. Use a calculator or computer implementation of the improved Euler method to approximate $v(t)$ for $0 \le t \le 10$ using both $n = 50$ and $n = 100$ subintervals. Display the results at intervals of 1 second. Do the two approximations—each rounded to two decimal places—agree both with each other and with the exact solution? If the exact solution were unavailable, explain how you could use the improved Euler method to approximate closely **(a)** the bolt's time of ascent to its apex (given in Section 2.3 as 4.56 s) and **(b)** its impact velocity after 9.41 s in the air.

30. Consider now the crossbow bolt of Example 3 in Section 2.3. It still is shot straight upward from the ground with an initial velocity of 49 m/s, but because of air resistance proportional to the square of its velocity, its velocity function $v(t)$ satisfies the initial value problem

$$\frac{dv}{dt} = -(0.0011)v|v| - 9.8, \quad v(0) = 49.$$

The symbolic solution discussed in Section 2.3 required separate investigations of the bolt's ascent and its descent, with $v(t)$ given by a tangent function during ascent and by a hyperbolic tangent function during descent. But the improved Euler method requires no such distinction. Use a calculator or computer implementation of the improved Euler method to approximate $v(t)$ for $0 \leq t \leq 10$ using both $n = 100$ and $n = 200$ subintervals. Display the results at intervals of 1 second. Do the two approximations—each rounded to two decimal places—agree with each other? If an exact solution were unavailable, explain how you could use the improved Euler method to approximate closely (**a**) the bolt's time of ascent to its apex (given in Section 2.3 as 4.61 s) and (**b**) its impact velocity after 9.41 s in the air.

2.5 Application Improved Euler Implementation

Figure 2.5.10 lists TI-85 and BASIC programs implementing the improved Euler method to approximate the solution of the initial value problem

$$\frac{dy}{dx} = x + y, \quad y(0) = 1$$

considered in Example 2 of this section. The comments provided in the final column should make these programs intelligible even if you have little familiarity with the BASIC and TI programming languages.

TI-85	BASIC	Comment
PROGRAM:IMPEULER	Program IMPEULER	Program title
:F=X+Y	DEF FN F(X,Y) = X + Y	Define function f
:10→N	N = 10	No. of steps
:0→X	X = 0	Initial x
:1→Y	Y = 1	Initial y
:1→X1	X1 = 1	Final x
:(X1-X)/N→H	H = (X1-X)/N	Step size
:For(I,1,N)	FOR I=1 TO N	Begin loop
:Y→Y0	Y0 = Y	Save previous y
:F→K1	K1 = FNF(X,Y)	First slope
:Y0+H*K1→Y	Y = Y0 + H*K1	Predictor
:X+H→X	X = X + H	New x
:F→K2	K2 = FNF(X,Y)	Second slope
:(K1+K2)/2→K	K = (K1 + K2)/2	Average slope
:Y0+H*K→Y	Y = Y0 + H*K	Corrector
:Disp X,Y	PRINT X,Y	Display results
:End	NEXT I	End loop

FIGURE 2.5.10.   TI-85 and BASIC improved Euler programs.

To apply the improved Euler method to a differential equation $dy/dx = f(x, y)$, one need only change the initial line of the program, in which the function f is defined. To increase the number of steps (and thereby decrease the step size) one need only change the value of **N** specified in the second line of the program.

Figure 2.5.11 exhibits one MATLAB implementation of the improved Euler method. The **impeuler** function takes as input the initial value **x**, the initial value **y**, the final value **x1** of x, and the desired number **n** of subintervals. As output it produces the resulting column vectors **X** and **Y** of x- and y-values. For instance, the MATLAB command

```
[X, Y] = impeuler(0, 1, 1, 10)
```

then generates the first and fourth columns of data shown in Fig. 2.5.4.

```
function yp = f(x,y)
yp = x + y;                          % yp = y'

function [X,Y] = impeuler(x,y,x1,n)
h = (x1 - x)/n;                      % step size
X = x;                               % initial x
Y = y;                               % initial y
for i = 1:n;                         % begin loop
    k1 = f(x,y);                     % first slope
    k2 = f(x+h,y+h*k1);              % second slope
    k = (k1 + k2)/2;;                % average slope
    x = x + h;                       % new x
    y = y + h*k;                     % new y
    X = [X;x];                       % update x-column
    Y = [Y;y];                       % update y-column
    end                              % end loop
```

FIGURE 2.5.11. MATLAB implementation of improved Euler method.

You should begin this project by implementing the improved Euler method with your own calculator or computer system. Test your program by applying it first to the initial value problem of Example 1, then to some of the problems for this section.

Famous Numbers Revisited

The following problems describe the numbers $e \approx 2.7182818$, $\ln 2 \approx 0.6931472$, and $\pi \approx 3.1415927$ as specific values of certain initial value problems. In each case, apply the improved Euler method with $n = 10, 20, 40, \ldots$ subintervals (doubling n each time). How many subintervals are needed to obtain—twice in succession—the correct value of the target number rounded to five decimal places?

1. The number $e = y(1)$, where $y(x)$ is the solution of the initial value problem $dy/dx = y$, $y(0) = 1$.
2. The number $\ln 2 = y(2)$, where $y(x)$ is the solution of the initial value problem $dy/dx = 1/x$, $y(1) = 0$.
3. The number $\pi = y(1)$, where $y(x)$ is the solution of the initial value problem $dy/dx = 4/(1 + x^2)$, $y(0) = 0$.

Logistic Population Investigation

Apply your improved Euler program to the initial value problem $dy/dx = \frac{1}{3}y(8-y)$, $y(0) = 1$ of Example 3. In particular, verify (as claimed) that the approximate solution with step size $h = 1$ levels off at $y \approx 4.3542$ rather than at the limiting value $y = 8$ of the exact solution. Perhaps a table of values for $0 \leqq x \leqq 100$ will make this apparent.

For your own logistic population to investigate, consider the initial value problem

$$\frac{dy}{dx} = \frac{1}{n} y(m - y), \quad y(0) = 1,$$

where m and n are (for instance) the largest and smallest nonzero digits in your student ID number. Does the improved Euler approximation with step size $h = 1$ level off at the "correct" limiting value of the exact solution? If not, find a smaller value of h so that it does.

Periodic Harvesting and Restocking

The differential equation

$$\frac{dy}{dt} = ky(M - y) - h \sin\left(\frac{2\pi t}{P}\right)$$

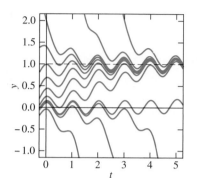

FIGURE 2.5.12. Solution curves of $dy/dt = y(1 - y) - \sin 2\pi t$.

models a logistic population that is periodically harvested and restocked with period P and maximal harvesting/restocking rate h. A numerical approximation program was used to plot the typical solution curves for the case $k = M = h = P = 1$ that are shown in Fig. 2.5.12. This figure suggests—although it does not prove—the existence of a threshold initial population such that

- Beginning with an initial population above this threshold, the population oscillates (perhaps with period P?) around the (unharvested) stable limiting population $y(t) \equiv M$, whereas
- The population dies out if it begins with an initial population below this threshold.

Use an appropriate plotting utility to investigate your own logistic population with periodic harvesting and restocking (selecting typical values of the parameters k, M, h, and P). Do the observations indicated here appear to hold for your population?

2.6 The Runge–Kutta Method

We now discuss a method for approximating the solution $y = y(x)$ of the initial value problem

$$\frac{dy}{dx} = f(x, y), \quad y(x_0) = y_0 \tag{1}$$

that is considerably more accurate than the improved Euler method and is more widely used in practice than any of the numerical methods discussed in Sections 2.4 and 2.5. It is called the *Runge–Kutta method*, after the German mathematicians who developed it, Carl Runge (1856–1927) and Wilhelm Kutta (1867–1944).

With the usual notation, suppose that we have computed the approximations y_1, y_2, y_3, ..., y_n to the actual values $y(x_1)$, $y(x_2)$, $y(x_3)$, ..., $y(x_n)$ and now want to compute $y_{n+1} \approx y(x_{n+1})$. Then

$$y(x_{n+1}) - y(x_n) = \int_{x_n}^{x_{n+1}} y'(x)\, dx = \int_{x_n}^{x_n + h} y'(x)\, dx \tag{2}$$

by the fundamental theorem of calculus. Next, Simpson's rule for numerical integration yields

$$y(x_{n+1}) - y(x_n) \approx \frac{h}{6}\left[y'(x_n) + 4y'\left(x_n + \frac{h}{2}\right) + y'(x_{n+1})\right]. \tag{3}$$

Hence we want to define y_{n+1} so that

$$y_{n+1} \approx y_n + \frac{h}{6}\left[y'(x_n) + 2y'\left(x_n + \frac{h}{2}\right) + 2y'\left(x_n + \frac{h}{2}\right) + y'(x_{n+1})\right]; \tag{4}$$

we have split $4y'\left(x_n + \frac{1}{2}h\right)$ into a sum of two terms because we intend to approximate the slope $y'\left(x_n + \frac{1}{2}h\right)$ at the midpoint $x_n + \frac{1}{2}h$ of the interval $[x_n, x_{n+1}]$ in two different ways.

On the right-hand side in (4), we replace the [true] slope values $y'(x_n)$, $y'\left(x_n + \frac{1}{2}h\right)$, $y'\left(x_n + \frac{1}{2}h\right)$, and $y'(x_{n+1})$, respectively, with the following estimates.

➤
$$k_1 = f(x_n, y_n) \tag{5a}$$

- This is the Euler method slope at x_n.

➤
$$k_2 = f\left(x_n + \tfrac{1}{2}h, y_n + \tfrac{1}{2}hk_1\right) \tag{5b}$$

- This is an estimate of the slope at the midpoint of the interval $[x_n, x_{n+1}]$ using the Euler method to predict the ordinate there.

➤
$$k_3 = f\left(x_n + \tfrac{1}{2}h, y_n + \tfrac{1}{2}hk_2\right) \tag{5c}$$

- This is an improved Euler value for the slope at the midpoint.

➤
$$k_4 = f(x_{n+1}, y_n + hk_3) \tag{5d}$$

- This is the Euler method slope at x_{n+1}, using the improved slope k_3 at the midpoint to step to x_{n+1}.

When these substitutions are made in (4), the result is the iterative formula

➤
$$y_{n+1} = y_n + \frac{h}{6}(k_1 + 2k_2 + 2k_3 + k_4). \tag{6}$$

The use of this formula to compute the approximations $y_1, y_2, y_3, \ldots$ successively constitutes the **Runge–Kutta method.** Note that Eq. (6) takes the "Euler form"

$$y_{n+1} = y_n + h \cdot k$$

if we write

$$k = \frac{1}{6}(k_1 + 2k_2 + 2k_3 + k_4) \tag{7}$$

for the approximate *average slope* on the interval $[x_n, x_{n+1}]$.

The Runge–Kutta method is a *fourth-order* method—it can be proved that the cumulative error on a bounded interval $[a, b]$ with $a = x_0$ is of order h^4. (Thus the iteration in (6) is sometimes called the *fourth-order* Runge–Kutta method because it is possible to develop Runge–Kutta methods of other orders.) That is,

➤
$$|y(x_n) - y_n| \leqq Ch^4, \tag{8}$$

where the constant C depends on the function $f(x, y)$ and the interval $[a, b]$, but does not depend on the step size h. The following example illustrates this high accuracy in comparison with the lower-order accuracy of our previous numerical methods.

Example 1   We first apply the Runge–Kutta method to the illustrative initial value problem

$$\frac{dy}{dx} = x + y, \quad y(0) = 1 \tag{9}$$

that we considered in Fig. 2.4.8 of Section 2.4 and again in Example 2 of Section 2.5. The exact solution of this problem is $y(x) = 2e^x - x - 1$. To make a point we use $h = 0.5$, a larger step size than in any previous example, so only two steps are required to go from $x = 0$ to $x = 1$.

In the first step we use the formulas in (5) and (6) to calculate

$$k_1 = 0 + 1 = 1,$$
$$k_2 = (0 + 0.25) + (1 + (0.25) \cdot (1)) = 1.5,$$
$$k_3 = (0 + 0.25) + (1 + (0.25) \cdot (1.5)) = 1.625,$$
$$k_4 = (0.5) + (1 + (0.5) \cdot (1.625)) = 2.3125,$$

and then

$$y_1 = 1 + \frac{0.5}{6}[1 + 2 \cdot (1.5) + 2 \cdot (1.625) + 2.3125] \approx 1.7969.$$

Similarly, the second step yields $y_2 \approx 3.4347$.

Figure 2.6.1 presents these results together with the results (from Fig. 2.5.4) of applying the improved Euler method with step size $h = 0.1$. We see that even with the larger step size, the Runge–Kutta method gives (for this problem) four to five times the accuracy (in terms of relative percentage errors) of the improved Euler method. ■

	Improved Euler		Runge–Kutta		
x	y with $h = 0.1$	Percent Error	y with $h = 0.5$	Percent Error	Actual y
0.0	1.0000	0.00%	1.0000	0.00%	1.0000
0.5	1.7949	0.14%	1.7969	0.03%	1.7974
1.0	3.4282	0.24%	3.4347	0.05%	3.4366

FIGURE 2.6.1. Runge–Kutta and improved Euler results for the initial value problem $dy/dx = x + y$, $y(0) = 1$.

It is customary to measure the computational labor involved in solving $dy/dx = f(x, y)$ numerically by counting the number of evaluations of the function $f(x, y)$ that are required. In Example 1, the Runge–Kutta method required eight evaluations of $f(x, y) = x + y$ (four at each step), whereas the improved Euler method required 20 such evaluations (two for each of 10 steps). Thus the Runge–Kutta method gave over four times the accuracy with only 40% of the labor.

Computer programs implementing the Runge–Kutta method are listed in the project material for this section. Figure 2.6.2 shows the results obtained by applying the improved Euler and Runge–Kutta methods to the problem $dy/dx = x + y$, $y(0) = 1$ with the same step size $h = 0.1$. The relative error in the improved Euler value at $x = 1$ is about 0.24%, but for the Runge–Kutta value it is 0.00012%. In this comparison the Runge–Kutta method is about 2000 times as accurate, but requires only twice as many function evaluations, as the improved Euler method.

x	Improved Euler y	Runge–Kutta y	Actual y
0.1	1.1100	1.110342	1.110342
0.2	1.2421	1.242805	1.242806
0.3	1.3985	1.399717	1.399718
0.4	1.5818	1.583648	1.583649
0.5	1.7949	1.797441	1.797443
0.6	2.0409	2.044236	2.044238
0.7	2.3231	2.327503	2.327505
0.8	2.6456	2.651079	2.651082
0.9	3.0124	3.019203	3.019206
1.0	3.4282	3.436559	3.436564

FIGURE 2.6.2. Runge–Kutta and improved Euler results for the initial value problem $dy/dx = x + y$, $y(0) = 1$, with the same step size $h = 0.1$.

The error bound

$$|y(x_n) - y_n| \leqq Ch^4 \tag{8}$$

for the Runge–Kutta method results in a rapid decrease in the magnitude of errors when the step size h is reduced (except for the possibility that very small step sizes may result in unacceptable roundoff errors). It follows from the inequality in (8) that (on a fixed bounded interval) halving the step size decreases the absolute error by a factor of $\left(\frac{1}{2}\right)^4 = \frac{1}{16}$. Consequently, the common practice of successively halving the step size until the computed results "stabilize" is particularly effective with the Runge–Kutta method.

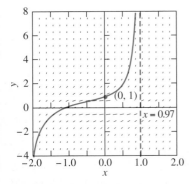

FIGURE 2.6.3. Solutions of $dy/dx = x^2 + y^2$, $y(0) = 1$.

Example 2 In Example 5 of Section 2.4 we saw that Euler's method is not adequate to approximate the solution $y(x)$ of the initial value problem

$$\frac{dy}{dx} = x^2 + y^2, \quad y(0) = 1 \tag{10}$$

as x approaches the infinite discontinuity near $x = 0.969811$ (see Fig. 2.6.3). Now we apply the Runge–Kutta method to this initial value problem.

Figure 2.6.4 shows Runge–Kutta results on the interval $[0.0, 0.9]$, computed with step sizes $h = 0.1$, $h = 0.05$, and $h = 0.025$. There is still some difficulty near $x = 0.9$, but it seems safe to conclude from these data that $y(0.5) \approx 2.0670$.

x	y with $h = 0.1$	y with $h = 0.05$	y with $h = 0.025$
0.1	1.1115	1.1115	1.1115
0.3	1.4397	1.4397	1.4397
0.5	2.0670	2.0670	2.0670
0.7	3.6522	3.6529	3.6529
0.9	14.0218	14.2712	14.3021

FIGURE 2.6.4. Approximating the solution of the initial value problem in Eq. (10).

We therefore begin anew and apply the Runge–Kutta method to the initial value problem

$$\frac{dy}{dx} = x^2 + y^2, \quad y(0.5) = 2.0670. \tag{11}$$

Figure 2.6.5 shows results on the interval $[0.5, 0.9]$, obtained with step sizes $h = 0.01$, $h = 0.005$, and $h = 0.0025$. We now conclude that $y(0.9) \approx 14.3049$.

x	y with $h = 0.01$	y with $h = 0.005$	y with $h = 0.0025$
0.5	2.0670	2.0670	2.0670
0.6	2.6440	2.6440	2.6440
0.7	3.6529	3.6529	3.6529
0.8	5.8486	5.8486	5.8486
0.9	14.3048	14.3049	14.3049

FIGURE 2.6.5. Approximating the solution of the initial value problem in Eq. (11).

Finally, Fig. 2.6.6 shows results on the interval $[0.90, 0.95]$ for the initial value problem

$$\frac{dy}{dx} = x^2 + y^2, \quad y(0.9) = 14.3049, \tag{12}$$

obtained using step sizes $h = 0.002$, $h = 0.001$, and $h = 0.0005$. Our final approximate result is $y(0.95) \approx 50.4723$. The actual value of the solution at $x = 0.95$ is $y(0.95) \approx 50.471867$. Our slight overestimate results mainly from the fact that the four-place initial value in (12) is (in effect) the result of rounding *up* the actual value $y(0.9) \approx 14.304864$; such errors are magnified considerably as we approach the vertical asymptote. ■

x	y with $h = 0.002$	y with $h = 0.001$	y with $h = 0.0005$
0.90	14.3049	14.3049	14.3049
0.91	16.7024	16.7024	16.7024
0.92	20.0617	20.0617	20.0617
0.93	25.1073	25.1073	25.1073
0.94	33.5363	33.5363	33.5363
0.95	50.4722	50.4723	50.4723

FIGURE 2.6.6. Approximating the solution of the initial value problem in Eq. (12).

Example 3   A skydiver with a mass of 60 kg jumps from a helicopter hovering at an initial altitude of 5 kilometers. Assume that she falls vertically with initial velocity zero and experiences an upward force F_R of air resistance given in terms of her velocity v (in meters per second) by

$$F_R = (0.0096)(100v + 10v^2 + v^3)$$

(in newtons, and with the coordinate axis directed downward so that $v > 0$ during her descent to the ground). If she does not open her parachute, what will be her terminal velocity? How fast will she be falling after 5 s have elapsed? After 10 s? After 20 s?

Solution   Newton's law $F = ma$ gives

$$m\frac{dv}{dt} = mg - F_R;$$

that is,

$$60\frac{dv}{dt} = (60)(9.8) - (0.0096)(100v + 10v^2 + v^3) \qquad (13)$$

because $m = 60$ and $g = 9.8$. Thus the velocity function $v(t)$ satisfies the initial value problem

$$\frac{dv}{dt} = f(v), \quad v(0) = 0, \qquad (14)$$

where

$$f(v) = 9.8 - (0.00016)(100v + 10v^2 + v^3). \qquad (15)$$

The skydiver reaches her terminal velocity when the forces of gravity and air resistance balance, so $f(v) = 0$. We can therefore calculate her terminal velocity immediately by solving the equation

$$f(v) = 9.8 - (0.00016)(100v + 10v^2 + v^3) = 0. \qquad (16)$$

Figure 2.6.7 shows the graph of the function $f(v)$ and exhibits the single real solution $v \approx 35.5780$ (found graphically or by using a calculator or computer **Solve** procedure). Thus the skydiver's terminal speed is approximately 35.578 m/s, about 128 km/h (almost 80 mi/h).

Figure 2.6.8 shows the results of Runge–Kutta approximations to the solution of the initial value problem in (14); the step sizes $h = 0.2$ and $h = 0.1$ yield the same results (to three decimal places). Observe that the terminal velocity is effectively attained in only 15 s. But the skydiver's velocity is 91.85% of her terminal velocity after only 5 s, and 99.78% after 10 s. ■

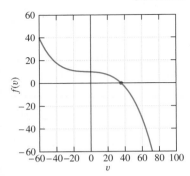

FIGURE 2.6.7.   Graph of $f(v) = 9.8 - (0.00016)(100v + 10v^2 + v^3)$.

t (s)	v (m/s)	t (s)	v (m/s)
0	0	11	35.541
1	9.636	12	35.560
2	18.386	13	35.569
3	25.299	14	35.574
4	29.949	15	35.576
5	32.678	16	35.577
6	34.137	17	35.578
7	34.875	18	35.578
8	35.239	19	35.578
9	35.415	20	35.578
10	35.500		

FIGURE 2.6.8.   The skydiver's velocity data.

The final example of this section contains a *warning*: For certain types of initial value problems, the numerical methods we have discussed are not nearly so successful as in the previous examples.

Example 4   Consider the seemingly innocuous initial value problem

$$\frac{dy}{dx} = 5y - 6e^{-x}, \quad y(0) = 1 \qquad (17)$$

whose exact solution is $y(x) = e^{-x}$. The table in Fig. 2.6.9 shows the results obtained by applying the Runge–Kutta method on the interval $[0, 4]$ with step sizes

x	Runge–Kutta y with h = 0.2	Runge–Kutta y with h = 0.1	Runge–Kutta y with h = 0.05	Actual y
0.4	0.66880	0.67020	0.67031	0.67032
0.8	0.43713	0.44833	0.44926	0.44933
1.2	0.21099	0.29376	0.30067	0.30199
1.6	−0.46019	0.14697	0.19802	0.20190
2.0	−4.72142	−0.27026	0.10668	0.13534
2.4	−35.53415	−2.90419	−0.12102	0.09072
2.8	−261.25023	−22.05352	−1.50367	0.06081
3.2	−1,916.69395	−163.25077	−11.51868	0.04076
3.6	−14059.35494	−1205.71249	−85.38156	0.02732
4.0	−103,126.5270	−8903.12866	−631.03934	0.01832

FIGURE 2.6.9. Runge–Kutta attempts to solve numerically the initial value problem in Eq. (17).

$h = 0.2$, $h = 0.1$, and $h = 0.05$. Obviously these attempts are spectacularly unsuccessful. Although $y(x) = e^{-x} \to 0$ as $x \to +\infty$, it appears that our numerical approximations are headed toward $-\infty$ rather than zero.

The explanation lies in the fact that the general solution of the equation $dy/dx = 5y - 6e^{-x}$ is

$$y(x) = e^{-x} + Ce^{5x}. \tag{18}$$

The particular solution of (17) satisfying the initial condition $y(0) = 1$ is obtained with $C = 0$. But any departure, however small, from the exact solution $y(x) = e^{-x}$—even if due only to roundoff error—introduces [in effect] a nonzero value of C in Eq. (18). And as indicated in Fig. 2.6.10, all solution curves of the form in (18) with $C \neq 0$ diverge rapidly away from the one with $C = 0$, even if their initial values are close to 1. ■

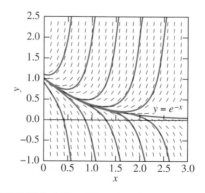

FIGURE 2.6.10. Direction field and solution curves for $dy/dx = 5y - 6e^{-x}$.

Difficulties of the sort illustrated by Example 4 sometimes are unavoidable, but one can at least hope to recognize such a problem when it appears. Approximate values whose order of magnitude varies with changing step size are a common indicator of such instability. These difficulties are discussed in numerical analysis textbooks and are the subject of current research in the field.

2.6 Problems

A hand-held calculator will suffice for Problems 1 through 10, where an initial value problem and its exact solution are given. Apply the Runge–Kutta method to approximate this solution on the interval $[0, 0.5]$ with step size $h = 0.25$. Construct a table showing five-decimal-place values of the approximate solution and actual solution at the points $x = 0.25$ and 0.5.

1. $y' = -y$, $y(0) = 2$; $y(x) = 2e^{-x}$
2. $y' = 2y$, $y(0) = \frac{1}{2}$; $y(x) = \frac{1}{2}e^{2x}$
3. $y' = y + 1$, $y(0) = 1$; $y(x) = 2e^x - 1$
4. $y' = x - y$, $y(0) = 1$; $y(x) = 2e^{-x} + x - 1$
5. $y' = y - x - 1$, $y(0) = 1$; $y(x) = 2 + x - e^x$
6. $y' = -2xy$, $y(0) = 2$; $y(x) = 2e^{-x^2}$
7. $y' = -3x^2 y$, $y(0) = 3$; $y(x) = 3e^{-x^3}$
8. $y' = e^{-y}$, $y(0) = 0$; $y(x) = \ln(x + 1)$
9. $y' = \frac{1}{4}(1 + y^2)$, $y(0) = 1$; $y(x) = \tan \frac{1}{4}(x + \pi)$
10. $y' = 2xy^2$, $y(0) = 1$; $y(x) = \dfrac{1}{1 - x^2}$

Note: The application following this problem set lists illustrative calculator/computer programs that can be used in the remaining problems.

A programmable calculator or a computer will be useful for Problems 11 through 16. In each problem find the exact solution of the given initial value problem. Then apply the Runge–Kutta method twice to approximate (to five decimal places) this solution on the given interval, first with step size $h = 0.2$, then with step size $h = 0.1$. Make a table showing the approximate values and the actual value, together with the percentage error in the more accurate approximation, for x an integral multiple of 0.2. Throughout, primes denote derivatives with respect to x.

11. $y' = y - 2$, $y(0) = 1$; $0 \leq x \leq 1$
12. $y' = \frac{1}{2}(y - 1)^2$, $y(0) = 2$; $0 \leq x \leq 1$
13. $yy' = 2x^3$, $y(1) = 3$; $1 \leq x \leq 2$
14. $xy' = y^2$, $y(1) = 1$; $1 \leq x \leq 2$
15. $xy' = 3x - 2y$, $y(2) = 3$; $2 \leq x \leq 3$
16. $y^2 y' = 2x^5$, $y(2) = 3$; $2 \leq x \leq 3$

A computer with a printer is required for Problems 17 through 24. In these initial value problems, use the Runge–Kutta method with step sizes $h = 0.2, 0.1, 0.05,$ and 0.025 to approximate to six decimal places the values of the solution at five equally spaced points of the given interval. Print the results in tabular form with appropriate headings to make it easy to gauge the effect of varying the step size h. Throughout, primes denote derivatives with respect to x.

17. $y' = x^2 + y^2$, $y(0) = 0$; $0 \leq x \leq 1$
18. $y' = x^2 - y^2$, $y(0) = 1$; $0 \leq x \leq 2$
19. $y' = x + \sqrt{y}$, $y(0) = 1$; $0 \leq x \leq 2$
20. $y' = x + \sqrt[3]{y}$, $y(0) = -1$; $0 \leq x \leq 2$

21. $y' = \ln y$, $y(1) = 2$; $1 \leq x \leq 2$
22. $y' = x^{2/3} + y^{2/3}$, $y(0) = 1$; $0 \leq x \leq 2$
23. $y' = \sin x + \cos y$, $y(0) = 0$; $0 \leq x \leq 1$
24. $y' = \dfrac{x}{1 + y^2}$, $y(-1) = 1$; $-1 \leq x \leq 1$

25. As in Problem 25 of Section 2.5, you bail out of a helicopter and immediately open your parachute, so your downward velocity satisfies the initial value problem

$$\frac{dv}{dt} = 32 - 1.6v, \quad v(0) = 0$$

(with t in seconds and v in ft/s). Use the Runge–Kutta method with a programmable calculator or computer to approximate the solution for $0 \leq t \leq 2$, first with step size $h = 0.1$ and then with $h = 0.05$, rounding off approximate v-values to three decimal places. What percentage of the limiting velocity 20 ft/s has been attained after 1 second? After 2 seconds?

26. As in Problem 26 of Section 2.5, suppose the deer population $P(t)$ in a small forest initially numbers 25 and satisfies the logistic equation

$$\frac{dP}{dt} = 0.0225P - 0.0003P^2$$

(with t in months). Use the Runge–Kutta method with a programmable calculator or computer to approximate the solution for 10 years, first with step size $h = 6$ and then with $h = 3$, rounding off approximate P-values to four decimal places. What percentage of the limiting population of 75 deer has been attained after 5 years? After 10 years?

Use the Runge–Kutta method with a computer system to find the desired solution values in Problems 27 and 28. Start with step size $h = 1$, and then use successively smaller step sizes until successive approximate solution values at $x = 2$ agree rounded off to five decimal places.

27. $y' = x^2 + y^2 - 1$, $y(0) = 0$; $y(2) = ?$
28. $y' = x + \frac{1}{2}y^2$, $y(-2) = 0$; $y(2) = ?$

Velocity-Acceleration Problems

In Problems 29 and 30, the linear acceleration $a = dv/dt$ of a moving particle is given by a formula $dv/dt = f(t, v)$, where the velocity $v = dy/dt$ is the derivative of the function $y = y(t)$ giving the position of the particle at time t. Suppose that the velocity $v(t)$ is approximated using the Runge–Kutta method to solve numerically the initial value problem

$$\frac{dv}{dt} = f(t, v), \quad v(0) = v_0. \tag{19}$$

That is, starting with $t_0 = 0$ and v_0, the formulas in Eqs. (5) and (6) are applied—with t and v in place of x and y—to calculate the successive approximate velocity values $v_1, v_2,$

$v_3, \ldots, v_m$ *at the successive times* $t_1, t_2, t_3, \ldots, t_m$ *(with* $t_{n+1} = t_n + h$*). Now suppose that we also want to approximate the* distance $y(t)$ *traveled by the particle. We can do this by beginning with the initial position* $y(0) = y_0$ *and calculating*

$$y_{n+1} = y_n + v_n h + \tfrac{1}{2} a_n h^2 \tag{20}$$

$(n = 1, 2, 3, \ldots)$*, where* $a_n = f(t_n, v_n) \approx v'(t_n)$ *is the particle's approximate acceleration at time* t_n*. The formula in (20) would give the correct increment (from* y_n *to* y_{n+1}*) if the acceleration* a_n *remained constant during the time interval* $[t_n, t_{n+1}]$*.*

Thus, once a table of approximate velocities has been calculated, Eq. (20) provides a simple way to calculate a table of corresponding successive positions. This process is illustrated in the project for this section, by beginning with the velocity data in Fig. 2.6.8 (Example 3) and proceeding to follow the skydiver's position during her descent to the ground.

29. Consider again the crossbow bolt of Example 2 in Section 2.3, shot straight upward from the ground with an initial velocity of 49 m/s. Because of linear air resistance, its velocity function $v = dy/dt$ satisfies the initial value problem

$$\frac{dv}{dt} = -(0.04)v - 9.8, \quad v(0) = 49$$

with exact solution $v(t) = 294e^{-t/25} - 245$. **(a)** Use a calculator or computer implementation of the Runge–Kutta method to approximate $v(t)$ for $0 \leq t \leq 10$ using both $n = 100$ and $n = 200$ subintervals. Display the results at intervals of 1 second. Do the two approximations—each rounded to four decimal places—agree both with each other and with the exact solution? **(b)** Now use the velocity data from part (a) to approximate $y(t)$ for $0 \leq t \leq 10$ using $n = 200$ subintervals. Display the results at intervals of 1 second. Do these approximate position values—each rounded to two decimal places—agree with the exact

solution

$$y(t) = 7350 \left(1 - e^{-t/25}\right) - 245t?$$

(c) If the exact solution were unavailable, explain how you could use the Runge–Kutta method to approximate closely the bolt's times of ascent and descent and the maximum height it attains.

30. Now consider again the crossbow bolt of Example 3 in Section 2.3. It still is shot straight upward from the ground with an initial velocity of 49 m/s, but because of air resistance proportional to the square of its velocity, its velocity function $v(t)$ satisfies the initial value problem

$$\frac{dv}{dt} = -(0.0011)v|v| - 9.8, \quad v(0) = 49.$$

Beginning with this initial value problem, repeat parts (a) through (c) of Problem 25 (except that you may need $n = 200$ subintervals to get four-place accuracy in part (a) and $n = 400$ subintervals for two-place accuracy in part (b)). According to the results of Problems 17 and 18 in Section 2.3, the bolt's velocity and position functions during ascent and descent are given by the following formulas.

Ascent:
$$v(t) = (94.388) \tan(0.478837 - [0.103827]t),$$
$$y(t) = 108.465$$
$$\quad + (909.091) \ln (\cos(0.478837 - [0.103827]t)) ;$$

Descent:
$$v(t) = -(94.388) \tanh(0.103827[t - 4.6119]),$$
$$y(t) = 108.465$$
$$\quad - (909.091) \ln (\cosh(0.103827[t - 4.6119])) .$$

2.6 Application Runge–Kutta Implementation

Figure 2.6.11 lists TI-85 and BASIC programs implementing the Runge–Kutta method to approximate the solution of the initial value problem

$$\frac{dy}{dx} = x + y, \quad y(0) = 1$$

considered in Example 1 of this section. The comments provided in the final column should make these programs intelligible even if you have little familiarity with the BASIC and TI programming languages.

To apply the Runge–Kutta method to a different equation $dy/dx = f(x, y)$, one need only change the initial line of the program, in which the function f is defined. To increase the number of steps (and thereby decrease the step size), one need only change the value of **N** specified in the second line of the program.

TI-85	BASIC	Comment
`PROGRAM:RK`	`Program RK`	`Program title`
`:F=X+Y`	`DEF FN F(X,Y) = X + Y`	`Define function f`
`:10→N`	`N = 10`	`No. of steps`
`:0→X`	`X = 0`	`Initial x`
`:1→Y`	`Y = 1`	`Initial y`
`:1→X1`	`X1 = 1`	`Final x`
`:(X1-X)/N→H`	`H = (X1-X)/N`	`Step size`
`:For(I,1,N)`	`FOR I=1 TO N`	`Begin loop`
`:X→X0`	`X0 = X`	`Save previous x`
`:Y→Y0`	`Y0 = Y`	`Save previous y`
`:F→K1`	`K1 = FNF(X,Y)`	`First slope`
`:X0+H/2→X`	`X = X0 + H/2`	`Midpoint`
`:Y0+H*K1/2→Y`	`Y = Y0 + H*K1/2`	`Midpt predictor`
`:F→K2`	`K2 = FNF(X,Y)`	`Second slope`
`:Y0+H*K2/2→Y`	`Y = Y0 + H*K2/2`	`Midpt predictor`
`:F→K3`	`K3 = FNF(X,Y)`	`Third slope`
`:X0+H→X`	`X = X0 + H`	`New x`
`:Y0+H*K3→Y`	`Y = Y0 + H*K3`	`Endpt predictor`
`:F→K4`	`K4 = FNF(X,Y)`	`Fourth slope`
`:(K1+2*K2+2*K3`	`K = (K1+2*K2+2*K3`	`Average slope`
`  +K4)/6→K`	`  +K4)/6`	
`:Y0+H*K→Y`	`Y = Y0 + K*K`	`Corrector`
`:Disp X,Y`	`PRINT X,Y`	`Display results`
`:End`	`NEXT I`	`End loop`

FIGURE 2.6.11. TI-85 and BASIC Runge–Kutta programs.

Figure 2.6.12 exhibits a MATLAB implementation of the Runge–Kutta method. Suppose that the function f describing the differential equation $y' = f(x, y)$ has been defined. Then the **rk** function takes as input the initial value **x**, the initial value **y**, the final value **x1** of x, and the desired number **n** of subintervals. As output it produces the resulting column vectors **x** and **y** of x- and y-values. For instance, the MATLAB command

    [X, Y] = rk(0, 1, 1, 10)

then generates the first and third columns of data shown in the table in Fig. 2.6.2.

You should begin this project by implementing the Runge–Kutta method with your own calculator or computer system. Test your program by applying it first to the initial value problem in Example 1, then to some of the problems for this section.

Famous Numbers Revisited, One Last Time

The following problems describe the numbers

$$e \approx 2.71828182846, \quad \ln 2 \approx 0.69314718056, \quad \text{and} \quad \pi \approx 3.14159265359$$

as specific values of certain initial value problems. In each case, apply the Runge–Kutta method with $n = 10, 20, 40, \ldots$ subintervals (doubling n each time). How

```
function yp = f(x,y)
yp = x + y;                                % yp = y'

function [X,Y] = rk(x,y,x1,n)
h = (x1 - x)/n;                            % step size
X = x;                                     % initial x
Y = y;                                     % initial y
for i = 1:n                                % begin loop
    k1 = f(x,y);                           % first slope
    k2 = f(x+h/2,y+h*k1/2);                % second slope
    k3 = f(x+h/2,y+h*k2/2);                % third slope
    k4 = f(x+h,y+h*k3);                    % fourth slope
    k  = (k1+2*k2+2*k3+k4)/6;              % average slope
    x  = x + h;                            % new x
    y  = y + h*k;                          % new y
    X = [X;x];                             % update x-column
    Y = [Y;y];                             % update y-column
    end                                    % end loop
```

FIGURE 2.6.12.   MATLAB implementation of the Runge–Kutta method.

many subintervals are needed to obtain—twice in succession—the correct value of the target number rounded to nine decimal places?

1. The number $e = y(1)$, where $y(x)$ is the solution of the initial value problem $dy/dx = y$, $y(0) = 1$.
2. The number $\ln 2 = y(2)$, where $y(x)$ is the solution of the initial value problem $dy/dx = 1/x$, $y(1) = 0$.
3. The number $\pi = y(1)$, where $y(x)$ is the solution of the initial value problem $dy/dx = 4/(1 + x^2)$, $y(0) = 0$.

The Skydiver's Descent

The following MATLAB function describes the skydiver's acceleration function in Example 3.

```
function    vp = f(t,v)
vp = 9.8 - 0.00016*(100*v + 10*v^2 + v^3);
```

Then the commands

```
k = 200                      % 200 subintervals
[t,v] = rk(0, 20, 0, k);     % Runge--Kutta approxima-
tion
[t(1:10:k+1); v(1:10:k+1)]   % Display every 10th entry
```

produce the table of approximate velocities shown in Fig. 2.6.8. Finally, the commands

```
y = zeros(k+1,1):                  % initialize y
h = 0.1;                           % step size
for n = 1:k                        % for n = 1 to k
  a = f(t(n),v(n)):                % acceleration
  y(n+1) = y(n) + v(n)*h + 0.5*a*h^2;   % Equation (20)
```

```
end                                      % end loop
[t(1:20:k+1),v(1:20:k+1),y(1:20:k+1)]    % each 20th entry
```

carry out the position function calculations described in Eq. (20) in the instructions for Problems 29 and 30. The results of these calculations are shown in the table in Fig. 2.6.13. It appears that the skydiver falls 629.866 m during her first 20 s of descent, and then free falls the remaining 4370.134 meters to the ground at her terminal speed of 35.578 m/s. Hence her total time of descent is $20 + (4370.134/35.578) \approx 142.833$ s, or about 2 min 23 s.

t (s)	v (m/s)	y (m)
0	0	0
2	18.386	18.984
4	29.949	68.825
6	34.137	133.763
8	35.239	203.392
10	35.500	274.192
12	35.560	345.266
14	35.574	416.403
16	35.577	487.555
18	35.578	558.710
20	35.578	629.866

FIGURE 2.6.13. The skydiver's velocity and position data.

For an individual problem to solve after implementing these methods using an available computer system, analyze your own skydive (perhaps from a different height), using your own mass m and a plausible air-resistance force of the form $F_R = av + bv^2 + cv^3$.

Linear Equations of Higher Order

Introduction: Second-Order Linear Equations

In Chapters 1 and 2 we investigated first-order differential equations. We now turn to equations of higher order $n \geq 2$, beginning in this chapter with equations that are linear. The general theory of linear differential equations parallels the second-order case ($n = 2$), which we outline in this initial section.

Recall that a second-order differential equation in the (unknown) function $y(x)$ is one of the form

$$G(x, y, y', y'') = 0. \tag{1}$$

This differential equation is said to be **linear** provided that G is linear in the dependent variable y and its derivatives y' and y''. Thus a linear second-order equation takes (or can be written in) the form

$$A(x)y'' + B(x)y' + C(x)y = F(x). \tag{2}$$

Unless otherwise noted, we will always assume that the (known) coefficient functions $A(x)$, $B(x)$, $C(x)$, and $F(x)$ are continuous on some open interval I (perhaps unbounded) on which we wish to solve this differential equation, but we do *not* require that they be linear functions of x. Thus the differential equation

$$e^x y'' + (\cos x)y' + (1 + \sqrt{x})y = \tan^{-1} x$$

is linear because the dependent variable y and its derivatives y' and y'' appear linearly. By contrast, the equations

$$y'' = yy' \quad \text{and} \quad y'' + 3(y')^2 + 4y^3 = 0$$

are not linear because products and powers of y or its derivatives appear.

147

If the function $F(x)$ on the right-hand side of Eq. (2) vanishes identically on I, then we call Eq. (2) a **homogeneous** linear equation; otherwise, it is **nonhomogeneous**. For example, the second-order equation

$$x^2 y'' + 2xy' + 3y = \cos x$$

is nonhomogeneous; its *associated* homogeneous equation is

$$x^2 y'' + 2xy' + 3y = 0.$$

In general, the homogeneous linear equation **associated** with Eq. (2) is

$$\blacktriangleright \qquad A(x)y'' + B(x)y' + C(x)y = 0. \qquad (3)$$

In case the differential equation in (2) models a physical system, the nonhomogeneous term $F(x)$ frequently corresponds to some *external* influence on the system.

> **Remark:** Note that the meaning of the term "homogeneous" for a second-order linear differential equation is quite different from its meaning for a first-order differential equation (as in Section 1.6). Of course, it is not unusual—either in mathematics or in the English language more generally—for the same word to have different meanings in different contexts.

A Typical Application

Linear differential equations frequently appear as mathematical models of mechanical systems and electrical circuits. For example, suppose that a mass m is attached both to a spring that exerts on it a force F_S and to a dashpot (shock absorber) that exerts a force F_R on the mass (Fig. 3.1.1). Assume that the restoring force F_S of the spring is proportional to the *displacement* x of the mass from its equilibrium position and acts opposite to the direction of displacement. Then

Spring   Mass   Dashpot

$x(t)$

$x = 0$ $x > 0$

Equilibrium position

FIGURE 3.1.1. A mass–spring–dashpot system.

m

$F_S \longleftarrow \quad \longleftarrow F_R$

$x, v > 0$

FIGURE 3.1.2. Directions of the forces acting on m.

$$F_S = -kx \quad \text{(with } k > 0\text{)}$$

so $F_S < 0$ if $x > 0$ (spring stretched) while $F_S > 0$ if $x < 0$ (spring compressed). We assume that the dashpot force F_R is proportional to the *velocity* $v = dx/dt$ of the mass and acts opposite to the direction of motion. Then

$$F_R = -cv = -c\frac{dx}{dt} \quad \text{(with } c > 0\text{)}$$

so $F_R < 0$ if $v > 0$ (motion to the right) while $F_R > 0$ if $v < 0$ (motion to the left). If F_R and F_S are the only forces acting on the mass m and its resulting acceleration is $a = dv/dt$, then Newton's law $F = ma$ gives

$$mx'' = F_S + F_R; \qquad (4)$$

that is,

$$\blacktriangleright \qquad m\frac{d^2 x}{dt^2} + c\frac{dx}{dt} + kx = 0. \qquad (5)$$

Thus we have a differential equation satisfied by the position function $x(t)$ of the mass m. This homogeneous second-order linear equation governs the *free vibrations* of the mass; we will return to this problem in detail in Section 3.4.

If, in addition to F_S and F_R, the mass m is acted on by an external force $F(t)$—which must then be added to the right-hand side in Eq. (4)—the resulting equation is

$$m\frac{d^2x}{dt^2} + c\frac{dx}{dt} + kx = F(t). \tag{6}$$

This nonhomogeneous linear differential equation governs the *forced vibrations* of the mass under the influence of the external force $F(t)$.

Homogeneous Second-Order Linear Equations

Consider the general second-order linear equation

$$A(x)y'' + B(x)y' + C(x)y = F(x), \tag{7}$$

where the coefficient functions A, B, C, and F are continuous on the open interval I. Here we assume in addition that $A(x) \neq 0$ at each point of I, so we can divide each term in Eq. (7) by $A(x)$ and write it in the form

$$y'' + p(x)y' + q(x)y = f(x). \tag{8}$$

We will discuss first the associated homogeneous equation

$$y'' + p(x)y' + q(x)y = 0. \tag{9}$$

A particularly useful property of this *homogeneous* linear equation is the fact that the sum of any two solutions of Eq. (9) is again a solution, as is any constant multiple of a solution. This is the central idea of the following theorem.

THEOREM 1 Principle of Superposition for Homogeneous Equations

Let y_1 and y_2 be two solutions of the homogeneous linear equation in (9) on the interval I. If c_1 and c_2 are constants, then the linear combination

$$y = c_1y_1 + c_2y_2 \tag{10}$$

is also a solution of Eq. (9) on I.

Proof: The conclusion follows almost immediately from the linearity of the operation of differentiation, which gives

$$y' = c_1y_1' + c_2y_2' \quad \text{and} \quad y'' = c_1y_1'' + c_2y_2''.$$

Then

$$\begin{aligned}
y'' + py' + qy &= (c_1y_1 + c_2y_2)'' + p(c_1y_1 + c_2y_2)' + q(c_1y_1 + c_2y_2) \\
&= (c_1y_1'' + c_2y_2'') + p(c_1y_1' + c_2y_2') + q(c_1y_1 + c_2y_2) \\
&= c_1(y_1'' + py_1' + qy_1) + c_2(y_2'' + py_2' + qy_2) \\
&= c_1 \cdot 0 + c_2 \cdot 0 = 0
\end{aligned}$$

because y_1 and y_2 are solutions. Thus $y = c_1y_1 + c_2y_2$ is also a solution. ▲

Example 1   We can see by inspection that

$$y_1(x) = \cos x \quad \text{and} \quad y_2(x) = \sin x$$

are two solutions of the equation

$$y'' + y = 0.$$

Theorem 1 tells us that any linear combination of these solutions, such as

$$y(x) = 3y_1(x) - 2y_2(x) = 3\cos x - 2\sin x,$$

is also a solution. We will see later that, conversely, *every* solution of $y'' + y = 0$ is a linear combination of these two particular solutions y_1 and y_2. Thus a general solution of $y'' + y = 0$ is given by

$$y(x) = c_1 \cos x + c_2 \sin x.$$

It is important to understand that this single formula for the general solution encompasses a "twofold infinity" of particular solutions, because the two coefficients c_1 and c_2 can be selected independently. Figures 3.1.3 through 3.1.5 illustrate some of the possibilities, with either c_1 or c_2 set equal to zero, or with both nonzero. ■

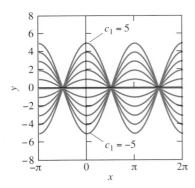

FIGURE 3.1.3. Solutions $y(x) = c_1 \cos x$ of $y'' + y = 0$.

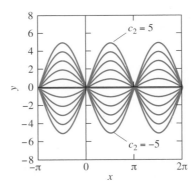

FIGURE 3.1.4. Solutions $y(x) = c_2 \sin x$ of $y'' + y = 0$.

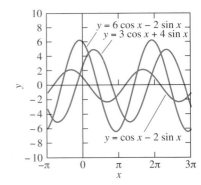

FIGURE 3.1.5. Solutions of $y'' + y = 0$ with c_1 and c_2 both nonzero.

Earlier in this section we gave the linear equation $mx'' + cx' + kx = F(t)$ as a mathematical model of the motion of the mass shown in Fig. 3.1.1. Physical considerations suggest that the motion of the mass should be determined by its initial position and initial velocity. Hence, given any preassigned values of $x(0)$ and $x'(0)$, Eq. (6) ought to have a *unique* solution satisfying these initial conditions. More generally, in order to be a "good" mathematical model of a deterministic physical situation, a differential equation must have unique solutions satisfying any appropriate initial conditions. The following existence and uniqueness theorem (proved in the Appendix) gives us this assurance for the general second-order equation.

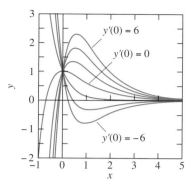

FIGURE 3.1.6. Solutions of $y'' + 3y' + 2y = 0$ with the same initial value $y(0) = 1$ but different initial slopes.

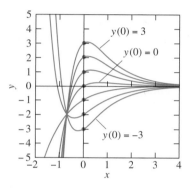

FIGURE 3.1.7. Solutions of $y'' + 3y' + 2y = 0$ with the same initial slope $y'(0) = 1$ but different initial values.

THEOREM 2　Existence and Uniqueness for Linear Equations

Suppose that the functions p, q, and f are continuous on the open interval I containing the point a. Then, given any two numbers b_0 and b_1, the equation

$$y'' + p(x)y' + q(x)y = f(x) \tag{8}$$

has a unique (that is, one and only one) solution on the entire interval I that satisfies the initial conditions

$$y(a) = b_0, \quad y'(a) = b_1. \tag{11}$$

Remark 1:　Equation (8) and the conditions in (11) constitute a second-order linear **initial value problem.** Theorem 2 tells us that any such initial value problem has a unique solution on the *whole* interval I where the coefficient functions in (8) are continuous. Recall from Section 1.3 that a *nonlinear* differential equation generally has a unique solution on only a smaller interval.

Remark 2:　Whereas a *first-order* differential equation $dy/dx = F(x, y)$ generally admits only a single solution curve $y = y(x)$ passing through a given initial point (a, b), Theorem 2 implies that the *second-order* equation in (8) has infinitely many solution curves passing through the point (a, b_0)—namely, one for each (real number) value of the initial slope $y'(a) = b_1$. That is, instead of there being only one line through (a, b_0) tangent to a solution curve, *every* nonvertical straight line through (a, b_0) is tangent to some solution curve of Eq. (8). Figure 3.1.6 shows a number of solution curves of the equation $y'' + 3y' + 2y = 0$ all having the same initial value $y(0) = 1$, while Fig. 3.1.7 shows a number of solution curves all having the same initial slope $y'(0) = 1$. The application at the end of this section suggests how to construct such families of solution curves for a given homogeneous second-order linear differential equation. ∎

Example 1
Continued

We saw in the first part of Example 1 that $y(x) = 3\cos x - 2\sin x$ is a solution (on the entire real line) of $y'' + y = 0$. It has the initial values $y(0) = 3$, $y'(0) = -2$. Theorem 2 tells us that this is the *only* solution with these initial values. More generally, the solution

$$y(x) = b_0 \cos x + b_1 \sin x$$

satisfies the *arbitrary* initial conditions $y(0) = b_0$, $y'(0) = b_1$; this illustrates the *existence* of such a solution, also as guaranteed by Theorem 2. ∎

Example 1 suggests how, given a *homogeneous* second-order linear equation, we might actually find the solution $y(x)$ whose existence is assured by Theorem 2. First, we find two "essentially different" solutions y_1 and y_2; second, we attempt to impose on the general solution

$$y = c_1 y_1 + c_2 y_2 \tag{12}$$

the initial conditions $y(a) = b_0$, $y'(a) = b_1$. That is, we attempt to solve the simultaneous equations

$$\begin{aligned} c_1 y_1(a) + c_2 y_2(a) &= b_0, \\ c_1 y_1'(a) + c_2 y_2'(a) &= b_1 \end{aligned} \tag{13}$$

for the coefficients c_1 and c_2.

Example 2   Verify that the functions

$$y_1(x) = e^x \quad \text{and} \quad y_2(x) = xe^x$$

are solutions of the differential equation

$$y'' - 2y' + y = 0,$$

and then find a solution satisfying the initial conditions $y(0) = 3$, $y'(0) = 1$.

Solution   The verification is routine; we omit it. We impose the given initial conditions on the general solution

$$y(x) = c_1 e^x + c_2 x e^x,$$

for which

$$y'(x) = (c_1 + c_2)e^x + c_2 x e^x,$$

to obtain the simultaneous equations

$$
\begin{aligned}
y(0) &= c_1 &&= 3, \\
y'(0) &= c_1 + c_2 &&= 1.
\end{aligned}
$$

The resulting solution is $c_1 = 3$, $c_2 = -2$. Hence the solution of the original initial value problem is

$$y(x) = 3e^x - 2xe^x.$$

Figure 3.1.8 shows several additional solutions of $y'' - 2y' + y = 0$, all having the same initial value $y(0) = 3$. ∎

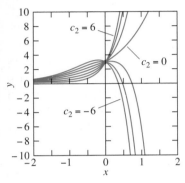

FIGURE 3.1.8.   Different solutions $y(x) = 3e^x + c_2 x e^x$ of $y'' - 2y' + y = 0$ with the same initial value $y(0) = 3$.

In order for the procedure of Example 2 to succeed, the two solutions y_1 and y_2 must have the elusive property that the equations in (13) can always be solved for c_1 and c_2, no matter what the initial conditions b_0 and b_1 might be. The following definition tells precisely how different the two functions y_1 and y_2 must be.

DEFINITION   Linear Independence of Two Functions

Two functions defined on an open interval I are said to be **linearly independent** on I provided that neither is a constant multiple of the other.

Two functions are said to be **linearly dependent** on an open interval provided that they are not linearly independent there; that is, one of them is a constant multiple of the other. We can always determine whether two given functions f and g are linearly dependent on an interval I by noting at a glance whether either of the two quotients f/g or g/f is a constant-valued function on I.

Example 3   Thus it is clear that the following pairs of functions are linearly independent on the entire real line:

$$
\begin{aligned}
\sin x \quad &\text{and} \quad \cos x; \\
e^x \quad &\text{and} \quad e^{-2x}; \\
e^x \quad &\text{and} \quad xe^x; \\
x + 1 \quad &\text{and} \quad x^2; \\
x \quad &\text{and} \quad |x|.
\end{aligned}
$$

That is, neither $\sin x / \cos x = \tan x$ nor $\cos x / \sin x = \cot x$ is a constant-valued function; neither $e^x / e^{-2x} = e^{3x}$ nor e^{-2x} / e^x is a constant-valued function; and so forth. But the identically zero function $f(x) \equiv 0$ and any other function g are linearly dependent on every interval, because $0 \cdot g(x) = 0 = f(x)$. Also, the functions

$$f(x) = \sin 2x \quad \text{and} \quad g(x) = \sin x \cos x$$

are linearly dependent on any interval because $f(x) = 2g(x)$ is the familiar trigonometric identity $\sin 2x = 2 \sin x \cos x$. ∎

General Solutions

But does the homogeneous equation $y'' + py' + qy = 0$ always have two linearly independent solutions? Theorem 2 says yes! We need only choose y_1 and y_2 so that

$$y_1(a) = 1, \ y_1'(a) = 0 \quad \text{and} \quad y_2(a) = 0, \ y_2'(a) = 1.$$

It is then impossible that either $y_1 = ky_2$ or $y_2 = ky_1$ because $k \cdot 0 \neq 1$ for any constant k. Theorem 2 tells us that two such linearly independent solutions *exist*; actually finding them is a crucial matter that we will discuss briefly at the end of this section, and in greater detail beginning in Section 3.3.

We want to show, finally, that given *any* two linearly independent solutions y_1 and y_2 of the homogeneous equation

$$y''(x) + p(x)y'(x) + q(x)y(x) = 0, \tag{9}$$

every solution y of Eq. (9) can be expressed as a linear combination

$$y = c_1 y_1 + c_2 y_2 \tag{12}$$

of y_1 and y_2. This means that the function in (12) is a *general solution* of Eq. (9)—it provides all possible solutions of the differential equation.

As suggested by the equations in (13), the determination of the constants c_1 and c_2 in (12) depends on a certain 2×2 determinant of values of y_1, y_2, and their derivatives. Given two functions f and g, the **Wronskian** of f and g is the determinant

$$W = \begin{vmatrix} f & g \\ f' & g' \end{vmatrix} = fg' - f'g.$$

We write either $W(f, g)$ or $W(x)$, depending on whether we wish to emphasize the two functions or the point x at which the Wronskian is to be evaluated. For example,

$$W(\cos x, \sin x) = \begin{vmatrix} \cos x & \sin x \\ -\sin x & \cos x \end{vmatrix} = \cos^2 x + \sin^2 x = 1$$

and

$$W(e^x, xe^x) = \begin{vmatrix} e^x & xe^x \\ e^x & e^x + xe^x \end{vmatrix} = e^{2x}.$$

These are examples of linearly *independent* pairs of solutions of differential equations (see Examples 1 and 2). Note that in both cases the Wronskian is everywhere *nonzero*.

On the other hand, if the functions f and g are linearly dependent, with $f = kg$ (for example), then

$$W(f, g) = \begin{vmatrix} kg & g \\ kg' & g' \end{vmatrix} = kgg' - kg'g \equiv 0.$$

Thus the Wronskian of two linearly *dependent* functions is identically zero. In Section 3.2 we will prove that, if the two functions y_1 and y_2 are solutions of a homogeneous second-order linear equation, then the strong converse stated in part (b) of Theorem 3 holds.

THEOREM 3   Wronskians of Solutions

Suppose that y_1 and y_2 are two solutions of the homogeneous second-order linear equation (Eq. (9))
$$y'' + p(x)y' + q(x)y = 0$$
on an open interval I on which p and q are continuous.
(a) If y_1 and y_2 are linearly dependent, then $W(y_1, y_2) \equiv 0$ on I.
(b) If y_1 and y_2 are linearly independent, then $W(y_1, y_2) \neq 0$ at each point of I.

Thus, given two solutions of Eq. (9), there are just two possibilities: The Wronskian W is identically zero if the solutions are linearly dependent; the Wronskian is never zero if the solutions are linearly independent. The latter fact is what we need to show that $y = c_1y_1 + c_2y_2$ is the general solution of Eq. (9) if y_1 and y_2 are linearly independent solutions.

THEOREM 4   General Solutions of Homogeneous Equations

Let y_1 and y_2 be two linearly independent solutions of the homogeneous equation (Eq. (9))
$$y'' + p(x)y' + q(x)y = 0$$
with p and q continuous on the open interval I. If Y is any solution whatsoever of Eq. (9) on I, then there exist numbers c_1 and c_2 such that

$$Y(x) = c_1y_1(x) + c_2y_2(x)$$

for all x in I.

In essence, Theorem 4 tells us that when we have found *two* linearly independent solutions of the second-order homogeneous equation in (9), then we have found *all* of its solutions. We therefore call the linear combination $Y = c_1y_1 + c_2y_2$ a *general solution* of the differential equation.

Proof of Theorem 4: Choose a point a of I, and consider the simultaneous equations

$$\begin{aligned} c_1y_1(a) + c_2y_2(a) &= Y(a), \\ c_1y_1'(a) + c_2y_2'(a) &= Y'(a). \end{aligned} \tag{14}$$

The determinant of the coefficients in this system of linear equations in the unknowns c_1 and c_2 is simply the Wronskian $W(y_1, y_2)$ evaluated at $x = a$. By

Theorem 3, this determinant is nonzero, so by elementary algebra it follows that the equations in (14) can be solved for c_1 and c_2. With these values of c_1 and c_2, we define the solution

$$G(x) = c_1 y_1(x) + c_2 y_2(x)$$

of Eq. (9); then

$$G(a) = c_1 y_1(a) + c_2 y_2(a) = Y(a)$$

and

$$G'(a) = c_1 y_1'(a) + c_2 y_2'(a) = Y'(a).$$

Thus the two solutions Y and G have the same initial values at a; likewise, so do Y' and G'. By the uniqueness of a solution determined by such initial values (Theorem 2), it follows that Y and G agree on I. Thus we see that

$$Y(x) \equiv G(x) = c_1 y_1(x) + c_2 y_2(x),$$

as desired.   ▲

Example 4   If $y_1(x) = e^{2x}$ and $y_2(x) = e^{-2x}$, then

$$y_1'' = (2)(2)e^{2x} = 4e^{2x} = 4y_1 \quad \text{and} \quad y_2'' = (-2)(-2)e^{-2x} = 4e^{-2x} = 4y_2.$$

Therefore, y_1 and y_2 are linearly independent solutions of

$$y'' - 4y = 0. \tag{15}$$

But $y_3(x) = \cosh 2x$ and $y_4(x) = \sinh 2x$ are also solutions of Eq. (15), because

$$\frac{d^2}{dx^2}(\cosh 2x) = \frac{d}{dx}(2 \sinh 2x) = 4 \cosh 2x$$

and, similarly, $(\sinh 2x)'' = 4 \sinh 2x$. It therefore follows from Theorem 4 that the functions $\cosh 2x$ and $\sinh 2x$ can be expressed as linear combinations of $y_1(x) = e^{2x}$ and $y_2(x) = e^{-2x}$. Of course, this is no surprise, because

$$\cosh 2x = \tfrac{1}{2}e^{2x} + \tfrac{1}{2}e^{-2x} \quad \text{and} \quad \sinh 2x = \tfrac{1}{2}e^{2x} - \tfrac{1}{2}e^{-2x}$$

by the definitions of the hyperbolic cosine and hyperbolic sine.   ■

Remark: Because e^{2x}, e^{-2x} and $\cosh x$, $\sinh x$ are two different pairs of linearly independent solutions of the equation $y'' - 4y = 0$ in (15), Theorem 4 implies that every particular solution $Y(x)$ of this equation can be written both in the form

$$Y(x) = c_1 e^{2x} + c_2 e^{-2x}$$

and in the form

$$Y(x) = a \cosh x + b \sinh x.$$

Thus these two different linear combinations (with arbitrary constant coefficients) provide two different descriptions of the set of all solutions of the same differential equation $y'' - 4y = 0$. Hence each of these two linear combinations is a general solution of the equation. Indeed, this is why it is accurate to refer to a specific such linear combination as "*a* general solution" rather than as "*the* general solution."   ■

Linear Second-Order Equations with Constant Coefficients

As an illustration of the general theory introduced in this section, we discuss the homogeneous second-order linear differential equation

$$ay'' + by' + cy = 0 \tag{16}$$

with *constant* coefficients a, b, and c. We first look for a *single* solution of Eq. (16) and begin with the observation that

$$(e^{rx})' = re^{rx} \quad \text{and} \quad (e^{rx})'' = r^2 e^{rx}, \tag{17}$$

so any derivative of e^{rx} is a constant multiple of e^{rx}. Hence, if we substituted $y = e^{rx}$ in Eq. (16), then each term would be a constant multiple of e^{rx}, with the constant coefficients dependent on r and the coefficients a, b, and c. This suggests that we try to find a value of r so that these multiples of e^{rx} will have sum zero. If we succeed, then $y = e^{rx}$ will be a solution of Eq. (16).

For example, if we substitute $y = e^{rx}$ in the equation

$$y'' - 5y' + 6y = 0,$$

we obtain

$$r^2 e^{rx} - 5re^{rx} + 6e^{rx} = 0.$$

Thus

$$(r^2 - 5r + 6)e^{rx} = 0; \quad (r-2)(r-3)e^{rx} = 0.$$

Hence $y = e^{rx}$ will be a solution if either $r = 2$ or $r = 3$. So, in searching for a single solution, we actually have found two solutions: $y_1(x) = e^{2x}$ and $y_2(x) = e^{3x}$.

To carry out this procedure in the general case, we substitute $y = e^{rx}$ in Eq. (16). With the aid of the equations in (17), we find the result to be

$$ar^2 e^{rx} + bre^{rx} + ce^{rx} = 0.$$

Because e^{rx} is never zero, we conclude that $y(x) = e^{rx}$ will satisfy the differential equation in (16) precisely when r is a root of the *algebraic* equation

$$ar^2 + br + c = 0. \tag{18}$$

This quadratic equation is called the **characteristic equation** of the homogeneous linear differential equation

$$ay'' + by' + cy = 0. \tag{16}$$

If Eq. (18) has two *distinct* (unequal) roots r_1 and r_2, then the corresponding solutions $y_1(x) = e^{r_1 x}$ and $y_2(x) = e^{r_2 x}$ of (16) are linearly independent. (Why?) This gives the following result.

THEOREM 5   Distinct Real Roots

If the roots r_1 and r_2 of the characteristic equation in (18) are real and distinct, then

$$y(x) = c_1 e^{r_1 x} + c_2 e^{r_2 x} \tag{19}$$

is a general solution of Eq. (16).

| Example 5 | Find the general solution of

$$2y'' - 7y' + 3y = 0.$$

Solution   We can solve the characteristic equation

$$2r^2 - 7r + 3 = 0$$

by factoring:

$$(2r - 1)(r - 3) = 0.$$

The roots $r_1 = \frac{1}{2}$ and $r_2 = 3$ are real and distinct, so Theorem 5 yields the general solution

$$y(x) = c_1 e^{x/2} + c_2 e^{3x}. \qquad \blacksquare$$

| Example 6 | The differential equation $y'' + 2y' = 0$ has characteristic equation

$$r^2 + 2r = r(r + 2) = 0$$

with distinct real roots $r_1 = 0$ and $r_2 = -2$. Because $e^{0 \cdot x} \equiv 1$, we get the general solution

$$y(x) = c_1 + c_2 e^{-2x}.$$

Figure 3.1.9 shows several different solution curves with $c_1 = 1$, all appearing to approach the solution curve $y(x) \equiv 1$ (with $c_2 = 0$) as $x \to +\infty$. $\qquad \blacksquare$

Remark: Note that Theorem 5 changes a problem involving a differential equation into one involving only the solution of an *algebraic* equation. $\qquad \blacksquare$

If the characteristic equation in (18) has equal roots $r_1 = r_2$, we get (at first) only the single solution $y_1(x) = e^{r_1 x}$ of Eq. (16). The problem in this case is to produce the "missing" second solution of the differential equation.

A double root $r = r_1$ will occur precisely when the characteristic equation is a constant multiple of the equation

$$(r - r_1)^2 = r^2 - 2r_1 r + r_1^2 = 0.$$

Any differential equation with this characteristic equation is equivalent to

$$y'' - 2r_1 y' + r_1^2 y = 0. \qquad (20)$$

But it is easy to verify by direct substitution that $y = x e^{r_1 x}$ is a second solution of Eq. (20). It is clear (but you should verify) that

$$y_1(x) = e^{r_1 x} \quad \text{and} \quad y_2(x) = x e^{r_1 x}$$

are linearly independent functions, so the general solution of the differential equation in (20) is

$$y(x) = c_1 e^{r_1 x} + c_2 x e^{r_1 x}.$$

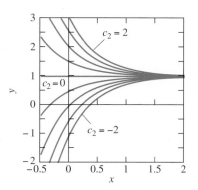

FIGURE 3.1.9.   Solutions $y(x) = 1 + c_2 e^{-2x}$ of $y'' + 2y' = 0$ with different values of c_2.

THEOREM 6 Repeated Roots

If the characteristic equation in (18) has equal (necessarily real) roots $r_1 = r_2$, then

$$y(x) = (c_1 + c_2 x)e^{r_1 x} \qquad (21)$$

is a general solution of Eq. (16).

Example 7   To solve the initial value problem

$$y'' + 2y' + y = 0;$$
$$y(0) = 5, \quad y'(0) = -3,$$

we note first that the characteristic equation

$$r^2 + 2r + 1 = (r+1)^2 = 0$$

has equal roots $r_1 = r_2 = -1$. Hence the general solution provided by Theorem 6 is

$$y(x) = c_1 e^{-x} + c_2 x e^{-x}.$$

Differentiation yields

$$y'(x) = -c_1 e^{-x} + c_2 e^{-x} - c_2 x e^{-x},$$

so the initial conditions yield the equations

$$\begin{aligned} y(0) &= c_1 &= 5, \\ y'(0) &= -c_1 + c_2 &= -3, \end{aligned}$$

which imply that $c_1 = 5$ and $c_2 = 2$. Thus the desired particular solution of the initial value problem is

$$y(x) = 5e^{-x} + 2xe^{-x}.$$

This particular solution, together with several others of the form $y(x) = c_1 e^{-x} + 2xe^{-x}$, is illustrated in Fig. 3.1.10. ∎

The characteristic equation in (18) may have either real or complex roots. The case of complex roots will be discussed in Section 3.3.

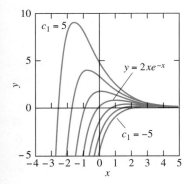

FIGURE 3.1.10. Solutions $y(x) = c_1 e^{-x} + 2xe^{-x}$ of $y'' + 2y' + y = 0$ with different values of c_1.

3.1 Problems

In Problems 1 through 16, a homogeneous second-order linear differential equation, two functions y_1 and y_2, and a pair of initial conditions are given. First verify that y_1 and y_2 are solutions of the differential equation. Then find a particular solution of the form $y = c_1 y_1 + c_2 y_2$ that satisfies the given initial conditions. Primes denote derivatives with respect to x.

1. $y'' - y = 0$; $y_1 = e^x$, $y_2 = e^{-x}$; $y(0) = 0$, $y'(0) = 5$

2. $y'' - 9y = 0$; $y_1 = e^{3x}$, $y_2 = e^{-3x}$; $y(0) = -1$, $y'(0) = 15$
3. $y'' + 4y = 0$; $y_1 = \cos 2x$, $y_2 = \sin 2x$; $y(0) = 3$, $y'(0) = 8$
4. $y'' + 25y = 0$; $y_1 = \cos 5x$, $y_2 = \sin 5x$; $y(0) = 10$, $y'(0) = -10$
5. $y'' - 3y' + 2y = 0$; $y_1 = e^x$, $y_2 = e^{2x}$; $y(0) = 1$, $y'(0) = 0$
6. $y'' + y' - 6y = 0$; $y_1 = e^{2x}$, $y_2 = e^{-3x}$; $y(0) = 7$, $y'(0) = -1$

7. $y'' + y' = 0$; $y_1 = 1$, $y_2 = e^{-x}$; $y(0) = -2$, $y'(0) = 8$

8. $y'' - 3y' = 0$; $y_1 = 1$, $y_2 = e^{3x}$; $y(0) = 4$, $y'(0) = -2$

9. $y'' + 2y' + y = 0$; $y_1 = e^{-x}$, $y_2 = xe^{-x}$; $y(0) = 2$, $y'(0) = -1$

10. $y'' - 10y' + 25y = 0$; $y_1 = e^{5x}$, $y_2 = xe^{5x}$; $y(0) = 3$, $y'(0) = 13$

11. $y'' - 2y' + 2y = 0$; $y_1 = e^x \cos x$, $y_2 = e^x \sin x$; $y(0) = 0$, $y'(0) = 5$

12. $y'' + 6y' + 13y = 0$; $y_1 = e^{-3x} \cos 2x$, $y_2 = e^{-3x} \sin 2x$; $y(0) = 2$, $y'(0) = 0$

13. $x^2 y'' - 2xy' + 2y = 0$; $y_1 = x$, $y_2 = x^2$; $y(1) = 3$, $y'(1) = 1$

14. $x^2 y'' + 2xy' - 6y = 0$; $y_1 = x^2$, $y_2 = x^{-3}$; $y(2) = 10$, $y'(2) = 15$

15. $x^2 y'' - xy' + y = 0$; $y_1 = x$, $y_2 = x \ln x$; $y(1) = 7$, $y'(1) = 2$

16. $x^2 y'' + xy' + y = 0$; $y_1 = \cos(\ln x)$, $y_2 = \sin(\ln x)$; $y(1) = 2$, $y'(1) = 3$

The following three problems illustrate the fact that the superposition principle does not generally hold for nonlinear equations.

17. Show that $y = 1/x$ is a solution of $y' + y^2 = 0$, but that if $c \neq 0$ and $c \neq 1$, then $y = c/x$ is not a solution.

18. Show that $y = x^3$ is a solution of $yy'' = 6x^4$, but that if $c^2 \neq 1$, then $y = cx^3$ is not a solution.

19. Show that $y_1 \equiv 1$ and $y_2 = \sqrt{x}$ are solutions of $yy'' + (y')^2 = 0$, but that their sum $y = y_1 + y_2$ is not a solution.

Determine whether the pairs of functions in Problems 20 through 26 are linearly independent or linearly dependent on the real line.

20. $f(x) = \pi$, $g(x) = \cos^2 x + \sin^2 x$

21. $f(x) = x^3$, $g(x) = x^2 |x|$

22. $f(x) = 1 + x$, $g(x) = 1 + |x|$

23. $f(x) = xe^x$, $g(x) = |x| e^x$

24. $f(x) = \sin^2 x$, $g(x) = 1 - \cos 2x$

25. $f(x) = e^x \sin x$, $g(x) = e^x \cos x$

26. $f(x) = 2\cos x + 3\sin x$, $g(x) = 3\cos x - 2\sin x$

27. Let y_p be a particular solution of the nonhomogeneous equation $y'' + py' + qy = f(x)$ and let y_c be a solution of its associated homogeneous equation. Show that $y = y_c + y_p$ is a solution of the given nonhomogeneous equation.

28. With $y_p = 1$ and $y_c = c_1 \cos x + c_2 \sin x$ in the notation of Problem 27, find a solution of $y'' + y = 1$ satisfying the initial conditions $y(0) = -1 = y'(0)$.

29. Show that $y_1 = x^2$ and $y_2 = x^3$ are two different solutions of $x^2 y'' - 4xy' + 6y = 0$, both satisfying the initial conditions $y(0) = 0 = y'(0)$. Explain why these facts do not contradict Theorem 2 (with respect to the guaranteed uniqueness).

30. **(a)** Show that $y_1 = x^3$ and $y_2 = |x^3|$ are linearly independent solutions on the real line of the equation $x^2 y'' - 3xy' + 3y = 0$. **(b)** Verify that $W(y_1, y_2)$ is identically zero. Why do these facts not contradict Theorem 3?

31. Show that $y_1 = \sin x^2$ and $y_2 = \cos x^2$ are linearly independent functions, but that their Wronskian vanishes at $x = 0$. Why does this imply that there is *no* differential equation of the form $y'' + p(x)y' + q(x)y = 0$, with both p and q continuous everywhere, having both y_1 and y_2 as solutions?

32. Let y_1 and y_2 be two solutions of $A(x)y'' + B(x)y' + C(x)y = 0$ on an open interval I where A, B, and C are continuous and $A(x)$ is never zero. **(a)** Let $W = W(y_1, y_2)$. Show that

$$A(x)\frac{dW}{dx} = (y_1)(Ay_2'') - (y_2)(Ay_1'').$$

Then substitute for Ay_2'' and Ay_1'' from the original differential equation to show that

$$A(x)\frac{dW}{dx} = -B(x)W(x).$$

(b) Solve this first-order equation to deduce **Abel's formula**

$$W(x) = K \exp\left(-\int \frac{B(x)}{A(x)}\,dx\right),$$

where K is a constant. **(c)** Why does Abel's formula imply that the Wronskian $W(y_1, y_2)$ is either zero everywhere or nonzero everywhere (as stated in Theorem 3)?

Apply Theorems 5 and 6 to find general solutions of the differential equations given in Problems 33 through 42. Primes denote derivatives with respect to x.

33. $y'' - 3y' + 2y = 0$

34. $y'' + 2y' - 15y = 0$

35. $y'' + 5y' = 0$

36. $2y'' + 3y' = 0$

37. $2y'' - y' - y = 0$

38. $4y'' + 8y' + 3y = 0$

39. $4y'' + 4y' + y = 0$

40. $9y'' - 12y' + 4y = 0$

41. $6y'' - 7y' - 20y = 0$

42. $35y'' - y' - 12y = 0$

Each of Problems 43 through 48 gives a general solution $y(x)$ of a homogeneous second-order differential equation $ay'' + by' + cy = 0$ with constant coefficients. Find such an equation.

43. $y(x) = c_1 + c_2 e^{-10x}$

44. $y(x) = c_1 e^{10x} + c_2 e^{-10x}$

45. $y(x) = c_1 e^{-10x} + c_2 xe^{-10x}$

46. $y(x) = c_1 e^{10x} + c_2 e^{100x}$

47. $y(x) = c_1 + c_2 x$

48. $y(x) = e^x \left(c_1 e^{x\sqrt{2}} + c_2 e^{-x\sqrt{2}}\right)$

Problems 49 and 50 deal with the solution curves of $y'' + 3y' + 2y = 0$ shown in Figs. 3.1.6 and 3.1.7.

49. Find the highest point on the solution curve with $y(0) = 1$ and $y'(0) = 6$ in Fig. 3.1.6.

50. Find the third-quadrant point of intersection of the solution curves shown in Fig. 3.1.7.

51. A second-order **Euler equation** is one of the form

$$ax^2y'' + bxy' + cy = 0 \tag{22}$$

where a, b, c are constants. **(a)** Show that if $x > 0$, then the substitution $v = \ln x$ transforms Eq. (22) into the constant-coefficient linear equation

$$a\frac{d^2y}{dv^2} + (b-a)\frac{dy}{dv} + cy = 0 \tag{23}$$

with independent variable v. **(b)** If the roots r_1 and r_2 of the characteristic equation of Eq. (23) are real and distinct,

conclude that a general solution of the Euler equation in (22) is $y(x) = c_1x^{r_1} + c_2x^{r_2}$.

Make the substitution $v = \ln x$ of Problem 51 to find general solutions (for $x > 0$) of the Euler equations in Problems 52–56.

52. $x^2y'' + xy' - y = 0$ **53.** $x^2y'' + 2xy' - 12y = 0$

54. $4x^2y'' + 8xy' - 3y = 0$ **55.** $x^2y'' + xy' = 0$

56. $x^2y'' - 3xy' + 4y = 0$

3.1 Application   Plotting Second-Order Solution Families

This application deals with the plotting by computer of families of solutions such as those illustrated in Figs. 3.1.6 and 3.1.7. Show first that the general solution of the differential equation

$$y'' + 3y' + 2y = 0 \tag{1}$$

is

$$y(x) = c_1e^{-x} + c_2e^{-2x}. \tag{2}$$

For Fig. 3.1.6, show that the particular solution of Eq. (1) satisfying the initial conditions $y(0) = 1$, $y'(0) = b$ is given by

$$y(x) = (b+2)e^{-x} - (b+1)e^{-2x}. \tag{3}$$

The MATLAB loop

```
x = - 1 : 0.02 : 5       % x-vector from x = - 1 to x = 5
for b = -6 : 2 : 6       % for b = -6 to 6 with db = 2 do
    y = (b + 2)*exp(-x)  - (b + 1)*exp(-2*x);
    plot(x,y)
end
```

was used to generate Fig. 3.1.6.

For Fig. 3.1.7, show that the particular solution of Eq. (1) satisfying the initial conditions $y(0) = a$, $y'(0) = 1$ is given by

$$y(x) = (2a+1)e^{-x} - (a+1)e^{-2x}. \tag{4}$$

The MATLAB loop

```
x = -2 : 0.02 : 4        % x-vector from x = -2 to x = 4
for a = -3 : 1 : 3       % for a = -3 to 3 with da = 1 do
    y = (2*a + 1)*exp(-x)  - (a + 1)*exp(-2*x);
    plot(x,y)
end
```

was used to generate Fig. 3.1.7.

Computer algebra systems such as *Maple* and *Mathematica*, as well as graphing calculators, have commands to carry out for-loops such as the two shown here. Begin by reproducing Figs. 3.1.6 and 3.1.7. Then, for each of the following differential equations, construct both a family of solution curves satisfying $y(0) = 1$ and a family of solution curves satisfying the initial condition $y'(0) = 1$.

1. $y'' - y = 0$

2. $y'' - 3y' + 2y = 0$

3. $2y'' + 3y' + y = 0$

4. $y'' + y = 0$ (see Example 1)

5. $y'' + 2y' + 2y = 0$, which has general solution $y(x) = e^{-x}(c_1 \cos x + c_2 \sin x)$.

3.2 General Solutions of Linear Equations

We now show that our discussion in Section 3.1 of second-order linear equations generalizes in a very natural way to the general *n*th-order **linear** differential equation of the form

$$P_0(x)y^{(n)} + P_1(x)y^{(n-1)} + \cdots + P_{n-1}(x)y' + P_n(x)y = F(x). \tag{1}$$

Unless otherwise noted, we will always assume that the coefficient functions $P_i(x)$ and $F(x)$ are continuous on some open interval I (perhaps unbounded) where we wish to solve the equation. Under the additional assumption that $P_0(x) \neq 0$ at each point of I, we can divide each term in Eq. (1) by $P_0(x)$ to obtain an equation with leading coefficient 1, of the form

➤ $$y^{(n)} + p_1(x)y^{(n-1)} + \cdots + p_{n-1}(x)y' + p_n(x)y = f(x). \tag{2}$$

The **homogeneous** linear equation **associated with** Eq. (2) is

➤ $$y^{(n)} + p_1(x)y^{(n-1)} + \cdots + p_{n-1}(x)y' + p_n(x)y = 0. \tag{3}$$

Just as in the second-order case, a *homogeneous* nth-order linear differential equation has the valuable property that any superposition, or *linear combination,* of solutions of the equation is again a solution. The proof of the following theorem is essentially the same—a routine verification—as that of Theorem 1 of Section 3.1.

THEOREM 1   Principle of Superposition for Homogeneous Equations

Let $y_1, y_2, \ldots, y_n$ be n solutions of the homogeneous linear equation in (3) on the interval I. If $c_1, c_2, \ldots, c_n$ are constants, then the linear combination

➤ $$y = c_1 y_1 + c_2 y_2 + \cdots + c_n y_n \tag{4}$$

is also a solution of Eq. (3) on I.

Example 1   It is easy to verify that the three functions

$$y_1(x) = e^{-3x}, \quad y_2(x) = \cos 2x, \quad \text{and} \quad y_3(x) = \sin 2x$$

are all solutions of the homogeneous third-order equation

$$y^{(3)} + 3y'' + 4y' + 12y = 0$$

on the entire real line. Theorem 1 tells us that any linear combination of these solutions, such as

$$y(x) = -3y_1(x) + 3y_2(x) - 2y_3(x) = -3e^{-3x} + 3\cos 2x - 2\sin 2x,$$

is also a solution on the entire real line. We will see that, conversely, every solution of the differential equation of this example is a linear combination of the three particular solutions y_1, y_2, and y_3. Thus a general solution is given by

$$y(x) = c_1 e^{-3x} + c_2 \cos 2x + c_3 \sin 2x. \qquad \blacksquare$$

Existence and Uniqueness of Solutions

We saw in Section 3.1 that a particular solution of a *second-order* linear differential equation is determined by *two* initial conditions. Similarly, a particular solution of an nth-order linear differential equation is determined by n initial conditions. The following theorem, proved in the Appendix, is the natural generalization of Theorem 2 of Section 3.1.

THEOREM 2   Existence and Uniqueness for Linear Equations

Suppose that the functions p_1, p_2, ..., p_n, and f are continuous on the open interval I containing the point a. Then, given n numbers b_0, b_1, ..., b_{n-1}, the nth-order linear equation (Eq. (2))

$$y^{(n)} + p_1(x)y^{(n-1)} + \cdots + p_{n-1}(x)y' + p_n(x)y = f(x)$$

has a unique (that is, one and only one) solution on the entire interval I that satisfies the n initial conditions

$$y(a) = b_0, \quad y'(a) = b_1, \quad \ldots, \quad y^{(n-1)}(a) = b_{n-1}. \qquad (5)$$

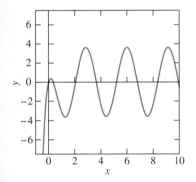

FIGURE 3.2.1. The particular solution $y(x) = -3e^{-3x} + 3\cos 2x - 2\sin 2x$.

Equation (2) and the conditions in (5) constitute an nth-order **initial value problem.** Theorem 2 tells us that any such initial value problem has a unique solution on the *whole* interval I where the coefficient functions in (2) are continuous. It tells us nothing, however, about how to find this solution. In Section 3.3 we will see how to construct explicit solutions of initial value problems in the *constant-coefficient* case that occurs often in applications.

Example 1

Continued

We saw earlier that

$$y(x) = -3e^{-3x} + 3\cos 2x - 2\sin 2x$$

is a solution of

$$y^{(3)} + 3y'' + 4y' + 12y = 0$$

on the entire real line. This particular solution has initial values $y(0) = 0$, $y'(0) = 5$, and $y''(0) = -39$, and Theorem 2 implies that there is no other solution with these same initial values. Note that its graph (in Fig. 3.2.1) looks periodic on the right. Indeed, because of the negative exponent, we see that $y(x) \approx 3\cos 2x - 2\sin 2x$ for large positive x. $\blacksquare$

Remark: Because its general solution involves the three arbitrary constants c_1, c_2, and c_3, the third-order equation in Example 1 has a "threefold infinity" of solutions, including three families of especially simple solutions:

- $y(x) = c_1 e^{-3x}$ (obtained from the general solution with $c_2 = c_3 = 0$),
- $y(x) = c_2 \cos 2x$ (with $c_1 = c_3 = 0$), and
- $y(x) = c_3 \sin 2x$ (with $c_1 = c_2 = 0$).

Alternatively, Theorem 2 suggests a threefold infinity of particular solutions corresponding to independent choices of the three initial values $y(0) = b_0$, $y'(0) = b_1$, and $y''(0) = b_2$. Figures 3.2.2 through 3.2.4 illustrate three corresponding families of solutions—for each of which, two of these three initial values are zero. ■

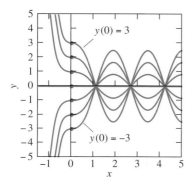

FIGURE 3.2.2. Solutions of $y^{(3)} + 3y'' + 4y' + 12y = 0$ with $y'(0) = y''(0) = 0$ but with different values for $y(0)$.

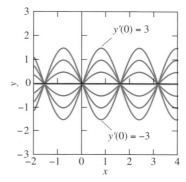

FIGURE 3.2.3. Solutions of $y^{(3)} + 3y'' + 4y' + 12y = 0$ with $y(0) = y''(0) = 0$ but with different values for $y'(0)$.

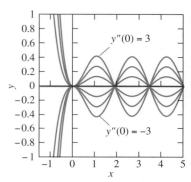

FIGURE 3.2.4. Solutions of $y^{(3)} + 3y'' + 4y' + 12y = 0$ with $y(0) = y'(0) = 0$ but with different values for $y''(0)$.

Note that Theorem 2 implies that the *trivial* solution $y(x) \equiv 0$ is the only solution of the *homogeneous* equation

$$y^{(n)} + p_1(x)y^{(n-1)} + \cdots + p_{n-1}(x)y' + p_n(x)y = 0 \tag{3}$$

that satisfies the *trivial* initial conditions

$$y(a) = y'(a) = \cdots = y^{(n-1)}(a) = 0.$$

Example 2 It is easy to verify that

$$y_1(x) = x^2 \quad \text{and} \quad y_2(x) = x^3$$

are two different solutions of

$$x^2 y'' - 4xy' + 6y = 0,$$

and that both satisfy the initial conditions $y(0) = y'(0) = 0$. Why does this not contradict the uniqueness part of Theorem 2? It is because the leading coefficient in this differential equation vanishes at $x = 0$, so this equation cannot be written in the form of Eq. (3) with coefficient functions *continuous* on an open interval containing the point $x = 0$. ■

Linearly Independent Solutions

On the basis of our knowledge of general solutions of second-order linear equations, we anticipate that a general solution of the *homogeneous* nth-order linear equation

$$y^{(n)} + p_1(x)y^{(n-1)} + \cdots + p_{n-1}(x)y' + p_n(x)y = 0 \tag{3}$$

will be a linear combination

$$y = c_1 y_1 + c_2 y_2 + \cdots + c_n y_n, \tag{4}$$

where $y_1, y_2, \ldots, y_n$ are particular solutions of Eq. (3). But these n particular solutions must be "sufficiently independent" that we can always choose the coefficients $c_1, c_2, \ldots, c_n$ in (4) to satisfy arbitrary initial conditions of the form in (5). The question is this: What should be meant by *independence* of three or more functions?

Recall that *two* functions f_1 and f_2 are linearly *dependent* if one is a constant multiple of the other; that is, if either $f_1 = k f_2$ or $f_2 = k f_1$ for some constant k. If we write these equations as

$$(1) f_1 + (-k) f_2 = 0 \quad \text{or} \quad (k) f_1 + (-1) f_2 = 0,$$

we see that the linear dependence of f_1 and f_2 implies that there exist two constants c_1 and c_2 *not both zero* such that

$$c_1 f_1 + c_2 f_2 = 0. \tag{6}$$

Conversely, if c_1 and c_2 are not both zero, then Eq. (6) certainly implies that f_1 and f_2 are linearly dependent.

In analogy with Eq. (6), we say that n functions $f_1, f_2, \ldots, f_n$ are *linearly dependent* provided that some *nontrivial* linear combination

$$c_1 f_1 + c_2 f_2 + \cdots + c_n f_n$$

of them vanishes identically; *nontrivial* means that *not all* of the coefficients $c_1, c_2, \ldots, c_n$ are zero (although some of them may be zero).

DEFINITION   **Linear Dependence of Functions**

The n functions $f_1, f_2, \ldots, f_n$ are said to be **linearly dependent** on the interval I provided that there exist constants $c_1, c_2, \ldots, c_n$ not all zero such that

$$c_1 f_1 + c_2 f_2 + \cdots + c_n f_n = 0 \tag{7}$$

on I; that is,

$$c_1 f_1(x) + c_2 f_2(x) + \cdots + c_n f_n(x) = 0$$

for all x in I.

If not all the coefficients in Eq. (7) are zero, then clearly we can solve for at least one of the functions as a linear combination of the others, and conversely. Thus the functions $f_1, f_2, \ldots, f_n$ are linearly dependent if and only if at least one of them is a linear combination of the others.

Example 3	The functions

$$f_1(x) = \sin 2x, \quad f_2(x) = \sin x \cos x, \quad \text{and} \quad f_3(x) = e^x$$

are linearly dependent on the real line because

$$(1) f_1 + (-2) f_2 + (0) f_3 = 0 \tag{1}$$

(by the familiar trigonometric identity $\sin 2x = 2 \sin x \cos x$). ∎

The n functions $f_1, f_2, \ldots, f_n$ are called **linearly independent** on the interval I provided that they are not linearly dependent there. Equivalently, they are linearly independent on I provided that the identity

$$c_1 f_1 + c_2 f_2 + \cdots + c_n f_n = 0 \tag{7}$$

holds on I only in the trivial case

$$c_1 = c_2 = \cdots = c_n = 0;$$

that is, *no* nontrivial linear combination of these functions vanishes on I. Put yet another way, the functions $f_1, f_2, \ldots, f_n$ are linearly independent if no one of them is a linear combination of the others. (Why?)

Sometimes one can show that n given functions are linearly dependent by finding, as in Example 3, nontrivial values of the coefficients so that Eq. (7) holds. But in order to show that n given functions are linearly independent, we must prove that nontrivial values of the coefficients *cannot* be found, and this is seldom easy to do in any direct or obvious manner.

Fortunately, in the case of n solutions of a homogeneous nth-order linear equation, there is a tool that makes the determination of their linear dependence or independence a routine matter in many examples. This tool is the Wronskian determinant, which we introduced (for the case $n = 2$) in Section 3.1. Suppose that the n functions $f_1, f_2, \ldots, f_n$ are each $n - 1$ times differentiable. Then their **Wronskian** is the $n \times n$ determinant

$$\blacktriangleright \qquad W = \begin{vmatrix} f_1 & f_2 & \cdots & f_n \\ f_1' & f_2' & \cdots & f_n' \\ \vdots & \vdots & & \vdots \\ f_1^{(n-1)} & f_2^{(n-1)} & \cdots & f_n^{(n-1)} \end{vmatrix}. \tag{8}$$

We write $W(f_1, f_2, \ldots, f_n)$ or $W(x)$, depending on whether we wish to emphasize the functions or the point x at which their Wronskian is to be evaluated. The Wronskian is named after the Polish mathematician J. M. H. Wronski (1778–1853).

We saw in Section 3.1 that the Wronskian of two linearly dependent functions vanishes identically. More generally, *the Wronskian of n linearly dependent functions $f_1, f_2, \ldots, f_n$ is identically zero.* To prove this, assume that Eq. (7) holds on the interval I for some choice of the constants $c_1, c_2, \ldots, c_n$ not all zero. We then differentiate this equation $n - 1$ times in succession, obtaining the n equations

$$\begin{aligned} c_1 f_1(x) + c_2 f_2(x) \quad &+ \cdots + \quad c_n f_n(x) = 0, \\ c_1 f_1'(x) + c_2 f_2'(x) \quad &+ \cdots + \quad c_n f_n'(x) = 0, \\ &\vdots \\ c_1 f_1^{(n-1)}(x) + c_2 f_2^{(n-1)}(x) &+ \cdots + c_n f_n^{(n-1)}(x) = 0, \end{aligned} \tag{9}$$

which hold for all x in I. We recall from linear algebra that a system of n linear *homogeneous* equations in n unknowns has a nontrivial solution if and only if the determinant of coefficients vanishes. In Eq. (9) the unknowns are the constants $c_1, c_2, \ldots, c_n$ and the determinant of coefficients is simply the Wronskian $W(f_1, f_2, \ldots, f_n)$ evaluated at the typical point x of I. Because we know that the c_i are not all zero, it follows that $W(x) \equiv 0$, as we wanted to prove.

Therefore, to show that the functions $f_1, f_2, \ldots, f_n$ are *linearly independent* on the interval I, it suffices to show that their Wronskian is nonzero at just one point of I.

Example 4 Show that the functions $y_1(x) = e^{-3x}$, $y_2(x) = \cos 2x$, and $y_3(x) = \sin 2x$ (of Example 1) are linearly independent.

Solution Their Wronskian is

$$
W = \begin{vmatrix} e^{-3x} & \cos 2x & \sin 2x \\ -3e^{-3x} & -2\sin 2x & 2\cos 2x \\ 9e^{-3x} & -4\cos 2x & -4\sin 2x \end{vmatrix}
$$

$$
= e^{-3x} \begin{vmatrix} -2\sin 2x & 2\cos 2x \\ -4\cos 2x & -4\sin 2x \end{vmatrix} + 3e^{-3x} \begin{vmatrix} \cos 2x & \sin 2x \\ -4\cos 2x & -4\sin 2x \end{vmatrix}
$$

$$
+ 9e^{-3x} \begin{vmatrix} \cos 2x & \sin 2x \\ -2\sin 2x & 2\cos 2x \end{vmatrix} = 26e^{-3x} \neq 0.
$$

Because $W \neq 0$ everywhere, it follows that y_1, y_2, and y_3 are linearly independent on any open interval (including the entire real line). ∎

Example 5 Show first that the three solutions

$$y_1(x) = x, \quad y_2(x) = x\ln x, \quad \text{and} \quad y_3(x) = x^2$$

of the third-order equation

$$x^3 y^{(3)} - x^2 y'' + 2xy' - 2y = 0 \tag{10}$$

are linearly independent on the open interval $x > 0$. Then find a particular solution of Eq. (10) that satisfies the initial conditions

$$y(1) = 3, \quad y'(1) = 2, \quad y''(1) = 1. \tag{11}$$

Solution Note that for $x > 0$, we could divide each term in (10) by x^3 to obtain a homogeneous linear equation of the standard form in (3). When we compute the Wronskian of the three given solutions, we find that

$$
W = \begin{vmatrix} x & x\ln x & x^2 \\ 1 & 1+\ln x & 2x \\ 0 & \dfrac{1}{x} & 2 \end{vmatrix} = x.
$$

Thus $W(x) \neq 0$ for $x > 0$, so y_1, y_2, and y_3 are linearly independent on the interval $x > 0$. To find the desired particular solution, we impose the initial conditions in (11) on

$$y(x) = c_1 x + c_2 x \ln x + c_3 x^2,$$
$$y'(x) = c_1 + c_2(1 + \ln x) + 2c_3 x,$$
$$y''(x) = 0 + \frac{c_2}{x} + 2c_3.$$

This yields the simultaneous equations

$$y(1) = c_1 + c_3 = 3,$$
$$y'(1) = c_1 + c_2 + 2c_3 = 2,$$
$$y''(1) = c_2 + 2c_3 = 1;$$

we solve to find $c_1 = 1$, $c_2 = -3$, and $c_3 = 2$. Thus the particular solution in question is

$$y(x) = x - 3x \ln x + 2x^2.$$ ∎

Provided that $W(y_1, y_2, \ldots, y_n) \neq 0$, it turns out (Theorem 4) that we can always find values of the coefficients in the linear combination

$$y = c_1 y_1 + c_2 y_2 + \cdots + c_n y_n$$

that satisfy any given initial conditions of the form in (5). Theorem 3 provides the necessary nonvanishing of W in the case of linearly independent solutions.

THEOREM 3   Wronskians of Solutions

Suppose that y_1, y_2, ..., y_n are n solutions of the homogeneous nth-order linear equation

$$y^{(n)} + p_1(x)y^{(n-1)} + \cdots + p_{n-1}(x)y' + p_n(x)y = 0 \qquad (3)$$

on an open interval I, where each p_i is continuous. Let

$$W = W(y_1, y_2, \ldots, y_n).$$

(a) If y_1, y_2, ..., y_n are linearly dependent, then $W \equiv 0$ on I.
(b) If y_1, y_2, ..., y_n are linearly independent, then $W \neq 0$ at each point of I.

Thus there are just two possibilities: Either $W = 0$ everywhere on I, or $W \neq 0$ everywhere on I.

Proof: We have already proven part (a). To prove part (b), it is sufficient to assume that $W(a) = 0$ at some point of I, and show this implies that the solutions y_1, y_2, ..., y_n are linearly dependent. But $W(a)$ is simply the determinant of coefficients of the system of n homogeneous linear equations

$$
\begin{aligned}
c_1 y_1(a) + \quad & c_2 y_2(a) + \cdots + \quad c_n y_n(a) = 0, \\
c_1 y_1'(a) + \quad & c_2 y_2'(a) + \cdots + \quad c_n y_n'(a) = 0, \\
& \vdots \\
c_1 y_1^{(n-1)}(a) + & c_2 y_2^{(n-1)}(a) + \cdots + c_n y_n^{(n-1)}(a) = 0
\end{aligned} \tag{12}
$$

in the n unknowns $c_1, c_2, \ldots, c_n$. Because $W(a) = 0$, the basic fact from linear algebra quoted just after (9) implies that the equations in (12) have a nontrivial solution. That is, the numbers $c_1, c_2, \ldots, c_n$ are not all zero.

We now use these values to define the particular solution

$$
Y(x) = c_1 y_1(x) + c_2 y_2(x) + \cdots + c_n y_n(x) \tag{13}
$$

of Eq. (3). The equations in (12) then imply that Y satisfies the trivial initial conditions

$$
Y(a) = Y'(a) = \cdots = Y^{(n-1)}(a) = 0.
$$

Theorem 2 (uniqueness) therefore implies that $Y(x) \equiv 0$ on I. In view of (13) and the fact that $c_1, c_2, \ldots, c_n$ are not all zero, this is the desired conclusion that the solutions $y_1, y_2, \ldots, y_n$ are linearly dependent. This completes the proof of Theorem 3. ▲

General Solutions

We can now show that, given any fixed set of n linearly independent solutions of a *homogeneous* nth-order equation, *every* (other) solution of the equation can be expressed as a linear combination of those n particular solutions. Using the fact from Theorem 3 that the Wronskian of n linearly independent solutions is nonzero, the proof of the following theorem is essentially the same as the proof of Theorem 4 of Section 3.1 (the case $n = 2$).

THEOREM 4   General Solutions of Homogeneous Equations

Let $y_1, y_2, \ldots, y_n$ be n linearly independent solutions of the homogeneous equation

$$
y^{(n)} + p_1(x) y^{(n-1)} + \cdots + p_{n-1}(x) y' + p_n(x) y = 0 \tag{3}
$$

on an open interval I where the p_i are continuous. If Y is any solution whatsoever of Eq. (3), then there exist numbers $c_1, c_2, \ldots, c_n$ such that

$$
Y(x) = c_1 y_1(x) + c_2 y_2(x) + \cdots + c_n y_n(x)
$$

for all x in I.

Thus *every* solution of a homogeneous nth-order linear differential equation is a linear combination

➤ $$ y = c_1 y_1 + c_2 y_2 + \cdots + c_n y_n $$

of any n given linearly independent solutions. On this basis we call such a linear combination a **general solution** of the differential equation.

Example 6	According to Example 4, the particular solutions $y_1(x) = e^{-3x}$, $y_2(x) = \cos 2x$, and $y_3(x) = \sin 2x$ of the linear differential equation $y^{(3)} + 3y'' + 4y' + 12y = 0$ are linearly independent. Now Theorem 2 says that—given b_0, b_1, and b_2—there exists a particular solution $y(x)$ satisfying the initial conditions $y(0) = b_0$, $y'(0) = b_1$, and $y''(0) = b_2$. Hence Theorem 4 implies that *this* particular solution is a linear combination of y_1, y_2, and y_3. That is, there exist coefficients c_1, c_2, and c_3 such that

$$y(x) = c_1 e^{-3x} + c_2 \cos 2x + c_3 \sin 2x.$$

Upon successive differentiation and substitution of $x = 0$, we discover that to find these coefficients, we need only solve the three linear equations

$$\begin{aligned} c_1 + c_2 \quad\quad\quad &= b_0, \\ -3c_1 \quad\quad + 2c_3 &= b_1, \\ 9c_1 - 4c_2 \quad\quad &= b_2. \end{aligned}$$

(See the application for this section.) ∎

Nonhomogeneous Equations

We now consider the *nonhomogeneous* nth-order linear differential equation

➤
$$y^{(n)} + p_1(x)y^{(n-1)} + \cdots + p_{n-1}(x)y' + p_n(x)y = f(x) \qquad (2)$$

with associated homogeneous equation

➤
$$y^{(n)} + p_1(x)y^{(n-1)} + \cdots + p_{n-1}(x)y' + p_n(x)y = 0. \qquad (3)$$

Suppose that a single fixed particular solution y_p of the nonhomogeneous equation in (2) is known, and that Y is any other solution of Eq. (2). If $y_c = Y - y_p$, then subsitution of y_c in the differential equation gives (using the linearity of differentiation)

$$\begin{aligned} y_c^{(n)} + p_1 y_c^{(n-1)} &+ \cdots + p_{n-1}y_c' + p_n y_c \\ &= \left[(Y^{(n)} + p_1 Y^{(n-1)} + \cdots + p_{n-1}Y' + p_n Y) \right] \\ &\quad - \left[(y_p^{(n)} + p_1 y_p^{(n-1)} + \cdots + p_{n-1}y_p' + p_n y_p) \right] \\ &= f(x) - f(x) = 0. \end{aligned}$$

Thus $y_c = Y - y_p$ is a solution of the associated homogeneous equation in (3). Then

➤
$$Y = y_c + y_p, \qquad (14)$$

and it follows from Theorem 4 that

➤
$$y_c = c_1 y_1 + c_2 y_2 + \cdots + c_n y_n, \qquad (15)$$

where $y_1, y_2, \ldots, y_n$ are linearly independent solutions of the associated *homogeneous* equation. We call y_c a **complementary function** of the nonhomogeneous equation and have thus proved that a *general solution* of the nonhomogeneous equation in (2) is the sum of its complementary function y_c and a single particular solution y_p of Eq. (2).

> **THEOREM 5   Solutions of Nonhomogeneous Equations**
>
> Let y_p be a particular solution of the nonhomogeneous equation in (2) on an open interval I where the functions p_i and f are continuous. Let $y_1, y_2, \ldots, y_n$ be linearly independent solutions of the associated homogeneous equation in (3). If Y is any solution whatsoever of Eq. (2) on I, then there exist numbers $c_1, c_2, \ldots, c_n$ such that
>
> $$Y(x) = c_1 y_1(x) + c_2 y_2(x) + \cdots + c_n y_n(x) + y_p(x) \qquad (16)$$
>
> for all x in I.

Example 7   It is evident that $y_p = 3x$ is a particular solution of the equation

$$y'' + 4y = 12x, \qquad (17)$$

and that $y_c(x) = c_1 \cos 2x + c_2 \sin 2x$ is its complementary solution. Find a solution of Eq. (17) that satisfies the initial conditions $y(0) = 5$, $y'(0) = 7$.

Solution   The general solution of Eq. (17) is

$$y(x) = c_1 \cos 2x + c_2 \sin 2x + 3x.$$

Now

$$y'(x) = -2c_1 \sin 2x + 2c_2 \cos 2x + 3.$$

Hence the initial conditions give

$$y(0) = \quad c_1 \qquad = 5,$$
$$y'(0) = 2c_2 + 3 = 7.$$

We find that $c_1 = 5$ and $c_2 = 2$. Thus the desired solution is

$$y(x) = 5 \cos 2x + 2 \sin 2x + 3x. \qquad \blacksquare$$

3.2   Problems

In Problems 1 through 6, show directly that the given functions are linearly dependent on the real line. That is, find a nontrivial linear combination of the given functions that vanishes identically.

1. $f(x) = 2x$, $g(x) = 3x^2$, $h(x) = 5x - 8x^2$
2. $f(x) = 5$, $g(x) = 2 - 3x^2$, $h(x) = 10 + 15x^2$
3. $f(x) = 0$, $g(x) = \sin x$, $h(x) = e^x$
4. $f(x) = 17$, $g(x) = 2\sin^2 x$, $h(x) = 3\cos^2 x$
5. $f(x) = 17$, $g(x) = \cos^2 x$, $h(x) = \cos 2x$
6. $f(x) = e^x$, $g(x) = \cosh x$, $h(x) = \sinh x$

In Problems 7 through 12, use the Wronskian to prove that the given functions are linearly independent on the indicated interval.

7. $f(x) = 1$, $g(x) = x$, $h(x) = x^2$; the real line
8. $f(x) = e^x$, $g(x) = e^{2x}$, $h(x) = e^{3x}$; the real line
9. $f(x) = e^x$, $g(x) = \cos x$, $h(x) = \sin x$; the real line
10. $f(x) = e^x$, $g(x) = x^{-2}$, $h(x) = x^{-2} \ln x$; $x > 0$
11. $f(x) = x$, $g(x) = xe^x$, $h(x) = x^2 e^x$; the real line
12. $f(x) = x$, $g(x) = \cos(\ln x)$, $h(x) = \sin(\ln x)$; $x > 0$

In Problems 13 through 20, a third-order homogeneous linear equation and three linearly independent solutions are given. Find a particular solution satisfying the given initial conditions.

13. $y^{(3)} + 2y'' - y' - 2y = 0$; $y(0) = 1$, $y'(0) = 2$, $y''(0) = 0$;
$y_1 = e^x$, $y_2 = e^{-x}$, $y_3 = e^{-2x}$

14. $y^{(3)} - 6y'' + 11y' - 6y = 0$; $y(0) = 0$, $y'(0) = 0$, $y''(0) = 3$; $y_1 = e^x$, $y_2 = e^{2x}$, $y_3 = e^{3x}$

15. $y^{(3)} - 3y'' + 3y' - y = 0$; $y(0) = 2$, $y'(0) = 0$, $y''(0) = 0$; $y_1 = e^x$, $y_2 = xe^x$, $y_3 = x^2 e^x$

16. $y^{(3)} - 5y'' + 8y' - 4y = 0$; $y(0) = 1$, $y'(0) = 4$, $y''(0) = 0$; $y_1 = e^x$, $y_2 = e^{2x}$, $y_3 = xe^{2x}$

17. $y^{(3)} + 9y' = 0$; $y(0) = 3$, $y'(0) = -1$, $y''(0) = 2$; $y_1 = 1$, $y_2 = \cos 3x$, $y_3 = \sin 3x$

18. $y^{(3)} - 3y'' + 4y' - 2y = 0$; $y(0) = 1$, $y'(0) = 0$, $y''(0) = 0$; $y_1 = e^x$, $y_2 = e^x \cos x$, $y_3 = e^x \sin x$.

19. $x^3 y^{(3)} - 3x^2 y'' + 6xy' - 6y = 0$; $y(1) = 6$, $y'(1) = 14$, $y''(1) = 22$; $y_1 = x$, $y_2 = x^2$, $y_3 = x^3$

20. $x^3 y^{(3)} + 6x^2 y'' + 4xy' - 4y = 0$; $y(1) = 1$, $y'(1) = 5$, $y''(1) = -11$; $y_1 = x$, $y_2 = x^{-2}$, $y_3 = x^{-2} \ln x$

In Problems 21 through 24, a nonhomogeneous differential equation, a complementary solution y_c, and a particular solution y_p are given. Find a solution satisfying the given initial conditions.

21. $y'' + y = 3x$; $y(0) = 2$, $y'(0) = -2$; $y_c = c_1 \cos x + c_2 \sin x$; $y_p = 3x$

22. $y'' - 4y = 12$; $y(0) = 0$, $y'(0) = 10$; $y_c = c_1 e^{2x} + c_2 e^{-2x}$; $y_p = -3$

23. $y'' - 2y' - 3y = 6$; $y(0) = 3$, $y'(0) = 11$; $y_c = c_1 e^{-x} + c_2 e^{3x}$; $y_p = -2$

24. $y'' - 2y' + 2y = 2x$; $y(0) = 4$, $y'(0) = 8$; $y_c = c_1 e^x \cos x + c_2 e^x \sin x$; $y_p = x + 1$

25. Let $Ly = y'' + py' + qy$. Suppose that y_1 and y_2 are two functions such that

$$Ly_1 = f(x) \quad \text{and} \quad Ly_2 = g(x).$$

Show that their sum $y = y_1 + y_2$ satisfies the nonhomogeneous equation $Ly = f(x) + g(x)$.

26. **(a)** Find by inspection particular solutions of the two nonhomogeneous equations

$$y'' + 2y = 4 \quad \text{and} \quad y'' + 2y = 6x.$$

(b) Use the method of Problem 25 to find a particular solution of the differential equation $y'' + 2y = 6x + 4$.

27. Prove directly that the functions

$$f_1(x) \equiv 1, \quad f_2(x) = x, \quad \text{and} \quad f_3(x) = x^2$$

are linearly independent on the whole real line. (*Suggestion*: Assume that $c_1 + c_2 x + c_3 x^2 = 0$. Differentiate this equation twice, and conclude from the equations you get that $c_1 = c_2 = c_3 = 0$.)

28. Generalize the method of Problem 27 to prove directly that the functions

$$f_0(x) \equiv 1, \quad f_1(x) = x, \quad f_2(x) = x^2, \ldots, \quad f_n(x) = x^n$$

are linearly independent on the real line.

29. Use the result of Problem 28 and the definition of linear independence to prove directly that, for any constant r, the functions

$$f_0(x) = e^{rx}, \quad f_1(x) = xe^{rx}, \quad \ldots, \quad f_n(x) = x^n e^{rx}$$

are linearly independent on the whole real line.

30. Verify that $y_1 = x$ and $y_2 = x^2$ are linearly independent solutions on the entire real line of the equation

$$x^2 y'' - 2xy' + 2y = 0,$$

but that $W(x, x^2)$ vanishes at $x = 0$. Why do these observations not contradict part (b) of Theorem 3?

31. This problem indicates why we can impose *only* n initial conditions on a solution of an nth-order linear differential equation. **(a)** Given the equation

$$y'' + py' + qy = 0,$$

explain why the value of $y''(a)$ is determined by the values of $y(a)$ and $y'(a)$. **(b)** Prove that the equation

$$y'' - 2y' - 5y = 0$$

has a solution satisfying the conditions

$$y(0) = 1, \quad y'(0) = 0, \quad \text{and} \quad y''(0) = C$$

if and only if $C = 5$.

32. Prove that an nth-order homogeneous linear differential equation satisfying the hypotheses of Theorem 2 has n linearly independent solutions $y_1, y_2, \ldots, y_n$. (*Suggestion*: Let y_i be the unique solution such that

$$y_i^{(i-1)}(a) = 1 \quad \text{and} \quad y_i^{(k)}(a) = 0 \quad \text{if } k \neq i - 1.)$$

33. Suppose that the three numbers r_1, r_2, and r_3 are distinct. Show that the three functions $\exp(r_1 x)$, $\exp(r_2 x)$, and $\exp(r_3 x)$ are linearly independent by showing that their Wronskian

$$W = \exp[(r_1 + r_2 + r_3)x] \cdot \begin{vmatrix} 1 & 1 & 1 \\ r_1 & r_2 & r_3 \\ r_1^2 & r_2^2 & r_3^2 \end{vmatrix}$$

is nonzero for all x.

34. Assume as known that the **Vandermonde determinant**

$$V = \begin{vmatrix} 1 & 1 & \cdots & 1 \\ r_1 & r_2 & \cdots & r_n \\ r_1^2 & r_2^2 & \cdots & r_n^2 \\ \vdots & \vdots & & \vdots \\ r_1^{n-1} & r_2^{n-1} & \cdots & r_n^{n-1} \end{vmatrix}$$

is nonzero if the numbers $r_1, r_2, \ldots, r_n$ are distinct. Prove by the method of Problem 33 that the functions

$$f_i(x) = \exp(r_i x), \quad 1 \leq i \leq n$$

are linearly independent.

35. According to Problem 32 of Section 3.1, the Wronskian $W(y_1, y_2)$ of two solutions of the second-order equation

$$y'' + p_1(x)y' + p_2(x)y = 0$$

is given by Abel's's formula

$$W(x) = K \exp\left(-\int p_1(x)\,dx\right)$$

for some constant K. It can be shown that the Wronskian of n solutions $y_1, y_2, \ldots, y_n$ of the nth-order equation

$$y^{(n)} + p_1(x)y^{(n-1)} + \cdots + p_{n-1}(x)y' + p_n(x)y = 0$$

satisfies the same identity. Prove this for the case $n = 3$ as follows: **(a)** The derivative of a determinant of functions is the sum of the determinants obtained by separately differentiating the rows of the original determinant. Conclude that

$$W' = \begin{vmatrix} y_1 & y_2 & y_3 \\ y_1' & y_2' & y_3' \\ y_1^{(3)} & y_2^{(3)} & y_3^{(3)} \end{vmatrix}.$$

(b) Substitute for $y_1^{(3)}$, $y_2^{(3)}$, and $y_3^{(3)}$ from the equation

$$y^{(3)} + p_1 y'' + p_2 y' + p_3 y = 0,$$

and then show that $W' = -p_1 W$. Integration now gives Abel's formula.

36. Suppose that one solution $y_1(x)$ of the homogeneous second-order linear differential equation

$$y'' + p(x)y' + q(x)y = 0 \qquad (18)$$

is known (on an interval I where p and q are continuous functions). The method of **reduction of order** consists of substituting $y_2(x) = v(x)y_1(x)$ in (18) and attempting to determine the function $v(x)$ so that $y_2(x)$ is a second linearly independent solution of (18). After substituting $y = v(x)y_1(x)$ in Eq. (18), use the fact that $y_1(x)$ is a solution to deduce that

$$y_1 v'' + (2y_1' + p y_1)v' = 0. \qquad (19)$$

If $y_1(x)$ is known, then (19) is a separable equation that is readily solved for the derivative $v'(x)$ of $v(x)$. Integration of $v'(x)$ then gives the desired (nonconstant) function $v(x)$.

37. Before applying Eq. (19) with a given homogeneous second-order linear differential equation and a known solution $y_1(x)$, the equation must first be written in the form of (18) with leading coefficient 1 in order to correctly determine the coefficient function $p(x)$. Frequently it is more convenient to simply substitute $y = v(x)y_1(x)$ in the given differential equation and then proceed directly to find $v(x)$. Thus, starting with the readily verified solution $y_1(x) = x^3$ of the equation

$$x^2 y'' - 5xy' + 9y = 0 \quad (x > 0),$$

substitute $y = vx^3$ and deduce that $xv'' + v' = 0$. Thence solve for $v(x) = C \ln x$, and thereby obtain (with $C = 1$) the second solution $y_2(x) = x^3 \ln x$.

In each of Problems 38 through 42, a differential equation and one solution y_1 are given. Use the method of reduction of order as in Problem 37 to find a second linearly independent solution y_2.

38. $x^2 y'' + xy' - 9y = 0 \ (x > 0); \ y_1(x) = x^3$

39. $4y'' - 4y' + y = 0; \ y_1(x) = e^{x/2}$

40. $x^2 y'' - x(x+2)y' + (x+2)y = 0 \ (x > 0); \ y_1(x) = x$

41. $(x+1)y'' - (x+2)y' + y = 0 \ (x > -1); \ y_1(x) = e^x$

42. $(1 - x^2)y'' + 2xy' - 2y = 0 \ (-1 < x < 1); \ y_1(x) = x$

43. First note that $y_1(x) = x$ is one solution of Legendre's equation of order 1,

$$(1 - x^2)y'' - 2xy' + 2y = 0.$$

Then use the method of reduction of order to derive the second solution

$$y_2(x) = 1 - \frac{x}{2} \ln \frac{1+x}{1-x} \quad \text{(for } -1 < x < 1\text{)}.$$

44. First verify by substitution that $y_1(x) = x^{-1/2} \cos x$ is one solution (for $x > 0$) of Bessel's equation of order $\frac{1}{2}$,

$$x^2 y'' + xy' + (x^2 - \tfrac{1}{4})y = 0.$$

Then derive by reduction of order the second solution $y_2(x) = x^{-1/2} \sin x$.

3.2 Application Plotting Third-Order Solution Families

This application deals with the plotting by computer of families of solutions such as those illustrated in Figs. 3.2.2 through 3.2.4. We know from Example 6 that the general solution of

$$y^{(3)} + 3y'' + 4y' + 12y = 0 \qquad (1)$$

is

$$y(x) = c_1 e^{-3x} + c_2 \cos 2x + c_3 \sin 2x. \qquad (2)$$

For Fig. 3.2.2, use the method of Example 6 to show that the particular solution of Eq. (1) satisfying the initial conditions $y(0) = a$, $y'(0) = 0$, and $y''(0) = 0$ is given by

$$y(x) = \frac{a}{13} \left(4e^{-3x} + 9 \cos 2x + 6 \sin 2x \right). \tag{3}$$

The MATLAB loop

```
x = -1.5 : 0.02 : 5      % x-vector from x = -1.5 to x = 5
for a = -3 : 1 : 3       % for a = -3 to 3 with da = 1 do
    c1 = 4*a/13;
    c2 = 9*a/13;
    c3 = 6*a/13;
    y = c1*exp(-3*x) + c2*cos(2*x) + c3*sin(2*x);
    plot(x,y)
end
```

was used to generate Fig. 3.2.2.

For Fig. 3.2.3, show that the particular solution of Eq. (1) satisfying the initial conditions $y(0) = 0$, $y'(0) = b$, and $y''(0) = 0$ is given by

$$y(x) = \frac{b}{2} \sin 2x, \tag{4}$$

and alter the preceding for-loop accordingly.

For Fig. 3.2.3, show that the particular solution of Eq. (1) satisfying the initial conditions $y(0) = 0$, $y'(0) = 0$, and $y''(0) = c$ is given by

$$y(x) = \frac{c}{26} \left(2e^{-3x} - 2 \cos 2x + 3 \sin 2x \right). \tag{5}$$

Computer algebra systems such as *Maple* and *Mathematica,* as well as graphing calculators, have commands to carry out for-loops such as the one shown here. Begin by reproducing Figs. 3.2.2 through 3.2.4. Then plot similar families of solution curves for the differential equations in Problems 13 through 20.

3.3 Homogeneous Equations with Constant Coefficients

In Section 3.2 we saw that a general solution of an nth-order homogeneous linear equation is a linear combination of n linearly independent particular solutions, but we said little about how actually to find even a single solution. The solution of a linear differential equation with *variable* coefficients ordinarily requires numerical methods (Chapter 2) or infinite series methods (Chapter 8). But we can now show how to find, explicitly and in a rather straightforward way, n linearly independent solutions of a given nth-order linear equation if it has *constant* coefficients. The general such equation may be written in the form

$$\blacktriangleright \qquad a_n y^{(n)} + a_{n-1} y^{(n-1)} + \cdots + a_2 y'' + a_1 y' + a_0 y = 0, \tag{1}$$

where the coefficients $a_0, a_1, a_2, \ldots, a_n$ are real constants with $a_n \neq 0$.

The Characteristic Equation

We first look for a *single* solution of Eq. (1), and begin with the observation that

$$\frac{d^k}{dx^k}(e^{rx}) = r^k e^{rx}, \tag{2}$$

so any derivative of e^{rx} is a constant multiple of e^{rx}. Hence, if we substituted $y = e^{rx}$ in Eq. (1), each term would be a constant multiple of e^{rx}, with the constant coefficients depending on r and the coefficients a_k. This suggests that we try to find r so that all these multiples of e^{rx} will have sum zero, in which case $y = e^{rx}$ will be a solution of Eq. (1).

For example, in Section 3.1 we substituted $y = e^{rx}$ in the second-order equation

$$ay'' + by' + cy = 0$$

to derive the characteristic equation

$$ar^2 + br + c = 0$$

that r must satisfy.

To carry out this technique in the general case, we substitute $y = e^{rx}$ in Eq. (1), and with the aid of Eq. (2) we find the result to be

$$a_n r^n e^{rx} + a_{n-1} r^{n-1} e^{rx} + \cdots + a_2 r^2 e^{rx} + a_1 r e^{rx} + a_0 e^{rx} = 0;$$

that is,

$$e^{rx}\left(a_n r^n + a_{n-1} r^{n-1} + \cdots + a_2 r^2 + a_1 r + a_0\right) = 0.$$

Because e^{rx} is never zero, we see that $y = e^{rx}$ will be a solution of Eq. (1) precisely when r is a root of the equation

$$\blacktriangleright \qquad a_n r^n + a_{n-1} r^{n-1} + \cdots + a_2 r^2 + a_1 r + a_0 = 0. \tag{3}$$

This equation is called the **characteristic equation** or **auxiliary equation** of the differential equation in (1). Our problem, then, is reduced to the solution of this purely algebraic equation.

According to the fundamental theorem of algebra, every nth-degree polynomial—such as the one in Eq. (3)—has n zeros, though not necessarily distinct and not necessarily real. Finding the exact values of these zeros may be difficult or even impossible; the quadratic formula is sufficient for second-degree equations, but for equations of higher degree we may need either to spot a fortuitous factorization or to apply a numerical technique such as Newton's method (or use a calculator/computer **solve** command).

Distinct Real Roots

Whatever the method we use, let us suppose that we have solved the characteristic equation. Then we can always write a general solution of the differential equation. The situation is slightly more complicated in the case of repeated roots or complex roots of Eq. (3), so let us first examine the simplest case—in which the characteristic equation has n distinct (no two equal) *real* roots $r_1, r_2, \ldots, r_n$. Then the functions

$$e^{r_1 x}, e^{r_2 x} \ldots, e^{r_n x}$$

are all solutions of Eq. (1), and (by Problem 34 of Section 3.2) these n solutions are linearly independent on the entire real line. In summary, we have proved Theorem 1.

> **THEOREM 1   Distinct Real Roots**
>
> If the roots $r_1, r_2, \ldots, r_n$ of the characteristic equation in (3) are real and distinct, then
>
> $$\blacktriangleright \qquad y(x) = c_1 e^{r_1 x} + c_2 e^{r_2 x} + \cdots + c_n e^{r_n x} \qquad\qquad (4)$$
>
> is a general solution of Eq. (1).

Example 1 Solve the initial value problem

$$y^{(3)} + 3y'' - 10y' = 0;$$
$$y(0) = 7, \quad y'(0) = 0, \quad y''(0) = 70.$$

Solution The characteristic equation of the given differential equation is

$$r^3 + 3r^2 - 10r = 0.$$

We solve by factoring:

$$r(r^2 + 3r - 10) = r(r + 5)(r - 2) = 0,$$

and so the characteristic equation has the three distinct real roots $r = 0$, $r = -5$, and $r = 2$. Because $e^0 = 1$, Theorem 1 gives the general solution

$$y(x) = c_1 + c_2 e^{-5x} + c_3 e^{2x}.$$

Then the given initial conditions yield the linear equations

$$
\begin{aligned}
y(0) &= c_1 + & c_2 + & c_3 = & 7, \\
y'(0) &= & -5c_2 + & 2c_3 = & 0, \\
y''(0) &= & 25c_2 + & 4c_3 = & 70
\end{aligned}
$$

in the coefficients c_1, c_2, and c_3. The last two equations give $y''(0) - 2y'(0) = 35c_2 = 70$, so $c_2 = 2$. Then the second equation gives $c_3 = 5$, and finally the first equation gives $c_1 = 0$. Thus the desired particular solution is

$$y(x) = 2e^{-5x} + 5e^{2x}. \qquad\qquad \blacksquare$$

Polynomial Differential Operators

If the roots of the characteristic equation in (3) are *not* distinct—there are repeated roots—then we cannot produce n linearly independent solutions of Eq. (1) by the method of Theorem 1. For example, if the roots are 1, 2, 2, and 2, we obtain only the *two* functions e^x and e^{2x}. The problem, then, is to produce the missing linearly independent solutions. For this purpose, it is convenient to adopt "operator notation" and write Eq. (1) in the form $Ly = 0$, where the **operator**

$$L = a_n \frac{d^n}{dx^n} + a_{n-1} \frac{d^{n-1}}{dx^{n-1}} + \cdots + a_2 \frac{d^2}{dx^2} + a_1 \frac{d}{dx} + a_0 \qquad\qquad (5)$$

operates on the n-times differentiable function $y(x)$ to produce the linear combination

$$Ly = a_n y^{(n)} + a_{n-1} y^{(n-1)} + \cdots + a_2 y^{(2)} + a_1 y' + a_0 y$$

of y and its first n derivatives. We also denote by $D = d/dx$ the operation of differentiation with respect to x, so that

$$Dy = y', \quad D^2 y = y'', \quad D^3 y = y^{(3)},$$

and so on. In terms of D, the operator L in (5) may be written

$$L = a_n D^n + a_{n-1} D^{n-1} + \cdots + a_2 D^2 + a_1 D + a_0, \tag{6}$$

and we will find it useful to think of the right-hand side in Eq. (6) as a (formal) nth-degree polynomial in the "variable" D; it is a **polynomial differential operator.**

A first-degree polynomial operator with leading coefficient 1 has the form $D - a$, where a is a real number. It operates on a function $y = y(x)$ to produce

$$(D - a)y = Dy - ay = y' - ay.$$

The important fact about such operators is that any two of them *commute*:

$$(D - a)(D - b)y = (D - b)(D - a)y \tag{7}$$

for any twice differentiable function $y = y(x)$. The proof of the formula in (7) is the following computation:

$$\begin{aligned}
(D - a)(D - b)y &= (D - a)(y' - by) \\
&= D(y' - by) - a(y' - by) \\
&= y'' - (b + a)y' + aby = y'' - (a + b)y' + bay \\
&= D(y' - ay) - b(y' - ay) \\
&= (D - b)(y' - ay) = (D - b)(D - a)y.
\end{aligned}$$

We see here also that $(D - a)(D - b) = D^2 - (a + b)D + ab$. Similarly, it can be shown by induction on the number of factors that an operator product of the form $(D - a_1)(D - a_2) \cdots (D - a_n)$ expands—by multiplying out and collecting coefficients—in the same way as does an ordinary product $(x - a_1)(x - a_2) \cdots (x - a_n)$ of linear factors, with x denoting a real variable. Consequently, the algebra of polynomial differential operators closely resembles the algebra of ordinary real polynomials.

Repeated Real Roots

Let us now consider the possibility that the characteristic equation

$$a_n r^n + a_{n-1} r^{n-1} + \cdots + a_2 r^2 + a_1 r + a_0 = 0 \tag{3}$$

has *repeated* roots. For example, suppose that Eq. (3) has only two distinct roots, r_0 of multiplicity 1 and r_1 of multiplicity $k = n - 1 > 1$. Then (after dividing by a_n) Eq. (3) can be rewritten in the form

$$(r - r_1)^k (r - r_0) = (r - r_0)(r - r_1)^k = 0. \tag{8}$$

Similarly, the corresponding operator L in (6) can be written as

$$L = (D - r_1)^k (D - r_0) = (D - r_0)(D - r_1)^k, \tag{9}$$

the order of the factors making no difference because of the formula in (7).

Two solutions of the differential equation $Ly = 0$ are certainly $y_0 = e^{r_0 x}$ and $y_1 = e^{r_1 x}$. This is, however, not sufficient; we need $k + 1$ linearly independent solutions in order to construct a general solution, because the equation is of order $k + 1$. To find the missing $k - 1$ solutions, we note that

$$Ly = (D - r_0)[(D - r_1)^k y] = 0.$$

Consequently, *every* solution of the kth-order equation

$$(D - r_1)^k y = 0 \tag{10}$$

will also be a solution of the original equation $Ly = 0$. Hence our problem is reduced to that of finding a general solution of the differential equation in (10).

The fact that $y_1 = e^{r_1 x}$ is one solution of Eq. (10) suggests that we try the substitution

$$y(x) = u(x)y_1(x) = u(x)e^{r_1 x}, \tag{11}$$

where $u(x)$ is a function yet to be determined. Observe that

$$(D - r_1)\left[ue^{r_1 x}\right] = (Du)e^{r_1 x} + u(r_1 e^{r_1 x}) - r_1(ue^{r_1 x}) = (Du)e^{r_1 x}. \tag{12}$$

Upon k applications of this fact, it follows that

$$(D - r_1)^k \left[ue^{r_1 x}\right] = (D^k u)e^{r_1 x} \tag{13}$$

for any sufficiently differentiable function $u(x)$. Hence $y = ue^{r_1 x}$ will be a solution of Eq. (10) if and only if $D^k u = u^{(k)} = 0$. But this is so if and only if

$$u(x) = c_1 + c_2 x + c_3 x^2 + \cdots + c_k x^{k-1},$$

a polynomial of degree at most $k - 1$. Hence our desired solution of Eq. (10) is

$$y(x) = ue^{r_1 x} = (c_1 + c_2 x + c_3 x^2 + \cdots + c_k x^{k-1})e^{r_1 x}.$$

In particular, we see here the additional solutions $xe^{r_1 x}, x^2 e^{r_1 x}, \ldots, x^{k-1}e^{r_1 x}$ of the original differential equation $Ly = 0$.

The preceding analysis can be carried out with the operator $D - r_1$ replaced with an arbitrary polynomial operator. When this is done, the result is a proof of the following theorem.

THEOREM 2   Repeated Roots

If the characteristic equation in (3) has a repeated root r of multiplicity k, then the part of a general solution of the differential equation in (1) corresponding to r is of the form

> $$(c_1 + c_2 x + c_3 x^2 + \cdots + c_k x^{k-1})e^{rx}. \tag{14}$$

We may observe that, according to Problem 29 of Section 3.2, the k functions $e^{rx}, xe^{rx}, x^2 e^{rx}, \ldots,$ and $x^{k-1}e^{rx}$ involved in (14) are linearly independent on the real line. Thus a root of multiplicity k corresponds to k linearly independent solutions of the differential equation.

Example 2 Find a general solution of the fifth-order differential equation

$$9y^{(5)} - 6y^{(4)} + y^{(3)} = 0.$$

Solution The characteristic equation is

$$9r^5 - 6r^4 + r^3 = r^3(9r^2 - 6r + 1) = r^3(3r - 1)^2 = 0.$$

It has the triple root $r = 0$ and the double root $r = \frac{1}{3}$. The triple root $r = 0$ contributes

$$c_1 e^{0 \cdot x} + c_2 x e^{0 \cdot x} + c_3 x^2 e^{0 \cdot x} = c_1 + c_2 x + c_3 x^2$$

to the solution, while the double root $r = \frac{1}{3}$ contributes $c_4 e^{x/3} + c_5 x e^{x/3}$. Hence a general solution of the given differential equation is

$$y(x) = c_1 + c_2 x + c_3 x^2 + c_4 e^{x/3} + c_5 x e^{x/3}.$$ ∎

Complex-Valued Functions and Euler's Formula

Because we have assumed that the coefficients of the differential equation and its characteristic equation are real, any complex (nonreal) roots will occur in complex conjugate pairs $a \pm bi$ where a and b are real and $i = \sqrt{-1}$. This raises the question of what might be meant by an exponential such as $e^{(a+bi)x}$.

To answer this question, we recall from elementary calculus the Taylor (or MacLaurin) series for the exponential function

$$e^t = \sum_{n=0}^{\infty} \frac{t^n}{n!} = 1 + t + \frac{t^2}{2!} + \frac{t^3}{3!} + \frac{t^4}{4!} + \cdots.$$

If we substitute $t = i\theta$ in this series and recall that $i^2 = -1$, $i^3 = -i$, $i^4 = 1$, and so on, we get

$$e^{i\theta} = \sum_{n=0}^{\infty} \frac{(i\theta)^n}{n!}$$

$$= 1 + i\theta - \frac{\theta^2}{2!} - \frac{i\theta^3}{3!} + \frac{\theta^4}{4!} + \frac{i\theta^5}{5!} - \cdots$$

$$= \left(1 - \frac{\theta^2}{2!} + \frac{\theta^4}{4!} - \cdots\right) + i\left(\theta - \frac{\theta^3}{3!} + \frac{\theta^5}{5!} - \cdots\right).$$

Because the two real series in the last line are the Taylor series for $\cos\theta$ and $\sin\theta$, respectively, this implies that

$$e^{i\theta} = \cos\theta + i\sin\theta. \tag{15}$$

This result is known as **Euler's formula**. Because of it, we *define* the exponential function e^z, for $z = x + iy$ an arbitrary complex number, to be

$$e^z = e^{x+iy} = e^x e^{iy} = e^x(\cos y + i\sin y). \tag{16}$$

Thus it appears that complex roots of the characteristic equation will lead to complex-valued solutions of the differential equation. A **complex-valued function**

F of the real variable x associates with each real number x (in its domain of definition) the complex number

$$F(x) = f(x) + ig(x). \tag{17}$$

The real-valued functions f and g are called the **real** and **imaginary** parts, respectively, of F. If they are differentiable, we define the **derivative** F' of F by

$$F'(x) = f'(x) + ig'(x). \tag{18}$$

Thus we simply differentiate the real and imaginary parts of F separately.

We say that the complex-valued function $F(x)$ satisfies the homogeneous linear differential equation $L[F(x)] = 0$ provided that its real and imaginary parts in (17) separately satisfy this equation—so $L[F(x)] = L[f(x)] + iL[g(x)] = 0$.

The particular complex-valued functions of interest here are of the form $F(x) = e^{rx}$, where $r = a \pm bi$. We note from Euler's formula that

$$e^{(a+bi)x} = e^{ax} e^{ibx} = e^{ax}(\cos bx + i \sin bx) \tag{19a}$$

and

$$e^{(a-bi)x} = e^{ax} e^{-ibx} = e^{ax}(\cos bx - i \sin bx). \tag{19b}$$

The most important property of e^{rx} is that

$$D_x(e^{rx}) = re^{rx}, \tag{20}$$

if r is a complex number. The proof of this assertion is a straightforward computation based on the definitions and formulas given earlier:

$$\begin{aligned}
D_x(e^{rx}) &= D_x(e^{ax} \cos bx) + i D_x(e^{ax} \sin bx) \\
&= \left(ae^{ax} \cos bx - be^{ax} \sin bx\right) + i \left(ae^{ax} \sin bx + be^{ax} \cos bx\right) \\
&= (a + bi)(e^{ax} \cos bx + ie^{ax} \sin bx) = re^{rx}.
\end{aligned}$$

Complex Roots

It follows from Eq. (20) that when r is complex (just as when r is real), e^{rx} will be a solution of the differential equation in (1) if and only if r is a root of its characteristic equation. If the complex conjugate pair of roots $r_1 = a + bi$ and $r_2 = a - bi$ are simple (nonrepeated), then the corresponding part of a general solution of Eq. (1) is

$$\begin{aligned}
y(x) &= C_1 e^{r_1 x} + C_2 e^{r_2 x} = C_1 e^{(a+bi)x} + C_2 e^{(a-bi)x} \\
&= C_1 e^{ax}(\cos bx + i \sin bx) + C_2 e^{ax}(\cos bx - i \sin bx) \\
y(x) &= (C_1 + C_2)e^{ax} \cos bx + i(C_1 - C_2)e^{ax} \sin bx,
\end{aligned}$$

where the arbitrary constants C_1 and C_2 can be complex. For instance, the choice $C_1 = C_2 = \frac{1}{2}$ gives the real-valued solution $y_1(x) = e^{ax} \cos bx$, while the choice $C_1 = -\frac{1}{2}i, C_2 = \frac{1}{2}i$ gives the independent real-valued solution $y_2(x) = e^{ax} \sin bx$. This yields the following result.

> **THEOREM 3   Complex Roots**
>
> If the characteristic equation in (3) has an unrepeated pair of complex conjugate roots $a \pm bi$ (with $b \neq 0$), then the corresponding part of a general solution of Eq. (1) has the form
>
> $$e^{ax}(c_1 \cos bx + c_2 \sin bx). \tag{21}$$

Example 3   The characteristic equation of

$$y'' + b^2 y = 0 \quad (b > 0)$$

is $r^2 + b^2 = 0$, with roots $r = \pm bi$. So Theorem 3 (with $a = 0$) gives the general solution

$$y(x) = c_1 \cos bx + c_2 \sin bx.$$ ∎

Example 4   Find the particular solution of

$$y'' - 4y' + 5y = 0$$

for which $y(0) = 1$ and $y'(0) = 5$.

Solution   Completion of the square in the characteristic equation yields

$$r^2 - 4r + 5 = (r - 2)^2 + 1 = 0,$$

so $r - 2 = \pm\sqrt{-1} = \pm i$. Thus we obtain the complex conjugate roots $2 \pm i$ (which could also be found directly using the quadratic formula). Hence Theorem 3 with $a = 2$ and $b = 1$ gives the general solution

$$y(x) = e^{2x}(c_1 \cos x + c_2 \sin x).$$

Then

$$y'(x) = 2e^{2x}(c_1 \cos x + c_2 \sin x) + e^{2x}(-c_1 \sin x + c_2 \cos x),$$

so the initial conditions give

$$y(0) = c_1 = 1 \quad \text{and} \quad y'(0) = 2c_1 + c_2 = 5.$$

It follows that $c_2 = 3$, and so the desired particular solution is

$$y(x) = e^{2x}(\cos x + 3 \sin x).$$ ∎

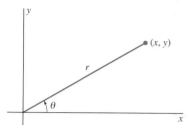

FIGURE 3.3.1. Modulus and argument of the complex number $x + iy$.

In Example 5 below we employ the **polar form**

$$z = x + iy = re^{i\theta} \qquad (22)$$

of the complex number z. This form follows from Euler's formula upon writing

$$z = r\left(\frac{x}{r} + i\frac{y}{r}\right) = r(\cos\theta + i\sin\theta) = re^{i\theta}$$

in terms of the **modulus** $r = \sqrt{x^2 + y^2} > 0$ of the number z and its **argument** θ indicated in Fig. 3.3.1. For instance, the imaginary number i has modulus 1 and argument $\pi/2$, so $i = e^{i\pi/2}$. Similarly, $-i = e^{3\pi/2}$. Another consequence is the fact that the nonzero complex number $z = re^{i\theta}$ has the two square roots

$$\sqrt{z} = \pm(re^{i\theta})^{1/2} = \pm\sqrt{r}e^{i\theta/2}, \qquad (23)$$

where $\sqrt{r}$ denotes (as usual for a positive real number) the positive square root of the modulus of z.

Example 5 Find a general solution of $y^{(4)} + 4y = 0$.

Solution The characteristic equation is

$$r^4 - 4 = (r^2)^2 - (2i)^2 = (r^2 + 2i)(r^2 - 2i) = 0,$$

and its four roots are $\pm\sqrt{\pm 2i}$. Since $i = e^{i\pi/2}$ and $-i = e^{i3\pi/2}$, we find that

$$\sqrt{2i} = \left(2e^{i\pi/2}\right)^{1/2} = \sqrt{2}e^{i\pi/4} = \sqrt{2}\left(\cos\frac{\pi}{4} + i\sin\frac{\pi}{4}\right) = 1 + i$$

and

$$\sqrt{-2i} = \left(2e^{i3\pi/2}\right)^{1/2} = \sqrt{2}e^{i3\pi/4} = \sqrt{2}\left(\cos\frac{3\pi}{4} + i\sin\frac{3\pi}{4}\right) = -1 + i.$$

Thus the four (distinct) roots of the characteristic equation are $r = \pm(\pm 1 + i)$. These two pairs of complex conjugate roots, $1 \pm i$ and $-1 \pm i$, give a general solution

$$y(x) = e^x(c_1\cos x + c_2\sin x) + e^{-x}(c_3\cos x + c_4\sin x)$$

of the differential equation $y^{(4)} + 4y = 0$. ∎

Repeated Complex Roots

Theorem 2 holds for repeated complex roots. If the conjugate pair $a \pm bi$ has multiplicity k, then the corresponding part of the general solution has the form

$$(A_1 + A_2x + \cdots + A_kx^{k-1})e^{(a+bi)x} + (B_1 + B_2x + \cdots + B_kx^{k-1})e^{(a-bi)x}$$

$$= \sum_{p=0}^{k-1} x^p e^{ax}(c_i\cos bx + d_i\sin bx). \qquad (24)$$

It can be shown that the $2k$ functions

$$x^p e^{ax}\cos bx, \quad x^p e^{ax}\sin bx, \quad 0 \leqq p \leqq k - 1$$

that appear in Eq. (24) are linearly independent.

Example 6   Find a general solution of $(D^2 + 6D + 13)^2 y = 0$.

Solution   By completing the square, we see that the characteristic equation

$$(r^2 + 6r + 13)^2 = [(r+3)^2 + 4]^2 = 0$$

has as its roots the conjugate pair $-3 \pm 2i$ of multiplicity $k = 2$. Hence Eq. (24) gives the general solution

$$y(x) = e^{-3x}(c_1 \cos 2x + d_1 \sin 2x) + xe^{-3x}(c_2 \cos 2x + d_2 \sin 2x).$$ ■

In applications we are seldom presented in advance with a factorization as convenient as the one in Example 6. Often the most difficult part of solving a homogeneous linear equation is finding the roots of its characteristic equation. Example 7 illustrates an approach that may succeed when a root of the characteristic equation can be found by inspection. The project material for this section illustrates other possibilities.

Example 7   The characteristic equation of the differential equation

$$y^{(3)} + y' - 10y = 0$$

is the cubic equation

$$r^3 + r - 10 = 0.$$

By a standard theorem of elementary algebra, the only possible rational roots are the factors ± 1, ± 2, ± 5, and ± 10 of the constant term 10. By trial and error (if not by inspection) we discover the root 2. The factor theorem of elementary algebra implies that $r - 2$ is a factor of $r^3 + r - 10$, and division of the former into the latter produces as quotient the quadratic polynomial

$$r^2 + 2r + 5 = (r+1)^2 + 4.$$

The roots of this quotient are the complex conjugates $-1 \pm 2i$. The three roots we have found now yield the general solution

$$y(x) = c_1 e^{2x} + e^{-x}(c_2 \cos 2x + c_3 \sin 2x).$$ ■

Example 8   The roots of the characteristic equation of a certain differential equation are 3, -5, 0, 0, 0, 0, -5, $2 \pm 3i$, and $2 \pm 3i$. Write a general solution of this homogeneous differential equation.

Solution   The solution can be read directly from the list of roots. It is

$$y(x) = c_1 + c_2 x + c_3 x^2 + c_4 x^3 + c_5 e^{3x} + c_6 e^{-5x} + c_7 x e^{-5x}$$
$$+ e^{2x}(c_8 \cos 3x + c_9 \sin 3x) + xe^{2x}(c_{10} \cos 3x + c_{11} \sin 3x).$$ ■

3.3 Problems

Find the general solutions of the differential equations in Problems 1 through 20.

1. $y'' - 4y = 0$

2. $2y'' - 3y' = 0$

3. $y'' + 3y' - 10y = 0$

4. $2y'' - 7y' + 3y = 0$

5. $y'' + 6y' + 9y = 0$

6. $y'' + 5y' + 5y = 0$

7. $4y'' - 12y' + 9y = 0$

8. $y'' - 6y' + 13y = 0$

9. $y'' + 8y' + 25y = 0$

10. $5y^{(4)} + 3y^{(3)} = 0$

11. $y^{(4)} - 8y^{(3)} + 16y'' = 0$

12. $y^{(4)} - 3y^{(3)} + 3y'' - y' = 0$

13. $9y^{(3)} + 12y'' + 4y' = 0$

14. $y^{(4)} + 3y'' - 4y = 0$

15. $y^{(4)} - 8y'' + 16y = 0$

16. $y^{(4)} + 18y'' + 81y = 0$

17. $6y^{(4)} + 11y'' + 4y = 0$

18. $y^{(4)} = 16y$

19. $y^{(3)} + y'' - y' - y = 0$

20. $y^{(4)} + 2y^{(3)} + 3y'' + 2y' + y = 0$ (*Suggestion:* Expand $(r^2 + r + 1)^2$.)

Solve the initial value problems given in Problems 21 through 26.

21. $y'' - 4y' + 3y = 0$; $y(0) = 7$, $y'(0) = 11$

22. $9y'' + 6y' + 4y = 0$; $y(0) = 3$, $y'(0) = 4$

23. $y'' - 6y' + 25y = 0$; $y(0) = 3$, $y'(0) = 1$

24. $2y^{(3)} - 3y'' - 2y' = 0$; $y(0) = 1$, $y'(0) = -1$, $y''(0) = 3$

25. $3y^{(3)} + 2y'' = 0$; $y(0) = -1$, $y'(0) = 0$, $y''(0) = 1$

26. $y^{(3)} + 10y'' + 25y' = 0$; $y(0) = 3$, $y'(0) = 4$, $y''(0) = 5$

Find general solutions of the equations in Problems 27 through 32. First find a small integral root of the characteristic equation by inspection; then factor by division.

27. $y^{(3)} + 3y'' - 4y = 0$

28. $2y^{(3)} - y'' - 5y' - 2y = 0$

29. $y^{(3)} + 27y = 0$

30. $y^{(4)} - y^{(3)} + y'' - 3y' - 6y = 0$

31. $y^{(3)} + 3y'' + 4y' - 8y = 0$

32. $y^{(4)} + y^{(3)} - 3y'' - 5y' - 2y = 0$

In Problems 33 through 36, one solution of the differential equation is given. Find the general solution.

33. $y^{(3)} + 3y'' - 54y = 0$; $y = e^{3x}$

34. $3y^{(3)} - 2y'' + 12y' - 8y = 0$; $y = e^{2x/3}$

35. $6y^{(4)} + 5y^{(3)} + 25y'' + 20y' + 4y = 0$; $y = \cos 2x$

36. $9y^{(3)} + 11y'' + 4y' - 14y = 0$; $y = e^{-x} \sin x$

37. Find a function $y(x)$ such that $y^{(4)}(x) = y^{(3)}(x)$ for all x and $y(0) = 18$, $y'(0) = 12$, $y''(0) = 13$, and $y^{(3)}(0) = 7$.

38. Solve the initial value problem

$$y^{(3)} - 5y'' + 100y' - 500y = 0;$$
$$y(0) = 0, \quad y'(0) = 10, \quad y''(0) = 250$$

given that $y_1(x) = e^{5x}$ is one particular solution of the differential equation.

In Problems 39 through 42, find a linear homogeneous constant-coefficient equation with the given general solution.

39. $y(x) = (A + Bx + Cx^2)e^{2x}$

40. $y(x) = Ae^{2x} + B\cos 2x + C\sin 2x$

41. $y(x) = A\cos 2x + B\sin 2x + C\cosh 2x + D\sinh 2x$

42. $y(x) = (A + Bx + Cx^2)\cos 2x + (D + Ex + Fx^2)\sin 2x$

Problems 43 through 47 pertain to the solution of differential equations with complex coefficients.

43. **(a)** Use Euler's formula to show that every complex number can be written in the form $re^{i\theta}$, where $r \geq 0$ and $-\pi < \theta \leq \pi$. **(b)** Express the numbers 4, -2, $3i$, $1 + i$, and $-1 + i\sqrt{3}$ in the form $re^{i\theta}$. **(c)** The two square roots of $re^{i\theta}$ are $\pm\sqrt{r}\,e^{i\theta/2}$. Find the square roots of the numbers $2 - 2i\sqrt{3}$ and $-2 + 2i\sqrt{3}$.

44. Use the quadratic formula to solve the following equations. Note in each case that the roots are not complex conjugates.

(a) $x^2 + ix + 2 = 0$ **(b)** $x^2 - 2ix + 3 = 0$

45. Find a general solution of $y'' - 2iy' + 3y = 0$.

46. Find a general solution of $y'' - iy' + 6y = 0$

47. Find a general solution of $y'' = (-2 + 2i\sqrt{3})y$.

48. Solve the initial value problem

$$y^{(3)} = y; \quad y(0) = 1, \quad y'(0) = y''(0) = 0.$$

(*Suggestion:* Impose the given initial conditions on the general solution

$$y(x) = Ae^x + Be^{\alpha x} + Ce^{\beta x},$$

where α and β are the complex conjugate roots of $r^3 - 1 = 0$, to discover that

$$y(x) = \frac{1}{3}\left(e^x + 2e^{-x/2}\cos\frac{x\sqrt{3}}{2}\right)$$

is a solution.)

49. Solve the initial value problem

$$y^{(4)} = y^{(3)} + y'' + y' + 2y;$$
$$y(0) = y'(0) = y''(0) = 0, \, 2y^{(3)}(0) = 30.$$

50. The differential equation

$$y'' + (\text{sgn}\,x)y = 0 \tag{25}$$

has the discontinuous coefficient function

$$\text{sgn}\,x = \begin{cases} +1 & \text{if } x > 0, \\ -1 & \text{if } x < 0. \end{cases}$$

Show that Eq. (25) nevertheless has two linearly independent solutions $y_1(x)$ and $y_2(x)$ defined for all x such that

- Each satisfies Eq. (25) at each point $x \neq 0$;
- Each has a continuous derivative at $x = 0$;
- $y_1(0) = y_2'(0) = 1$ and $y_2(0) = y_1'(0) = 0$.

(*Suggestion*: Each $y_i(x)$ will be defined by one formula for $x < 0$ and by another for $x \geq 0$.) The graphs of these two solutions are shown in Fig. 3.3.2.

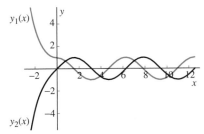

FIGURE 3.3.2. Graphs of $y_1(x)$ and $y_2(x)$ in Problem 50.

51. According to Problem 51 in Section 3.1, the substitution $v = \ln x$ $(x > 0)$ transforms the second-order Euler equation $ax^2 y'' + bxy' + cy = 0$ to a constant-coefficient homogeneous linear equation. Show similarly that this same

substitution transforms the third-order Euler equation

$$ax^3 y''' + bx^2 y'' + cxy' + dy = 0$$

(where a, b, c, d are constants) into the constant-coefficient equation

$$a\frac{d^3 y}{dv^3} + (b - 3a)\frac{d^2 y}{dv^2} + (c - b + 2a)\frac{dy}{dv} + dy = 0.$$

Make the substitution $v = \ln x$ of Problem 51 to find general solutions (for $x > 0$) of the Euler equations in Problems 52 through 58.

52. $x^2 y'' + xy' + 9y = 0$
53. $x^2 y'' + 7xy' + 25y = 0$
54. $x^3 y''' + 6x^2 y'' + 4xy' = 0$
55. $x^3 y''' - x^2 y'' + xy' = 0$
56. $x^3 y''' + 3x^2 y'' + xy' = 0$
57. $x^3 y''' - 3x^2 y'' + xy' = 0$
58. $x^3 y''' + 6x^2 y'' + 7xy' + y = 0$

3.3 Application Approximate Solutions of Linear Equations

To meet the needs of applications such as those of this section, polynomial-solving utilities are now a common feature of calculator and computer systems and can be used to solve a characteristic equation numerically even when no simple factorization is evident or even possible. For instance, suppose that we want to solve the homogeneous linear differential equation

$$y^{(3)} - 3y'' + y = 0 \qquad (1)$$

with characteristic equation

$$r^3 - 3r^2 + 1 = 0. \qquad (2)$$

A typical graphing calculator has a **solve** command that can be used to find the approximate roots of a polynomial equation. As indicated in Figs. 3.3.3 and 3.3.4, we find that the roots of Eq. (2) are given by $r \approx -0.5321$, 0.6527, and 2.8794. Some analogous computer algebra system commands are

```
solve(R^3-3R²+1,
R,-1)
               -.5321
solve(R^3-3R²+1,
R,1)
                .6527
solve(R^3-3R²+1,
R,3)
```

```
F1▾  F2▾  F3▾ F4▾  F5    F6▾
Tools Algebra Calc Other PrgmIO Clean Up
▪ solve(r³ - 3·r² + 1 = 0,r)
  r = 2.8794 or r = .6527 or▶
solve(r^3-3r^2+1=0,r)
MAIN     RAD AUTO    DE      1/30
```

FIGURE 3.3.3. Solving the equation $r^3 - 3r^2 + 1 = 0$ with a TI-83 calculator that requires an estimate of each root.

FIGURE 3.3.4. Solving the characteristic equation with a TI-89 calculator having a more sophisticated **solve** facility.

```
fsolve(r^3 - 3*r^2 + 1 = 0, r);
NSolve[r^3 - 3*r^2 + 1 == 0, r]
roots([1  -3   0   1])
```

(*Maple*)
(*Mathematica*)
(MATLAB)

(In the MATLAB command, one enters the polynomial's vector `[1 -3 0 1]` of coefficients, listed in descending order.) However we find these approximate roots, it follows that a general solution of the differential equation in (1) is given (approximately) by

$$y(x) = c_1 e^{-(0.5321)x} + c_2 e^{(0.6527)x} + c_3 e^{(2.8794)x}. \tag{3}$$

Use calculator or computer methods like those indicated here to find general solutions (in approximate numerical form) of the following differential equations.

1. $y^{(3)} - 3y' + y = 0$
2. $y^{(3)} + 3y'' - 3y = 0$
3. $y^{(3)} + y' + y = 0$
4. $y^{(3)} + 3y' + 5y = 0$
5. $y^{(4)} + 2y^{(3)} - 3y = 0$
6. $y^{(4)} + 3y' - 4y = 0$

3.4 Mechanical Vibrations

FIGURE 3.4.1. A mass–spring–dashpot system.

The motion of a mass attached to a spring serves as a relatively simple example of the vibrations that occur in more complex mechanical systems. For many such systems, the analysis of these vibrations is a problem in the solution of linear differential equations with constant coefficients.

We consider a body of mass m attached to one end of an ordinary spring that resists compression as well as stretching; the other end of the spring is attached to a fixed wall, as shown in Fig. 3.4.1. Assume that the body rests on a frictionless horizontal plane, so that it can move only back and forth as the spring compresses and stretches. Denote by x the distance of the body from its **equilibrium position**— its position when the spring is unstretched. We take $x > 0$ when the spring is stretched, and thus $x < 0$ when it is compressed.

According to Hooke's law, the restorative force F_S that the spring exerts on the mass is proportional to the distance x that the spring has been stretched or compressed. Because this is the same as the displacement x of the mass m from its equilibrium position, it follows that

$$F_S = -kx. \tag{1}$$

The positive constant of proportionality k is called the **spring constant.** Note that F_S and x have opposite signs: $F_S < 0$ when $x > 0$, $F_S > 0$ when $x < 0$.

Figure 3.4.1 shows the mass attached to a dashpot—a device, like a shock absorber, that provides a force directed opposite to the instantaneous direction of motion of the mass m. We assume the dashpot is so designed that this force F_R is proportional to the velocity $v = dx/dt$ of the mass; that is,

$$F_R = -cv = -c\frac{dx}{dt}. \tag{2}$$

The positive constant c is the **damping constant** of the dashpot. More generally, we may regard Eq. (2) as specifying frictional forces in our system (including air resistance to the motion of m).

If, in addition to the forces F_S and F_R, the mass is subjected to a given **external force** $F_E = F(t)$, then the total force acting on the mass is $F = F_S + F_R + F_E$. Using Newton's law

$$F = ma = m\frac{d^2x}{dt^2} = mx'',$$

we obtain the second-order linear differential equation

$$\blacktriangleright \qquad mx'' + cx' + kx = F(t) \qquad (3)$$

that governs the motion of the mass.

If there is no dashpot (and we ignore all frictional forces), then we set $c = 0$ in Eq. (3) and call the motion **undamped**; it is **damped** motion if $c > 0$. If there is no external force, we replace $F(t)$ with 0 in Eq. (3). We refer to the motion as **free** in this case and **forced** in the case $F(t) \neq 0$. Thus the homogeneous equation

$$\blacktriangleright \qquad mx'' + cx' + kx = 0 \qquad (4)$$

describes free motion of a mass on a spring with dashpot but with no external forces applied. We will defer discussion of forced motion until Section 3.6.

For an alternative example, we might attach the mass to the lower end of a spring that is suspended vertically from a fixed support, as in Fig. 3.4.2. In this case the weight $W = mg$ of the mass would stretch the spring a distance s_0 determined by Eq. (1) with $F_S = -W$ and $x = s_0$. That is, $mg = ks_0$, so that $s_0 = mg/k$. This gives the **static** equilibrium position of the mass. If y denotes the displacement of the mass in motion, measured downward from its static equilibrium position, then we ask you to show in Problem 9 that y satisfies Eq. (3); specifically, that

$$my'' + cy' + ky = F(t) \qquad (5)$$

if we include damping and external forces (meaning those other than gravity).

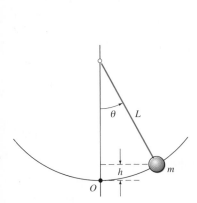

FIGURE 3.4.2. A mass suspended vertically from a spring.

The Simple Pendulum

The importance of the differential equation that appears in Eqs. (3) and (5) stems from the fact that it describes the motion of many other simple mechanical systems. For example, a **simple pendulum** consists of a mass m swinging back and forth on the end of a string (or better, a *massless rod*) of length L, as shown in Fig. 3.4.3. We may specify the position of the mass at time t by giving the counterclockwise angle $\theta = \theta(t)$ that the string or rod makes with the vertical at time t. To analyze the motion of the mass m, we will apply the law of the *conservation of mechanical energy*, according to which the sum of the kinetic energy and the potential energy of m remains constant.

The distance along the circular arc from 0 to m is $s = L\theta$, so the velocity of the mass is $v = ds/dt = L(d\theta/dt)$, and therefore its kinetic energy is

$$T = \frac{1}{2}mv^2 = \frac{1}{2}m\left(\frac{ds}{dt}\right)^2 = \frac{1}{2}mL^2\left(\frac{d\theta}{dt}\right)^2.$$

FIGURE 3.4.3. The simple pendulum.

We next choose as reference point the lowest point O reached by the mass (see Fig. 3.4.3). Then its potential energy V is the product of its weight mg and its vertical height $h = L(1 - \cos\theta)$ above O, so

$$V = mgL(1 - \cos\theta).$$

The fact that the sum of T and V is a constant C therefore gives

$$\frac{1}{2}mL^2\left(\frac{d\theta}{dt}\right)^2 + mgL(1 - \cos\theta) = C.$$

We differentiate both sides of this identity with respect to t to obtain

$$mL^2\left(\frac{d\theta}{dt}\right)\left(\frac{d^2\theta}{dt^2}\right) + mgL(\sin\theta)\frac{d\theta}{dt} = 0,$$

so

$$\frac{d^2\theta}{dt^2} + \frac{g}{L}\sin\theta = 0 \tag{6}$$

after removal of the common factor $mL^2(d\theta/dt)$. This differential equation can be derived in a seemingly more elementary manner using the familiar second law $F = ma$ of Newton (applied to tangential components of the acceleration of the mass and the force acting on it). However, derivations of differential equations based on conservation of energy are often seen in more complex situations where Newton's law is not so directly applicable, and it may be instructive to see the energy method in a simpler application like the pendulum.

Now recall that if θ is small, then $\sin\theta \approx \theta$ (this approximation obtained by retaining just the first term in the Taylor series for $\sin\theta$). In fact, $\sin\theta$ and θ agree to two decimal places when $|\theta|$ is at most $\pi/12$ (that is, $15°$). In a typical pendulum clock, for example, θ would never exceed $15°$. It therefore seems reasonable to simplify our mathematical model of the simple pendulum by replacing $\sin\theta$ with θ in Eq. (6). If we also insert a term $c\theta'$ to account for the frictional resistance of the surrounding medium, the result is an equation in the form of Eq. (4):

$$\theta'' + c\theta' + k\theta = 0, \tag{7}$$

where $k = g/L$. Note that this equation is independent of the mass m on the end of the rod. We might, however, expect the effects of the discrepancy between θ and $\sin\theta$ to accumulate over a period of time, so that Eq. (7) will probably not describe accurately the actual motion of the pendulum over a long period of time.

In the remainder of this section, we first analyze free undamped motion and then free damped motion.

Free Undamped Motion

If we have only a mass on a spring, with neither damping nor external force, then Eq. (3) takes the simpler form

$$mx'' + kx = 0. \tag{8}$$

It is convenient to define

$$\omega_0 = \sqrt{\frac{k}{m}} \tag{9}$$

and rewrite Eq. (8) as

$$x'' + \omega_0^2 x = 0. \tag{8'}$$

The general solution of Eq. (8′) is

$$x(t) = A\cos\omega_0 t + B\sin\omega_0 t. \tag{10}$$

To analyze the motion described by this solution, we choose constants C and α so that

$$C = \sqrt{A^2 + B^2}, \quad \cos\alpha = \frac{A}{C}, \quad \text{and} \quad \sin\alpha = \frac{B}{C}, \tag{11}$$

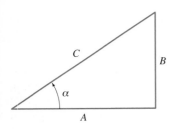

FIGURE 3.4.4. The angle α.

as indicated in Fig. 3.4.4. Note that, although $\tan\alpha = B/A$, the angle α is *not* given by the principal branch of the inverse tangent function (which gives values only in the interval $-\pi/2 < x < \pi/2$). Instead, α is the angle between 0 and 2π whose cosine and sine have the signs given in (11), where either A or B or both may be negative. Thus

$$\alpha = \begin{cases} \tan^{-1}(B/A) & \text{if } A > 0, B > 0 \text{ (first quadrant),} \\ \pi + \tan^{-1}(B/A) & \text{if } A < 0 \text{ (second or third quadrant),} \\ 2\pi + \tan^{-1}(B/A) & \text{if } A > 0, B < 0 \text{ (fourth quadrant),} \end{cases}$$

where $\tan^{-1}(B/A)$ is the angle in $(-\pi/2, \pi/2)$ given by a calculator or computer. In any event, from (10) and (11) we get

$$x(t) = C\left(\frac{A}{C}\cos\omega_0 t + \frac{B}{C}\sin\omega_0 t\right) = C(\cos\alpha\cos\omega_0 t + \sin\alpha\sin\omega_0 t).$$

With the aid of the cosine addition formula, we find that

$$x(t) = C\cos(\omega_0 t - \alpha). \tag{12}$$

Thus the mass oscillates to and fro about its equilibrium position with

1. **Amplitude** C,
2. **Circular frequency** ω_0, and
3. **Phase angle** α.

Such motion is called **simple harmonic motion**.

If time t is measured in seconds, the circular frequency ω_0 has dimensions of radians per second (rad/s). The **period** of the motion is the time required for the system to complete one full oscillation, so is given by

$$T = \frac{2\pi}{\omega_0} \tag{13}$$

seconds; its **frequency** is

$$\nu = \frac{1}{T} = \frac{\omega_0}{2\pi} \tag{14}$$

in hertz (Hz), which measures the number of complete cycles per second. Note that frequency is measured in cycles per second, whereas circular frequency has the dimensions of radians per second.

A typical graph of a simple harmonic position function

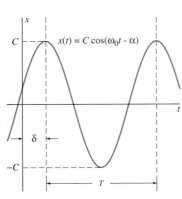

FIGURE 3.4.5. Simple harmonic motion.

$$x(t) = C\cos(\omega_0 t - \alpha) = C\cos\left(\omega_0\left(t - \frac{\alpha}{\omega_0}\right)\right) = C\cos(\omega_0(t - \delta))$$

is shown in Fig. 3.4.5, where the geometric significance of the amplitude C, the period T, and the **time lag**

$$\delta = \frac{\alpha}{\omega_0}$$

are indicated.

   If the initial position $x(0) = x_0$ and initial velocity $x'(0) = v_0$ of the mass are given, we first determine the values of the coefficients A and B in Eq. (10), then find the amplitude C and phase angle α by carrying out the transformation of $x(t)$ to the form in Eq. (12), as indicated previously.

Example 1   A body with mass $m = \frac{1}{2}$ kilogram (kg) is attached to the end of a spring that is stretched 2 meters (m) by a force of 100 newtons (N). It is set in motion with initial position $x_0 = 1$ (m) and initial velocity $v_0 = -5$ (m/s). (Note that these initial conditions indicate that the body is displaced to the right and is moving to the left at time $t = 0$.) Find the position function of the body as well as the amplitude, frequency, period of oscillation, and time lag of its motion.

Solution   The spring constant is $k = (100 \text{ N})/(2 \text{ m}) = 50$ (N/m), so Eq. (8) yields $\frac{1}{2}x'' + 50x = 0$; that is,

$$x'' + 100x = 0.$$

Consequently, the circular frequency of the resulting simple harmonic motion of the body will be $\omega_0 = \sqrt{100} = 10$ (rad/s). Hence it will oscillate with period

$$T = \frac{2\pi}{\omega_0} = \frac{2\pi}{10} \approx 0.6283 \text{ s}$$

and with frequency

$$\nu = \frac{1}{T} = \frac{\omega_0}{2\pi} = \frac{10}{2\pi} \approx 1.5915 \text{ Hz.}$$

   We now impose the initial conditions $x(0) = 1$ and $x'(0) = -5$ on the position function

$$x(t) = A \cos 10t + B \sin 10t \quad \text{with} \quad x'(t) = -10A \sin 10t + 10B \cos 10t.$$

It follows readily that $A = 1$ and $B = -\frac{1}{2}$, so the position function of the body is

$$x(t) = \cos 10t - \frac{1}{2} \sin 10t.$$

Hence its amplitude of motion is

$$C = \sqrt{(1)^2 + (-\tfrac{1}{2})^2} = \tfrac{1}{2}\sqrt{5} \text{ m.}$$

To find the time lag, we write

$$x(t) = \frac{\sqrt{5}}{2}\left(\frac{2}{\sqrt{5}} \cos 10t - \frac{1}{\sqrt{5}} \sin 10t\right) = \frac{\sqrt{5}}{2}\cos(10t - \alpha),$$

where the phase angle α satisfies

$$\cos \alpha = \frac{2}{\sqrt{5}} > 0 \quad \text{and} \quad \sin \alpha = -\frac{1}{\sqrt{5}} < 0.$$

Hence α is the fourth-quadrant angle

$$\alpha = 2\pi + \tan^{-1}\left(\frac{-1/\sqrt{5}}{2/\sqrt{5}}\right) = 2\pi - \tan^{-1}(\tfrac{1}{2}) \approx 5.8195,$$

and the time lag of the motion is

$$\delta = \frac{\alpha}{\omega_0} \approx 0.5820 \text{ s}.$$

With the amplitude and approximate phase angle shown explicitly, the position function of the body takes the form

$$x(t) \approx \tfrac{1}{2}\sqrt{5}\cos(10t - 5.8195),$$

and its graph is shown in Fig. 3.4.6. ∎

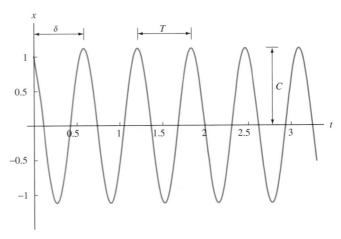

FIGURE 3.4.6.   Graph of the position function
$x(t) = C\cos(\omega_0 t - \alpha)$ in Example 1, with amplitude
$C \approx 1.118$, period $T \approx 0.628$, and time lag $\delta \approx 0.582$.

Free Damped Motion

With damping but no external force, the differential equation we have been studying takes the form $mx'' + cx' + kx = 0$; alternatively,

$$x'' + 2px' + \omega_0^2 x = 0, \tag{15}$$

where $\omega_0 = \sqrt{k/m}$ is the corresponding *undamped* circular frequency and

$$p = \frac{c}{2m} > 0. \tag{16}$$

The characteristic equation $r^2 + 2pr + \omega_0^2 = 0$ of Eq. (15) has roots

$$r_1, \; r_2 = -p \pm (p^2 - \omega_0^2)^{1/2} \tag{17}$$

that depend on the sign of

$$p^2 - \omega_0^2 = \frac{c^2}{4m^2} - \frac{k}{m} = \frac{c^2 - 4km}{4m^2}. \qquad (18)$$

The **critical damping** c_{cr} is given by $c_{cr} = \sqrt{4km}$, and we distinguish three cases, according as $c > c_{cr}$, $c = c_{cr}$, or $c < c_{cr}$.

OVERDAMPED CASE: $c > c_{cr}(c^2 > 4km)$. Because c is relatively large in this case, we are dealing with a strong resistance in comparison with a relatively weak spring or a small mass. Then (17) gives distinct real roots r_1 and r_2, both of which are negative. The position function has the form

$$x(t) = c_1 e^{r_1 t} + c_2 e^{r_2 t}. \qquad (19)$$

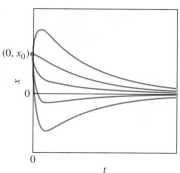

FIGURE 3.4.7. Overdamped motion: $x(t) = c_1 e^{r_1 t} + c_2 e^{r_2 t}$ with $r_1 < 0$ and $r_2 < 0$. Solution curves are graphed with the same initial position x_0 and different initial velocities.

It is easy to see that $x(t) \to 0$ as $t \to +\infty$ and that the body settles to its equilibrium position without any oscillations (Problem 29). Figure 3.4.7 shows some typical graphs of the position function for the overdamped case; we chose x_0 a fixed positive number and illustrated the effects of changing the initial velocity v_0. In every case the would-be oscillations are damped out.

CRITICALLY DAMPED CASE: $c = c_{cr}(c^2 = 4km)$. In this case, (17) gives equal roots $r_1 = r_2 = -p$ of the characteristic equation, so the general solution is

$$x(t) = e^{-pt}(c_1 + c_2 t). \qquad (20)$$

Because $e^{-pt} > 0$ and $c_1 + c_2 t$ has at most one positive zero, the body passes through its equilibrium position at most once, and it is clear that $x(t) \to 0$ as $t \to +\infty$. Some graphs of the motion in the critically damped case appear in Fig. 3.4.8, and they resemble those of the overdamped case (Fig. 3.4.7). In the critically damped case, the resistance of the dashpot is just large enough to damp out any oscillations, but even a slight reduction in resistance will bring us to the remaining case, the one that shows the most dramatic behavior.

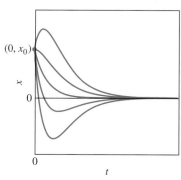

FIGURE 3.4.8. Critically damped motion: $x(t) = (c_1 + c_2 t)e^{-pt}$ with $p > 0$. Solution curves are graphed with the same initial position x_0 and different initial velocities.

UNDERDAMPED CASE: $c < c_{cr}(c^2 < 4km)$. The characteristic equation now has two complex conjugate roots $-p \pm i\sqrt{\omega_0^2 - p^2}$, and the general solution is

$$x(t) = e^{-pt}(A \cos \omega_1 t + B \sin \omega_1 t), \qquad (21)$$

where

$$\omega_1 = \sqrt{\omega_0^2 - p^2} = \frac{\sqrt{4km - c^2}}{2m}. \qquad (22)$$

Using the cosine addition formula as in the derivation of Eq. (12), we may rewrite Eq. (20) as

$$x(t) = Ce^{-pt}\left(\frac{A}{C} \cos \omega_1 t + \frac{B}{C} \sin \omega_1 t\right),$$

so

$$x(t) = Ce^{-pt} \cos(\omega_1 t - \alpha) \qquad (23)$$

where

$$C = \sqrt{A^2 + B^2}, \quad \cos \alpha = \frac{A}{C}, \quad \text{and} \quad \sin \alpha = \frac{B}{C}.$$

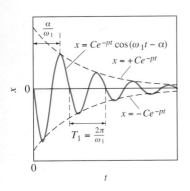

FIGURE 3.4.9. Underdamped oscillations:
$x(t) = Ce^{-pt} \cos(\omega_1 t - \alpha)$.

The solution in (22) represents exponentially damped oscillations of the body around its equilibrium position. The graph of $x(t)$ lies between the "amplitude envelope" curves $x = -Ce^{-pt}$ and $x = Ce^{-pt}$ and touches them when $\omega_1 t - \alpha$ is an integral multiple of π. The motion is not actually periodic, but it is nevertheless useful to call ω_1 its **circular frequency** (more properly, its **pseudofrequency**), $T_1 = 2\pi/\omega_1$ its **pseudoperiod** of oscillation, and Ce^{-pt} its **time-varying amplitude.** Most of these quantities are shown in the typical graph of underdamped motion in Fig. 3.4.9. Note from Eq. (21) that in this case ω_1 is less than the undamped circular frequency ω_0, so T_1 is larger than the period T of oscillation of the same mass without damping on the same spring. Thus the action of the dashpot has at least two effects:

1. It exponentially damps the oscillations, in accord with the time-varying amplitude.
2. It slows the motion; that is, the dashpot decreases the frequency of the motion.

As the following example illustrates, damping typically also delays the motion further—that is, increases the time lag—as compared with undamped motion with the same initial conditions.

Example 2 The mass and spring of Example 1 are now attached also to a dashpot that provides 1 N of resistance for each meter per second of velocity. The mass is set in motion with the same initial position $x(0) = 1$ and initial velocity $x'(0) = -5$ as in Example 1. Now find the position function of the mass, its new frequency and pseudoperiod of motion, its new time lag, and the times of its first four passages through the initial position $x = 0$.

Solution Rather than memorizing the various formulas given in the preceding discussion, it is better practice in a particular case to set up the differential equation and then solve it directly. Recall that $m = \frac{1}{2}$ and $k = 50$; we are now given $c = 1$ in mks units. Hence Eq. (4) is $\frac{1}{2}x'' + x' + 50x = 0$; that is,

$$x'' + 2x' + 100x = 0.$$

The characteristic equation $r^2 + 2r + 100 = (r + 1)^2 + 99 = 0$ has roots r_1, $r_2 = -1 \pm \sqrt{99}\,i$, so the general solution is

$$x(t) = e^{-t}(A \cos \sqrt{99}\,t + B \sin \sqrt{99}\,t). \tag{24}$$

Consequently, the new circular (pseudo)frequency is $\omega_1 = \sqrt{99} \approx 9.9499$ (as compared with $\omega_0 = 10$ in Example 1). The new (pseudo)period and frequency are

$$T_1 = \frac{2\pi}{\omega_1} = \frac{2\pi}{\sqrt{99}} \approx 0.6315 \text{ s}$$

and

$$\nu_1 = \frac{1}{T_1} = \frac{\omega_1}{2\pi} = \frac{\sqrt{99}}{2\pi} \approx 1.5836 \text{ Hz}$$

(as compared with $T \approx 0.6283 < T_1$ and $\nu \approx 1.5915 > \nu_1$ in Example 1).

We now impose the initial conditions $x(0) = 1$ and $x'(0) = -5$ on the position function in (23) and the resulting velocity function

$$x'(t) = -e^{-t}(A \cos \sqrt{99}\, t + B \sin \sqrt{99}\, t) + \sqrt{99}\, e^{-t}(-A \sin \sqrt{99}\, t + B \cos \sqrt{99}\, t).$$

It follows that

$$x(0) = A = 1 \quad \text{and} \quad x'(0) = -A + B\sqrt{99} = -5,$$

whence we find that $A = 1$ and $B = -4/\sqrt{99}$. Thus the new position function of the body is

$$x(t) = e^{-t}\left(\cos \sqrt{99}\, t - \frac{4}{\sqrt{99}} \sin \sqrt{99}\, t\right).$$

Hence its time-varying amplitude of motion is

$$C_1 e^{-t} = \sqrt{(1)^2 + \left(-\frac{4}{\sqrt{99}}\right)^2}\, e^{-t} = \sqrt{\frac{115}{99}}\, e^{-t}.$$

We therefore write

$$x(t) = \frac{\sqrt{115}}{\sqrt{99}} e^{-t}\left(\frac{\sqrt{99}}{\sqrt{115}} \cos \sqrt{99}\, t - \frac{4}{\sqrt{115}} \sin \sqrt{99}\, t\right)$$

$$= \sqrt{\frac{115}{99}}\, e^{-t} \cos(\sqrt{99}\, t - \alpha_1),$$

where the phase angle α_1 satisfies

$$\cos \alpha_1 = \frac{\sqrt{99}}{\sqrt{115}} > 0 \quad \text{and} \quad \sin \alpha_1 = -\frac{4}{\sqrt{115}} < 0.$$

Hence α_1 is the fourth-quadrant angle

$$\alpha_1 = 2\pi + \tan^{-1}\left(\frac{-4/\sqrt{115}}{\sqrt{99}/\sqrt{115}}\right) = 2\pi - \tan^{-1}\left(\frac{4}{\sqrt{99}}\right) \approx 5.9009,$$

and the time lag of the motion is

$$\delta_1 = \frac{\alpha_1}{\omega_1} \approx 0.5931 \text{ s}$$

(as compared with $\delta \approx 0.5820 < \delta_1$ in Example 1). With the time-varying amplitude and approximate phase angle shown explicitly, the position function of the mass takes the form

$$x(t) \approx \sqrt{\frac{115}{99}}\, e^{-t} \cos(\sqrt{99}\, t - 5.9009), \tag{25}$$

and its graph is the damped exponential that is shown in Fig. 3.4.10 (in comparison with the undamped oscillations of Example 1).

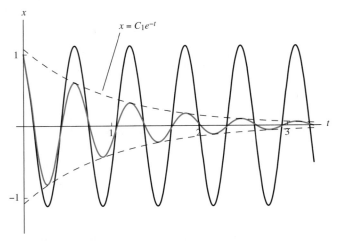

FIGURE 3.4.10.   Graphs of the position function $x(t) = C_1 e^{-t} \cos(\omega_1 t - \alpha_1)$ of Example 2 (damped oscillations), the position function $x(t) = C \cos(\omega_0 t - \alpha)$ of Example 1 (undamped oscillations), and the envelope curves $x(t) = \pm C_1 e^{-t}$.

From (24) we see that the mass passes through its equilibrium position $x = 0$ when $\cos(\omega_1 t - \alpha_1) = 0$, and thus when

$$\omega_1 t - \alpha_1 = -\frac{3\pi}{2}, \quad -\frac{\pi}{2}, \quad \frac{\pi}{2}, \quad \frac{3\pi}{2}, \quad \dots;$$

that is, when

$$t = \delta_1 - \frac{3\pi}{2\omega_1}, \quad \delta_1 - \frac{\pi}{2\omega_1}, \quad \delta_1 + \frac{\pi}{2\omega_1}, \quad \delta_1 + \frac{3\pi}{2\omega_1}, \quad \dots.$$

We see similarly that the undamped mass of Example 1 passes through equilibrium when

$$t = \delta_0 - \frac{3\pi}{2\omega_0}, \quad \delta_0 - \frac{\pi}{2\omega_0}, \quad \delta_0 + \frac{\pi}{2\omega_0}, \quad \delta_0 + \frac{3\pi}{2\omega_0}, \quad \dots.$$

The following table compares the first four values t_1, t_2, t_3, t_4 we calculate for the undamped and damped cases, respectively.

n	1	2	3	4
t_n (undamped)	0.1107	0.4249	0.7390	1.0532
t_n (damped)	0.1195	0.4352	0.7509	1.0667

Accordingly, in Fig. 3.4.11 (where only the first three equilibrium passages are shown) we see the damped oscillations lagging slightly behind the undamped ones. ∎

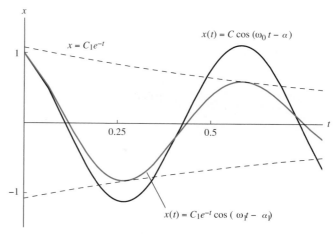

FIGURE 3.4.11. Graphs on the interval $0 \leq t \leq 0.8$ illustrating the additional delay associated with damping.

3.4 Problems

1. Determine the period and frequency of the simple harmonic motion of a 4-kg mass on the end of a spring with spring constant 16 N/m.

2. Determine the period and frequency of the simple harmonic motion of a body of mass 0.75 kg on the end of a spring with spring constant 48 N/m.

3. A mass of 3 kg is attached to the end of a spring that is stretched 20 cm by a force of 15 N. It is set in motion with initial position $x_0 = 0$ and initial velocity $v_0 = -10$ m/s. Find the amplitude, period, and frequency of the resulting motion.

4. A body with mass 250 g is attached to the end of a spring that is stretched 25 cm by a force of 9 N. At time $t = 0$ the body is pulled 1 m to the right, stretching the spring, and set in motion with an initial velocity of 5 m/s to the left. **(a)** Find $x(t)$ in the form $C \cos(\omega_0 t - \alpha)$. **(b)** Find the amplitude and period of motion of the body.

In Problems 5 through 8, assume that the differential equation of a simple pendulum of length L is $L\theta'' + g\theta = 0$, where $g = GM/R^2$ is the gravitational acceleration at the location of the pendulum (at distance R from the center of the earth; M denotes the mass of the earth).

5. Two pendulums are of lengths L_1 and L_2 and—when located at the respective distances R_1 and R_2 from the center of the earth—have periods p_1 and p_2. Show that

$$\frac{p_1}{p_2} = \frac{R_1\sqrt{L_1}}{R_2\sqrt{L_2}}.$$

6. A certain pendulum keeps perfect time in Paris, where the radius of the earth is $R = 3956$ (mi). But this clock loses 2 min 40 s per day at a location on the equator. Use the result of Problem 5 to find the amount of the equatorial bulge of the earth.

7. A pendulum of length 100.10 in., located at a point at sea level where the radius of the earth is $R = 3960$ (mi), has the same period as does a pendulum of length 100.00 in. atop a nearby mountain. Use the result of Problem 5 to find the height of the mountain.

8. Most grandfather clocks have pendulums with adjustable lengths. One such clock loses 10 min per day when the length of its pendulum is 30 in. With what length pendulum will this clock keep perfect time?

9. Derive Eq. (5) describing the motion of a mass attached to the bottom of a vertically suspended spring. (*Suggestion:* First denote by $x(t)$ the displacement of the mass below the unstretched position of the spring; set up the differential equation for x. Then substitute $y = x - x_0$ in this differential equation.)

10. Consider a floating cylindrical buoy with radius r, height h, and uniform density $\rho \leq 0.5$ (recall that the density of water is 1 g/cm^3). The buoy is initially suspended at rest with its bottom at the top surface of the water and is released at time $t = 0$. Thereafter it is acted on by two forces: a downward gravitational force equal to its weight $mg = \pi r^2 h g$ and (by Archimedes' principle of buoyancy) an upward force equal to the weight $\pi r^2 x g$ of water displaced, where $x = x(t)$ is the depth of the bottom of the buoy beneath the surface at time t (Fig. 3.4.12). Conclude that the buoy undergoes simple harmonic motion around its equilibrium position $x_e = \rho h$ with period $p = 2\pi \sqrt{\rho h/g}$. Compute p and the amplitude of the motion if $\rho = 0.5$ g/cm^3, $h = 200$ cm, and $g = 980$ cm/s^2.

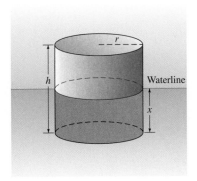

FIGURE 3.4.12. The buoy of Problem 10.

11. A cylindrical buoy weighing 100 lb (thus of mass $m = 3.125$ slugs in ft-lb-s (fps) units) floats in water with its axis vertical (as in Problem 10). When depressed slightly and released, it oscillates up and down four times every 10 s. Assume that friction is negligible. Find the radius of the buoy.

12. Assume that the earth is a solid sphere of uniform density, with mass M and radius $R = 3960$ (mi). For a particle of mass m *within* the earth at distance r from the center of the earth, the gravitational force attracting m toward the center is $F_r = -GM_r m/r^2$, where M_r is the mass of the part of the earth within a sphere of radius r. **(a)** Show that $F_r = -GMmr/R^3$. **(b)** Now suppose that a small hole is drilled straight through the center of the earth, thus connecting two antipodal points on its surface. Let a particle of mass m be dropped at time $t = 0$ into this hole with initial speed zero, and let $r(t)$ be its distance from the center of the earth at time t (Fig. 3.4.13). Conclude from Newton's second law and part (a) that $r''(t) = -k^2 r(t)$, where $k^2 = GM/R^3 = g/R$.

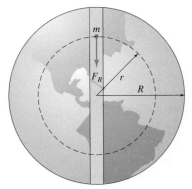

FIGURE 3.4.13. A mass m falling down a hole through the center of the earth (Problem 12).

(c) Take $g = 32.2$ ft/s^2, and conclude from part (b) that the particle undergoes simple harmonic motion back and forth between the ends of the hole, with a period of about 84 min. **(d)** Look up (or derive) the period of a satellite that just skims the surface of the earth; compare with the result in part (c). How do you explain the coincidence? Or *is* it a coincidence? **(e)** With what speed (in miles per hour) does the particle pass through the center of the earth? **(f)** Look up (or derive) the orbital velocity of a satellite that just skims the surface of the earth; compare with the result in part (e). How do you explain the coincidence? Or *is* it a coincidence?

13. Suppose that the mass in a mass–spring–dashpot system with $m = 10$, $c = 9$, and $k = 2$ is set in motion with $x(0) = 0$ and $x'(0) = 5$. **(a)** Find the position function $x(t)$ and show that its graph looks as indicated in Fig. 3.4.14. **(b)** Find how far the mass moves to the right before starting back toward the origin.

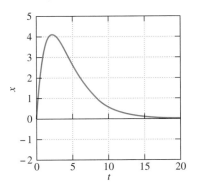

FIGURE 3.4.14. The position function $x(t)$ of Problem 13.

14. Suppose that the mass in a mass–spring–dashpot system with $m = 25$, $c = 10$, and $k = 226$ is set in motion with $x(0) = 20$ and $x'(0) = 41$. **(a)** Find the position function $x(t)$ and show that its graph looks as indicated in Fig. 3.4.15. **(b)** Find the pseudoperiod of the oscillations and the equations of the "envelope curves" that are dashed in the figure.

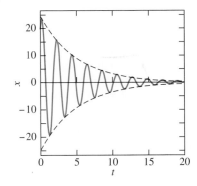

FIGURE 3.4.15. The position function $x(t)$ of Problem 14.

The remaining problems in this section deal with free damped motion. In Problems 15 through 21, a mass m is attached to both a spring (with given spring constant k) and a dashpot (with given damping constant c). The mass is set in motion with initial position x_0 and initial velocity v_0. Find the position function $x(t)$ and determine whether the motion is overdamped, critically damped, or underdamped. If it is underdamped, write the position function in the form $x(t) = C_1 e^{-pt} \cos(\omega_1 t - \alpha_1)$. Also, find the undamped position function $u(t) = C_0 \cos(\omega_0 t - \alpha_0)$ that would result if the mass on the spring were set in motion with the same initial position and velocity, but with the dashpot disconnected (so $c = 0$). Finally, construct a figure that illustrates the effect of damping by comparing the graphs of $x(t)$ and $u(t)$.

15. $m = \frac{1}{2}, c = 3, k = 4; x_0 = 2, v_0 = 0$
16. $m = 3, c = 30, k = 63; x_0 = 2, v_0 = 2$
17. $m = 1, c = 8, k = 16; x_0 = 5, v_0 = -10$
18. $m = 2, c = 12, k = 50; x_0 = 0, v_0 = -8$
19. $m = 4, c = 20, k = 169; x_0 = 4, v_0 = 16$
20. $m = 2, c = 16, k = 40; x_0 = 5, v_0 = 4$
21. $m = 1, c = 10, k = 125; x_0 = 6, v_0 = 50$
22. A 12-lb weight (mass $m = 0.375$ slugs in fps units) is attached both to a vertically suspended spring that it stretches 6 in. and to a dashpot that provides 3 lb of resistance for every foot per second of velocity. **(a)** If the weight is pulled down 1 ft below its static equilibrium position and then released from rest at time $t = 0$, find its position function $x(t)$. **(b)** Find the frequency, time-varying amplitude, and phase angle of the motion.
23. This problem deals with a highly simplified model of a car of weight 3200 lb (mass $m = 100$ slugs in fps units). Assume that the suspension system acts like a single spring and its shock absorbers like a single dashpot, so that its vertical vibrations satisfy Eq. (4) with appropriate values of the coefficients. **(a)** Find the stiffness coefficient k of the spring if the car undergoes free vibrations at 80 cycles per minute (cycles/min) when its shock absorbers are disconnected. **(b)** With the shock absorbers connected, the car is set into vibration by driving it over a bump, and the resulting damped vibrations have a frequency of 78 cycles/min. After how long will the time-varying amplitude be 1% of its initial value?

Problems 24 through 34 deal with a mass–spring–dashpot system having position function $x(t)$ satisfying Eq. (4). We write $x_0 = x(0)$ and $v_0 = x'(0)$ and recall that $p = c/(2m)$, $\omega_0^2 = k/m$, and $\omega_1^2 = \omega_0^2 - p^2$. The system is critically damped, overdamped, or underdamped, as specified in each problem.

24. (Critically damped) Show in this case that
$$x(t) = (x_0 + v_0 t + p x_0 t)e^{-pt}.$$

25. (Critically damped) Deduce from Problem 24 that the mass passes through $x = 0$ at some instant $t > 0$ if and only if x_0 and $v_0 + p x_0$ have opposite signs.
26. (Critically damped) Deduce from Problem 24 that $x(t)$ has a local maximum or minimum at some instant $t > 0$ if and only if v_0 and $v_0 + p x_0$ have the same sign.
27. (Overdamped) Show in this case that
$$x(t) = \frac{1}{2\gamma}\left[(v_0 - r_2 x_0)e^{r_1 t} - (v_0 - r_1 x_0)e^{r_2 t}\right],$$
where $r_1, r_2 = -p \pm \sqrt{p^2 - \omega_0^2}$ and $\gamma = (r_1 - r_2)/2 > 0$.

28. (Overdamped) If $x_0 = 0$, deduce from Problem 27 that
$$x(t) = \frac{v_0}{\gamma}e^{-pt}\sinh \gamma t.$$

29. (Overdamped) Prove that in this case the mass can pass through its equilibrium position $x = 0$ at most once.
30. (Underdamped) Show that in this case
$$x(t) = e^{-pt}\left(x_0 \cos \omega_1 t + \frac{v_0 + p x_0}{\omega_1}\sin \omega_1 t\right).$$

31. (Underdamped) If the damping constant c is small in comparison with $\sqrt{8mk}$, apply the binomial series to show that
$$\omega_1 \approx \omega_0 \left(1 - \frac{c^2}{8mk}\right).$$

32. (Underdamped) Show that the local maxima and minima of
$$x(t) = Ce^{-pt}\cos(\omega_1 t - \alpha)$$
occur where
$$\tan(\omega_1 t - \alpha) = -\frac{p}{\omega_1}.$$
Conclude that $t_2 - t_1 = 2\pi/\omega_1$ if two consecutive maxima occur at times t_1 and t_2.
33. (Underdamped) Let x_1 and x_2 be two consecutive local maximum values of $x(t)$. Deduce from the result of Problem 32 that
$$\ln \frac{x_1}{x_2} = \frac{2\pi p}{\omega_1}.$$
The constant $\Delta = 2\pi p/\omega_1$ is called the **logarithmic decrement** of the oscillation. Note also that $c = m\omega_1 \Delta/\pi$ because $p = c/(2m)$.

Note: *The result of Problem 33 provides an accurate method for measuring the* viscosity *of a fluid, which is an important parameter in fluid dynamics but is not easy to measure directly. According to Stokes's drag law, a spherical body of radius a moving at a (relatively slow) speed through a fluid of viscosity μ experiences a resistive force $F_R = 6\pi \mu a v$. Thus if a spherical mass on a spring is immersed in the fluid and set in motion, this drag resistance damps its oscillations with damping constant $c = 6\pi a\mu$. The frequency ω_1 and logarithmic decrement Δ of the oscillations can be measured by direct observation. The final formula in Problem 33 then gives c and hence the viscosity of the fluid.*

34. (Underdamped) A body weighing 100 lb (mass $m = 3.125$ slugs in fps units) is oscillating attached to a spring and a dashpot. Its first two maximum displacements of 6.73 in. and 1.46 in. are observed to occur at times 0.34 s and 1.17 s, respectively. Compute the damping constant (in pound-seconds per foot) and spring constant (in pounds per foot).

Differential Equations and Determinism

Given a mass m, a dashpot constant c, and a spring constant k, Theorem 2 of Section 3.1 implies that the equation
$$mx'' + cx' + kx = 0 \tag{26}$$

has a unique *solution for $t \geq 0$ satisfying given initial conditions $x(0) = x_0$, $x'(0) = v_0$. Thus the future motion of an ideal mass–spring–dashpot system is completely determined by the differential equation and the initial conditions. Of course in a real physical system it is impossible to measure the parameters m, c, and k precisely. Problems 35 through 38 explore the resulting uncertainty in predicting the future behavior of a physical system.*

35. Suppose that $m = 1$, $c = 2$, and $k = 1$ in Eq. (26). Show that the solution with $x(0) = 0$ and $x'(0) = 1$ is

$$x_1(t) = te^{-t}.$$

36. Suppose that $m = 1$ and $c = 2$ but $k = 1 - 10^{-2n}$. Show that the solution of Eq. (26) with $x(0) = 0$ and $x'(0) = 1$ is

$$x_2(t) = 10^n e^{-t} \sinh 10^{-n} t.$$

37. Suppose that $m = 1$ and $c = 2$ but that $k = 1 + 10^{-2n}$. Show that the solution of Eq. (26) with $x(0) = 0$ and $x'(0) = 1$ is

$$x_3(t) = 10^n e^{-t} \sin 10^{-n} t.$$

38. Whereas the graphs of $x_1(t)$ and $x_2(t)$ resemble those shown in Figs. 3.4.7 and 3.4.8, the graph of $x_3(t)$ exhibits damped oscillations like those illustrated in Fig. 3.4.9, but with a very long pseudoperiod. Nevertheless, show that for each fixed $t > 0$ it is true that

$$\lim_{n \to \infty} x_2(t) = \lim_{n \to \infty} x_3(t) = x_1(t).$$

Conclude that *on a given finite time interval* the three solutions are in "practical" agreement if n is sufficiently large.

3.5 Nonhomogeneous Equations and Undetermined Coefficients

We learned in Section 3.3 how to solve homogeneous linear equations with constant coefficients, but we saw in Section 3.4 that an external force in a simple mechanical system contributes a nonhomogeneous term to its differential equation. The general nonhomogeneous nth-order linear equation with constant coefficients has the form

$$a_n y^{(n)} + a_{n-1} y^{(n-1)} + \cdots + a_1 y' + a_0 y = f(x). \tag{1}$$

By Theorem 5 of Section 3.2, a general solution of Eq. (1) has the form

$$y = y_c + y_p \tag{2}$$

where the complementary function $y_c(x)$ is a general solution of the associated homogeneous equation

$$a_n y^{(n)} + a_{n-1} y^{(n-1)} + \cdots + a_1 y' + a_0 y = 0, \tag{3}$$

and $y_p(x)$ is a particular solution of Eq. (1). Thus our remaining task is to find y_p.

The **method of undetermined coefficients** is a straightforward way of doing this when the given function $f(x)$ in Eq. (1) is sufficiently simple that we can make an intelligent guess as to the general form of y_p. For example, suppose that $f(x)$ is a polynomial of degree m. Then, because the derivatives of a polynomial are themselves polynomials of lower degree, it is reasonable to suspect a particular solution

$$y_p(x) = A_m x^m + A_{m-1} x^{m-1} + \cdots + A_1 x + A_0$$

that is also a polynomial of degree m, but with as yet undetermined coefficients. We may, therefore, substitute this expression for y_p into Eq. (1), and then—by equating coefficients of like powers of x on the two sides of the resulting equation—attempt to determine the coefficients $A_0, A_1, \ldots, A_m$ so that y_p will, indeed, be a particular solution of Eq. (1).

Similarly, suppose that

$$f(x) = a \cos kx + b \sin kx.$$

Then it is reasonable to expect a particular solution of the same form:

$$y_p(x) = A \cos kx + B \sin kx,$$

a linear combination with undetermined coefficients A and B. The reason is that any derivative of such a linear combination of $\cos kx$ and $\sin kx$ has the same form. We may therefore substitute this form of y_p in Eq. (1), and then—by equating coefficients of $\cos kx$ and $\sin kx$ on both sides of the resulting equation—attempt to determine the coefficients A and B so that y_p will, indeed, be a particular solution.

It turns out that this approach does succeed whenever all the derivatives of $f(x)$ have the same form as $f(x)$ itself. Before describing the method in full generality, we illustrate it with several preliminary examples.

Example 1   Find a particular solution of $y'' + 3y' + 4y = 3x + 2$.

Solution   Here $f(x) = 3x + 2$ is a polynomial of degree 1, so our guess is that

$$y_p(x) = Ax + B.$$

Then $y_p' = A$ and $y_p'' = 0$, so y_p will satisfy the differential equation provided that

$$(0) + 3(A) + 4(Ax + B) = 3x + 2,$$

that is,

$$(4A)x + (3A + 4B) = 3x + 2$$

for all x. This will be true if the x-terms and constant terms on the two sides of this equation agree. It therefore suffices for A and B to satisfy the two linear equations $4A = 3$ and $3A + 4B = 2$ that we readily solve for $A = \frac{3}{4}$ and $B = -\frac{1}{16}$. Thus we have found the particular solution

$$y_p(x) = \tfrac{3}{4}x - \tfrac{1}{16}. \qquad \blacksquare$$

Example 2   Find a particular solution of $y'' - 4y = 2e^{3x}$.

Solution   Any derivative of e^{3x} is a constant multiple of e^{3x}, so it is reasonable to try

$$y_p(x) = Ae^{3x}.$$

Then $y_p'' = 9Ae^{3x}$, so the given differential equation will be satisfied provided that

$$9Ae^{3x} - 4(Ae^{3x}) = 2e^{3x};$$

that is, $5A = 2$, so that $A = \frac{2}{5}$. Thus our particular solution is $y_p(x) = \frac{2}{5}e^{3x}$. $\qquad \blacksquare$

Example 3   Find a particular solution of $3y'' + y' - 2y = 2\cos x$.

Solution   A first guess might be $y_p(x) = A \cos x$, but the presence of y' on the left-hand side signals that we probably need a term involving $\sin x$ as well. So we try

$$\begin{aligned} y_p(x) &= A \cos x + B \sin x; \\ y_p'(x) &= -A \sin x + B \cos x, \\ y_p''(x) &= -A \cos x - B \sin x. \end{aligned}$$

Then substitution of y_p and its derivatives into the given differential equation yields

$$3(-A\cos x - B\sin x) + (-A\sin x + B\cos x) - 2(A\cos x + B\sin x) = 2\cos x,$$

that is (collecting coefficients on the left),

$$(-5A + B)\cos x + (-A - 5B)\sin x = 2\cos x.$$

This will be true for all x provided that the cosine and sine terms on the two sides of this equation agree. It therefore suffices for A and B to satisfy the two linear equations

$$-5A + B = 2,$$
$$-A - 5B = 0$$

with readily found solution $A = -\frac{5}{13}$, $B = \frac{1}{13}$. Hence a particular solution is

$$y_p(x) = -\frac{5}{13}\cos x + \frac{1}{13}\sin x.$$ ∎

The following example, which superficially resembles Example 2, indicates that the method of undetermined coefficients is not always quite so simple as we have made it appear.

Example 4 Find a particular solution of $y'' - 4y = 2e^{2x}$.

Solution If we try $y_p(x) = Ae^{2x}$, we find that

$$y_p'' - 4y_p = 4Ae^{2x} - 4Ae^{2x} = 0 \neq 2e^{2x}.$$

Thus, no matter how A is chosen, Ae^{2x} cannot satisfy the given nonhomogeneous equation. In fact, the preceding computation shows that Ae^{2x} satisfies instead the associated *homogeneous* equation. Therefore, we should begin with a trial function $y_p(x)$ whose derivative involves both e^{2x} *and something else* that can cancel upon substitution into the differential equation to leave the e^{2x} term that we need. A reasonable guess is

$$y_p(x) = Axe^{2x},$$

for which

$$y_p'(x) = Ae^{2x} + 2Axe^{2x} \quad \text{and} \quad y_p''(x) = 4Ae^{2x} + 4Axe^{2x}.$$

Substitution into the original differential equation yields

$$(4Ae^{2x} + 4Axe^{2x}) - 4(Axe^{2x}) = 2e^{2x}.$$

The terms involving xe^{2x} obligingly cancel, leaving only $4Ae^{2x} = 2e^{2x}$, so that $A = \frac{1}{2}$. Consequently, a particular solution is

$$y_p(x) = \tfrac{1}{2}xe^{2x}.$$ ∎

The General Approach

Our initial difficulty in Example 4 resulted from the fact that $f(x) = 2e^{2x}$ satisfies the associated homogeneous equation. Rule 1, given shortly, tells what to do when we do not have this difficulty, and Rule 2 tells what to do when we do have it.

The method of undetermined coefficients applies whenever the function $f(x)$ in Eq. (1) is a linear combination of (finite) products of functions of the following three types:

1. A polynomial in x;
2. An exponential function e^{rx};   (4)
3. $\cos kx$ or $\sin kx$.

Any such function—for example,

$$f(x) = (3 - 4x^2)e^{5x} - 4x^3 \cos 10x,$$

has the crucial property that only *finitely* many linearly independent functions appear as terms (summands) in $f(x)$ and its derivatives of all orders. In Rules 1 and 2 we assume that $Ly = f(x)$ is a nonhomogeneous linear equation with constant coefficients and that $f(x)$ is a function of this kind.

RULE 1   Method of Undetermined Coefficients

Suppose that no term appearing either in $f(x)$ or in any of its derivatives satisfies the associated homogeneous equation $Ly = 0$. Then take as a trial solution for y_p a linear combination of all linearly independent such terms and their derivatives. Then determine the coefficients by substitution of this trial solution into the nonhomogeneous equation $Ly = f(x)$.

Note that this rule is not a theorem requiring proof; it is merely a procedure to be followed in searching for a particular solution y_p. If we succeed in finding y_p, then nothing more need be said. (It can be proved, however, that this procedure will always succeed under the conditions specified here.)

In practice we check the supposition made in Rule 1 by first using the characteristic equation to find the complementary function y_c, and then write a list of all the terms appearing in $f(x)$ and its successive derivatives. If none of the terms in this list duplicates a term in y_c, then we proceed with Rule 1.

Example 5   Find a particular solution of

$$y'' + 4y = 3x^3.$$ (5)

Solution   The (familiar) complementary solution of Eq. (5) is

$$y_c(x) = c_1 \cos 2x + c_2 \sin 2x.$$

The function $f(x) = 3x^3$ and its derivatives are constant multiples of the linearly independent functions x^3, x^2, x, and 1. Because none of these appears in y_c, we try

$$y_p = Ax^3 + Bx^2 + Cx + D,$$
$$y_p' = 3Ax^2 + 2Bx + C,$$
$$y_p'' = 6Ax + 2B.$$

Substitution in Eq. (5) gives

$$y_p'' + 4y_p = (6Ax + 2B) + 4(Ax^3 + Bx^2 + Cx + D)$$
$$= 4Ax^3 + 4Bx^2 + (6A + 4C)x + (2B + D) = 3x^3.$$

We equate coefficients of like powers of x in the last equation to get

$$4A = 3, \qquad 4B = 0,$$
$$6A + 4C = 0, \qquad 2B + D = 0$$

with solution $A = \frac{3}{4}$, $B = 0$, $C = -\frac{9}{8}$, and $D = 0$. Hence a particular solution of Eq. (5) is

$$y_p(x) = \frac{3}{4}x^3 - \frac{9}{8}x. \qquad \blacksquare$$

Example 6   Solve the initial value problem

$$y'' - 3y' + 2y = 3e^{-x} - 10\cos 3x;$$
$$y(0) = 1, \quad y'(0) = 2. \tag{6}$$

Solution   The characteristic equation $r^2 - 3r + 2 = 0$ has roots $r = 1$ and $r = 2$, so the complementary function is

$$y_c(x) = c_1 e^x + c_2 e^{2x}.$$

The terms involved in $f(x) = 3e^{-x} - 10\cos 3x$ and its derivatives are e^{-x}, $\cos 3x$, and $\sin 3x$. Because none of these appears in y_c, we try

$$y_p = \quad Ae^{-x} + \quad B\cos 3x + \quad C\sin 3x,$$
$$y_p' = -Ae^{-x} - \quad 3B\sin 3x + 3C\cos 3x,$$
$$y_p'' = \quad Ae^{-x} - 9B\cos 3x - \quad 9C\sin 3x.$$

After we substitute these expressions into the differential equation in (6) and collect coefficients, we get

$$y_p'' - 3y_p' + 2y_p = 6Ae^{-x} + (-7B - 9C)\cos 3x + (9B - 7C)\sin 3x$$
$$= 3e^{-x} - 10\cos 3x.$$

We equate the coefficients of the terms involving e^{-x}, those involving $\cos 3x$, and those involving $\sin 3x$. The result is the system

$$6A = \quad 3,$$
$$-7B - 9C = -10,$$
$$9B - 7C = \quad 0$$

with solution $A = \frac{1}{2}$, $B = \frac{7}{13}$, and $C = \frac{9}{13}$. This gives the particular solution

$$y_p(x) = \tfrac{1}{2}e^{-x} + \tfrac{7}{13}\cos 3x + \tfrac{9}{13}\sin 3x,$$

which, however, does not have the required initial values in (6).

To satisfy those initial conditions, we begin with the *general* solution

$$y(x) = y_c(x) + y_p(x)$$
$$= c_1 e^x + c_2 e^{2x} + \tfrac{1}{2} e^{-x} + \tfrac{7}{13} \cos 3x + \tfrac{9}{13} \sin 3x,$$

with derivative

$$y'(x) = c_1 e^x + 2c_2 e^{2x} - \tfrac{1}{2} e^{-x} - \tfrac{21}{13} \sin 3x + \tfrac{27}{13} \cos 3x.$$

The initial conditions in (6) lead to the equations

$$y(0) = c_1 + c_2 + \tfrac{1}{2} + \tfrac{7}{13} = 1,$$
$$y'(0) = c_1 + 2c_2 - \tfrac{1}{2} + \tfrac{27}{13} = 2$$

with solution $c_1 = -\tfrac{1}{2}$, $c_2 = \tfrac{6}{13}$. The desired particular solution is therefore

$$y(x) = -\tfrac{1}{2} e^x + \tfrac{6}{13} e^{2x} + \tfrac{1}{2} e^{-x} + \tfrac{7}{13} \cos 3x + \tfrac{9}{13} \sin 3x. \qquad \blacksquare$$

Example 7 Find the general form of a particular solution of

$$y^{(3)} + 9y' = x \sin x + x^2 e^{2x}. \tag{7}$$

Solution The characteristic equation $r^3 + 9r = 0$ has roots $r = 0$, $r = -3i$, and $r = 3i$. So the complementary function is

$$y_c(x) = c_1 + c_2 \cos 3x + c_3 \sin 3x.$$

The derivatives of the right-hand side in Eq. (7) involve the terms

$$\cos x, \quad \sin x, \quad x \cos x, \quad x \sin x,$$
$$e^{2x}, \quad x e^{2x}, \quad \text{and} \quad x^2 e^{2x}.$$

Because there is no duplication with the terms of the complementary function, the trial solution takes the form

$$y_p(x) = A \cos x + B \sin x + Cx \cos x + Dx \sin x + E e^{2x} + F x e^{2x} + G x^2 e^{2x}.$$

Upon substituting y_p in Eq. (7) and equating coefficients of like terms, we get seven equations determining the seven coefficients A, B, C, D, E, F, and G. $\qquad \blacksquare$

The Case of Duplication

Now we turn our attention to the situation in which Rule 1 does not apply: Some of the terms involved in $f(x)$ and its derivatives satisfy the associated homogeneous equation. For instance, suppose that we want to find a particular solution of the differential equation

$$(D - r)^3 y = (2x - 3)e^{rx}. \tag{8}$$

Proceeding as in Rule 1, our first guess would be

$$y_p(x) = Ae^{rx} + Bxe^{rx}. \tag{9}$$

This form of $y_p(x)$ will not be adequate because the complementary function of Eq. (8) is

$$y_c(x) = c_1 e^{rx} + c_2 x e^{rx} + c_3 x^2 e^{rx}, \tag{10}$$

so substitution of (9) in the left-hand side of (8) would yield zero rather than $(2x - 3)e^{rx}$.

To see how to amend our first guess, we observe that

$$(D - r)^2 [(2x - 3)e^{rx}] = [D^2(2x - 3)]e^{rx} = 0$$

by Eq. (13) of Section 3.3. If $y(x)$ is *any* solution of Eq. (8) and we apply the operator $(D - r)^2$ to both sides, we see that $y(x)$ is also a solution of the equation $(D - r)^5 y = 0$. The general solution of this *homogeneous* equation can be written as

$$y(x) = \underbrace{c_1 e^{rx} + c_2 x e^{rx} + c_3 x^2 e^{rx}}_{y_c} + \underbrace{Ax^3 e^{rx} + Bx^4 e^{rx}}_{y_p}.$$

Thus *every* solution of our original equation in (8) is the sum of a complementary function and a *particular solution* of the form

$$y_p(x) = Ax^3 e^{rx} + Bx^4 e^{rx}. \tag{11}$$

Note that the right-hand side in Eq. (11) can be obtained by multiplying each term of our first guess in (9) by the least positive integral power of x (in this case, x^3) that suffices to eliminate duplication between the terms of the resulting trial solution $y_p(x)$ and the complementary function $y_c(x)$ given in (10). This procedure succeeds in the general case.

To simplify the general statement of Rule 2, we observe that to find a particular solution of the nonhomogeneous linear differential equation

$$Ly = f_1(x) + f_2(x), \tag{12}$$

it suffices to find *separately* particular solutions $Y_1(x)$ and $Y_2(x)$ of the two equations

$$Ly = f_1(x) \quad \text{and} \quad Ly = f_2(x), \tag{13}$$

respectively. For linearity then gives

$$L[Y_1 + Y_2] = LY_1 + LY_2 = f_1(x) + f_2(x),$$

and therefore $y_p = Y_1 + Y_2$ is a particular solution of Eq. (12). (This is a type of "superposition principle" for nonhomogeneous linear equations.)

Now our problem is to find a particular solution of the equation $Ly = f(x)$, where $f(x)$ is a linear combination of products of the elementary functions listed in (4). Thus $f(x)$ can be written as a sum of terms each of the form

$$P_m(x)e^{rx}\cos kx \quad \text{or} \quad P_m(x)e^{rx}\sin kx, \tag{14}$$

where $P_m(x)$ is a polynomial in x of degree m. Note that any derivative of such a term is of the same form but with *both* sines and cosines appearing. The procedure by which we arrived earlier at the particular solution in (11) of Eq. (8) can be generalized to show that the following procedure is always successful.

> ### RULE 2   Method of Undetermined Coefficients
>
> If the function $f(x)$ is of either form in (14), take as the trial solution
>
> $$y_p(x) = x^s[(A_0 + A_1 x + A_2 x^2 + \cdots + A_m x^m)e^{rx}\cos kx$$
> $$+ (B_0 + B_1 x + B_2 x^2 + \cdots + B_m x^m)e^{rx}\sin kx], \tag{15}$$
>
> where s is the smallest nonnegative integer such that such that no term in y_p duplicates a term in the complementary function y_c. Then determine the coefficients in Eq. (15) by substituting y_p into the nonhomogeneous equation.

In practice we seldom need to deal with a function $f(x)$ exhibiting the full generality in (14). The table in Fig. 3.5.1 lists the form of y_p in various common cases, corresponding to the possibilities $m = 0$, $r = 0$, and $k = 0$.

On the other hand, it is common to have

$$f(x) = f_1(x) + f_2(x),$$

where $f_1(x)$ and $f_2(x)$ are different functions of the sort listed in the table in Fig. 3.5.1. In this event we take as y_p the sum of the trial solutions for $f_1(x)$ and $f_2(x)$, choosing s *separately* for each part to eliminate duplication with the complementary function. This procedure is illustrated in Examples 8 through 10.

$f(x)$	y_p
$P_m = b_0 + b_1 x + b_2 x^2 + \cdots + b_m x^m$	$x^s(A_0 + A_1 x + A_2 x^2 + \cdots + A_m x^m)$
$a\cos kx + b\sin kx$	$x^s(A\cos kx + B\sin kx)$
$e^{rx}(a\cos kx + b\sin kx)$	$x^s e^{rx}(A\cos kx + B\sin kx)$
$P_m(x)e^{rx}$	$x^s(A_0 + A_1 x + A_2 x^2 + \cdots + A_m x^m)e^{rx}$
$P_m(x)(a\cos kx + b\sin kx)$	$x^s[(A_0 + A_1 x + \cdots + A_m x^m)\cos kx$
	$\qquad + (B_0 + B_1 x + \cdots + B_m x^m)\sin kx]$

FIGURE 3.5.1.   Substitutions in the method of undetermined coefficients.

Example 8   Find a particular solution of

$$y^{(3)} + y'' = 3e^x + 4x^2. \tag{16}$$

Solution The characteristic equation $r^3 + r^2 = 0$ has roots $r_1 = r_2 = 0$ and $r_3 = -1$, so the complementary function is

$$y_c(x) = c_1 + c_2 x + c_3 e^{-x}.$$

As a first step toward our particular solution, we form the sum

$$(Ae^x) + (B + Cx + Dx^2).$$

The part Ae^x corresponding to $3e^x$ does not duplicate any part of the complementary function, but the part $B + Cx + Dx^2$ must be multiplied by x^2 to eliminate duplication. Hence we take

$$y_p = Ae^x + Bx^2 + Cx^3 + Dx^4,$$

$$y_p' = Ae^x + 2Bx + 3Cx^2 + 4Dx^3,$$

$$y_p'' = Ae^x + 2B + 6Cx + 12Dx^2, \quad \text{and}$$

$$y_p^{(3)} = Ae^x + 6C + 24Dx.$$

Substitution of these derivatives in Eq. (16) yields

$$2Ae^x + (2B + 6C) + (6C + 24D)x + 12Dx^2 = 3e^x + 4x^2.$$

The system of equations

$$2A = 3, \qquad 2B + 6C = 0,$$
$$6C + 24D = 0, \qquad 12D = 4$$

has the solution $A = \frac{3}{2}$, $B = 4$, $C = -\frac{4}{3}$, and $D = \frac{1}{3}$. Hence the desired particular solution is

$$y_p(x) = \tfrac{3}{2}e^x + 4x^2 - \tfrac{4}{3}x^3 + \tfrac{1}{3}x^4. \qquad \blacksquare$$

Example 9 Determine the appropriate form for a particular solution of

$$y'' + 6y' + 13y = e^{-3x} \cos 2x.$$

Solution The characteristic equation $r^2 + 6r + 13 = 0$ has roots $-3 \pm 2i$, so the complementary function is

$$y_c(x) = e^{-3x}(c_1 \cos 2x + c_2 \sin 2x).$$

This is the same form as a first attempt $e^{-3x}(A \cos 2x + B \sin 2x)$ at a particular solution, so we must multiply by x to eliminate duplication. Hence we would take

$$y_p(x) = e^{-3x}(Ax \cos 2x + Bx \sin 2x). \qquad \blacksquare$$

Example 10 Determine the appropriate form for a particular solution of the fifth-order equation

$$(D - 2)^3(D^2 + 9)y = x^2 e^{2x} + x \sin 3x.$$

Solution The characteristic equation $(r - 2)^3(r^2 + 9) = 0$ has roots $r = 2, 2, 2, 3i$, and $-3i$, so the complementary function is

$$y_c(x) = c_1e^{2x} + c_2xe^{2x} + c_3x^2e^{2x} + c_4\cos 3x + c_5\sin 3x.$$

As a first step toward the form of a particular solution, we examine the sum

$$[(A + Bx + Cx^2)e^{2x}] + [(D + Ex)\cos 3x + (F + Gx)\sin 3x].$$

To eliminate duplication with terms of $y_c(x)$, the first part—corresponding to x^2e^{2x}— must be multiplied by x^3, and the second part—corresponding to $x\sin 3x$—must be multiplied by x. Hence we would take

$$y_p(x) = (Ax^3 + Bx^4 + Cx^5)e^{2x} + (Dx + Ex^2)\cos 3x + (Fx + Gx^2)\sin 3x. \quad \blacksquare$$

Variation of Parameters

Finally, let us point out the kind of situation in which the method of undetermined coefficients cannot be used. Consider, for example, the equation

$$y'' + y = \tan x, \tag{17}$$

which at first glance may appear similar to those considered in the preceding examples. Not so; the function $f(x) = \tan x$ has *infinitely many* linearly independent derivatives

$$\sec^2 x, \quad 2\sec^2 x \tan x, \quad 4\sec^2 x \tan^2 x + 2\sec^4 x, \quad \dots .$$

Therefore, we do not have available a *finite* linear combination to use as a trial solution.

We discuss here the method of **variation of parameters**, which—in principle (that is, if the integrals that appear can be evaluated)—can always be used to find a particular solution of the nonhomogeneous linear differential equation

$$y^{(n)} + p_{n-1}(x)y^{(n-1)} + \cdots + p_1(x)y' + p_0(x)y = f(x), \tag{18}$$

provided that we already know the general solution

$$y_c = c_1y_1 + c_2y_2 + \cdots + c_ny_n \tag{19}$$

of the associated homogeneous equation

$$y^{(n)} + p_{n-1}(x)y^{(n-1)} + \cdots + p_1(x)y' + p_0(x)y = 0. \tag{20}$$

Here, in brief, is the basic idea of the method of variation of parameters. Suppose that we replace the constants, or *parameters, $c_1, c_2, \dots, c_n$* in the complementary function in Eq. (19) with *variables*: functions $u_1, u_2, \dots, u_n$ of x. We ask whether it is possible to choose these functions in such a way that the combination

$$y_p(x) = u_1(x)y_1(x) + u_2(x)y_2(x) + \cdots + u_n(x)y_n(x) \tag{21}$$

is a particular solution of the nonhomogeneous equation in (18). It turns out that this *is* always possible.

The method is essentially the same for all orders $n \geq 2$, but we will describe it in detail only for the case $n = 2$. So we begin with the second-order nonhomogeneous equation

$$L[y] = y'' + P(x)y' + Q(x)y = f(x) \tag{22}$$

with complementary function

$$y_c(x) = c_1 y_1(x) + c_2 y_2(x) \tag{23}$$

on some open interval I where the functions P and Q are continuous. We want to find functions u_1 and u_2 such that

$$y_p(x) = u_1(x)y_1(x) + u_2(x)y_2(x) \tag{24}$$

is a particular solution of Eq. (22).

One condition on the two functions u_1 and u_2 is that $L[y_p] = f(x)$. Because two conditions are required to determine two functions, we are free to impose an additional condition of our choice. We will do so in a way that simplifies the computations as much as possible. But first, to impose the condition $L[y_p] = f(x)$, we must compute the derivatives y_p' and y_p''. The product rule gives

$$y_p' = (u_1 y_1' + u_2 y_2') + (u_1' y_1 + u_2' y_2).$$

To avoid the appearance of the second derivatives u_1'' and u_2'', the additional condition that we now impose is that the second sum here must vanish:

$$u_1' y_1 + u_2' y_2 = 0. \tag{25}$$

Then

$$y_p' = u_1 y_1' + u_2 y_2', \tag{26}$$

and the product rule gives

$$y_p'' = (u_1 y_1'' + u_2 y_2'') + (u_1' y_1' + u_2' y_2'). \tag{27}$$

But both y_1 and y_2 satisfy the homogeneous equation

$$y'' + Py' + Qy = 0$$

associated with the nonhomogeneous equation in (22), so

$$y_i'' = -Py_i' - Qy_i \tag{28}$$

for $i = 1, 2$. It therefore follows from Eq. (27) that

$$y_p'' = (u_1' y_1' + u_2' y_2') - P \cdot (u_1 y_1' + u_2 y_2') - Q \cdot (u_1 y_1 + u_2 y_2).$$

In view of Eqs. (24) and (26), this means that

$$y_p'' = (u_1' y_1' + u_2' y_2') - Py_p' - Qy_p;$$

hence

$$L[y_p] = u_1' y_1' + u_2' y_2'. \tag{29}$$

The requirement that y_p satisfy the nonhomogeneous equation in (22)—that is, that $L[y_p] = f(x)$—therefore implies that

$$u_1' y_1' + u_2' y_2' = f(x). \tag{30}$$

Finally, Eqs. (25) and (30) determine the functions u_1 and u_2 that we need. Collecting these equations, we obtain a system

$$\begin{aligned} u_1' y_1 + u_2' y_2 &= 0, \\ u_1' y_1' + u_2' y_2' &= f(x) \end{aligned} \tag{31}$$

of two linear equations in the two *derivatives* u_1' and u_2'. Note that the determinant of coefficients in (31) is simply the Wronskian $W(y_1, y_2)$. Once we have solved the equations in (31) for the derivatives u_1' and u_2', we integrate each to obtain the functions u_1 and u_2 such that

$$y_p = u_1 y_1 + u_2 y_2 \tag{32}$$

is the desired particular solution of Eq. (22). In Problem 63 we ask you to carry out this process explicitly and thereby verify the formula for $y_p(x)$ in the following theorem.

THEOREM 1 Variation of Parameters

If the nonhomogeneous equation $y'' + P(x)y' + Q(x)y = f(x)$ has complementary function $y_c(x) = c_1 y_1(x) + c_2 y_2(x)$, then a particular solution is given by

$$y_p(x) = -y_1(x) \int \frac{y_2(x) f(x)}{W(x)} \, dx + y_2(x) \int \frac{y_1(x) f(x)}{W(x)} \, dx, \tag{33}$$

where $W = W(y_1, y_2)$ is the Wronskian of the two independent solutions y_1 and y_2 of the associated homogeneous equation.

Example 11   Find a particular solution of the equation $y'' + y = \tan x$.

Solution   The complementary function is $y_c(x) = c_1 \cos x + c_2 \sin x$, and we could simply substitute directly in Eq. (33). But it is more instructive to set up the equations in (31) and solve for u_1' and u_2', so we begin with

$$\begin{aligned} y_1 &= \cos x, & y_2 &= \sin x, \\ y_1' &= -\sin x, & y_2' &= \cos x. \end{aligned}$$

Hence the equations in (31) are

$$\begin{aligned} (u_1')(\cos x) + (u_2')(\sin x) &= 0, \\ (u_1')(-\sin x) + (u_2')(\cos x) &= \tan x. \end{aligned}$$

We easily solve these equations for

$$u_1' = -\sin x \tan x = -\frac{\sin^2 x}{\cos x} = \cos x - \sec x,$$

$$u_2' = \cos x \tan x = \sin x.$$

Hence we take

$$u_1 = \int (\cos x - \sec x)\, dx = \sin x - \ln|\sec x + \tan x|$$

and

$$u_2 = \int \sin x\, dx = -\cos x.$$

(Do you see why we choose the constants of integration to be zero?) Thus our particular solution is

$$\begin{aligned} y_p(x) &= u_1(x)y_1(x) + u_2(x)y_2(x) \\ &= (\sin x - \ln|\sec x + \tan x|)\cos x + (-\cos x)(\sin x); \end{aligned}$$

that is,

$$y_p(x) = -(\cos x)\ln|\sec x + \tan x|.$$ ∎

3.5 Problems

In Problems 1 through 20, find a particular solution y_p of the given equation. In all these problems, primes denote derivatives with respect to x.

1. $y'' + 16y = e^{3x}$

2. $y'' - y' - 2y = 3x + 4$

3. $y'' - y' - 6y = 2\sin 3x$

4. $4y'' + 4y' + y = 3xe^x$

5. $y'' + y' + y = \sin^2 x$

6. $2y'' + 4y' + 7y = x^2$

7. $y'' - 4y = \sinh x$

8. $y'' - 4y = \cosh 2x$

9. $y'' + 2y' - 3y = 1 + xe^x$

10. $y'' + 9y = 2\cos 3x + 3\sin 3x$

11. $y^{(3)} + 4y' = 3x - 1$

12. $y^{(3)} + y' = 2 - \sin x$

13. $y'' + 2y' + 5y = e^x \sin x$

14. $y^{(4)} - 2y'' + y = xe^x$

15. $y^{(5)} + 5y^{(4)} - y = 17$

16. $y'' + 9y = 2x^2 e^{3x} + 5$

17. $y'' + y = \sin x + x \cos x$

18. $y^{(4)} - 5y'' + 4y = e^x - xe^{2x}$

19. $y^{(5)} + 2y^{(3)} + 2y'' = 3x^2 - 1$

20. $y^{(3)} - y = e^x + 7$

In Problems 21 through 30, set up the appropriate form of a particular solution y_p, but do not determine the values of the coefficients.

21. $y'' - 2y' + 2y = e^x \sin x$

22. $y^{(5)} - y^{(3)} = e^x + 2x^2 - 5$

23. $y'' + 4y = 3x \cos 2x$

24. $y^{(3)} - y'' - 12y' = x - 2xe^{-3x}$

25. $y'' + 3y' + 2y = x(e^{-x} - e^{-2x})$

26. $y'' - 6y' + 13y = xe^{3x} \sin 2x$

27. $y^{(4)} + 5y'' + 4y = \sin x + \cos 2x$

28. $y^{(4)} + 9y'' = (x^2 + 1)\sin 3x$

29. $(D-1)^3(D^2 - 4)y = xe^x + e^{2x} + e^{-2x}$

30. $y^{(4)} - 2y'' + y = x^2 \cos x$

Solve the initial value problems in Problems 31 through 40.

31. $y'' + 4y = 2x$; $y(0) = 1$, $y'(0) = 2$

32. $y'' + 3y' + 2y = e^x$; $y(0) = 0$, $y'(0) = 3$

33. $y'' + 9y = \sin 2x$; $y(0) = 1$, $y'(0) = 0$

34. $y'' + y = \cos x$; $y(0) = 1$, $y'(0) = -1$

35. $y'' - 2y' + 2y = x + 1$; $y(0) = 3$, $y'(0) = 0$

36. $y^{(4)} - 4y'' = x^2$; $y(0) = y'(0) = 1$, $y''(0) = y^{(3)}(0) = -1$

37. $y^{(3)} - 2y'' + y' = 1 + xe^x$; $y(0) = y'(0) = 0$, $y''(0) = 1$

38. $y'' + 2y' + 2y = \sin 3x$; $y(0) = 2$, $y'(0) = 0$

39. $y^{(3)} + y'' = x + e^{-x}$; $y(0) = 1$, $y'(0) = 0$, $y''(0) = 1$

40. $y^{(4)} - y = 5$; $y(0) = y'(0) = y''(0) = y^{(3)}(0) = 0$

41. Find a particular solution of the equation

$$y^{(4)} - y^{(3)} - y'' - y' - 2y = 8x^5.$$

42. Find the solution of the initial value problem consisting of the differential equation of Problem 41 and the initial conditions

$$y(0) = y'(0) = y''(0) = y^{(3)}(0) = 0.$$

43. (a) Write

$$\cos 3x + i \sin 3x = e^{3ix} = (\cos x + i \sin x)^3$$

by Euler's formula, expand, and equate real and imaginary parts to derive the identities

$$\cos^3 x = \tfrac{3}{4} \cos x + \tfrac{1}{4} \cos 3x,$$
$$\sin^3 x = \tfrac{3}{4} \sin x - \tfrac{1}{4} \sin 3x.$$

(b) Use the result of part (a) to find a general solution of

$$y'' + 4y = \cos^3 x.$$

Use trigonometric identities to find general solutions of the equations in Problems 44 through 46.

44. $y'' + y' + y = \sin x \sin 3x$
45. $y'' + 9y = \sin^4 x$
46. $y'' + y = x \cos^3 x$

In Problems 47 through 56, use the method of variation of parameters to find a particular solution of the given differential equation.

47. $y'' + 3y' + 2y = 4e^x$ **48.** $y'' - 2y' - 8y = 3e^{-2x}$
49. $y'' - 4y' + 4y = 2e^{2x}$ **50.** $y'' - 4y = \sinh 2x$
51. $y'' + 4y = \cos 3x$ **52.** $y'' + 9y = \sin 3x$
53. $y'' + 9y = 2 \sec 3x$ **54.** $y'' + y = \csc^2 x$
55. $y'' + 4y = \sin^2 x$ **56.** $y'' - 4y = xe^x$

57. You can verify by substitution that $y_c = c_1 x + c_2 x^{-1}$ is a complementary function for the nonhomogeneous second-order equation

$$x^2 y'' + xy' - y = 72x^5.$$

But before applying the method of variation of parameters, you must first divide this equation by its leading coefficient x^2 to rewrite it in the standard form

$$y'' + \frac{1}{x} y' - \frac{1}{x^2} y = 72x^3.$$

Thus $f(x) = 72x^3$ in Eq. (22). Now proceed to solve the equations in (31) and thereby derive the particular solution $y_p = 3x^5$.

In Problems 58 through 62, a nonhomogeneous second-order linear equation and a complementary function y_c are given. Apply the method of Problem 57 to find a particular solution of the equation.

58. $x^2 y'' - 4xy' + 6y = x^3$; $y_c = c_1 x^2 + c_2 x^3$
59. $x^2 y'' - 3xy' + 4y = x^4$; $y_c = x^2(c_1 + c_2 \ln x)$
60. $4x^2 y'' - 4xy' + 3y = 8x^{4/3}$; $y_c = c_1 x + c_2 x^{3/4}$
61. $x^2 y'' + xy' + y = \ln x$; $y_c = c_1 \cos(\ln x) + c_2 \sin(\ln x)$
62. $(x^2 - 1)y'' - 2xy' + 2y = x^2 - 1$; $y_c = c_1 x + c_2(1 + x^2)$
63. Carry out the solution process indicated in the text to derive the variation of parameters formula in (33) from Eqs. (31) and (32).
64. Apply the variation of parameters formula in (33) to find the particular solution $y_p(x) = -x \cos x$ of the nonhomogeneous equation $y'' + y = 2 \sin x$.

3.5 Application   **Automated Variation of Parameters**

The variation of parameters formula in (33) is especially amenable to implementation in a computer algebra system when the indicated integrals would be too tedious or inconvenient for manual evaluation. For example, suppose that we want to find a particular solution of the nonhomogeneous equation

$$y'' + y = \tan x$$

of Example 11, with complementary function $y_c(x) = c_1 \cos x + c_2 \sin x$. Then the *Maple* commands

```
y1 := cos(x):
y2 := sin(x):
f  := tan(x):
W  := y1*diff(y2,x) - y2*diff(y1,x):
W  := simplify(W):
yp := -y1*int(y2*f/W,x) + y2*int(y1*f/W,x):
simplify(yp);
```

implement (33) and produce the result

$$y_p(x) = -(\cos x) \ln \left(\frac{1 + \sin x}{\cos x} \right)$$

equivalent to the result $y_p(x) = -(\cos x)\ln(\sec x + \tan x)$ found in Example 11. The analogous *Mathematica* commands

```
y1 = Cos[x];
y2 = Sin[x];
f = Tan[x];
W = y1*D[y2,x] - y2*D[y1,x]   //   Simplify
yp = -y1*Integrate[y2*f/W,x] + y2*Integrate[y1*f/W,x];
Simplify[yp]
```

produce the result

$$y_p(x) = -(\cos x)\ln\left(\frac{\cos(x/2) + \sin(x/2)}{\cos(x/2) - \sin(x/2)}\right),$$

which (by the usual difference-of-squares technique) also is equivalent to the result found in Example 11.

To solve similarly a second-order linear equation $y'' + P(x)y' + Q(x)y = f(x)$ whose complementary function $y_c(x) = c_1 y_1(x) + c_2 y_2(x)$ is known, we need only insert the corresponding definitions of $y_1(x)$, $y_2(x)$, and $f(x)$ in the initial lines shown here. Find in this way the indicated particular solution $y_p(x)$ of the nonhomogeneous equations in Problems 1 through 6.

1. $y'' + y = 2\sin x$ $y_p(x) = -x\cos x$
2. $y'' + y = 4x\sin x$ $y_p(x) = x\sin x - x^2\cos x$
3. $y'' + y = 12x^2\sin x$ $y_p(x) = 3x^2\sin x + (3x - 2x^3)\cos x$
4. $y'' - 2y' + 2y = 2e^x\sin x$ $y_p(x) = -xe^x\cos x$
5. $y'' - 2y' + 2y = 4xe^x\sin x$ $y_p(x) = e^x(x\sin x - x^2\cos x)$
6. $y'' - 2y' + 2y = 12x^2e^x\sin x$ $y_p(x) = e^x\left[3x^2\sin x + (3x - 2x^3)\cos x\right]$

3.6 Forced Oscillations and Resonance

In Section 3.4 we derived the differential equation

$$mx'' + cx' + kx = F(t) \tag{1}$$

that governs the one-dimensional motion of a mass m that is attached to a spring (with constant k) and a dashpot (with constant c) and is also acted on by an external force $F(t)$. Machines with rotating components commonly involve mass-spring systems (or their equivalents) in which the external force is simple harmonic:

$$F(t) = F_0\cos\omega t \quad \text{or} \quad F(t) = F_0\sin\omega t, \tag{2}$$

where the constant F_0 is the amplitude of the periodic force and ω is its circular frequency.

For an example of how a rotating machine component can provide a simple harmonic force, consider the cart with a rotating vertical flywheel shown in Fig. 3.6.1. The cart has mass $m - m_0$, not including the flywheel of mass m_0. The centroid of the flywheel is off center at a distance a from its center, and its angular speed is ω radians per second. The cart is attached to a spring (with constant k) as shown. Assume that the centroid of the cart itself is directly beneath the center of the flywheel, and denote by $x(t)$ its displacement from its equilibrium position

FIGURE 3.6.1. The cart-with-flywheel system.

(where the spring is unstretched). Figure 3.6.1 helps us to see that the displacement $\bar{x}$ of the centroid of the combined cart plus flywheel is given by

$$\bar{x} = \frac{(m - m_0)x + m_0(x + a \cos \omega t)}{m} = x + \frac{m_0 a}{m} \cos \omega t.$$

Let us ignore friction and apply Newton's second law $m\bar{x}'' = -kx$, because the force exerted by the spring is $-kx$. We substitute for $\bar{x}$ in the last equation to obtain

$$mx'' - m_0 a\omega^2 \cos \omega t = -kx;$$

that is,

$$mx'' + kx = m_0 a\omega^2 \cos \omega t. \tag{3}$$

Thus the cart with its rotating flywheel acts like a mass on a spring under the influence of a simple harmonic external force with amplitude $F_0 = m_0 a\omega^2$. Such a system is a reasonable model of a front-loading washing machine with the clothes being washed loaded off center. This illustrates the practical importance of analyzing solutions of Eq. (1) with external forces as in (2).

Undamped Forced Oscillations

To study undamped oscillations under the influence of the external force $F(t) = F_0 \cos \omega t$, we set $c = 0$ in Eq. (1), and thereby begin with the equation

➤ $$mx'' + kx = F_0 \cos \omega t \tag{4}$$

whose complementary function is $x_c = c_1 \cos \omega_0 t + c_2 \sin \omega_0 t$. Here

➤ $$\omega_0 = \sqrt{\frac{k}{m}}$$

(as in Eq. (9) of Section 3.4) is the (circular) **natural frequency** of the mass–spring system. The fact that the angle $\omega_0 t$ is measured in (dimensionless) radians reminds us that if t is measured in seconds (s), then ω_0 is measured in radians per second—that is, in inverse seconds (s^{-1}). Also recall from Eq. (14) in Section 3.4 that division of a circular frequency ω by the number 2π of radians in a cycle gives the corresponding (ordinary) **frequency** $\nu = \omega/2\pi$ in Hz (hertz = cycles per second).

Let us assume initially that the external and natural frequencies are *unequal*: $\omega \neq \omega_0$. We substitute $x_p = A \cos \omega t$ in Eq. (4) to find a particular solution. (No sine term is needed in x_p because there is no term involving x' on the left-hand side in Eq. (4).) This gives

$$-m\omega^2 A \cos \omega t + kA \cos \omega t = F_0 \cos \omega t,$$

so

$$A = \frac{F_0}{k - m\omega^2} = \frac{F_0/m}{\omega_0^2 - \omega^2}, \tag{5}$$

and thus

$$x_p(t) = \frac{F_0/m}{\omega_0^2 - \omega^2} \cos \omega t. \tag{6}$$

Therefore, the general solution $x = x_c + x_p$ is given by

$$x(t) = c_1 \cos \omega_0 t + c_2 \sin \omega_0 t + \frac{F_0/m}{\omega_0^2 - \omega^2} \cos \omega t, \qquad (7)$$

where the constants c_1 and c_2 are determined by the initial values $x(0)$ and $x'(0)$. Equivalently, as in Eq. (12) of Section 3.4, we can rewrite Eq. (7) as

$$x(t) = C \cos(\omega_0 t - \alpha) + \frac{F_0/m}{\omega_0^2 - \omega^2} \cos \omega t, \qquad (8)$$

so we see that the resulting motion is a superposition of two oscillations, one with natural circular frequency ω_0, the other with the frequency ω of the external force.

Example 1   Suppose that $m = 1$, $k = 9$, $F_0 = 80$, and $\omega = 5$, so the differential equation in (4) is

$$x'' + 9x = 80 \cos 5t.$$

Find $x(t)$ if $x(0) = x'(0) = 0$.

Solution   Here the natural frequency $\omega_0 = 3$ and the frequency $\omega = 5$ of the external force are unequal, as in the preceding discussion. First we substitute $x_p = A \cos 5t$ in the differential equation and find that $-25A + 9A = 80$, so that $A = -5$. Thus a particular solution is

$$x_p(t) = -5 \cos 5t.$$

The complementary function is $x_c = c_1 \cos 3t + c_2 \sin 3t$, so the general solution of the given nonhomogeneous equation is

$$x(t) = c_1 \cos 3t + c_2 \sin 3t - 5 \cos 5t,$$

with derivative

$$x'(t) = -3c_1 \sin 3t + 3c_2 \cos 3t + 25 \sin 5t.$$

The initial conditions $x(0) = 0$ and $x'(0) = 0$ now yield $c_1 = 5$ and $c_2 = 0$, so the desired particular solution is

$$x(t) = 5 \cos 3t - 5 \cos 5t.$$

As indicated in Fig. 3.6.2, the period of $x(t)$ is the least common multiple 2π of the periods $2\pi/3$ and $2\pi/5$ of the two cosine terms.   ∎

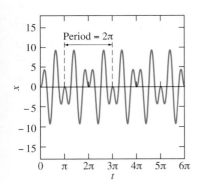

FIGURE 3.6.2. The response $x(t) = 5 \cos 3t - 5 \cos 5t$ in Example 1.

Beats

If we impose the initial conditions $x(0) = x'(0) = 0$ on the solution in (7), we find that

$$c_1 = -\frac{F_0}{m(\omega_0^2 - \omega^2)} \quad \text{and} \quad c_2 = 0,$$

so the particular solution is

$$x(t) = \frac{F_0}{m(\omega_0^2 - \omega^2)} (\cos \omega t - \cos \omega_0 t). \qquad (9)$$

The trigonometric identity $2 \sin A \sin B = \cos(A - B) - \cos(A + B)$, applied with $A = \frac{1}{2}(\omega_0 + \omega)t$ and $B = \frac{1}{2}(\omega_0 - \omega)t$, enables us to rewrite Eq. (9) in the form

$$x(t) = \frac{2F_0}{m(\omega_0^2 - \omega^2)} \sin \tfrac{1}{2}(\omega_0 - \omega)t \sin \tfrac{1}{2}(\omega_0 + \omega)t. \tag{10}$$

Suppose now that $\omega \approx \omega_0$, so that $\omega_0 + \omega$ is very large in comparison with $|\omega_0 - \omega|$. Then $\sin \frac{1}{2}(\omega_0 + \omega)t$ is a *rapidly* varying function, whereas $\sin \frac{1}{2}(\omega_0 - \omega)t$ is a *slowly* varying function. We may therefore interpret Eq. (10) as a rapid oscillation with circular frequency $\frac{1}{2}(\omega_0 + \omega)$,

$$x(t) = A(t) \sin \tfrac{1}{2}(\omega_0 + \omega)t,$$

but with a slowly varying amplitude

$$A(t) = \frac{2F_0}{m(\omega_0^2 - \omega^2)} \sin \tfrac{1}{2}(\omega_0 - \omega)t.$$

Example 2   With $m = 0.1$, $F_0 = 50$, $\omega_0 = 55$, and $\omega = 45$, Eq. (10) gives

$$x(t) = \sin 5t \sin 50t.$$

Figure 3.6.3 shows the corresponding oscillation of frequency $\frac{1}{2}(\omega_0 + \omega) = 50$ that is "modulated" by the amplitude function $A(t) = \sin 5t$ of frequency $\frac{1}{2}(\omega_0 - \omega) = 5$. ∎

A rapid oscillation with a (comparatively) slowly varying periodic amplitude exhibits the phenomenon of *beats*. For example, if two horns not exactly attuned to one another simultaneously play their middle C, one at $\omega_0/(2\pi) = 258$ Hz and the other at $\omega/(2\pi) = 254$ Hz, then one hears a beat—an audible variation in the *amplitude* of the combined sound—with a frequency of

$$\frac{(\omega_0 - \omega)/2}{2\pi} = \frac{258 - 254}{2} = 2 \text{ (Hz)}.$$

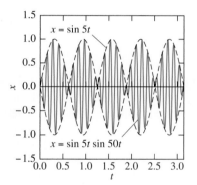

FIGURE 3.6.3. The phenomenon of beats.

Resonance

Looking at Eq. (6), we see that the amplitude A of x_p is large when the natural and external frequencies ω_0 and ω are approximately equal. It is sometimes useful to rewrite Eq. (5) in the form

$$A = \frac{F_0}{k - m\omega^2} = \frac{F_0/k}{1 - (\omega/\omega_0)^2} = \pm\frac{\rho F_0}{k}, \tag{11}$$

where F_0/k is the **static displacement** of a spring with constant k due to a *constant* force F_0, and the **amplification factor** ρ is defined to be

$$\rho = \frac{1}{|1 - (\omega/\omega_0)^2|}. \tag{12}$$

It is clear that $\rho \to +\infty$ as $\omega \to \omega_0$. This is the phenomenon of **resonance**—the increase without bound (as $\omega \to \omega_0$) in the amplitude of oscillations of an undamped system with natural frequency ω_0 in response to an external force with frequency $\omega \approx \omega_0$.

We have been assuming that $\omega \neq \omega_0$. What sort of catastrophe should one expect if ω and ω_0 are precisely equal? Then Eq. (4), upon division of each term by m, becomes

$$x'' + \omega_0^2 x = \frac{F_0}{m} \cos \omega_0 t. \tag{13}$$

Because $\cos \omega_0 t$ is a term of the complementary function, the method of undetermined coefficients calls for us to try

$$x_p(t) = t(A \cos \omega_0 t + B \sin \omega_0 t).$$

We substitute this in Eq. (13) and thereby find that $A = 0$ and $B = F_0/(2m\omega_0)$. Hence the particular solution is

$$x_p(t) = \frac{F_0}{2m\omega_0} t \sin \omega_0 t. \tag{14}$$

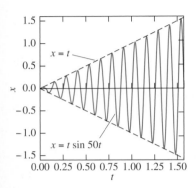

FIGURE 3.6.4. The phenomenon of resonance.

The graph of $x_p(t)$ in Fig. 3.6.4 (in which $m = 1$, $F_0 = 100$, and $\omega_0 = 50$) shows vividly how the amplitude of the oscillation theoretically would increase without bound in this case of *pure resonance,* $\omega = \omega_0$. We may interpret this phenomenon as reinforcement of the natural vibrations of the system by externally impressed vibrations at the same frequency.

Example 3   Suppose that $m = 5$ kg and $k = 500$ N/m in the cart with the flywheel of Fig. 3.6.1. Then the natural frequency is $\omega_0 = \sqrt{k/m} = 10$ rad/s; that is, $10/(2\pi) \approx 1.59$ Hz. We would therefore expect oscillations of very large amplitude to occur if the flywheel revolves at about $(1.59)(60) \approx 95$ revolutions per minute (rpm). ∎

In practice, a mechanical system with very little damping can be destroyed by resonance vibrations. A spectacular example can occur when a column of soldiers marches in step over a bridge. Any complicated structure such as a bridge has many natural frequencies of vibration. If the frequency of the soldiers' cadence is approximately equal to one of the natural frequencies of the structure, then—just as in our simple example of a mass on a spring—resonance will occur. Indeed, the resulting resonance vibrations can be of such large amplitude that the bridge will collapse. This has actually happened—for example, the collapse of Broughton Bridge near Manchester, England, in 1831—and it is the reason for the now-standard practice of breaking cadence when crossing a bridge. Resonance may have been involved in the 1981 Kansas City disaster in which a hotel balcony (called a *skywalk*) collapsed with dancers on it. The collapse of a building in an earthquake is sometimes due to resonance vibrations caused by the ground oscillating at one of the natural frequencies of the structure; this happened to many buildings in the Mexico City earthquake of September 19, 1985. On occasion an airplane has crashed because of resonant wing oscillations caused by vibrations of the engines. It is reported that for some of the first commercial jet aircraft, the natural frequency of the vertical vibrations of the airplane during turbulence was almost exactly that of the mass–spring system consisting of the pilot's head (mass) and spine (spring). Resonance occurred, causing pilots to have difficulty in reading the instruments. Large modern commercial jets have different natural frequencies, so that this resonance problem no longer occurs.

Modeling Mechanical Systems

The avoidance of destructive resonance vibrations is an ever-present consideration in the design of mechanical structures and systems of all types. Often the most important step in determining the natural frequency of vibration of a system is the formulation of its differential equation. In addition to Newton's law $F = ma$, the principle of conservation of energy is sometimes useful for this purpose (as in the derivation of the pendulum equation in Section 3.4). The following kinetic and potential energy formulas are often useful.

1. *Kinetic energy*: $T = \frac{1}{2}mv^2$ for translation of a mass m with velocity v;
2. *Kinetic energy*: $T = \frac{1}{2}I\omega^2$ for rotation of a body of a moment of inertia I with angular velocity ω;
3. *Potential energy*: $V = \frac{1}{2}kx^2$ for a spring with constant k stretched or compressed a distance x;
4. *Potential energy*: $V = mgh$ for the gravitational potential energy of a mass m at height h above the reference level (the level at which $V = 0$), provided that g may be regarded as essentially constant.

Example 4   Find the natural frequency of a mass m on a spring with constant k if, instead of sliding without friction, it is a uniform disk of radius a that rolls without slipping, as shown in Fig 3.6.5.

Solution   With the preceding notation, the principle of conservation of energy gives

$$\tfrac{1}{2}mv^2 + \tfrac{1}{2}I\omega^2 + \tfrac{1}{2}kx^2 = E$$

where E is a constant (the total mechanical energy of the system). We note that $v = a\omega$ and recall that $I = ma^2/2$ for a uniform circular disk. Then we may simplify the last equation to

$$\tfrac{3}{4}mv^2 + \tfrac{1}{2}kx^2 = E.$$

Because the right-hand side of this equation is constant, differentiation with respect to t (with $v = x'$ and $v' = x''$) now gives

$$\tfrac{3}{2}mx'x'' + kxx' = 0.$$

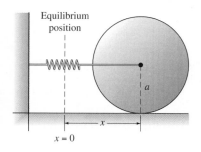

Equilibrium position

a

x

$x = 0$

FIGURE 3.6.5.   The rolling disk.   We divide each term by $\frac{3}{2}mx'$ to obtain

$$x'' + \frac{2k}{3m}x = 0.$$

Thus the natural frequency of horizontal back-and-forth oscillation of our rolling disk is $\sqrt{2k/3m}$, which is $\sqrt{2/3} \approx 0.8165$ times the familiar natural frequency $\sqrt{k/m}$ of a mass on a spring that is sliding without friction rather than rolling without sliding. It is interesting (and perhaps surprising) that this natural frequency does not depend on the *radius* of the disk. It could be either a dime or a large disk with a radius of one meter (but of the same mass).   ■

Example 5 Suppose that a car oscillates vertically as if it were a mass $m = 800$ kg on a single spring (with constant $k = 7 \times 10^4$ N/m), attached to a single dashpot (with constant $c = 3000$ N·s/m). Suppose that this car with the dashpot *disconnected* is driven along a washboard road surface with an amplitude of 5 cm and a wavelength of $L = 10$ m (Fig. 3.6.6). At what car speed will resonance vibrations occur?

FIGURE 3.6.6. The washboard road surface of Example 5.

FIGURE 3.6.7. The "unicycle model" of a car.

Solution We think of the car as a unicycle, as pictured in Fig. 3.6.7. Let $x(t)$ denote the upward displacement of the mass m from its equilibrium position; we ignore the force of gravity, because it merely displaces the equilibrium position as in Problem 9 of Section 3.4. We write the equation of the road surface as

$$y = a \cos \frac{2\pi s}{L} \quad (a = 0.05 \text{ m}, L = 10 \text{ m}). \tag{15}$$

When the car is in motion, the spring is stretched by the amount $x - y$, so Newton's second law, $F = ma$, gives

$$mx'' = -k(x - y);$$

that is,

$$mx'' + kx = ky \tag{16}$$

If the velocity of the car is v, then $s = vt$ in Eq. (15), so Eq. (16) takes the form

$$mx'' + kx = ka \cos \frac{2\pi vt}{L}. \tag{16'}$$

This is the differential equation that governs the vertical oscillations of the car. In comparing it with Eq. (4), we see that we have forced oscillations with circular frequency $\omega = 2\pi v/L$. Resonance will occur when $\omega = \omega_0 = \sqrt{k/m}$. We use our numerical data to find the speed of the car at resonance:

$$v = \frac{L}{2\pi}\sqrt{\frac{k}{m}} = \frac{10}{2\pi}\sqrt{\frac{7 \times 10^4}{800}} \approx 14.89 \text{ (m/s)};$$

that is, about 33.3 mi/h (using the conversion factor of 2.237 mi/h per m/s). ∎

Damped Forced Oscillations

In real physical systems there is always some damping, from frictional effects if nothing else. The complementary function x_c of the equation

$$mx'' + cx' + kx = F_0 \cos \omega t \qquad (17)$$

is given by Eq. (19), (20), or (21) of Section 3.4, depending on whether $c > c_{cr} = \sqrt{4km}$, $c = c_{cr}$, or $c < c_{cr}$. The specific form is not important here. What is important is that, in any case, these formulas show that $x_c(t) \to 0$ as $t \to +\infty$. Thus x_c is a **transient solution** of Eq. (17)—one that dies out with the passage of time, leaving only the particular solution x_p.

The method of undetermined coefficients indicates that we should substitute

$$x(t) = A \cos \omega t + B \sin \omega t$$

in Eq. (17). When we do this, collect terms, and equate coefficients of $\cos \omega t$ and $\sin \omega t$, we obtain the two equations

$$(k - m\omega^2)A + c\omega B = F_0, \qquad -c\omega A + (k - m\omega^2)B = 0 \qquad (18)$$

that we solve without difficulty for

$$A = \frac{(k - m\omega^2)F_0}{(k - m\omega^2)^2 + (c\omega)^2}, \qquad B = \frac{c\omega F_0}{(k - m\omega^2)^2 + (c\omega)^2}. \qquad (19)$$

If we write

$$A \cos \omega t + B \sin \omega t = C(\cos \omega t \cos \alpha + \sin \omega t \sin \alpha) = C \cos(\omega t - \alpha)$$

as usual, we see that the resulting steady periodic oscillation

$$x_p(t) = C \cos(\omega t - \alpha) \qquad (20)$$

has amplitude

$$C = \sqrt{A^2 + B^2} = \frac{F_0}{\sqrt{(k - m\omega^2)^2 + (c\omega)^2}}. \qquad (21)$$

Now (19) implies that $\sin \alpha = B/C > 0$, so it follows that the phase angle α lies in the first or second quadrant. Thus

$$\tan \alpha = \frac{B}{A} = \frac{c\omega}{k - m\omega^2} \quad \text{with} \quad 0 < \alpha < \pi, \qquad (22)$$

so

$$\alpha = \begin{cases} \tan^{-1} \dfrac{c\omega}{k - m\omega^2} & \text{if } k > m\omega^2, \\[2ex] \pi + \tan^{-1} \dfrac{c\omega}{k - m\omega^2} & \text{if } k < m\omega^2 \end{cases}$$

(whereas $\alpha = \pi/2$ if $k = m\omega^2$).

Note that if $c > 0$, then the "forced amplitude"—defined as a function $C(\omega)$ by (21)—always remains finite, in contrast with the case of resonance in the undamped case when the forcing frequency ω equals the critical frequency $\omega_0 = $

$\sqrt{k/m}$. But the forced amplitude may attain a maximum for some value of ω, in which case we speak of *practical resonance*. To see if and when practical resonance occurs, we need only graph C as a function of ω and look for a global maximum. It can be shown (Problem 27) that C is a steadily decreasing function of ω if $c \geq \sqrt{2km}$. But if $c < \sqrt{2km}$, then the amplitude of C attains a maximum value—and so practical resonance occurs—at some value of ω less than ω_0, and then approaches zero as $\omega \to +\infty$. It follows that an underdamped system typically will undergo forced oscillations whose amplitude is

- Large if ω is close to the critical resonance frequency;
- Close to F_0/k if ω is very small;
- Very small if ω is very large.

Example 6 Find the transient motion and steady periodic oscillations of a damped mass-and-spring system with $m = 1$, $c = 2$, and $k = 26$ under the influence of an external force $F(t) = 82 \cos 4t$ with $x(0) = 6$ and $x'(0) = 0$. Also investigate the possibility of practical resonance for this system.

Solution The resulting motion $x(t) = x_{tr}(t) + x_{sp}(t)$ of the mass satisfies the initial value problem

$$x'' + 2x' + 26x = 82 \cos 4t; \quad x(0) = 6, \quad x'(0) = 0. \tag{23}$$

Instead of applying the general formulas derived earlier in this section, it is better in a concrete problem to work it directly. The roots of the characteristic equation

$$r^2 + 2r + 26 = (r+1)^2 + 25 = 0$$

are $r = -1 \pm 5i$, so the complementary function is

$$x_c(t) = e^{-t}(c_1 \cos 5t + c_2 \sin 5t).$$

When we substitute the trial solution

$$x(t) = A \cos 4t + B \sin 4t$$

in the given equation, collect like terms, and equate coefficients of $\cos 4t$ and $\sin 4t$, we get the equations

$$10A + 8B = 82,$$
$$-8A + 10B = 0$$

with solution $A = 5$, $B = 4$. Hence the general solution of the equation in (23) is

$$x(t) = e^{-t}(c_1 \cos 5t + c_2 \sin 5t) + 5 \cos 4t + 4 \sin 4t.$$

At this point we impose the initial conditions $x(0) = 6$, $x'(0) = 0$ and find that $c_1 = 1$ and $c_2 = -3$. Therefore, the transient motion and the steady periodic oscillation of the mass are given by

$$x_{tr}(t) = e^{-t}(\cos 5t - 3 \sin 5t)$$

and

$$x_{sp}(t) = 5\cos 4t + 4\sin 4t = \sqrt{41}\left(\frac{5}{\sqrt{41}}\cos 4t + \frac{4}{\sqrt{41}}\sin 4t\right)$$

$$= \sqrt{41}\cos(4t - \alpha)$$

where $\alpha = \tan^{-1}\left(\frac{4}{5}\right) \approx 0.6747$.

Figure 3.6.8 shows graphs of the solution $x(t) = x_{tr}(t) + x_{sp}(t)$ of the initial value problem

$$x'' + 2x' + 26x = 82\cos 4t, \quad x(0) = x_0, \quad x'(0) = 0 \tag{24}$$

for the different values $x_0 = -20, -10, 0, 10,$ and 20 of the initial position. Here we see clearly what it means for the transient solution $x_{tr}(t)$ to "die out with the passage of time," leaving only the steady periodic motion $x_{sp}(t)$. Indeed, because $x_{tr}(t) \to 0$ exponentially, within a very few cycles the full solution $x(t)$ and the steady periodic solution $x_{sp}(t)$ are virtually indistinguishable (whatever the initial position x_0).

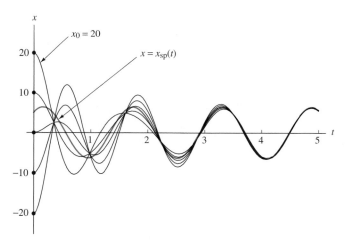

FIGURE 3.6.8.   Solutions of the initial value problem in (24) with $x_0 = -20, -10, 0, 10,$ and 20.

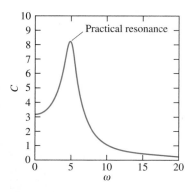

FIGURE 3.6.9.   Plot of amplitude C versus external frequency ω.

To investigate the possibility of practical resonance in the given system, we substitute the values $m = 1$, $c = 2$, and $k = 26$ in (21) and find that the forced amplitude at frequency ω is

$$C(\omega) = \frac{82}{\sqrt{676 - 48\omega^2 + \omega^4}}.$$

The graph of $C(\omega)$ is shown in Fig. 3.6.9. The maximum amplitude occurs when

$$C'(\omega) = \frac{-41(4\omega^3 - 96\omega)}{(676 - 48\omega^2 + \omega^4)^{3/2}} = \frac{-164\omega(\omega^2 - 24)}{(676 - 48\omega^2 + \omega^4)^{3/2}} = 0.$$

Thus practical resonance occurs when the external frequency is $\omega = \sqrt{24}$ (a bit less than the mass-and-spring's undamped critical frequency of $\omega_0 = \sqrt{k/m} = \sqrt{26}$).

3.6 Problems

In Problems 1 through 6, express the solution of the given initial value problem as a sum of two oscillations as in Eq. (8). Throughout, primes denote derivatives with respect to time t. In Problems 1–4, graph the solution function x(t) in such a way that you can identify and label (as in Fig. 3.6.2) its period.

1. $x'' + 9x = 10\cos 2t$; $x(0) = x'(0) = 0$
2. $x'' + 4x = 5\sin 3t$; $x(0) = x'(0) = 0$
3. $x'' + 100x = 225\cos 5t + 300\sin 5t$; $x(0) = 375$, $x'(0) = 0$
4. $x'' + 25x = 90\cos 4t$; $x(0) = 0$, $x'(0) = 90$
5. $mx'' + kx = F_0\cos\omega t$ with $\omega \neq \omega_0$; $x(0) = x_0$, $x'(0) = 0$
6. $mx'' + kx = F_0\cos\omega t$ with $\omega = \omega_0$; $x(0) = 0$, $x'(0) = v_0$

In each of Problems 7 through 10, find the steady periodic solution $x_{sp}(t) = C\cos(\omega t - \alpha)$ of the given equation $mx'' + cx' + kx = F(t)$ with periodic forcing function $F(t)$ of frequency ω. Then graph $x_{sp}(t)$ together with (for comparison) the adjusted forcing function $F_1(t) = F(t)/m\omega$.

7. $x'' + 4x' + 4x = 10\cos 3t$
8. $x'' + 3x' + 5x = -4\cos 5t$
9. $2x'' + 2x' + x = 3\sin 10t$
10. $x'' + 3x' + 3x = 8\cos 10t + 6\sin 10t$

In each of Problems 11 through 14, find and plot both the steady periodic solution $x_{sp}(t) = C\cos(\omega t - \alpha)$ of the given differential equation and the transient solution $x_{tr}(t)$ that satisfies the given initial conditions.

11. $x'' + 4x' + 5x = 10\cos 3t$; $x(0) = x'(0) = 0$
12. $x'' + 6x' + 13x = 10\sin 5t$; $x(0) = x'(0) = 0$
13. $x'' + 2x' + 26x = 600\cos 10t$; $x(0) = 10$, $x'(0) = 0$
14. $x'' + 8x' + 25x = 200\cos t + 520\sin t$; $x(0) = -30$, $x'(0) = -10$

Each of Problems 15 through 18 gives the parameters for a forced mass–spring–dashpot system with equation $mx'' + cx' + kx = F_0\cos\omega t$. Investigate the possibility of practical resonance of this system. In particular, find the amplitude $C(\omega)$ of steady periodic forced oscillations with frequency ω. Sketch the graph of $C(\omega)$ and find the practical resonance frequency ω (if any).

15. $m = 1$, $c = 2$, $k = 2$, $F_0 = 2$
16. $m = 1$, $c = 4$, $k = 5$, $F_0 = 10$
17. $m = 1$, $c = 6$, $k = 45$, $F_0 = 50$
18. $m = 1$, $c = 10$, $k = 650$, $F_0 = 100$
19. A mass weighing 100 lb (mass $m = 3.125$ slugs in fps units) is attached to the end of a spring that is stretched 1 in. by a force of 100 lb. A force $F_0\cos\omega t$ acts on the mass. At what frequency (in hertz) will resonance oscillations occur? Neglect damping.
20. A front-loading washing machine is mounted on a thick rubber pad that acts like a spring; the weight $W = mg$ (with $g = 9.8$ m/s^2) of the machine depresses the pad exactly 0.5 cm. When its rotor spins at ω radians per second, the rotor exerts a vertical force $F_0\cos\omega t$ newtons on the machine. At what speed (in revolutions per minute) will resonance vibrations occur? Neglect friction.

21. Figure 3.6.10 shows a mass m on the end of a pendulum (of length L) also attached to a horizontal spring (with constant k). Assume small oscillations of m so that the spring remains essentially horizontal and neglect damping. Find the natural circular frequency ω_0 of motion of the mass in terms of L, k, m, and the gravitational constant g.

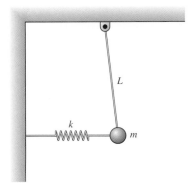

FIGURE 3.6.10. The pendulum-and-spring system of Problem 21.

22. A mass m hangs on the end of a cord around a pulley of radius a and moment of inertia I, as shown in Fig. 3.6.11. The rim of the pulley is attached to a spring (with constant k). Assume small oscillations so that the spring remains essentially horizontal and neglect friction. Find the natural circular frequency of the system in terms of m, a, k, I, and g.

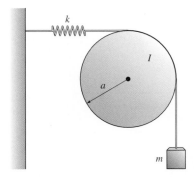

FIGURE 3.6.11. The mass–spring–pulley system of Problem 22.

23. A building consists of two floors. The first floor is attached rigidly to the ground, and the second floor is of mass $m = 1000$ slugs (fps units) and weighs 16 tons (32,000 lb). The elastic frame of the building behaves as a spring that resists horizontal displacements of the second floor; it requires a horizontal force of 5 tons to displace the second floor a distance of 1 ft. Assume that in an earthquake the ground oscillates horizontally with amplitude

A_0 and circular frequency ω, resulting in an external horizontal force $F(t) = mA_0\omega^2 \sin \omega t$ on the second floor. **(a)** What is the natural frequency (in hertz) of oscillations of the second floor?   **(b)** If the ground undergoes one oscillation every 2.25 s with an amplitude of 3 in., what is the amplitude of the resulting forced oscillations of the second floor?

24. A mass on a spring without damping is acted on by the external force $F(t) = F_0 \cos^3 \omega t$. Show that there are *two* values of ω for which resonance occurs, and find both.

25. Derive the steady periodic solution of

$$mx'' + cx' + kx = F_0 \sin \omega t.$$

In particular, show that it is what one would expect—the same as the formula in (20) with the same values of C and ω, except with $\sin(\omega t - \alpha)$ in place of $\cos(\omega t - \alpha)$.

26. Given the differential equation

$$mx'' + cx' + kx = E_0 \cos \omega t + F_0 \sin \omega t$$

—with both cosine and sine forcing terms—derive the steady periodic solution

$$x_{sp}(t) = \frac{\sqrt{E_0^2 + F_0^2}}{\sqrt{(k - m\omega^2)^2 + (c\omega)^2}} \cos(\omega t - \alpha - \beta),$$

where α is defined in Eq. (22) and $\beta = \tan^{-1}(F_0/E_0)$. (*Suggestion*: Add the steady periodic solutions separately corresponding to $E_0 \cos \omega t$ and $F_0 \sin \omega t$ (see Problem 25).)

27. According to Eq. (21), the amplitude of forced steady periodic oscillations for the system $mx'' + cx' + kx = F_0 \cos \omega t$ is given by

$$C(\omega) = \frac{F_0}{\sqrt{(k - m\omega^2)^2 + (c\omega)^2}}.$$

(a) If $c \geq c_{cr}/\sqrt{2}$, where $c_{cr} = \sqrt{4km}$, show that C steadily decreases as ω increases.   **(b)** If $c < c_{cr}/\sqrt{2}$, show that C attains a maximum value (practical resonance) when

$$\omega = \omega_m = \sqrt{\frac{k}{m} - \frac{c^2}{2m^2}} < \omega_0 = \sqrt{\frac{k}{m}}.$$

28. As indicated by the cart-with-flywheel example discussed in this section, an unbalanced rotating machine part typically results in a force having amplitude proportional to the *square* of the frequency ω.   **(a)** Show that the amplitude of the steady periodic solution of the differential equation

$$mx'' + cx' + kx = mA\omega^2 \cos \omega t$$

(with a forcing term similar to that in Eq. (17)) is given by

$$C(\omega) = \frac{mA\omega^2}{\sqrt{(k - m\omega^2)^2 + (c\omega)^2}}.$$

(b) Suppose that $c^2 < 2mk$. Show that the maximum amplitude occurs at the frequency ω_m given by

$$\omega_m = \sqrt{\frac{k}{m} \left(\frac{2mk}{2mk - c^2} \right)}.$$

Thus the resonance frequency in this case is *larger* (in contrast with the result of Problem 27) than the natural frequency $\omega_0 = \sqrt{k/m}$. (*Suggestion*: Maximize the *square* of C.)

Automobile Vibrations

Problems 29 and 30 deal further with the car of Example 5. Its upward displacement function satisfies the equation $mx'' + cx' + kx = cy' + ky$ when the shock absorber is connected (so that $c > 0$). With $y = a \sin \omega t$ for the road surface, this differential equation becomes

$$mx'' + cx' + kx = E_0 \cos \omega t + F_0 \sin \omega t$$

where $E_0 = c\omega a$ and $F_0 = ka$.

29. Apply the result of Problem 26 to show that the amplitude C of the resulting steady periodic oscillation for the car is given by

$$C = \frac{a\sqrt{k^2 + (c\omega)^2}}{\sqrt{(k - m\omega^2)^2 + (c\omega)^2}}.$$

Because $\omega = 2\pi v/L$ when the car is moving with velocity v, this gives C as a function of v.

30. Figure 3.6.12 shows the graph of the amplitude function $C(\omega)$ using the numerical data given in Example 5 (including $c = 3000$ N·s/m). It indicates that, as the car accelerates gradually from rest, it initially oscillates with amplitude slightly over 5 cm. Maximum resonance vibrations with amplitude about 14 cm occur around 32 mi/h, but then subside to more tolerable levels at high speeds. Verify these graphically based conclusions by analyzing the function $C(\omega)$. In particular, find the practical resonance frequency and the corresponding amplitude.

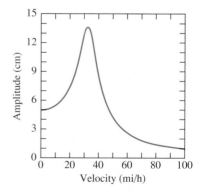

FIGURE 3.6.12.   Amplitude of vibrations of the car on a washboard surface.

3.6 Application   Forced Vibrations

Here we investigate forced vibrations of the mass–spring–dashpot system with equation

$$mx'' + cx' + kx = F(t). \tag{1}$$

To simplify the notation, let's take $m = p^2$, $c = 2p$, and $k = p^2q^2 + 1$, where $p > 0$ and $q > 0$. Then the complementary function of Eq. (1) is

$$x_c(t) = e^{-t/p}(c_1 \cos qt + c_2 \sin qt). \tag{2}$$

We will take $p = 5$, $q = 3$, and thus investigate the transient and steady periodic solutions corresponding to

$$25x'' + 10x' + 226x = F(t), \quad x(0) = 0, \quad x'(0) = 0 \tag{3}$$

with several illustrative possibilities for the external force $F(t)$. For your personal investigations to carry out similarly, you might select integers p and q with $6 \leq p \leq 9$ and $2 \leq q \leq 5$.

INVESTIGATION 1: With periodic external force $F(t) = 901 \cos 3t$, the MATLAB commands

```
x = dsolve('25*D2x+10*Dx+226*x=901*cos(3*t)',
    'x(0)=0, Dx(0)=0');
x = simple(x);
syms t, xsp = cos(3*t) + 30*sin(3*t);
ezplot(x, [0  6*pi]),hold on
ezplot(xsp, [0  6*pi])
```

produce the plot shown in Fig. 3.6.13. We see the (transient plus steady periodic) solution

$$x(t) = \cos 3t + 30 \sin 3t + e^{-t/5}\left(-\cos 3t - \tfrac{451}{15} \sin 3t\right)$$

rapidly "building up" to the steady periodic oscillation $x_{sp}(t) = \cos 3t + 30 \sin 3t$.

INVESTIGATION 2: With damped oscillatory external force

$$F(t) = 900e^{-t/5} \cos 3t,$$

we have duplication with the complementary function in (2). The *Maple* commands

```
de2 := 25*diff(x(t),t,t)+10*diff(x(t),t)+226*x(t) =
    900*exp(-t/5)*cos(3*t);
dsolve({de2,x(0)=0,D(x)(0)=0}, x(t));
x := simplify(combine(rhs(%),trig));
C := 6*t*exp(-t/5);
plot({x,C,-C},t=0..8*Pi);
```

produce the plot shown in Fig. 3.6.14. We see the solution

$$x(t) = 6te^{-t/5} \sin 3t$$

oscillating up-and-down between the envelope curves $x = \pm 6te^{-t/5}$. (Note the factor of t that signals a resonance situation.)

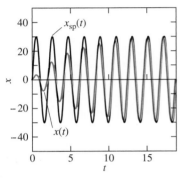

FIGURE 3.6.13. The solution $x(t) = x_{tr}(t) + x_{sp}(t)$ and the steady periodic solution $x(t) = x_{sp}(t)$ with periodic external force $F(t) = 901 \cos 3t$.

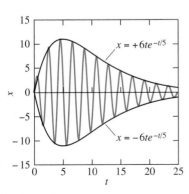

FIGURE 3.6.14. The solution $x(t) = 6te^{-t/5} \sin 3t$ and the envelope curves $x(t) = \pm 6te^{-t/5}$ with damped oscillatory force $F(t) = 900e^{-t/5} \cos 3t$.

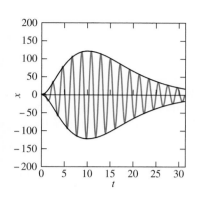

FIGURE 3.6.15. The solution
$x(t) =$
$e^{-t/5}[3t\cos t + (9t^2 - 1)\sin 3t]$
and the envelope curves
$x(t) = \pm e^{-t/5}\sqrt{(3t)^2 + (9t^2 - 1)^2}$
with external force
$F(t) = 2700te^{-t/5}\cos 3t$

INVESTIGATION 3:   With damped oscillatory external force

$$F(t) = 2700te^{-t/5}\cos 3t,$$

we have a still more complicated resonance situation. The *Mathematica* commands

```
de3 = 25 x''[t] + 10 x'[t] + 226 x[t] ==
        2700 t Exp[-t/5] Cos[3t]
soln = DSolve[{de3, x[0] == 0, x'[0] == 0}, x[t], t]
x = First[x[t]  /.  soln]
amp = Exp[-t/5] Sqrt[(3t)^2 + (9t^2 - 1)^2]
Plot[{x, amp, -amp}, {t, 0, 10 Pi}];
```

produce the plot shown in Fig. 3.6.15. We see the solution

$$x(t) = e^{-t/5}\left[3t\cos 3t + (9t^2 - 1)\sin 3t\right]$$

oscillating up-and-down between the envelope curves

$$x = \pm e^{-t/5}\sqrt{(3t)^2 + (9t^2 - 1)^2}.$$

3.7 Electrical Circuits

FIGURE 3.7.1. The series *RLC* circuit.

Here we examine the *RLC* circuit that is a basic building block in more complicated electrical circuits and networks. As shown in Fig. 3.7.1, it consists of

> A **resistor** with a resistance of *R ohms*,
> An **inductor** with an inductance of *L henries*, and
> A **capacitor** with a capacitance of *C farads*

in series with a source of electromotive force (such as a battery or a generator) that supplies a voltage of $E(t)$ *volts* at time *t*. If the switch shown in the circuit of Fig. 3.7.1 is closed, this results in a current of $I(t)$ *amperes* in the circuit and a charge of $Q(t)$ *coulombs* on the capacitor at time *t*. The relation between the functions Q and I is

$$\frac{dQ}{dt} = I(t). \tag{1}$$

Circuit Element	Voltage Drop
Inductor	$L\dfrac{dI}{dt}$
Resistor	RI
Capacitor	$\dfrac{1}{C}Q$

FIGURE 3.7.2. Table of voltage drops.

We will always use mks electric units, in which time is measured in seconds.

According to elementary principles of electricity, the **voltage drops** across the three circuit elements are those shown in the table in Fig. 3.7.2. We can analyze the behavior of the series circuit of Fig. 3.7.1 with the aid of this table and one of Kirchhoff's laws:

> The (algebraic) sum of the voltage drops across the elements in a simple loop of an electrical circuit is equal to the applied voltage.

As a consequence, the current and charge in the simple *RLC* circuit of Fig. 3.7.1 satisfy the basic circuit equation

$$L\frac{dI}{dt} + RI + \frac{1}{C}Q = E(t). \tag{2}$$

If we substitute (1) in Eq. (2), we get the second-order linear differential equation

$$LQ'' + RQ' + \frac{1}{C}Q = E(t) \tag{3}$$

for the charge $Q(t)$, under the assumption that the voltage $E(t)$ is known.

In most practical problems it is the current I rather than the charge Q that is of primary interest, so we differentiate both sides of Eq. (3) and substitute I for Q' to obtain

$$➤ \qquad LI'' + RI' + \frac{1}{C}I = E'(t). \tag{4}$$

We do *not* assume here a prior familiarity with electrical circuits. It suffices to regard the resistor, inductor, and capacitor in an electrical circuit as "black boxes" that are calibrated by the constants R, L, and C. A battery or generator is described by the voltage $E(t)$ that it supplies. When the switch is open, no current flows in the circuit; when the switch is closed, there is a current $I(t)$ in the circuit and a charge $Q(t)$ on the capacitor. All we need to know about these constants and functions is that they satisfy Eqs. (1) through (4), our mathematical model for the *RLC* circuit. We can then learn a good deal about electricity by studying this mathematical model.

The Mechanical–Electrical Analogy

It is striking that Eqs. (3) and (4) have precisely the same form as the equation

$$➤ \qquad mx'' + cx' + kx = F(t) \tag{5}$$

of a mass–spring–dashpot system with external force $F(t)$. The table in Fig. 3.7.3 details this important **mechanical–electrical analogy.** As a consequence, most of the results derived in Section 3.6 for mechanical systems can be applied at once to electrical circuits. The fact that the same differential equation serves as a mathematical model for such different physical systems is a powerful illustration of the unifying role of mathematics in the investigation of natural phenomena. More concretely, the correspondences in Fig. 3.7.3 can be used to construct an electrical model of a given mechanical system, using inexpensive and readily available circuit elements. The performance of the mechanical system can then be predicted by means of accurate but simple measurements in the electrical model. This is especially useful when the actual mechanical system would be expensive to construct or when measurements of displacements and velocities would be inconvenient, inaccurate, or even dangerous. This idea is the basis of *analog computers*—electrical models of mechanical systems. Analog computers modeled the first nuclear reactors for commercial power and submarine propulsion before the reactors themselves were built.

Mechanical System	Electrical System
Mass m	Inductance L
Damping constant c	Resistance R
Spring constant k	Reciprocal capacitance $1/C$
Position x	Charge Q (using (3) (or current I using (4)))
Force F	Electromotive force E (or its derivative E')

FIGURE 3.7.3. Mechanical–electrical analogies.

In the typical case of an alternating current voltage $E(t) = E_0 \sin \omega t$, Eq. (4) takes the form

$$LI'' + RI' + \frac{1}{C}I = \omega E_0 \cos \omega t. \tag{6}$$

As in a mass–spring–dashpot system with a simple harmonic external force, the solution of Eq. (6) is the sum of a **transient current** I_{tr} that approaches zero as $t \to +\infty$ (under the assumption that the coefficients in Eq. (6) are all positive, so the roots of the characteristic equation have negative real parts), and a **steady periodic current** I_{sp}; thus

$$I = I_{\text{tr}} + I_{\text{sp}}. \tag{7}$$

Recall from Section 3.6 (Eqs. (19) through (22) there) that the steady periodic solution of Eq. (5) with $F(t) = F_0 \cos \omega t$ is

$$x_{\text{sp}}(t) = \frac{F_0 \cos(\omega t - \alpha)}{\sqrt{(k - m\omega^2)^2 + (c\omega)^2}},$$

where

$$\alpha = \tan^{-1} \frac{c\omega}{k - m\omega^2}, \quad 0 \leq \alpha \leq \pi.$$

If we make the substitutions L for m, R for c, $1/C$ for k, and ωE_0 for F_0, we get the steady periodic current

$$I_{\text{sp}}(t) = \frac{E_0 \cos(\omega t - \alpha)}{\sqrt{R^2 + \left(\omega L - \dfrac{1}{\omega C}\right)^2}} \tag{8}$$

with the phase angle

$$\alpha = \tan^{-1} \frac{\omega RC}{1 - LC\omega^2}, \quad 0 \leq \alpha \leq \pi. \tag{9}$$

Reactance and Impedance

The quantity in the denominator in (8),

$$Z = \sqrt{R^2 + \left(\omega L - \frac{1}{\omega C}\right)^2} \quad \text{(ohms)}, \tag{10}$$

is called the **impedance** of the circuit. Then the steady periodic current

$$I_{\text{sp}}(t) = \frac{E_0}{Z} \cos(\omega t - \alpha) \tag{11}$$

has amplitude

$$I_0 = \frac{E_0}{Z}, \tag{12}$$

reminiscent of Ohm's law, $I = E/R$.

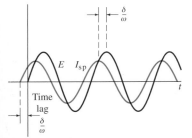

$$\delta = \alpha - \frac{\pi}{2}$$

FIGURE 3.7.4. Reactance and delay angle.

Equation (11) gives the steady periodic current as a cosine function, whereas the input voltage $E(t) = E_0 \sin \omega t$ was a sine function. To convert I_{sp} to a sine function, we first introduce the **reactance**

$$S = \omega L - \frac{1}{\omega C}. \tag{13}$$

Then $Z = \sqrt{R^2 + S^2}$, and we see from Eq. (9) that α is as in Fig. 3.7.4, with delay angle $\delta = \alpha - \frac{1}{2}\pi$. Equation (11) now yields

$$
\begin{aligned}
I_{sp}(t) &= \frac{E_0}{Z}(\cos \alpha \cos \omega t + \sin \alpha \sin \omega t) \\
&= \frac{E_0}{Z}\left(-\frac{S}{Z}\cos \omega t + \frac{R}{Z}\sin \omega t\right) \\
&= \frac{E_0}{Z}(\cos \delta \sin \omega t - \sin \delta \cos \omega t).
\end{aligned}
$$

Therefore,

$$I_{sp}(t) = \frac{E_0}{Z}\sin(\omega t - \delta), \tag{14}$$

where

$$\delta = \tan^{-1}\frac{S}{R} = \tan^{-1}\frac{LC\omega^2 - 1}{\omega RC}. \tag{15}$$

This finally gives the **time lag** δ/ω (in seconds) of the steady periodic current I_{sp} behind the input voltage (Fig. 3.7.5).

FIGURE 3.7.5. Time lag of current behind imposed voltage.

Initial Value Problems

When we want to find the transient current, we are usually given the initial values $I(0)$ and $Q(0)$. So we must first find $I'(0)$. To do so, we substitute $t = 0$ in Eq. (2) to obtain the equation

$$LI'(0) + RI(0) + \frac{1}{C}Q(0) = E(0) \tag{16}$$

to determine $I'(0)$ in terms of the initial values of current, charge, and voltage.

Example 1   Consider an RLC circuit with $R = 50$ ohms (Ω), $L = 0.1$ henry (H), and $C = 5 \times 10^{-4}$ farad (F). At time $t = 0$, when both $I(0)$ and $Q(0)$ are zero, the circuit is connected to a 110-V, 60-Hz alternating current generator. Find the current in the circuit and the time lag of the steady periodic current behind the voltage.

Solution   A frequency of 60 Hz means that $\omega = (2\pi)(60)$ rad/s, approximately 377 rad/s. So we take $E(t) = 110 \sin 377t$ and use equality in place of the symbol for approximate equality in this discussion. The differential equation in (6) takes the form

$$(0.1)I'' + 50I' + 2000I = (377)(110)\cos 377t.$$

We substitute the given values of R, L, C, and $\omega = 377$ in Eq. (10) to find that the impedance is $Z = 59.58\ \Omega$, so the steady periodic amplitude is

$$I_0 = \frac{110\ \text{(volts)}}{59.58\ \text{(ohms)}} = 1.846\ \text{amperes (A)}.$$

With the same data, Eq. (15) gives the sine phase angle:

$$\delta = \tan^{-1}(0.648) = 0.575.$$

Thus the time lag of current behind voltage is

$$\frac{\delta}{\omega} = \frac{0.575}{377} = 0.0015\ \text{s},$$

and the steady periodic current is

$$I_{sp} = (1.846)\sin(377t - 0.575).$$

The characteristic equation $(0.1)r^2 + 50r + 2000 = 0$ has the two roots $r_1 \approx -44$ and $r_2 \approx -456$. With these approximations, the general solution is

$$I(t) = c_1 e^{-44t} + c_2 e^{-456t} + (1.846)\sin(377t - 0.575),$$

with derivative

$$I'(t) = -44c_1 e^{-44t} - 456c_2 e^{-456t} + 696\cos(377t - 0.575).$$

Because $I(0) = Q(0) = 0$, Eq. (16) gives $I'(0) = 0$ as well. With these initial values substituted, we obtain the equations

$$I(0) = c_1 + c_2 - 1.004 = 0,$$
$$I'(0) = -44c_1 - 456c_2 + 584 = 0;$$

their solution is $c_1 = -0.307$, $c_2 = 1.311$. Thus the transient solution is

$$I_{tr}(t) = (-0.307)e^{-44t} + (1.311)e^{-456t}.$$

The observation that after one-fifth of a second we have $|I_{tr}(0.2)| < 0.000047$ A (comparable to the current in a single human nerve fiber) indicates that the transient solution dies out very rapidly, indeed. ∎

Example 2 Suppose that the *RLC* circuit of Example 1, still with $I(0) = Q(0) = 0$, is connected at time $t = 0$ to a battery supplying a constant 110 V. Now find the current in the circuit.

Solution   We now have $E(t) \equiv 110$, so Eq. (16) gives

$$I'(0) = \frac{E(0)}{L} = \frac{110}{0.1} = 1100 \text{ (A/s)},$$

and the differential equation is

$$(0.1)I'' + 50I' + 2000I = E'(t) = 0.$$

Its general solution is the complementary function we found in Example 1:

$$I(t) = c_1 e^{-44t} + c_2 e^{-456t}.$$

We solve the equations

$$I(0) = c_1 + c_2 = 0,$$
$$I'(0) = -44c_1 - 456c_2 = 1100$$

for $c_1 = -c_2 = 2.670$. Therefore,

$$I(t) = (2.670)(e^{-44t} - e^{-456t}).$$

Note that $I(t) \to 0$ as $t \to +\infty$ even though the voltage is constant.   ■

Electrical Resonance

Consider again the current differential equation in (6) corresponding to a sinusoidal input voltage $E(t) = E_0 \sin \omega t$. We have seen that the amplitude of its steady periodic current is

$$I_0 = \frac{E_0}{Z} = \frac{E_0}{\sqrt{R^2 + \left(\omega L - \dfrac{1}{\omega C}\right)^2}}. \tag{17}$$

FIGURE 3.7.6.   The effect of frequency on I_0.

For typical values of the constants R, L, C, and E_0, the graph of I_0 as a function of ω resembles the one shown in Fig. 3.7.6. It reaches a maximum value at $\omega_m = 1/\sqrt{LC}$ and then approaches zero as $\omega \to +\infty$; the critical frequency ω_m is the **resonance frequency** of the circuit.

In Section 3.6 we emphasized the importance of avoiding resonance in most mechanical systems (the cello is an example of a mechanical system in which resonance is *sought*). By contrast, many common electrical devices could not function properly without taking advantage of the phenomenon of resonance. The radio is a familiar example. A highly simplified model of its tuning circuit is the RLC circuit we have discussed. Its inductance L and resistance R are constant, but its capacitance C is varied as one operates the tuning dial.

Suppose that we wanted to pick up a particular radio station that is broadcasting at frequency ω, and thereby (in effect) provides an input voltage $E(t) = E_0 \sin \omega t$ to the tuning circuit of the radio. The resulting steady periodic current I_{sp} in the tuning circuit drives its amplifier, and in turn its loudspeaker, with the volume of sound we hear roughly proportional to the amplitude I_0 of I_{sp}. To hear our preferred station (of frequency ω) the loudest—and simultaneously tune out stations broadcasting at other frequencies—we therefore want to choose C to maximize I_0.

But examine Eq. (17), thinking of ω as a constant with C the only variable. We see at a glance—no calculus required—that I_0 is maximal when

$$\omega L - \frac{1}{\omega C} = 0;$$

that is, when

$$C = \frac{1}{L\omega^2}. \tag{18}$$

So we merely turn the dial to set the capacitance to this value.

This is the way that old crystal radios worked, but modern AM radios have a more sophisticated design. A *pair* of variable capacitors are used. The first controls the frequency selected as described earlier; the second controls the frequency of a signal that the radio itself generates, kept close to 455 kilohertz (kHz) above the desired frequency. The resulting *beat* frequency of 455 kHz, known as the *intermediate frequency,* is then amplified in several stages. This technique has the advantage that the several *RLC* circuits used in the amplification stages easily can be designed to resonate at 455 kHz and reject other frequencies, resulting in far more selectivity of the receiver as well as better amplification of the desired signal.

3.7 Problems

Problems 1 through 6 deal with the RL circuit of Fig. 3.7.7, a series circuit containing an inductor with an inductance of L henries, a resistor with a resistance of R ohms, and a source of electromotive force (emf), but no capacitor. In this case Eq. (2) reduces to the linear first-order equation

$$LI' + RI = E(t).$$

FIGURE 3.7.7. The circuit for Problems 1 through 6.

1. In the circuit of Fig. 3.7.7, suppose that $L = 5$ H, $R = 25$ Ω, and the source E of emf is a battery supplying 100 V to the circuit. Suppose also that the switch has been in position 1 for a long time, so that a steady current of 4 A is flowing in the circuit. At time $t = 0$, the switch is thrown to position 2, so that $I(0) = 4$ and $E = 0$ for $t \geq 0$. Find $I(t)$.
2. Given the same circuit as in Problem 1, suppose that the switch is initially in position 2, but is thrown to position 1 at time $t = 0$, so that $I(0) = 0$ and $E = 100$ for $t \geq 0$. Find $I(t)$ and show that $I(t) \to 4$ as $t \to +\infty$.

3. Suppose that the battery in Problem 2 is replaced with an alternating-current generator that supplies a voltage of $E(t) = 100 \cos 60t$ volts. With everything else the same, now find $I(t)$.

4. In the circuit of Fig. 3.7.7, with the switch in position 1, suppose that $L = 2$, $R = 40$, $E(t) = 100e^{-10t}$, and $I(0) = 0$. Find the maximum current in the circuit for $t \geq 0$.

5. In the circuit of Fig. 3.7.7, with the switch in position 1, suppose that $E(t) = 100e^{-10t} \cos 60t$, $R = 20$, $L = 2$, and $I(0) = 0$. Find $I(t)$.

6. In the circuit of Fig. 3.7.7, with the switch in position 1, take $L = 1$, $R = 10$, and $E(t) = 30 \cos 60t + 40 \sin 60t$. **(a)** Substitute $I_{sp}(t) = A \cos 60t + B \sin 60t$ and then determine A and B to find the steady-state current I_{sp} in the circuit. **(b)** Write the solution in the form $I_{sp}(t) = C \cos(\omega t - \alpha)$.

Problems 7 through 10 deal with the RC circuit in Fig. 3.7.8, containing a resistor (R ohms), a capacitor (C farads), a switch, a source of emf, but no inductor. Substitution of L = 0 in Eq. (3) gives the linear first-order differential equation

$$R\frac{dQ}{dt} + \frac{1}{C}Q = E(t)$$

for the charge $Q = Q(t)$ on the capacitor at time t. Note that $I(t) = Q'(t)$.

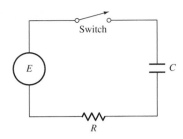

FIGURE 3.7.8. The circuit for Problems 7 through 10.

7. (a) Find the charge $Q(t)$ and current $I(t)$ in the RC circuit if $E(t) \equiv E_0$ (a constant voltage supplied by a battery) and the switch is closed at time $t = 0$, so that $Q(0) = 0$. **(b)** Show that

$$\lim_{t \to +\infty} Q(t) = E_0 C \quad \text{and that} \quad \lim_{t \to +\infty} I(t) = 0.$$

8. Suppose that in the circuit of Fig. 3.7.8, we have $R = 10$, $C = 0.02$, $Q(0) = 0$, and $E(t) = 100e^{-5t}$ (volts). **(a)** Find $Q(t)$ and $I(t)$. **(b)** What is the maximum charge on the capacitor for $t \geq 0$ and when does it occur?

9. Suppose that in the circuit of Fig. 3.7.8, $R = 200$, $C = 2.5 \times 10^{-4}$, $Q(0) = 0$, and $E(t) = 100 \cos 120t$. **(a)** Find $Q(t)$ and $I(t)$. **(b)** What is the amplitude of the steady-state current?

10. An emf of voltage $E(t) = E_0 \cos \omega t$ is applied to the RC circuit of Fig. 3.7.8 at time $t = 0$ (with the switch closed), and $Q(0) = 0$. Substitute $Q_{sp}(t) = A \cos \omega t + B \sin \omega t$ in the differential equation to show that the steady periodic charge on the capacitor is

$$Q_{sp}(t) = \frac{E_0 C}{\sqrt{1 + \omega^2 R^2 C^2}} \cos(\omega t - \beta)$$

where $\beta = \tan^{-1}(\omega RC)$.

In Problems 11 through 16, the parameters of an RLC circuit with input voltage $E(t)$ are given. Substitute

$$I_{sp}(t) = A \cos \omega t + B \sin \omega t$$

in Eq. (4), using the appropriate value of ω, to find the steady periodic current in the form $I_{sp}(t) = I_0 \sin(\omega t - \delta)$.

11. $R = 30\ \Omega$, $L = 10$ H, $C = 0.02$ F; $E(t) = 50 \sin 2t$ V
12. $R = 200\ \Omega$, $L = 5$ H, $C = 0.001$ F; $E(t) = 100 \sin 10t$ V
13. $R = 20\ \Omega$, $L = 10$ H, $C = 0.01$ F; $E(t) = 200 \cos 5t$ V
14. $R = 50\ \Omega$, $L = 5$ H, $C = 0.005$ F; $E(t) = 300 \cos 100t + 400 \sin 100t$ V
15. $R = 100\ \Omega$, $L = 2$ H, $C = 5 \times 10^{-6}$ F; $E(t) = 110 \sin 60\pi t$ V
16. $R = 25\ \Omega$, $L = 0.2$ H, $C = 5 \times 10^{-4}$ F; $E(t) = 120 \cos 377t$ V

In Problems 17 through 22, an RLC circuit with input voltage $E(t)$ is described. Find the current $I(t)$ using the given initial current (in amperes) and charge on the capacitor (in coulombs).

17. $R = 16\ \Omega$, $L = 2$ H, $C = 0.02$ F; $E(t) = 100$ V; $I(0) = 0$, $Q(0) = 5$
18. $R = 60\ \Omega$, $L = 2$ H, $C = 0.0025$ F; $E(t) = 100e^{-t}$ V; $I(0) = 0$, $Q(0) = 0$
19. $R = 60\ \Omega$, $L = 2$ H, $C = 0.0025$ F; $E(t) = 100e^{-10t}$ V; $I(0) = 0$, $Q(0) = 1$

In each of Problems 20 through 22, plot both the steady periodic current $I_{sp}(t)$ and the total current $I(t) = I_{sp}(t) + I_{tr}(t)$.

20. The circuit and input voltage of Problem 11 with $I(0) = 0$ and $Q(0) = 0$
21. The circuit and input voltage of Problem 13 with $I(0) = 0$ and $Q(0) = 3$
22. The circuit and input voltage of Problem 15 with $I(0) = 0$ and $Q(0) = 0$
23. Consider an LC circuit—that is, an RLC circuit with $R = 0$—with input voltage $E(t) = E_0 \sin \omega t$. Show that unbounded oscillations of current occur for a certain resonance frequency; express this frequency in terms of L and C.
24. It was stated in the text that, if R, L, and C are positive, then any solution of $LI'' + RI' + I/C = 0$ is a transient solution—it approaches zero as $t \to +\infty$. Prove this.
25. Prove that the amplitude I_0 of the steady periodic solution of Eq. (6) is maximal at frequency $\omega = 1/\sqrt{LC}$.

3.8 Endpoint Problems and Eigenvalues

You are now familiar with the fact that a solution of a second-order linear differential equation is uniquely determined by two initial conditions. In particular, the only solution of the initial value problem

$$y'' + p(x)y' + q(x)y = 0; \quad y(a) = 0, \quad y'(a) = 0 \tag{1}$$

is the trivial solution $y(x) \equiv 0$. Most of Chapter 3 has been based, directly or indirectly, on the uniqueness of solutions of linear initial value problems (as guaranteed by Theorem 2 of Section 3.2).

In this section we will see that the situation is radically different for a problem such as

$$y'' + p(x)y' + q(x)y = 0; \quad y(a) = 0, \quad y(b) = 0. \tag{2}$$

The difference between the problems in Eqs. (1) and (2) is that in (2) the two conditions are imposed at two *different* points a and b with (say) $a < b$. In (2) we are to find a solution of the differential equation on the interval (a, b) that satisfies the conditions $y(a) = 0$ and $y(b) = 0$ at the endpoints of the interval. Such a problem is called an **endpoint** or **boundary value problem.** Examples 1 and 2 illustrate the sorts of complications that can arise in endpoint problems.

Example 1 Consider the endpoint problem

$$y'' + 3y = 0; \quad y(0) = 0, \quad y(\pi) = 0. \tag{3}$$

The general solution of the differential equation is

$$y(x) = A \cos x\sqrt{3} + B \sin x\sqrt{3}.$$

Now $y(0) = A$, so the condition $y(0) = 0$ implies that $A = 0$. Therefore the only possible solutions are of the form $y(x) = B \sin x\sqrt{3}$. But then

$$y(\pi) = B \sin \pi\sqrt{3} \approx -0.7458B,$$

so the other condition $y(\pi) = 0$ requires that $B = 0$ also. Graphically, Fig. 3.8.1 illustrates the fact that *no* possible solution $y(x) = B \sin x\sqrt{3}$ with $B \neq 0$ hits the desired target value $y = 0$ when $x = \pi$. Thus the *only* solution of the endpoint value problem in (3) is the trivial solution $y(x) \equiv 0$ (which probably is no surprise). ∎

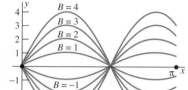

FIGURE 3.8.1. Various possible solutions $y(x) = B \sin x\sqrt{3}$ of the endpoint value problem in Example 1. For no $B \neq 0$ does the solution hit the target value $y = 0$ for $x = \pi$.

Example 2 Consider the endpoint problem

$$y'' + 4y = 0; \quad y(0) = 0, \quad y(\pi) = 0. \tag{4}$$

The general solution of the differential equation is

$$y(x) = A \cos 2x + B \sin 2x.$$

Again, $y(0) = A$, so the condition $y(0) = 0$ implies that $A = 0$. Therefore the only possible solutions are of the form $y(x) = B \sin 2x$. But now $y(\pi) = B \sin 2\pi = 0$ no matter what the value of the coefficient B is. Hence, as illustrated graphically in Fig. 3.8.2, *every* possible solution $y(x) = B \sin 2x$ hits automatically the desired target value $y = 0$ when $x = \pi$ (whatever the value of B). Thus the endpoint value problem in (4) has *infinitely many* different nontrivial solutions. Perhaps this does seem a bit surprising. ∎

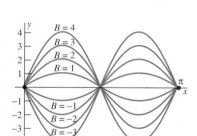

FIGURE 3.8.2. Various possible solutions $y(x) = B \sin 2x$ of the endoint value problem in Example 2. No matter what the coefficient B is, the solution automatically hits the target value $y = 0$ for $x = \pi$.

Remark 1: Note that the big difference in the results of Examples 1 and 2 stems from the seemingly small difference between the differential equations in (3) and (4), with the coefficient 3 in one replaced by the coefficient 4 in the other. In mathematics as elsewhere, sometimes "big doors turn on small hinges."

Remark 2: The "shooting" terminology used in Examples 1 and 2 is often useful in discussing endpoint value problems. We consider a possible solution which starts at the left endpoint value and ask whether it hits the "target" specified by the right endpoint value.

Eigenvalue Problems

Rather than being the exceptional cases, Examples 1 and 2 illustrate the typical situation for an endpoint problem as in (2): It may have no nontrivial solutions, or it may have infinitely many nontrivial solutions. Note that the problems in (3) and (4) both can be written in the form

$$\blacktriangleright \qquad y'' + p(x)y' + \lambda q(x)y = 0; \quad y(a) = 0, \quad y(b) = 0, \tag{5}$$

with $p(x) \equiv 0$, $q(x) \equiv 1$, $a = 0$, and $b = \pi$. The number λ is a parameter in the problem (nothing to do with the parameters that were varied in Section 3.5). If we take $\lambda = 3$, we get the equations in (3); with $\lambda = 4$, we obtain the equations in (4). Examples 1 and 2 show that the situation in an endpoint problem containing a parameter can (and generally will) depend strongly on the specific numerical value of the parameter.

An endpoint value problem such as the problem in (5)—one that contains an unspecified parameter λ—is called an **eigenvalue problem**. The question we ask in an eigenvalue problem is this: For what values of the parameter λ does there exist a nontrivial (i.e., nonzero) solution of the endpoint value problem? Such a value of λ is called an **eigenvalue** of the problem. One might think of such a value as a "proper" value of λ for which there exist proper (nonzero) solutions of the problem. Indeed, the prefix *eigen* is a German word that (in some contexts) may be translated as the English word *proper*, so eigenvalues are sometimes called *proper values* (or *characteristic values*).

Thus we saw in Example 2 that $\lambda = 4$ is an eigenvalue of the endpoint problem

$$y'' + \lambda y = 0, \quad y(0) = 0, \quad y(\pi) = 0, \tag{6}$$

whereas Example 1 shows that $\lambda = 3$ is not an eigenvalue of this problem.

Suppose that $\lambda_\star$ is an eigenvalue of the problem in (5) and that $y_\star(x)$ is a nontrivial solution of the endpoint problem that results when the parameter λ in (5) is replaced by the specific numerical value $\lambda_\star$, so

$$y''_\star + p(x)y'_\star + \lambda_\star q(x)y_\star = 0 \quad \text{and} \quad y_\star(a) = 0, \quad y_\star(b) = 0.$$

Then we call $y_\star$ an **eigenfunction** associated with the eigenvalue $\lambda_\star$. Thus we saw in Example 2 that $y_\star(x) = \sin 2x$ is an eigenfunction associated with the eigenvalue $\lambda_\star = 4$, as is any constant multiple of $\sin 2x$.

More generally, note that the problem in (5) is *homogeneous* in the sense that any constant multiple of an eigenfunction is again an eigenfunction—indeed, one associated with the same eigenvalue. That is, if $y = y_\star(x)$ satisfies the problem in (5) with $\lambda = \lambda_\star$, then so does any constant multiple $cy_\star(x)$. It can be proved (under mild restrictions on the coefficient functions p and q) that any two eigenfunctions associated with the same eigenvalue must be linearly dependent.

Example 3   Determine the eigenvalues and associated eigenfunctions for the endpoint problem

$$y'' + \lambda y = 0; \quad y(0) = 0, \quad y(L) = 0 \quad (L > 0). \tag{7}$$

Solution   We must consider all possible (real) values of λ—positive, zero, and negative. If $\lambda = 0$, then the equation is simply $y'' = 0$ and its general solution is

$$y(x) = Ax + B.$$

Then the endpoint conditions $y(0) = 0 = y(L)$ immediately imply that $A = B = 0$, so the only solution in this case is the trivial function $y(x) \equiv 0$. Therefore, $\lambda = 0$ is *not* an eigenvalue of the problem in (7).

If $\lambda < 0$, let us then write $\lambda = -\alpha^2$ (with $\alpha > 0$) to be specific. Then the differential equation takes the form

$$y'' - \alpha^2 y = 0,$$

and its general solution is

$$y(x) = c_1 e^{\alpha x} + c_2 e^{-\alpha x} = A \cosh \alpha x + B \sinh \alpha x,$$

where $A = c_1 + c_2$ and $B = c_1 - c_2$. (Recall that $\cosh \alpha x = (e^{\alpha x} + e^{-\alpha x})/2$ and that $\sinh \alpha x = (e^{\alpha x} - e^{-\alpha x})/2$.) The condition $y(0) = 0$ then gives

$$y(0) = A \cosh 0 + B \sinh 0 = A = 0,$$

so that $y(x) = B \sinh \alpha x$. But now the second endpoint condition, $y(L) = 0$, gives $y(L) = B \sinh \alpha L = 0$. This implies that $B = 0$, because $\alpha \neq 0$, and $\sinh x = 0$ only for $x = 0$ (examine the graphs of $y = \sinh x$ and $y = \cosh x$ in Fig. 3.8.3.) Thus the only solution of the problem in (7) in the case $\lambda < 0$ is the trivial solution $y \equiv 0$, and we may therefore conclude that the problem has *no* negative eigenvalues.

The only remaining possibility is that $\lambda = \alpha^2 > 0$ with $\alpha > 0$. In this case the differential equation is

$$y'' + \alpha^2 y = 0,$$

with general solution

$$y(x) = A \cos \alpha x + B \sin \alpha x.$$

The condition $y(0) = 0$ implies that $A = 0$, so $y(x) = B \sin \alpha x$. The condition $y(L) = 0$ then gives

$$y(L) = B \sin \alpha L = 0.$$

Can this occur if $B \neq 0$? Yes, but only provided that αL is a (positive) integral multiple of π:

$$\alpha L = \pi, \quad 2\pi, \quad 3\pi, \quad \dots, \quad n\pi, \quad \dots ;$$

that is, if

$$\lambda = \alpha^2 = \frac{\pi^2}{L^2}, \quad \frac{4\pi^2}{L^2}, \quad \frac{9\pi^2}{L^2}, \quad \dots, \quad \frac{n^2 \pi^2}{L^2}, \quad \dots .$$

Thus we have discovered that the problem in (7) has an *infinite sequence* of positive eigenvalues

$$\lambda_n = \frac{n^2 \pi^2}{L^2}, \quad n = 1, 2, 3, \dots . \tag{8}$$

With $B = 1$, the eigenfunction associated with the eigenvalue λ_n is

$$y_n(x) = \sin \frac{n\pi x}{L}, \quad n = 1, 2, 3, \dots . \tag{9}$$

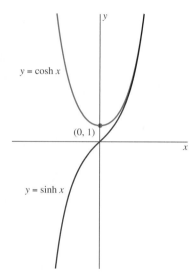

$y = \cosh x$

$(0, 1)$

$y = \sinh x$

FIGURE 3.8.3. The hyperbolic sine and cosine graphs.

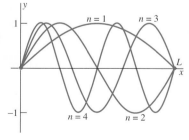

$n = 1$ $n = 3$

$n = 4$ $n = 2$

FIGURE 3.8.4. The eigenfunctions $y_n(x) = \sin \dfrac{n\pi x}{L}$ for $n = 1, 2, 3, 4$.

Figure 3.8.4 shows graphs of the first several of these eigenfunctions. We see visibly how the endpoint conditions $y(0) = y(L) = 0$ serve to select just those sine functions that start a period at $x = 0$ and wind up at $x = L$ precisely at the end of a half-period. ∎

Example 3 illustrates the general situation. According to a theorem whose precise statement we will defer until Section 10.1, under the assumption that $q(x) > 0$ on the interval $[a, b]$, any eigenvalue of the form in (5) has a divergent increasing sequence

$$\lambda_1 < \lambda_2 < \lambda_3 < \cdots < \lambda_n < \cdots \to +\infty$$

of eigenvalues, each with an associated eigenfunction. This is also true of the following more general type of eigenvalue problem, in which the endpoint conditions involve values of the derivative y' as well as values of y:

$$\begin{aligned} y'' + p(x)y' + \lambda q(x)y &= 0; \\ a_1 y(a) + a_2 y'(a) &= 0, \quad b_1 y(b) + b_2 y'(b) = 0, \end{aligned} \tag{10}$$

where a_1, a_2, b_1, and b_2 are given constants. With $a_1 = 1 = b_2$ and $a_2 = 0 = b_1$, we get the problem of Example 4 (in which $p(x) \equiv 0$ and $q(x) \equiv 1$, as in the previous example).

Example 4   Determine the eigenvalues and eigenfunctions of the problem

$$y'' + \lambda y = 0; \quad y(0) = 0, \quad y'(L) = 0. \tag{11}$$

Solution   Virtually the same argument as that used in Example 3 shows that the only possible eigenvalues are positive, so we take $\lambda = \alpha^2 > 0$ ($\alpha > 0$) to be specific. Then the differential equation is

$$y'' + \alpha^2 y = 0,$$

with general solution

$$y(x) = A \cos \alpha x + B \sin \alpha x.$$

The condition $y(0) = 0$ immediately gives $A = 0$, so

$$y(x) = B \sin \alpha x \quad \text{and} \quad y'(x) = B\alpha \cos \alpha x.$$

The second endpoint condition $y'(L) = 0$ now gives

$$y'(L) = B\alpha \cos \alpha L = 0.$$

This will hold with $B \neq 0$ provided that αL is an odd positive integral multiple of $\pi/2$:

$$\alpha L = \frac{\pi}{2}, \quad \frac{3\pi}{2}, \quad \dots, \quad \frac{(2n-1)\pi}{2}, \quad \dots ;$$

that is, if

$$\lambda = \frac{\pi^2}{4L^2}, \quad \frac{9\pi^2}{4L^2}, \quad \dots, \quad \frac{(2n-1)^2\pi^2}{4L^2}, \quad \dots .$$

Thus the nth eigenvalue λ_n and associated eigenfunction of the problem in (11) are given by

$$\lambda_n = \frac{(2n-1)^2\pi^2}{4L^2} \quad \text{and} \quad y_n(x) = \sin \frac{(2n-1)\pi x}{2L} \tag{12}$$

for $n = 1, 2, 3, \dots$. Figure 3.8.5 shows graphs of the first several of these eigenfunctions. We see visibly how the endpoint conditions $y(0) = y'(L) = 0$ serve to select just those sine functions that start a period at $x = 0$ but wind up at $x = L$ precisely in the middle of a half-period. ∎

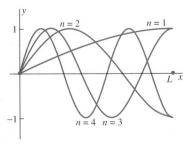

FIGURE 3.8.5. The eigenfunctions
$$y_n(x) = \sin \frac{(2n-1)\pi x}{2L}$$
for $n = 1, 2, 3, 4$.

A general procedure for determining the eigenvalues of the problem in (10) can be outlined as follows. We first write the general solution of the differential equation in the form

$$y = Ay_1(x, \lambda) + By_2(x, \lambda).$$

We write $y_i(x, \lambda)$ because y_1 and y_2 will depend on λ, as in Examples 3 and 4, in which

$$y_1(x) = \cos \alpha x = \cos x \sqrt{\lambda} \quad \text{and} \quad y_2(x) = \sin \alpha x = \sin x \sqrt{\lambda}.$$

Then we impose the two endpoint conditions, noting that each is linear in y and y', and hence also linear in A and B. When we collect coefficients of A and B in the resulting pair of equations, we therefore get a system of the form

$$\begin{aligned} \alpha_1(\lambda)A + \beta_1(\lambda)B &= 0, \\ \alpha_2(\lambda)A + \beta_2(\lambda)B &= 0. \end{aligned} \tag{13}$$

Now λ is an eigenvalue if and only if the system in (13) has a nontrivial solution (one with A and B not both zero). But such a homogeneous system of linear equations has a nontrivial solution if and only if the determinant of its coefficients vanishes. We therefore conclude that the eigenvalues of the problem in (10) are the (real) solutions of the equation

$$D(\lambda) = \alpha_1(\lambda)\beta_2(\lambda) - \alpha_2(\lambda)\beta_1(\lambda) = 0. \tag{14}$$

To illustrate Eq. (14) in a concrete problem, let's revisit the eigenvalue problem of Example 3. If $\lambda > 0$, then the differential equation $y'' + \lambda y = 0$ has the general solution $y(x) = A \cos(\sqrt{\lambda}x) + B \sin(\sqrt{\lambda}x)$. The endpoint conditions $y(0) = 0$ and $y(L) = 0$ then yield the equations

$$\begin{aligned} y(0) &= A \cdot 1 & + B \cdot 0 & = 0, \\ y(L) &= A \cos(\sqrt{\lambda}L) + B \sin(\sqrt{\lambda}L) & = 0 \end{aligned}$$

(in the unknowns A and B) which correspond to the equations in (13). The determinant equation $D(\lambda) = 0$ corresponding to (14) is then simply the equation $\sin(\sqrt{\lambda}L) = 0$, which implies that $\sqrt{\lambda}L = n\pi$, or $\lambda = n^2\pi^2/L^2$ for $n = 1, 2, 3, \ldots$ (as we saw in Example 3).

For more general problems, the solution of the equation $D(\lambda) = 0$ in (14) may present formidable difficulties and require a numerical approximation method (such as Newton's method) or recourse to a computer algebra system.

Most of the interest in eigenvalue problems is due to their very diverse physical applications. The remainder of this section is devoted to three such applications. Numerous additional applications are included in Chapters 9 and 10 (on partial differential equations and boundary value problems).

The Whirling String

Who of us has not wondered about the shape of a quickly spinning jump rope? Let us consider the shape assumed by a tightly stretched flexible string of length L and constant linear density ρ (mass per unit length) if it is rotated or whirled (like a jump rope) with constant angular speed ω (in radians per second) around its equilibrium position along the x-axis. We assume that the portion of the string to one side of any point exerts a constant tension force T on the portion of the string to the other

x = 0   x = L

Equilibrium position

(a)

x = 0   x = L

Whirling string

(b)

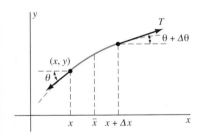

(x, y)

String

(c)

FIGURE 3.8.6. The whirling string.

FIGURE 3.8.7. Forces on a short segment of the whirling string.

side of the point, with the direction of T tangential to the string at that point. We further assume that, as the string whirls around the x-axis, each point moves in a circle centered at that point's equilibrium position on the x-axis. Thus the string is elastic, so that as it whirls it also stretches to assume a curved shape. Denote by $y(x)$ the displacement of the string from the point x on the axis of rotation. Finally, we assume that the deflection of the string is so slight that $\sin\theta \approx \tan\theta = y'(x)$ in Fig. 3.8.6(c).

We plan to derive a differential equation for $y(x)$ by application of Newton's law $F = ma$ to the piece of string of mass $\rho\,\Delta x$ corresponding to the interval $[x, x + \Delta x]$. The only forces acting on this piece are the tension forces at its two ends. From Fig. 3.8.7 we see that the net vertical force in the positive y-direction is

$$F = T\sin(\theta + \Delta\theta) - T\sin\theta \approx T\tan(\theta + \Delta\theta) - T\tan\theta,$$

so that

$$F \approx Ty'(x + \Delta x) - Ty'(x). \tag{15}$$

Next we recall from elementary calculus or physics the formula $a = r\omega^2$ for the (inward) centripetal acceleration of a body in uniform circular motion (r is the radius of the circle and ω is the angular velocity of the body). Here we have $r = y$, so the vertical acceleration of our piece of string is $a = -\omega^2 y$, the minus sign because the inward direction is the negative y-direction. Because $m = \rho\,\Delta x$, substitution of this and (15) in $F = ma$ yields

$$Ty'(x + \Delta x) - Ty'(x) \approx -\rho\omega^2 y\,\Delta x,$$

so that

$$T \cdot \frac{y'(x + \Delta x) - y'(x)}{\Delta x} \approx -\rho\omega^2 y.$$

We now take the limit as $\Delta x \to 0$ to get the differential equation of motion of the string:

$$Ty'' + \rho\omega^2 y = 0. \tag{16}$$

If we write

$$\lambda = \frac{\rho\omega^2}{T} \tag{17}$$

and impose the condition that the ends of the string are fixed, we finally get the eigenvalue problem

$$y'' + \lambda y = 0; \quad y(0) = 0, \quad y(L) = 0 \tag{7}$$

that we considered in Example 3. We found there that the eigenvalues of the problem in (7) are

$$\lambda_n = \frac{n^2\pi^2}{L^2}, \quad n = 1, 2, 3, \ldots, \tag{8}$$

with the eigenfunction $y_n(x) = \sin(n\pi x/L)$ associated with λ_n.

But what does all this mean in terms of the whirling string? It means that unless λ in (17) is one of the eigenvalues in (8), then the only solution of the problem in (7) is the trivial solution $y(x) \equiv 0$. In this case the string remains in its equilibrium position with zero deflection. But if we equate (17) and (8) and solve for the value ω_n corresponding to λ_n,

$$\omega_n = \sqrt{\frac{\lambda_n T}{\rho}} = \frac{n\pi}{L}\sqrt{\frac{T}{\rho}} \tag{18}$$

for $n = 1, 2, 3, \ldots$, we get a sequence of **critical speeds** of angular rotation. Only at these critical angular speeds can the string whirl up out of its equilibrium position. At angular speed ω it assumes a shape of the form $y_n = c_n \sin(n\pi x/L)$ illustrated in Fig. 3.8.4 (where $c_n \equiv 1$). Our mathematical model is not sufficiently complete (or realistic) to determine the coefficient c_n, but it assumes much smaller deflections than those observed in Fig. 3.8.4, so the numerical value of c_n would necessarily be significantly smaller than 1.

Suppose that we start the string rotating at speed

$$\omega < \omega_1 = \frac{\pi}{L}\sqrt{\frac{T}{\rho}},$$

then gradually increase its speed of rotation. So long as $\omega < \omega_1$, the string remains in its undeflected position $y \equiv 0$. But when $\omega = \omega_1$, the string pops into a whirling position $y = c_1 \sin(\pi x/L)$. And when ω is increased still further, the string pops back into its undeflected position along the axis of rotation!

The Deflection of a Uniform Beam

We include now an example of the use of a relatively simple endpoint value problem to explain a complicated physical phenomenon—the shape of a horizontal beam on which a vertical force is acting.

FIGURE 3.8.8.   Distortion of a horizontal beam.

Consider the horizontal beam shown in Fig. 3.8.8, uniform both in cross section and in material. If it is supported only at its ends, then the force of its own weight distorts its longitudinal axis of symmetry into the curve shown as a dashed line in the figure. We want to investigate the shape $y = y(x)$ of this curve, the **deflection curve** of the beam. We will use the coordinate system indicated in Fig. 3.8.9, with the positive y-axis directed downward.

A consequence of the theory of elasticity is that for relatively small deflections of such a beam (so small that $[y'(x)]^2$ is negligible in comparison with unity), an adequate mathematical model of the deflection curve is the fourth-order differential equation

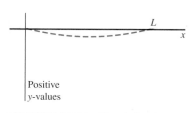

FIGURE 3.8.9.   The deflection curve.

$$EIy^{(4)} = F(x), \tag{19}$$

where

- E is a constant known as the *Young's modulus* of the material of the beam,
- I denotes the moment of inertia of the cross section of the beam around a horizontal line through the centroid of the cross section, and
- $F(x)$ denotes the density of *downward* force acting vertically on the beam at the point x.

Density of force? Yes; this means that the force acting downward on a very short segment $[x, x + \Delta x]$ of the beam is approximately $F(x)\,\Delta x$. The units of $F(x)$ are those of force per unit length, such as pounds per foot. We will consider here the case in which the only force distributed along the beam is its own weight, w pounds per foot, so that $F(x) \equiv w$. Then Eq. (19) takes the form

$$EIy^{(4)} = w \qquad\qquad (20)$$

where E, I, and w are all constant.

Note: We assume no previous familiarity with the theory of elasticity or with Eq. (19) or (20) here. It is important to be able to begin with a differential equation that arises in a specific applied discipline and then analyze its implications; thus we develop an understanding of the equation by examining its solutions. Observe that, in essence, Eq. (20) implies that the fourth derivative $y^{(4)}$ is proportional to the weight density w. This proportionality involves, however, *two* constants: E, which depends only on the material of the beam, and I, which depends only on the shape of the cross section of the beam. Values of the Young's modulus E of various materials can be found in handbooks of physical constants; $I = \frac{1}{4}\pi a^4$ for a circular cross section of radius a.

Although Eq. (20) is a fourth-order differential equation, its solution involves only the solution of simple first-order equations by successive simple integrations. One integration of Eq. (20) yields

$$EIy^{(3)} = wx + C_1;$$

a second yields

$$EIy'' = \tfrac{1}{2}wx^2 + C_1x + C_2;$$

another yields

$$EIy' = \tfrac{1}{6}wx^3 + \tfrac{1}{2}C_1x^2 + C_2x + C_3;$$

a final integration gives

$$EIy = \tfrac{1}{24}wx^4 + \tfrac{1}{6}C_1x^3 + \tfrac{1}{2}C_2x^2 + C_3x + C_4,$$

x = 0   x = L

Simply supported or hinged

x = 0   x = L

Built in

FIGURE 3.8.10. Two ways of supporting a beam.

where C_1, C_2, C_3, and C_4 are arbitrary constants. Thus we obtain a solution of Eq. (20) of the form

$$y(x) = \frac{w}{24EI}x^2 + Ax^3 + Bx^2 + Cx + D, \qquad\qquad (21)$$

where A, B, C, and D are constants resulting from the four integrations.

These last four constants are determined by the way in which the beam is supported at its ends, where $x = 0$ and $x = L$. Figure 3.8.10 shows two common types of support. A beam might also be supported one way at one end but another way at the other end. For instance, Fig. 3.8.11 shows a **cantilever**—a beam firmly fastened at $x = 0$ but *free* (no support whatsoever) at $x = L$. The following table shows the **boundary** or **endpoint conditions** corresponding to the three most common cases. We will see that these conditions are applied readily in beam problems, although a discussion here of their origin would take us too far afield.

Support	Endpoint Condition
Simply supported	$y = y'' = 0$
Built-in or fixed end	$y = y' = 0$
Free end	$y'' = y^{(3)} = 0$

For example, the deflection curve of the cantilever in Fig. 3.8.11 would be given by Eq. (21), with the coefficients A, B, C, and D determined by the conditions

$$y(0) = y'(0) = 0 \quad \text{and} \quad y''(L) = y^{(3)}(L) = 0, \tag{22}$$

Cantilever

FIGURE 3.8.11. The cantilever.

corresponding to the fixed end at $x = 0$ and the free end at $x = L$. The conditions in (22) together with the differential equation in (21) constitute an **endpoint value problem**.

Example 5

Determine the shape of the deflection curve of a uniform horizontal beam of length L and weight w per unit length and simply supported at each end.

Solution

We have the endpoint conditions

$$y(0) = y''(0) = 0 = y(L) = y''(L).$$

Rather than imposing then directly on Eq. (21), let us begin with the differential equation $EIy^{(4)} = w$ and determine the constants as we proceed with the four successive integrations. The first two integrations yield

$$EIy^{(3)} = wx + A; \quad EIy'' = \tfrac{1}{2}wx^2 + Ax + B.$$

Hence $y''(0) = 0$ implies that $B = 0$, and then $y''(L) = 0$ gives

$$0 = \tfrac{1}{2}wL^2 + AL.$$

It follows that $A = -wL/2$ and thus that

$$EIy'' = \tfrac{1}{2}x^2 - \tfrac{1}{2}wLx.$$

Then two more integrations give

$$EIy' = \tfrac{1}{6}wx^3 - \tfrac{1}{4}wLx^2 + C,$$

and finally,

$$EIy(x) = \tfrac{1}{24}wx^4 - \tfrac{1}{12}wLx^3 + Cx + D. \tag{23}$$

Now $y(0) = 0$ implies that $D = 0$; then, because $y(L) = 0$,

$$0 = \tfrac{1}{24}wL^4 - \tfrac{1}{12}wL^4 + CL.$$

It follows that $C = wL^3/24$. Hence from Eq. (23) we obtain

$$y(x) = \frac{w}{24EI}(x^4 - 2Lx^3 + L^3x) \tag{24}$$

as the shape of the simply supported beam. It is apparent from symmetry (see also Problem 17) that the *maximum deflection* y_{max} of the beam occurs at its midpoint $x = L/2$, and thus has the value

$$y_{max} = y\left(\frac{L}{2}\right) = \frac{w}{24EI}\left(\frac{1}{16}L^4 - \frac{2}{8}L^4 + \frac{1}{2}L^4\right);$$

that is,

$$y_{max} = \frac{5wL^4}{384EI}. \tag{25}$$

∎

Example 6　For instance, suppose that we want to calculate the maximum deflection of a simply supported steel rod 20 ft long with a circular cross section 1 in. in diameter. From a handbook we find that typical steel has density $\delta = 7.75$ g/cm³ and that its Young's modulus is $E = 2 \times 10^{12}$ g/cm·s², so it will be more convenient to work in cgs units. Thus our rod has

$$\text{length:} \quad L = (20 \text{ ft})\left(30.48 \frac{\text{cm}}{\text{ft}}\right) = 609.60 \text{ cm}$$

and

$$\text{radius:} \quad a = \left(\frac{1}{2} \text{ in.}\right)\left(2.54 \frac{\text{cm}}{\text{in.}}\right) = 1.27 \text{ cm}.$$

Its *linear* mass density (that is, its mass per unit length) is

$$\rho = \pi a^2 \delta = \pi(1.27)^2(7.75) \approx 39.27 \frac{\text{g}}{\text{cm}},$$

so

$$w = \rho g = \left(39.27 \frac{\text{g}}{\text{cm}}\right)\left(980 \frac{\text{cm}}{\text{s}^2}\right) \approx 38484.6 \frac{\text{dyn}}{\text{cm}}.$$

The area moment of inertia of a circular disk of radius a around a diameter is $I = \frac{1}{4}\pi a^4$, so

$$I = \frac{1}{4}\pi(1.27)^4 \approx 2.04 \text{ cm}^4.$$

Therefore Eq. (25) yields

$$y_{max} \approx \frac{(5)(38484.6)(609.60)^4}{(384)(2 \times 10^{12})(2.04)} \approx 16.96 \text{ cm},$$

about 6.68 in., as the maximum deflection of the rod at its midpoint. It is interesting to note that y_{max} is proportional to L^4, so if the rod were only 10 ft long, its maximum deflection would be only one-sixteenth as much—only about 0.42 in. Because $I = \frac{1}{4}\pi a^4$, we see from Eq. (25) that the same reduction in maximum deflection could be achieved by doubling the radius a of the rod. ∎

The Buckled Rod

FIGURE 3.8.12. The buckled rod.

Figure 3.8.12 shows a uniform rod of length L, hinged at each end, that has been "buckled" by an axial force of compression P applied at one end. We assume this buckling to be so slight that the deflection curve $y = y(x)$ of the rod may be regarded as defined on the interval $0 \leq x \leq L$.

In the theory of elasticity the linear endpoint boundary value problem

$$EIy'' + Py = 0, \quad y(0) = y(L) = 0 \tag{26}$$

is used to model the actual (nonlinear) behavior of the rod. As in our discussion of the deflection of a uniform beam, E denotes the Young's modulus of the material of the beam and I denotes the moment of inertia of each cross section of the beam around a horizontal line through its centroid.

If we write

$$\lambda = \frac{P}{EI}, \tag{27}$$

then the problem in (26) becomes the eigenvalue problem

$$y'' + \lambda y = 0; \quad y(0) = y(L) = 0 \tag{7}$$

that we considered in Example 3. We found that its eigenvalues $\{\lambda_n\}$ are given by

$$\lambda_n = \frac{n^2 \pi^2}{L^2}, \quad n = 1, 2, 3, \dots \tag{8}$$

with the eigenfunction $y_n = \sin(n\pi x/L)$ associated with λ_n. (Thus whirling strings and buckled rods lead to the same eigenvalues and eigenfunctions.)

To interpret this result in terms of the buckled rod, recall from Eq. (27) that $P = \lambda EI$. The forces

$$P_n = \lambda_n EI = \frac{n^2 \pi^2 EI}{L^2}, \quad n = 1, 2, 3, \dots \tag{28}$$

are the *critical buckling forces* of the rod. Only when the compressive force P is one of these critical forces should the rod "buckle" out of its straight (undeflected) shape. The smallest compressive force for which this occurs is

$$P_1 = \frac{\pi^2 EI}{L^2}. \tag{29}$$

This smallest critical force P_1 is called the *Euler buckling force* for the rod; it is the upper bound for those compressive forces to which the rod can safely be subjected without buckling. (In practice a rod may fail at a significantly smaller force due to a contribution of factors not taken into account by the mathematical model discussed here.)

| Example 7 | For instance, suppose that we want to compute the Euler buckling force for a steel rod 10 ft long having a circular cross section 1 in. in diameter. In cgs units we have |

$$E = 2 \times 10^{12} \text{ g/cm·s}^2,$$

$$L = (10 \text{ ft}) \left(30.48 \frac{\text{cm}}{\text{ft}} \right) = 304.8 \text{ cm}, \qquad \text{and}$$

$$I = \frac{\pi}{4} \left[(0.5 \text{ in.}) \left(2.54 \frac{\text{cm}}{\text{in.}} \right) \right]^4 \approx 2.04 \text{ cm}^4.$$

Upon substituting these values in Eq. (29) we find that the critical force for this rod is

$$P_1 \approx 4.34 \times 10^8 \text{ dyn} \approx 976 \text{ lb},$$

using the conversion factor 4.448×10^5 dyn/lb.   ■

3.8 Problems

The eigenvalues in Problems 1 through 5 are all nonnegative. First determine whether $\lambda = 0$ is an eigenvalue; then find the positive eigenvalues and associated eigenfunctions.

1. $y'' + \lambda y = 0$; $y'(0) = 0$, $y(1) = 0$
2. $y'' + \lambda y = 0$; $y'(0) = 0$, $y'(\pi) = 0$
3. $y'' + \lambda y = 0$; $y(-\pi) = 0$, $y(\pi) = 0$
4. $y'' + \lambda y = 0$; $y'(-\pi) = 0$, $y'(\pi) = 0$
5. $y'' + \lambda y = 0$; $y(-2) = 0$, $y'(2) = 0$
6. Consider the eigenvalue problem

$$y'' + \lambda y = 0; \quad y'(0) = 0, \quad y(1) + y'(1) = 0.$$

All the eigenvalues are nonnegative, so write $\lambda = \alpha^2$ where $\alpha \geqq 0$. **(a)** Show that $\lambda = 0$ is not an eigenvalue. **(b)** Show that $y = A \cos \alpha x + B \sin \alpha x$ satisfies the endpoint conditions if and only if $B = 0$ and α is a positive root of the equation $\tan z = 1/z$. These roots $\{\alpha_n\}_1^\infty$ are the abscissas of the points of intersection of the curves $y = \tan z$ and $y = 1/z$, as indicated in Fig. 3.8.13. Thus the eigenvalues and eigenfunctions of this problem are the numbers $\{\alpha_n^2\}_1^\infty$ and the functions $\{\cos \alpha_n x\}_1^\infty$, respectively.

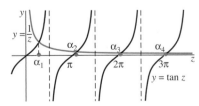

FIGURE 3.8.13. The eigenvalues are determined by the intersections of the graphs of $y = \tan z$ and $y = 1/z$ (Problem 6).

7. Consider the eigenvalue problem

$$y'' + \lambda y = 0; \quad y(0) = 0, \quad y(1) + y'(1) = 0;$$

all its eigenvalues are nonnegative. **(a)** Show that $\lambda = 0$ is not an eigenvalue. **(b)** Show that the eigenfunctions are the functions $\{\sin \alpha_n x\}_1^\infty$, where α_n is the nth positive root of the equation $\tan z = -z$. **(c)** Draw a sketch indicating the roots $\{\alpha_n\}_1^\infty$ as the points of intersection of the curves $y = \tan z$ and $y = -z$. Deduce from this sketch that $\alpha_n \approx (2n - 1)\pi/2$ when n is large.

8. Consider the eigenvalue problem

$$y'' + \lambda y = 0; \quad y(0) = 0, \quad y(1) = y'(1);$$

all its eigenvalues are nonnegative. **(a)** Show that $\lambda = 0$ is an eigenvalue with associated eigenfunction $y_0(x) = x$. **(b)** Show that the remaining eigenfunctions are given by $y_n(x) = \sin \beta_n x$, where β_n is the nth positive root of the equation $\tan z = z$. Draw a sketch showing these roots. Deduce from this sketch that $\beta_n \approx (2n + 1)\pi/2$ when n is large.

9. Prove that the eigenvalue problem of Example 4 has no negative eigenvalues.

10. Prove that the eigenvalue problem

$$y'' + \lambda y = 0; \quad y(0) = 0, \quad y(1) + y'(1) = 0$$

has no negative eigenvalues. (*Suggestion*: Show graphically that the only root of the equation $\tanh z = -z$ is $z = 0$.)

11. Use a method similar to that suggested in Problem 10 to show that the eigenvalue problem in Problem 6 has no negative eigenvalues.

12. Consider the eigenvalue problem

$$y'' + \lambda y = 0; \quad y(-\pi) = y(\pi), \quad y'(-\pi) = y'(\pi),$$

which is not of the type in (10) because the two endpoint conditions are not "separated" between the two endpoints. **(a)** Show that $\lambda_0 = 0$ is an eigenvalue with associated eigenfunction $y_0(x) \equiv 1$. **(b)** Show that there are no negative eigenvalues. **(c)** Show that the nth positive eigenvalue is n^2 and that it has two linearly independent associated eigenfunctions, $\cos nx$ and $\sin nx$.

13. Consider the eigenvalue problem

$$y'' + 2y' + \lambda y = 0; \quad y(0) = y(1) = 0.$$

(a) Show that $\lambda = 1$ is not an eigenvalue. **(b)** Show that there is no eigenvalue λ such that $\lambda < 1$. **(c)** Show that the nth positive eigenvalue is $\lambda_n = n^2\pi^2 + 1$, with associated eigenfunction $y_n(x) = e^{-x} \sin n\pi x$.

14. Consider the eigenvalue problem

$$y'' + 2y' + \lambda y = 0; \quad y(0) = 0, \quad y'(1) = 0.$$

Show that the eigenvalues are all positive and that the nth positive eigenvalue is $\lambda_n = \alpha_n^2 + 1$ with associated eigenfunction $y_n(x) = e^{-x} \sin \alpha_n x$, where α_n is the nth positive root of $\tan z = z$.

15. **(a)** A uniform cantilever beam is fixed at $x = 0$ and free at its other end, where $x = L$. Show that its shape is given by

$$y(x) = \frac{w}{24EI}(x^4 - 4Lx^3 + 6L^2x^2).$$

(b) Show that $y'(x) = 0$ only at $x = 0$, and thus that it follows (why?) that the maximum deflection of the cantilever is $y_{\max} = y(L) = wL^4/(8EI)$.

16. **(a)** Suppose that a beam is fixed at its ends $x = 0$ and $x = L$. Show that its shape is given by

$$y(x) = \frac{w}{24EI}(x^4 - 2Lx^3 + L^2x^2).$$

(b) Show that the roots of $y'(x) = 0$ are $x = 0$, $x = L$, and $x = L/2$, so it follows (why?) that the maximum deflection of the beam is

$$y_{\max} = y\left(\frac{L}{2}\right) = \frac{wL^4}{384EI},$$

one-fifth that of a beam with simply supported ends.

17. For the simply supported beam whose deflection curve is given by Eq. (24), show that the only root of $y'(x) = 0$ in $[0, L]$ is $x = L/2$, so it follows (why?) that the maximum deflection is indeed that given in Eq. (25).

18. **(a)** A beam is fixed at its left end $x = 0$ but is simply supported at the other end $x = L$. Show that its deflection curve is

$$y(x) = \frac{w}{48EI}(2x^4 - 5Lx^3 + 3L^2x^2).$$

(b) Show that its maximum deflection occurs where $x = (15 - \sqrt{33})L/16$ and is about 41.6% of the maximum deflection that would occur if the beam were simply supported at each end.

4 Introduction to Systems of Differential Equations

4.1 First-Order Systems and Applications

In the preceding chapters we have discussed methods for solving an ordinary differential equation that involves only one dependent variable. Many applications, however, require the use of two or more dependent variables, each a function of a single independent variable (typically time). Such a problem leads naturally to a *system* of simultaneous ordinary differential equations. We will usually denote the independent variable by t and the dependent variables (the unknown functions of t) by $x_1, x_2, x_3, \ldots$ or by $x, y, z, \ldots$. Primes will indicate derivatives with respect to t.

We will restrict our attention to systems in which the number of equations is the same as the number of dependent variables (unknown functions). For instance, a system of two first-order equations in the dependent variables x and y has the general form

$$
\begin{aligned}
f(t, x, y, x', y') &= 0, \\
g(t, x, y, x', y') &= 0,
\end{aligned}
\tag{1}
$$

where the functions f and g are given. A **solution** of this system is a pair $x(t)$, $y(t)$ of functions of t that satisfy both equations identically over some interval of values of t.

For an example of a second-order system, consider a particle of mass m that moves in space under the influence of a force field $\mathbf{F}$ that depends on time t, the position $(x(t), y(t), z(t))$ of the particle, and its velocity $(x'(t), y'(t), z'(t))$. Applying Newton's law $m\mathbf{a} = \mathbf{F}$ componentwise, we get the system

$$
\begin{aligned}
mx'' &= F_1(t, x, y, z, x', y', z'), \\
my'' &= F_2(t, x, y, z, x', y', z'), \\
mz'' &= F_3(t, x, y, z, x', y', z')
\end{aligned}
\tag{2}
$$

of three second-order equations with independent variable t and dependent variables x, y, z; the three right-hand-side functions F_1, F_2, F_3 are the components of the vector-valued function **F**.

Initial Applications

Examples 1 through 3 further illustrate how systems of differential equations arise naturally in scientific problems.

Example 1

Consider the system of two masses and two springs shown in Fig. 4.1.1, with a given external force $f(t)$ acting on the right-hand mass m_2. We denote by $x(t)$ the displacement (to the right) of the mass m_1 from its static equilibrium position (when the system is motionless and in equilibrium and $f(t) = 0$) and by $y(t)$ the displacement of the mass m_2 from its static position. Thus the two springs are neither stretched nor compressed when x and y are zero.

In the configuration in Fig. 4.1.1, the first spring is stretched x units and the second by $y - x$ units. We apply Newton's law of motion to the two "free body diagrams" shown in Fig. 4.1.2; we thereby obtain the system

$$m_1 x'' = -k_1 x + k_2 (y - x),$$
$$m_2 y'' = -k_2 (y - x) + f(t) \tag{3}$$

of differential equations that the position functions $x(t)$ and $y(t)$ must satisfy. For instance, if $m_1 = 2$, $m_2 = 1$, $k_1 = 4$, $k_2 = 2$, and $f(t) = 40 \sin 3t$ in appropriate physical units, then the system in (3) reduces to

$$2x'' = -6x + 2y,$$
$$y'' = 2x - 2y + 40 \sin 3t. \tag{4}$$

■

FIGURE 4.1.1. The mass-and-spring system of Example 1.

FIGURE 4.1.2. The "free body diagrams" for the system of Example 1.

Example 2

Consider two brine tanks connected as shown in Fig. 4.1.3. Tank 1 contains $x(t)$ pounds of salt in 100 gal of brine and tank 2 contains $y(t)$ pounds of salt in 200 gal of brine. The brine in each tank is kept uniform by stirring, and brine is pumped from each tank to the other at the rates indicated in Fig. 4.1.3. In addition, fresh water flows into tank 1 at 20 gal/min, and the brine in tank 2 flows out at 20 gal/min (so the total volume of brine in the two tanks remains constant). The salt concentrations in the two tanks are $x/100$ pounds per gallon and $y/200$ pounds per gallon, respectively. When we compute the rates of change of the amount of salt in the two tanks, we therefore get the system of differential equations that $x(t)$ and $y(t)$ must satisfy:

$$x' = -30 \cdot \frac{x}{100} + 10 \cdot \frac{y}{200} = -\frac{3}{10}x + \frac{1}{20}y,$$
$$y' = 30 \cdot \frac{x}{100} - 10 \cdot \frac{y}{200} - 20 \cdot \frac{y}{200} = \frac{3}{10}x - \frac{3}{20}y;$$

that is,

$$20x' = -6x + y,$$
$$20y' = 6x - 3y. \tag{5}$$

■

FIGURE 4.1.3. The two brine tanks of Example 2.

FIGURE 4.1.4. The electrical network of Example 3.

Circuit Element	Voltage Drop
Inductor	$L\dfrac{dI}{dt}$
Resistor	RI
Capacitor	$\dfrac{1}{C}Q$

FIGURE 4.1.5. Voltage drops across common circuit elements.

Example 3

Consider the electrical network shown in Fig. 4.1.4, where $I_1(t)$ denotes the current in the indicated direction through the inductor L and $I_2(t)$ denotes the current through the resistor R_2. The current through the resistor R_1 is $I = I_1 - I_2$ in the direction indicated. We recall Kirchhoff's voltage law to the effect that the (algebraic) sum of the voltage drops around any closed loop of such a network is zero. As in Section 3.7, the voltage drops across the three types of circuit elements are those shown in Fig. 4.1.5. We apply Kirchhoff's law to the left-hand loop of the network to obtain

$$2\frac{dI_1}{dt} + 50(I_1 - I_2) - 100 = 0, \tag{6}$$

because the voltage drop from the negative to the positive pole of the battery is -100. The right-hand loop yields the equation

$$125Q_2 + 25I_2 + 50(I_2 - I_1) = 0, \tag{7}$$

where $Q_2(t)$ is the charge on the capacitor. Because $dQ_2/dt = I_2$, differentiation of each side of Eq. (7) yields

$$125I_2 + 75\frac{dI_2}{dt} - 50\frac{dI_1}{dt} = 0. \tag{8}$$

After dividing Eqs. (6) and (8) by the factors 2 and -25, respectively, we get the system

$$\frac{dI_1}{dt} + 25I_1 - 25I_2 = 50,$$

$$2\frac{dI_1}{dt} - 3\frac{dI_2}{dt} - 5I_2 = 0 \tag{9}$$

of differential equations that the currents $I_1(t)$ and $I_2(t)$ must satisfy. ∎

First-Order Systems

Consider a system of differential equations that can be solved for the highest-order derivatives of the dependent variables that appear, as explicit functions of t and lower-order derivatives of the dependent variables. For instance, in the case of a system of two second-order equations, our assumption is that it can be written in the form

$$x_1'' = f_1(t, x_1, x_2, x_1', x_2'),$$
$$x_2'' = f_2(t, x_1, x_2, x_1', x_2'). \tag{10}$$

It is of both practical and theoretical importance that any such higher-order system can be transformed into an equivalent system of *first-order* equations.

To describe how such a transformation is accomplished, we consider first the "system" consisting of the single nth-order equation

➤
$$x^{(n)} = f(t, x, x', \ldots, x^{(n-1)}). \tag{11}$$

We introduce the dependent variables $x_1, x_2, \ldots, x_n$ defined as follows:

$$x_1 = x, \quad x_2 = x', \quad x_3 = x'', \quad \ldots, \quad x_n = x^{(n-1)}. \tag{12}$$

Note that $x_1' = x' = x_2$, $x_2' = x'' = x_3$, and so on. Hence the substitution of (12) in Eq. (11) yields the system

$$x_1' = x_2,$$
$$x_2' = x_3,$$

➤
$$\vdots \tag{13}$$

$$x_{n-1}' = x_n,$$
$$x_n' = f(t, x_1, x_2, \ldots, x_n)$$

of n *first-order* equations. Evidently, this system is equivalent to the original nth-order equation in (11), in the sense that $x(t)$ is a solution of Eq. (11) if and only if the functions $x_1(t), x_2(t), \ldots, x_n(t)$ defined in (12) satisfy the system of equations in (13).

Example 4

The third-order equation

$$x^{(3)} + 3x'' + 2x' - 5x = \sin 2t$$

is of the form in (11) with

$$f(t, x, x', x'') = 5x - 2x' - 3x'' + \sin 2t.$$

Hence the substitutions

$$x_1 = x, \quad x_2 = x' = x_1', \quad x_3 = x'' = x_2'$$

yield the system

$$x_1' = x_2,$$
$$x_2' = x_3,$$
$$x_3' = 5x_1 - 2x_2 - 3x_3 + \sin 2t$$

of three first-order equations. ∎

It may appear that the first-order system obtained in Example 4 offers little advantage because we could use the methods of Chapter 3 to solve the original (linear) third-order equation. But suppose that we were confronted with the nonlinear equation

$$x'' = x^3 + (x')^3,$$

to which none of our earlier methods can be applied. The corresponding first-order system is

$$x_1' = x_2,$$
$$x_2' = (x_1)^3 + (x_2)^3, \tag{14}$$

and we will see in Section 4.3 that there exist effective numerical techniques for approximating the solution of essentially any first-order system. So in this case the transformation to a first-order system *is* advantageous. From a practical viewpoint, large systems of higher-order differential equations typically are solved numerically with the aid of the computer, and the first step is to transform such a system into a first-order system for which a standard computer program is available.

Example 5 The system

$$2x'' = -6x + 2y,$$
$$y'' = \quad 2x - 2y + 40 \sin 3t \tag{4}$$

of second-order equations was derived in Example 1. Transform this system into an equivalent first-order system.

Solution Motivated by the equations in (12), we define

$$x_1 = x, \quad x_2 = x' = x_1', \quad y_1 = y, \quad y_2 = y' = y_1'.$$

Then the system in (4) yields the system

$$x_1' = x_2,$$
$$2x_2' = -6x_1 + 2y_1,$$
$$y_1' = y_2, \tag{15}$$
$$y_2' = 2x_1 - 2y_1 + 40 \sin 3t$$

of four first-order equations in the dependent variables x_1, x_2, y_1, and y_2. ∎

Simple Two-Dimensional Systems

The linear second-order differential equation

$$x'' + px' + qx = 0 \tag{16}$$

(with constant coefficients and independent variable t) transforms via the substitutions $x' = y$, $x'' = y'$ into the two-dimensional linear system

$$x' = y,$$
$$y' = -qx - py. \tag{17}$$

Conversely, we can solve this system in (17) by solving the familiar single equation in (16).

Example 6 To solve the two-dimensional system

$$x' = -2y,$$
$$y' = \tfrac{1}{2}x, \tag{18}$$

we begin with the observation that

$$x'' = -2y' = -2\left(\tfrac{1}{2}x\right) = -x.$$

This gives the single second-order equation $x'' + x = 0$ with general solution

$$x(t) = A\cos t + B\sin t = C\cos(t - \alpha)$$

where $A = C\cos\alpha$ and $B = C\sin\alpha$. Then

$$y(t) = -\tfrac{1}{2}x'(t) = -\tfrac{1}{2}(-A\sin t + B\cos t)$$
$$= \tfrac{1}{2}C\sin(t - \alpha).$$

The identity $\cos^2\theta + \sin^2\theta = 1$ therefore implies that, for each value of t, the point $(x(t), y(t))$ lies on the ellipse

$$\frac{x^2}{C^2} + \frac{y^2}{(C/2)^2} = 1$$

with semiaxes C and $C/2$. Figure 4.1.6 shows several such ellipses in the xy-plane. ∎

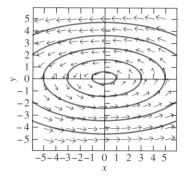

FIGURE 4.1.6. Direction field and solution curves for the system $x' = -2y$, $y' = \tfrac{1}{2}x$ of Example 6.

A solution $(x(t), y(t))$ of a two-dimensional system

$$x' = f(t, x, y),$$
$$y' = g(t, x, y)$$

may be regarded as a parametrization of a **solution curve** or **trajectory** of the system in the xy-plane. Thus the trajectories of the system in (18) are the ellipses of Fig. 4.1.6. The choice of an initial point $(x(0), y(0))$ determines which one of these trajectories a particular solution parametrizes.

The picture showing a system's trajectories in the xy-plane—its so-called *phase plane portrait*—fails to reveal precisely how the point $(x(t), y(t))$ moves along its trajectory. If the functions f and g do not involve the independent variable t, then a **direction field**—showing typical arrows representing vectors with components (proportional to) the derivatives $x' = f(x, y)$ and $y' = g(x, y)$—can be plotted. Because the moving point $(x(t), y(t))$ has velocity vector $(x'(t), y'(t))$, this direction field indicates the point's direction of motion along its trajectory. For instance, the direction field plotted in Fig. 4.1.6 indicates that each such point moves counterclockwise around its elliptical trajectory. Additional information can be shown in the separate graphs of $x(t)$ and $y(t)$ as functions of t.

Example 6
Continued

With initial values $x(0) = 2$, $y(0) = 0$, the general solution in Example 6 yields

$$x(0) = A = 2, \quad y(0) = -\tfrac{1}{2}B = 0.$$

The resulting particular solution is given by

$$x(t) = 2\cos t, \quad y(t) = \sin t.$$

The graphs of the two functions are shown in Fig. 4.1.7. We see that $x(t)$ initially decreases while $y(t)$ increases. It follows that, as t increases, the solution point $(x(t), y(t))$ traverses the trajectory $\tfrac{1}{4}x^2 + y^2 = 1$ in the counterclockwise direction, as indicated by the direction field vectors in Fig. 4.1.6. ■

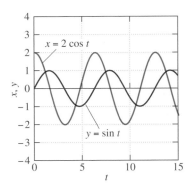

FIGURE 4.1.7. x- and y-solution curves for the initial value problem $x' = -2y$, $y' = \tfrac{1}{2}x$, $x(0) = 2$, $y(0) = 0$.

Example 7

To find a general solution of the system

$$\begin{aligned} x' &= y, \\ y' &= 2x + y, \end{aligned} \tag{19}$$

we begin with the observation that

$$x'' = y' = 2x + y = x' + 2x.$$

This gives the single linear second-order equation

$$x'' - x' - 2x = 0$$

with characteristic equation

$$r^2 - r - 2 = (r + 1)(r - 2) = 0$$

and general solution

$$x(t) = Ae^{-t} + Be^{2t}. \tag{20}$$

Then

$$y(t) = x'(t) = -Ae^{-t} + 2Be^{2t}. \tag{21}$$

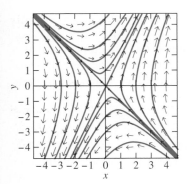

FIGURE 4.1.8. Direction field and solution curves for the system $x' = y$, $y' = 2x + y$ of Example 7.

Typical phase plane trajectories of the system in (19) parametrized by Eqs. (20) and (21) are shown in Fig. 4.1.8. These trajectories may resemble hyperbolas sharing common asymptotes, but Problem 23 shows that their actual form is somewhat more complicated. ■

| **Example 8** | To solve the initial value problem

$$x' = -y,$$
$$y' = (1.01)x - (0.2)y,$$
$$x(0) = 0, \quad y(0) = -1,$$

(22)

we begin with the observation that

$$x'' = -y' = -[(1.01)x - (0.2)y] = (-1.01)x - (0.2)x'.$$

This gives the single linear second-order equation

$$x'' + (0.2)x' + (1.01)x = 0$$

with characteristic equation

$$r^2 + (0.2)r + 1.01 = (r + 0.1)^2 + 1 = 0,$$

characteristic roots $-0.1 \pm i$, and general solution

$$x(t) = e^{-t/10}(A \cos t + B \sin t).$$

Then $x(0) = A = 0$, so

$$x(t) = Be^{-t/10} \sin t,$$
$$y(t) = -x'(t) = \tfrac{1}{10} Be^{-t/10} \sin t - Be^{-t/10} \cos t.$$

Finally, $y(0) = -B = -1$, so the desired solution of the system in (22) is

$$x(t) = e^{-t/10} \sin t,$$
$$y(t) = \tfrac{1}{10} e^{-t/10}(\sin t - 10 \cos t).$$

(23)

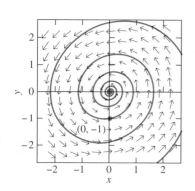

FIGURE 4.1.9. Direction field and solution curve for the system $x' = -y$, $y' = (1.01)x - (0.2)y$ of Example 8.

These equations parametrize the spiral trajectory in Fig. 4.1.9; the trajectory approaches the origin as $t \to +\infty$. Figure 4.1.10 shows the x- and y-solution curves given in (23). ∎

When we study linear systems in Chapter 5, we will learn why the superficially similar systems in Examples 6 through 8 have the markedly different trajectories shown in Figs. 4.1.6, 4.1.8, and 4.1.9.

Linear Systems

FIGURE 4.1.10. x- and y-solution curves for the initial value problem of Example 8.

In addition to practical advantages for numerical computation, the general theory of systems and systematic solution techniques are more easily and more concisely described for first-order systems than for higher-order systems. For instance, consider a *linear* first-order system of the form

$$
\begin{aligned}
x_1' &= p_{11}(t)x_1 + p_{12}(t)x_2 + \cdots + p_{1n}x_n + f_1(t), \\
x_2' &= p_{21}(t)x_1 + p_{22}(t)x_2 + \cdots + p_{2n}x_n + f_2(t), \\
&\vdots \\
x_n' &= p_{n1}(t)x_1 + p_{n2}(t)x_2 + \cdots + p_{nn}x_n + f_n(t).
\end{aligned}
$$

(24)

We say that this system is **homogeneous** if the functions $f_1, f_2, \ldots, f_n$ are all identically zero; otherwise, it is **nonhomogeneous.** Thus the linear system in (5) is homogeneous, whereas the linear system in (15) is nonhomogeneous. The system in (14) is nonlinear because the right-hand side of the second equation is not a linear function of the dependent variables x_1 and x_2.

A **solution** of the system in (24) is an n-tuple of functions $x_1(t), x_2(t), \ldots,$ $x_n(t)$ that (on some interval) identically satisfy each of the equations in (24). We will see that the general theory of a system of n linear first-order equations shares many similarities with the general theory of a single nth-order linear differential equation. Theorem 1 (proved in the Appendix) is analogous to Theorem 2 of Section 3.2. It tells us that if the coefficient functions p_{ij} and f_j in (24) are continuous, then the system has a unique solution satisfying given initial conditions.

THEOREM 1   Existence and Uniqueness for Linear Systems

Suppose that the functions $p_{11}, p_{12}, \ldots, p_{nn}$ and the functions $f_1, f_2, \ldots, f_n$ are continuous on the open interval I containing the point a. Then, given the n numbers $b_1, b_2, \ldots, b_n$, the system in (24) has a unique solution on the entire interval I that satisfies the n initial conditions

$$x_1(a) = b_1, \quad x_2(a) = b_2, \quad \ldots, \quad x_n(a) = b_n. \tag{25}$$

Thus n initial conditions are needed to determine a solution of a system of n linear first-order equations, and we therefore expect a general solution of such a system to involve n arbitrary constants. For instance, we saw in Example 5 that the second-order linear system

$$2x'' = -6x + 2y,$$
$$y'' = 2x - 2y + 40 \sin 3t,$$

which describes the position functions $x(t)$ and $y(t)$ of Example 1, is equivalent to the system of *four* first-order linear equations in (15). Hence four initial conditions would be needed to determine the subsequent motions of the two masses in Example 1. Typical initial values would be the initial positions $x(0)$ and $y(0)$ and the initial velocities $x'(0)$ and $y'(0)$. On the other hand, we found that the amounts $x(t)$ and $y(t)$ of salt in the two tanks of Example 2 are described by the system

$$20x' = -6x + y,$$
$$20y' = 6x - 3y$$

of *two* first-order linear equations. Hence the two initial values $x(0)$ and $y(0)$ should suffice to determine the solution. Given a higher-order system, we often must transform it into an equivalent first-order system to discover how many initial conditions are needed to determine a unique solution. Theorem 1 tells us that the number of such conditions is precisely the same as the number of equations in the equivalent first-order system.

4.1 Problems

In Problems 1 through 10, transform the given differential equation or system into an equivalent system of first-order differential equations.

1. $x'' + 3x' + 7x = t^2$
2. $x^{(4)} + 6x'' - 3x' + x = \cos 3t$
3. $t^2 x'' + tx' + (t^2 - 1)x = 0$
4. $t^3 x^{(3)} - 2t^2 x'' + 3tx' + 5x = \ln t$
5. $x^{(3)} = (x')^2 + \cos x$
6. $x'' - 5x + 4y = 0, \; y'' + 4x - 5y = 0$
7. $x'' = -\dfrac{kx}{(x^2+y^2)^{3/2}}, \; y'' = -\dfrac{ky}{(x^2+y^2)^{3/2}}$
8. $x'' + 3x' + 4x - 2y = 0, \; y'' + 2y' - 3x + y = \cos t$
9. $x'' = 3x - y + 2z, \; y'' = x + y - 4z, \; z'' = 5x - y - z$
10. $x'' = (1-y)x, \; y'' = (1-x)y$

Use the method of Examples 6, 7, and 8 to find general solutions of the systems in Problems 11 through 20. If initial conditions are given, find the corresponding particular solution. For each problem, use a computer system or graphing calculator to construct a direction field and typical solution curves for the given system.

11. $x' = y, \; y' = -x$
12. $x' = y, \; y' = x$
13. $x' = -2y, \; y' = 2x; \; x(0) = 1, \; y(0) = 0$
14. $x' = 10y, \; y' = -10x; \; x(0) = 3, \; y(0) = 4$
15. $x' = \frac{1}{2}y, \; y' = -8x$
16. $x' = 8y, \; y' = -2x$
17. $x' = y, \; y' = 6x - y; \; x(0) = 1, \; y(0) = 2$
18. $x' = -y, \; y' = 10x - 7y; \; x(0) = 2, \; y(0) = -7$
19. $x' = -y, \; y' = 13x + 4y; \; x(0) = 0, \; y(0) = 3$
20. $x' = y, \; y' = -9x + 6y$

21. **(a)** Calculate $[x(t)]^2 + [y(t)]^2$ to show that the trajectories of the system $x' = y, \; y' = -x$ of Problem 11 are circles. **(b)** Calculate $[x(t)]^2 - [y(t)]^2$ to show that the trajectories of the system $x' = y, \; y' = x$ of Problem 12 are hyperbolas.

22. **(a)** Beginning with the general solution of the system $x' = -2y, \; y' = 2x$ of Problem 13, calculate $x^2 + y^2$ to show that the trajectories are circles. **(b)** Show similarly that the trajectories of the system $x' = \frac{1}{2}y, \; y' = -8x$ of Problem 15 are ellipses with equations of the form $16x^2 + y^2 = C^2$.

23. First solve Eqs. (20) and (21) for e^{-t} and e^{2t} in terms of $x(t), y(t)$, and the constants A and B. Then substitute the results in $(e^{2t})(e^{-t})^2 = 1$ to show that the trajectories of the system $x' = y, \; y' = 2x + y$ in Example 7 satisfy an equation of the form

$$4x^3 - 3xy^2 + y^3 = C \quad \text{(constant)}.$$

Then show that $C = 0$ yields the straight lines $y = -x$ and $y = 2x$ that are visible in Fig. 4.1.8.

24. Derive the equations

$$\begin{aligned} m_1 x_1'' &= -(k_1 + k_2)x_1 + k_2 x_2, \\ m_2 x_2'' &= k_2 x_1 - (k_2 + k_3)x_2 \end{aligned}$$

for the displacements (from equilibrium) of the two masses shown in Fig. 4.1.11.

FIGURE 4.1.11. The system of Problem 24.

25. Two particles each of mass m are attached to a string under (constant) tension T, as indicated in Fig. 4.1.12. Assume that the particles oscillate vertically (that is, parallel to the y-axis) with amplitudes so small that the sines of the angles shown are accurately approximated by their tangents. Show that the displacements y_1 and y_2 satisfy the equations

$$ky_1'' = -2y_1 + y_2, \quad ky_2'' = y_1 - 2y_2$$

where $k = mL/T$.

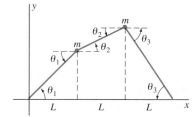

FIGURE 4.1.12. The mechanical system of Problem 25.

26. Three 100-gal fermentation vats are connected as indicated in Fig. 4.1.13, and the mixtures in each tank are kept uniform by stirring. Denote by $x_i(t)$ the amount (in pounds) of alcohol in tank T_i at time t ($i = 1, 2, 3$). Suppose that the mixture circulates between the tanks at the rate of 10 gal/min. Derive the equations

$$\begin{aligned} 10x_1' &= -x_1 \qquad\;\; + x_3 \\ 10x_2' &= \;\; x_1 - x_2 \\ 10x_3' &= \qquad\;\; x_2 - x_3. \end{aligned}$$

FIGURE 4.1.13. The fermentation tanks of Problem 26.

27. Set up a system of first-order differential equations for the indicated currents I_1 and I_2 in the electrical circuit of Fig. 4.1.14, which shows an inductor, two resistors, and a generator which supplies an alternating voltage drop of $E(t) = 100 \sin 60t$ V in the direction of the current I_1.

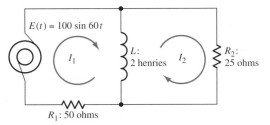

FIGURE 4.1.14. The electrical circuit of Problem 27.

28. Repeat Problem 27, except with the generator replaced with a battery supplying an emf of 100 V and with the inductor replaced with a 1-millifarad (mF) capacitor.

29. A particle of mass m moves in the plane with coordinates $(x(t), y(t))$ under the influence of a force that is directed toward the origin and has magnitude $k/(x^2 + y^2)$—an inverse-square central force field. Show that

$$mx'' = -\frac{kx}{r^3} \quad \text{and} \quad my'' = -\frac{ky}{r^3},$$

where $r = \sqrt{x^2 + y^2}$.

30. Suppose that a projectile of mass m moves in a vertical plane in the atmosphere near the surface of the earth under the influence of two forces: a downward gravitational force of magnitude mg, and a resistive force $\mathbf{F}_R$ that is directed opposite to the velocity vector $\mathbf{v}$ and has magnitude kv^2 (where $v = |\mathbf{v}|$ is the speed of the projectile; see Fig. 4.1.15). Show that the equations of motion of the projectile are

$$mx'' = -kvx', \quad my'' = -kvy' - mg,$$

where $v = \sqrt{(x')^2 + (y')^2}$.

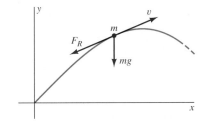

FIGURE 4.1.15. The trajectory of the projectile of Problem 30.

31. Suppose that a particle with mass m and electrical charge q moves in the xy-plane under the influence of the magnetic field $\mathbf{B} = B\mathbf{k}$ (thus a uniform field parallel to the z-axis), so the force on the particle is $\mathbf{F} = q\mathbf{v} \times \mathbf{B}$ if its velocity is $\mathbf{v}$. Show that the equations of motion of the particle are

$$mx'' = +qBy', \quad my'' = -qBx'.$$

4.1 Application   Gravitation and Kepler's Laws of Planetary Motion

Around the turn of the 17th century, Johannes Kepler analyzed a lifetime of planetary observations by the astronomer Tycho Brahe. Kepler concluded that the motion of the planets around the sun is described by the following three propositions, now known as **Kepler's laws of planetary motion:**

1. The orbit of each planet is an ellipse with the sun at one focus.
2. The radius vector from the sun to each planet sweeps out area at a constant rate.
3. The square of the planet's period of revolution is proportional to the cube of the major semiaxis of its elliptical orbit.

In his *Principia Mathematica* (1687) Isaac Newton deduced the inverse-square law of gravitation from Kepler's laws. In this application we lead you (in the opposite direction) through a derivation of Kepler's first two laws from Newton's law of gravitation.

Assume that the sun is located at the origin in the plane of motion of a planet, and write the position vector of the planet in the form

$$\mathbf{r}(t) = (x(t), y(t)) = x\mathbf{i} + y\mathbf{j}, \tag{1}$$

where $\mathbf{i} = (1, 0)$ and $\mathbf{j} = (0, 1)$ denote the unit vectors in the positive x- and y-directions. Then the inverse-square law of gravitation implies (Problem 29) that the acceleration vector $\mathbf{r}''(t)$ of the planet is given by

$$\mathbf{r}'' = -\frac{k\mathbf{r}}{r^3}, \tag{2}$$

where $r = \sqrt{x^2 + y^2}$ is the distance from the sun to the planet. If the polar co-ordinates of the planet at time t are $(r(t), \theta(t))$, then the radial and transverse unit vectors shown in Fig. 4.1.16 are given by

$$\mathbf{u}_r = \mathbf{i}\cos\theta + \mathbf{j}\sin\theta \quad \text{and} \quad \mathbf{u}_\theta = -\mathbf{i}\sin\theta + \mathbf{j}\cos\theta. \tag{3}$$

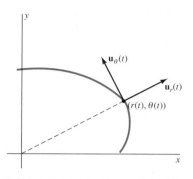

FIGURE 4.1.16. The radial and transverse unit vectors $\mathbf{u}_r$ and $\mathbf{u}_\theta$.

The radial unit vector $\mathbf{u}_r$ (when located at the planet's position) always points directly away from the origin, so $\mathbf{u}_r = \mathbf{r}/r$, and the transverse unit vector $\mathbf{u}_\theta$ is obtained from $\mathbf{u}_r$ by a 90° counterclockwise rotation.

STEP 1: Differentiate the equations in (3) componentwise to show that

$$\frac{d\mathbf{u}_r}{dt} = \mathbf{u}_\theta \frac{d\theta}{dt} \quad \text{and} \quad \frac{d\mathbf{u}_\theta}{dt} = -\mathbf{u}_r \frac{d\theta}{dt}. \tag{4}$$

STEP 2: Use the equations in (4) to differentiate the planet's position vector $\mathbf{r} = r\mathbf{u}_r$ and thereby show that its velocity vector is given by

$$\mathbf{v} = \frac{d\mathbf{r}}{dt} = \mathbf{u}_r \frac{dr}{dt} + r\frac{d\theta}{dt}\mathbf{u}_\theta. \tag{5}$$

STEP 3: Differentiate again to show that the planet's acceleration vector $\mathbf{a} = d\mathbf{v}/dt$ is given by

$$\mathbf{a} = \left[\frac{d^2r}{dt^2} - r\left(\frac{d\theta}{dt}\right)^2\right]\mathbf{u}_r + \left[\frac{1}{r}\frac{d}{dt}\left(r^2\frac{d\theta}{dt}\right)\right]\mathbf{u}_\theta. \tag{6}$$

STEP 4: The radial and transverse components on the right-hand sides in Eqs. (2) and (6) must agree. Equating the transverse components—that is, the coefficients of $\mathbf{u}_\theta$—we get

$$\frac{1}{r}\frac{d}{dt}\left(r^2\frac{d\theta}{dt}\right) = 0, \tag{7}$$

so it follows that

$$r^2\frac{d\theta}{dt} = h, \tag{8}$$

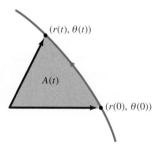

FIGURE 4.1.17. Area swept out by the radius vector.

where h is a constant. Because the polar-coordinate area element—for computation of the area $A(t)$ in Fig. 4.1.17—is given by $dA = \frac{1}{2}r^2 d\theta$, Eq. (8) implies that the derivative $A'(t)$ is *constant*, which is a statement of Kepler's second law.

STEP 5: Equate radial components in (2) and (6) and then use the result in (8) to show that the planet's radial coordinate function $r(t)$ satisfies the second-order differential equation

$$\frac{d^2r}{dt^2} - \frac{h^2}{r^3} = -\frac{k}{r^2}. \tag{9}$$

STEP 6: Although the differential equation in (9) is nonlinear, it can be transformed to a linear equation by means of a simple substitution. For this purpose, assume that the orbit can be written in the polar-coordinate form $r = r(\theta)$, and first use the chain rule and Eq. (8) to show that if $r = 1/z$, then

$$\frac{dr}{dt} = -h\frac{dz}{d\theta}.$$

Differentiate again to deduce from Eq. (9) that the function $z(\theta) = 1/r(\theta)$ satisfies the second-order equation

$$\frac{d^2z}{d\theta^2} + z = \frac{k}{h^2}. \tag{10}$$

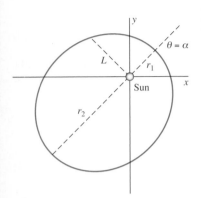

STEP 7: Show that the general solution of Eq. (10) is

$$z(\theta) = A\sin\theta + B\cos\theta + \frac{k}{h^2}. \tag{11}$$

STEP 8: Finally, deduce from Eq. (11) that $r(\theta) = 1/z(\theta)$ is given by

$$r(\theta) = \frac{L}{1 + e\cos(\theta - \alpha)} \tag{12}$$

FIGURE 4.1.18. The elliptical orbit

$$r = \frac{L}{1 + e\cos(\theta - \alpha)}$$

with perihelion distance $r_1 = L/(1 + e)$ and aphelion distance $r_2 = L/(1 - e)$.

with $e = Ch^2/k$, $C\cos\alpha = A$, $C\sin\alpha = B$, and $L = h^2/k$. The polar-coordinate graph of Eq. (12) is a conic section of eccentricity e—an ellipse if $0 \leqq e < 1$, a parabola if $e = 1$, and a hyperbola if $e > 1$—with focus at the origin. Planetary orbits are bounded and therefore are ellipses with eccentricity $e < 1$. As indicated in Fig. 4.1.18, the major axis of the ellipse lies along the radial line $\theta = \alpha$.

STEP 9: Plot some typical elliptical orbits as described by (12) with different eccentricities, sizes, and orientations. In rectangular coordinates you can write

$$x(t) = r(t)\cos t, \quad y(t) = r(t)\sin t, \quad 0 \leqq t \leqq 2\pi$$

FIGURE 4.1.19. The shape of the orbit of Halley's comet.

to plot an elliptical orbit with eccentricity e, semilatus rectum L (Fig. 4.1.18), and rotation angle α. The eccentricity of the earth's orbit is $e \approx 0.0167$, so close to zero that the orbit looks nearly circular (though with the sun off center), and the eccentricities of the other planetary orbits range from 0.0068 for Venus and 0.0933 for Mars to 0.2056 for Mercury and 0.2486 for Pluto. But many comets have highly eccentric orbits, like Halley's comet with $e \approx 0.97$ (Fig. 4.1.19).

4.2 The Method of Elimination

The most elementary approach to linear systems of differential equations involves the elimination of dependent variables by appropriately combining pairs of equations. The object of this procedure is to eliminate dependent variables in succession until there remains only a single equation containing only one dependent variable. This remaining equation will usually be a linear equation of high order and can frequently be solved by the methods of Chapter 3. After its solution has been found, the other dependent variables can be found in turn, using either the original differential equations or those that have appeared in the elimination process.

The **method of elimination** for linear differential systems is similar to the solution of a linear system of algebraic equations by a process of eliminating the unknowns one at a time until only a single equation with a single unknown remains. It is most convenient in the case of manageably small systems: those containing no more than two or three equations. For such systems the method of elimination provides a simple and concrete approach that requires little preliminary theory or formal machinery. But for larger systems of differential equations, as well as for theoretical discussion, the matrix methods of Chapter 5 are preferable.

Example 1 Find the particular solution of the system

$$x' = 4x - 3y, \quad y' = 6x - 7y \tag{1}$$

that satisfies the initial conditions $x(0) = 2$, $y(0) = -1$.

Solution If we solve the second equation in (1) for x, we get

$$x = \tfrac{1}{6}y' + \tfrac{7}{6}y, \tag{2}$$

so that

$$x' = \tfrac{1}{6}y'' + \tfrac{7}{6}y'. \tag{3}$$

We then substitute these expressions for x and x' in the first equation of the system in (1); this yields

$$\tfrac{1}{6}y'' + \tfrac{7}{6}y' = 4\left(\tfrac{1}{6}y' + \tfrac{7}{6}y\right) - 3y,$$

which we simplify to

$$y'' + 3y' - 10y = 0.$$

This second-order linear equation has characteristic equation

$$r^2 + 3r - 10 = (r - 2)(r + 5) = 0,$$

so its general solution is

$$y(t) = c_1 e^{2t} + c_2 e^{-5t}. \tag{4}$$

Next, substitution of (4) in (2) gives

$$x(t) = \tfrac{1}{6}\left(2c_1 e^{2t} - 5c_2 e^{-5t}\right) + \tfrac{7}{6}\left(c_1 e^{2t} + c_2 e^{-5t}\right);$$

that is,

$$x(t) = \tfrac{3}{2}c_1 e^{2t} + \tfrac{1}{3}c_2 e^{-5t}. \tag{5}$$

Thus Eqs. (4) and (5) constitute the general solution of the system in (1).

The given initial conditions imply that

$$x(0) = \tfrac{3}{2}c_1 + \tfrac{1}{3}c_2 = 2$$

and that

$$y(0) = c_1 + c_2 = -1;$$

these equations are readily solved for $c_1 = 2$ and $c_2 = -3$. Hence the desired solution is

$$x(t) = 3e^{2t} - e^{-5t}, \quad y(t) = 2e^{2t} - 3e^{-5t}.$$

FIGURE 4.2.1. Direction field and solution curves for the system $x' = 4x - 3y$, $y' = 6x - 7y$ of Example 1.

Figure 4.2.1 shows this and other typical solution curves parametrized by the equations $x(t) = \tfrac{3}{2}c_1 e^{2t} + \tfrac{1}{3}c_2 e^{-5t}$, $y(t) = c_1 e^{2t} + c_2 e^{-5t}$ with different values of the arbitrary constants c_1 and c_2. We see two families of curves resembling hyperbolas sharing the same pair of (oblique) asymptotes. ∎

Remark: The general solution defined by Eqs. (4) and (5) may be regarded as the pair or vector $(x(t), y(t))$. Recalling the componentwise addition of vectors (and multiplication of vectors by scalars), we can write the general solution in (4) and (5) in the form

$$(x(t), y(t)) = \left(\tfrac{3}{2}c_1 e^{2t} + \tfrac{1}{3}c_2 e^{-5t}, c_1 e^{2t} + c_2 e^{-5t}\right)$$

$$= c_1 \left(\tfrac{3}{2}e^{2t}, e^{2t}\right) + c_2 \left(\tfrac{1}{3}e^{-5t}, e^{-5t}\right).$$

This expression presents the general solution of the system in (1) as a linear combination of the two particular solutions

$$(x_1, y_1) = \left(\tfrac{3}{2}e^{2t}, e^{2t}\right) \quad \text{and} \quad (x_2, y_2) = \left(\tfrac{1}{3}e^{-5t}, e^{-5t}\right). \qquad \blacksquare$$

Polynomial Differential Operators

In Example 1 we used an ad hoc procedure to eliminate one of the independent variables by expressing it in terms of the other. We now describe a systematic elimination procedure. Operator notation is most convenient for these purposes. Recall from Section 3.3 that a **polynomial differential operator** is one of the form

$$L = a_n D^n + a_{n-1} D^{n-1} + \cdots + a_1 D + a_0, \qquad (6)$$

where D denotes differentiation with respect to the independent variable t.

If L_1 and L_2 are two such operators, then their product $L_1 L_2$ is defined this way:

➤ $$L_1 L_2[x] = L_1[L_2 x]. \qquad (7)$$

For instance, if $L_1 = D + a$ and $L_2 = D + b$, then

$$L_1 L_2[x] = (D+a)[(D+b)x] = D(Dx + bx) + a(Dx + bx)$$
$$= [D^2 + (a+b)D + ab]x.$$

This illustrates the fact that two polynomial operators with constant coefficients can be multiplied as if they were ordinary polynomials in the "variable" D. Because the multiplication of such polynomials is commutative, it follows that

$$L_1 L_2[x] = L_2 L_1[x] \qquad (8)$$

if the necessary derivatives of $x(t)$ exist. By contrast, this property of commutativity generally fails for polynomial operators with variable coefficients—see Problems 21 and 22.

Any system of two linear differential equations with constant coefficients can be written in the form

$$\begin{aligned} L_1 x + L_2 y &= f_1(t), \\ L_3 x + L_4 y &= f_2(t), \end{aligned} \qquad (9)$$

where L_1, L_2, L_3, and L_4 are polynomial differential operators (perhaps of different orders) as in Eq. (6), and $f_1(t)$ and $f_2(t)$ are given functions. For instance, the system in (1) (Example 1) can be written in the form

$$
\begin{aligned}
(D - 4)x + \quad\quad 3y &= 0, \\
-6x + (D + 7)y &= 0,
\end{aligned}
\tag{10}
$$

with $L_1 = D - 4$, $L_2 = 3$, $L_3 = -6$, and $L_4 = D + 7$.

To eliminate the dependent variable x from the system in (9), we operate with L_3 on the first equation and with L_1 on the second. Thus we obtain the system

$$
\begin{aligned}
L_3 L_1 x + L_3 L_2 y &= L_3 f_1(t), \\
L_1 L_3 x + L_1 L_4 y &= L_1 f_2(t).
\end{aligned}
\tag{11}
$$

Subtraction of the first from the second of these equations yields the single equation

$$
(L_1 L_4 - L_2 L_3)y = L_1 f_2(t) - L_3 f_1(t)
\tag{12}
$$

in the single dependent variable y. After solving for $y = y(t)$ we can substitute the result into either of the original equations in (9) and then solve for $x = x(t)$.

Alternatively, we could eliminate in like manner the dependent variable y from the original system in (9). If so, we would get the equation

$$
(L_1 L_4 - L_2 L_3)x = L_4 f_1(t) - L_2 f_2(t),
\tag{13}
$$

which can now be solved for $x = x(t)$.

Note that the same operator $L_1 L_4 - L_2 L_3$ appears on the left-hand side in both Eq. (12) and Eq. (13). This is the **operational determinant**

$$
\begin{vmatrix} L_1 & L_2 \\ L_3 & L_4 \end{vmatrix} = L_1 L_4 - L_2 L_3
\tag{14}
$$

of the system in (9). In determinant notation Eqs. (12) and (13) can be rewritten as

$$
\begin{aligned}
\begin{vmatrix} L_1 & L_2 \\ L_3 & L_4 \end{vmatrix} x &= \begin{vmatrix} f_1(t) & L_2 \\ f_2(t) & L_4 \end{vmatrix}, \\[2mm]
\begin{vmatrix} L_1 & L_2 \\ L_3 & L_4 \end{vmatrix} y &= \begin{vmatrix} L_1 & f_1(t) \\ L_3 & f_2(t) \end{vmatrix}.
\end{aligned}
\tag{15}
$$

It is important to note that the determinants on the right-hand side in (15) are evaluated by means of the operators operating on the functions. The equations in (15) are strongly reminiscent of Cramer's rule for the solution of two linear equations in two (algebraic) variables and are thereby easy to remember. Indeed, you can solve a system of two linear differential equations either by carrying out the systematic elimination procedure described here or by directly employing the determinant notation in (15). Either process is especially simple if the system is homogeneous ($f_1(t) \equiv 0$ and $f_2(t) \equiv 0$), because in this case the right-hand sides of the equations in (12), (13), and (15) are zero.

Example 2 Find a general solution of the system

$$
\begin{aligned}
(D-4)x + \quad 3y &= 0, \\
-6x + (D+7)y &= 0.
\end{aligned}
\tag{10}
$$

Solution The operational determinant of this system is

$$
(D-4)(D+7) - 3 \cdot (-6) = D^2 + 3D - 10.
\tag{16}
$$

Hence Eqs. (13) and (12) are

$$
\begin{aligned}
x'' + 3x' - 10x &= 0, \\
y'' + 3y' - 10y &= 0.
\end{aligned}
$$

The characteristic equation of each is

$$
r^2 + 3r - 10 = (r-2)(r+5) = 0,
$$

so their (separate) general solutions are

$$
\begin{aligned}
x(t) &= a_1 e^{2t} + a_2 e^{-5t}, \\
y(t) &= b_1 e^{2t} + b_2 e^{-5t}.
\end{aligned}
\tag{17}
$$

At this point we appear to have *four* arbitrary constants a_1, a_2, b_1, and b_2. But it follows from Theorem 1 in Section 4.1 that the general solution of a system of two first-order equations involves only two arbitrary constants. This apparent difficulty demands a resolution.

The explanation is simple: There must be some hidden relations among our four constants. We can discover them by substituting the solutions in (17) into either of the original equations in (10). On substitution in the first equation, we get

$$
\begin{aligned}
0 &= x' - 4x + 3y \\
&= (2a_1 e^{2t} - 5a_2 e^{-5t}) - 4(a_1 e^{2t} + a_2 e^{-5t}) + 3(b_1 e^{2t} + b_2 e^{-5t});
\end{aligned}
$$

that is,

$$
0 = (-2a_1 + 3b_1)e^{2t} + (-9a_2 + 3b_2)e^{-5t}.
$$

But e^{2t} and e^{-5t} are linearly independent functions, so it follows that $a_1 = \frac{3}{2}b_1$ and $a_2 = \frac{1}{3}b_2$. Therefore, the desired general solution is given by

$$
x(t) = \tfrac{3}{2}b_1 e^{2t} + \tfrac{1}{3}b_2 e^{-5t}, \quad y(t) = b_1 e^{2t} + b_2 e^{-5t}.
$$

Note that this result is in accord with the general solution (Eqs. (4) and (5)) that we obtained by a different method in Example 1. ∎

As illustrated by Example 2, the elimination procedure used to solve a linear system frequently will introduce a number of interdependent constants that may appear to be arbitrary, but actually are not independent. The "extra" constants must then be eliminated by substitution of the proposed general solution into one or more of the original differential equations. The appropriate number of arbitrary constants in a general solution of a linear system is determined by the following proposition:

If the operational determinant in (15) is *not identically zero*, then the number of independent arbitrary constants in a general solution of the system in (9) is equal to the order of its operational determinant—that is, its degree as a polynomial in D.

(For a proof of this fact, see pages 144–150 of E.L. Ince's *Ordinary Differential Equations* (New York: Dover, 1956).) Thus the general solution of the system in (10) of Example 2 involves two arbitrary constants, because its operational determinant $D^2 + 3D - 10$ is of order 2.

If the operational determinant is identically zero, then the system is said to be **degenerate**. A degenerate system may have either no solution or infinitely many independent solutions. For instance, the equations

$$Dx - Dy = 0,$$
$$2Dx - 2Dy = 1$$

with operational determinant zero are obviously inconsistent and thus have no solutions. On the other hand, the equations

$$Dx + Dy = t,$$
$$2Dx + 2Dy = 2t$$

with operational determinant zero are obviously redundant; we can substitute *any* (continuously differentiable) function for $x(t)$ and then integrate to obtain $y(t)$. Roughly speaking, every degenerate system is equivalent to either an inconsistent system or a redundant system.

Although the aforementioned procedures and results are described for the case of a system of two equations, they can be generalized readily to systems of three or more equations. For the system

$$L_{11}x + L_{12}y + L_{13}z = f_1(t),$$
$$L_{21}x + L_{22}y + L_{23}z = f_2(t), \qquad (18)$$
$$L_{31}x + L_{32}y + L_{33}z = f_3(t)$$

of three linear equations, the dependent variable $x(t)$ satisfies the single linear equation

$$\begin{vmatrix} L_{11} & L_{12} & L_{13} \\ L_{21} & L_{22} & L_{23} \\ L_{31} & L_{32} & L_{33} \end{vmatrix} x = \begin{vmatrix} f_1(t) & L_{12} & L_{13} \\ f_2(t) & L_{22} & L_{23} \\ f_3(t) & L_{32} & L_{33} \end{vmatrix} \qquad (19)$$

with analogous equations for $y = y(t)$ and $z = z(t)$. For most systems of more than three equations, however, the method of operational determinants is too tedious to be practical.

Mechanical Vibrations

A mechanical system typically vibrates or oscillates periodically in one or more specific ways. The methods of this section often can be applied to analyze the "natural modes of oscillation" of a given system. Example 3 illustrates this approach.

| **Example 3** | In Example 1 of Section 4.1, we derived the equations |

$$(D^2 + 3)x + \quad (-1)y = 0,$$
$$-2x + (D^2 + 2)y = 0 \tag{20}$$

for the displacements of the two masses in Fig. 4.2.2. Here $f(t) \equiv 0$ because we assume that there is no external force. Find the general solution of the system in (20).

Solution The operational determinant of the system in (20) is

$$(D^2 + 3)(D^2 + 2) - (-1)(-2) = D^4 + 5D^2 + 4 = (D^2 + 1)(D^2 + 4).$$

Hence the equations for $x(t)$ and $y(t)$ are

$$(D^2 + 1)(D^2 + 4)x = 0,$$
$$(D^2 + 1)(D^2 + 4)y = 0. \tag{21}$$

$k_1 = 4 \qquad k_2 = 2$

$m_1 = 2 \qquad m_2 = 1$

$x(t) \qquad\qquad y(t)$

Equilibrium positions

FIGURE 4.2.2. The mass–and–spring system of Example 3.

The characteristic equation $(r^2 + 1)(r^2 + 4) = 0$ has roots i, $-i$, $2i$, and $-2i$. So the general solutions of the equations in (21) are

$$x(t) = a_1 \cos t + a_2 \sin t + b_1 \cos 2t + b_2 \sin 2t,$$
$$y(t) = c_1 \cos t + c_2 \sin t + d_1 \cos 2t + d_2 \sin 2t. \tag{22}$$

Because the operational determinant is of order 4, the general solution should contain four (rather than eight) arbitrary constants. When we substitute $x(t)$ and $y(t)$ from (22) in the first equation in (20), we get

$$0 = x'' + 3x - y$$
$$= (-a_1 \cos t - a_2 \sin t - 4b_1 \cos 2t - 4b_2 \sin 2t)$$
$$+ 3(a_1 \cos t + a_2 \sin t + b_1 \cos 2t + b_2 \sin 2t)$$
$$- (c_1 \sin t + c_2 \sin t + d_1 \cos 2t + d_2 \sin 2t);$$

thus

$$0 = (2a_1 - c_1) \cos t + (2a_2 - c_2) \sin t$$
$$+ (-b_1 - d_1) \cos 2t + (-b_2 - d_2) \sin 2t.$$

Because $\cos t$, $\cos 2t$, $\sin t$, and $\sin 2t$ are linearly independent, it follows that their coefficients in the last equation are zero. Thus

$$c_1 = 2a_1, \quad c_2 = 2a_2, \quad d_1 = -b_1, \quad \text{and} \quad d_2 = -b_2.$$

Therefore

$$x(t) = \quad a_1 \cos t + \quad a_2 \sin t + b_1 \cos 2t + b_2 \sin 2t,$$
$$y(t) = 2a_1 \cos t + 2a_2 \sin t - b_1 \cos 2t - \quad b_2 \sin 2t \tag{23}$$

is the desired general solution of the system in (20). ∎

The equations in (23) describe **free oscillations** of the mass-and-spring system of Fig. 4.2.2—motion subject to *no* external forces. Four initial conditions (typically, initial displacements and velocities) would be required to determine the values of a_1, a_2, b_1, and b_2. The expression

$$(x(t), y(t)) = a_1(\cos t, 2\cos t) + a_2(\sin t, 2\sin t)$$
$$+ b_1(\cos 2t, -\cos 2t) + b_2(\sin 2t, -\sin 2t) \tag{24}$$

then presents the general solution of the system in (20) as a linear combination of four particular solutions. Moreover, the first two of these particular solutions represent physically similar oscillations of the masses, as do the latter two.

Indeed, we can (by the usual trigonometric machinations) write

$$a_1 \cos t + a_2 \sin t = A\cos(t - \alpha),$$
$$2a_1 \cos t + 2a_2 \sin t = 2A\cos(t - \alpha)$$

and

$$b_1 \cos 2t + b_2 \sin 2t = B\cos(2t - \beta),$$
$$-b_1 \cos 2t - b_2 \sin 2t = -B\cos(2t - \beta)$$

with $A = \sqrt{a_1^2 + a_2^2}$, $\tan\alpha = a_2/a_1$, $B = \sqrt{b_1^2 + b_2^2}$, and $\tan\beta = b_2/b_1$. Then Eq. (24) takes the form

$$(x, y) = A(x_1, y_1) + B(x_2, y_2), \tag{25}$$

where the particular solutions

$$(x_1(t), y_1(t)) = (\cos(t - \alpha), 2\cos(t - \alpha)) \tag{26}$$

and

$$(x_2(t), y_2(t)) = (\cos(2t - \beta), -\cos(2t - \beta)) \tag{27}$$

describe the two **natural modes of oscillation** of the mass-and-spring system. Moreover, they exhibit its two (circular) **natural frequencies** $\omega_1 = 1$ and $\omega_2 = 2$.

The linear combination in Eq. (25) represents an arbitrary free oscillation of the mass-and-spring system as a superposition of its two natural modes of oscillation, with the constants A, α, B, and β determined by the initial conditions. Figure

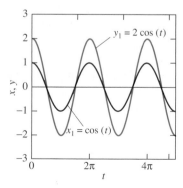

FIGURE 4.2.3. The two masses move in the same direction, each with frequency $\omega_1 = 1$.

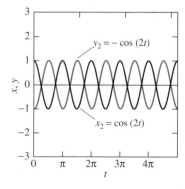

FIGURE 4.2.4. The two masses move in opposite directions with frequency $\omega_2 = 2$.

4.2.3 (where $\alpha = 0$) illustrates the natural mode (x_1, y_1) of Eq. (26), in which the two masses move in synchrony in the same direction with the same frequency of oscillation $\omega_1 = 1$, but with the amplitude of m_2 twice that of m_1 (because $y_1 = 2x_1$). Figure 4.2.4 (where $\beta = 0$) illustrates the natural mode (x_2, y_2) of Eq. (27), in which the masses move in synchrony in opposite directions, with the same frequency $\omega_2 = 2$ and with equal amplitudes of oscillation (because $y_2 = -x_2$).

4.2 Problems

Find general solutions of the linear systems in Problems 1 through 20. If initial conditions are given, find the particular solution that satisfies them. In Problems 1 through 6, use a computer system or graphing calculator to construct a direction field and typical solution curves for the given system.

1. $x' = -x + 3y, \ y' = 2y$
2. $x' = x - 2y, \ y' = 2x - 3y$
3. $x' = -3x + 2y, \ y' = -3x + 4y; \ x(0) = 0, \ y(0) = 2$
4. $x' = 3x - y, \ y' = 5x - 3y; \ x(0) = 1, \ y(0) = -1$
5. $x' = -3x - 4y, \ y' = 2x + y$
6. $x' = x + 9y, \ y' = -2x - 5y; \ x(0) = 3, \ y(0) = 2$
7. $x' = 4x + y + 2t, \ y' = -2x + y$
8. $x' = 2x + y, \ y' = x + 2y - e^{2t}$
9. $x' = 2x - 3y + 2\sin 2t, \ y' = x - 2y - \cos 2t$
10. $x' + 2y' = 4x + 5y, \ 2x' - y' = 3x; \ x(0) = 1, \ y(0) = -1$
11. $2y' - x' = x + 3y + e^t, \ 3x' - 4y' = x - 15y + e^{-t}$
12. $x'' = 6x + 2y, \ y'' = 3x + 7y$
13. $x'' = -5x + 2y, \ y'' = 2x - 8y$
14. $x'' = -4x + \sin t, \ y'' = 4x - 8y$
15. $x'' - 3y' - 2x = 0, \ y'' + 3x' - 2y = 0$
16. $x'' + 13y' - 4x = 6\sin t, \ y'' - 2x' - 9y = 0$
17. $x'' + y'' - 3x' - y' - 2x + 2y = 0,$
    $2x'' + 3y'' - 9x' - 2y' - 4x + 6y = 0$
18. $x' = x + 2y + z, \ y' = 6x - y, \ z' = -x - 2y - z$
19. $x' = 4x - 2y, \ y' = -4x + 4y - 2z, \ z' = -4y + 4z$
20. $x' = y + z + e^{-t}, \ y' = x + z, \ z' = x + y$ (*Suggestion:* Solve the characteristic equation by inspection.)
21. Suppose that $L_1 = a_1 D^2 + b_1 D + c_1$ and $L_2 = a_2 D^2 + b_2 D + c_2$, where the coefficients are all constants, and that $x(t)$ is a twice differentiable function. Verify that $L_1 L_2 x = L_2 L_1 x$.
22. Suppose that $L_1 x = t D x + x$ and that $L_2 x = D x + t x$. Show that $L_1 L_2 x \neq L_2 L_1 x$. Thus linear operators with *variable* coefficients generally do not commute.

Show that the systems in Problems 23 through 25 are degenerate. In each problem determine—by attempting to solve the system—whether it has infinitely many solutions or no solutions.

23. $(D + 2)x + (D + 2)y = e^{-3t}$
    $(D + 3)x + (D + 3)y = e^{-2t}$

24. $(D + 2)x + (D + 2)y = t$
    $(D + 3)x + (D + 3)y = t^2$
25. $(D^2 + 5D + 6)x + D(D + 2)y = 0$
    $(D + 3)x + Dy = 0$

In Problems 26 through 29, first calculate the operational determinant of the given system in order to determine how many arbitrary constants should appear in a general solution. Then attempt to solve the system explicitly so as to find such a general solution.

26. $(D^2 + 1)x + D^2 y = 2e^{-t}$
    $(D^2 - 1)x + D^2 y = 0$
27. $(D^2 + 1)x + (D^2 + 2)y = 2e^{-t}$
    $(D^2 - 1)x + D^2 y = 0$
28. $(D^2 + D)x + D^2 y = 2e^{-t}$
    $(D^2 - 1)x + (D^2 - D)y = 0$
29. $(D^2 + 1)x - D^2 y = 2e^{-t}$
    $(D^2 - 1)x + D^2 y = 0$
30. Suppose that the salt concentration in each of the two brine tanks of Example 2 of Section 4.1 initially $(t = 0)$ is 0.5 lb/gal. Then solve the system in Eq. (5) there to find the amounts $x(t)$ and $y(t)$ of salt in the two tanks at time t.
31. Suppose that the electrical network of Example 3 of Section 4.1 is initially open—no currents are flowing. Assume that it is closed at time $t = 0$; solve the system in Eq. (9) there to find $I_1(t)$ and $I_2(t)$.
32. Repeat Problem 31, except use the electrical network of Problem 27 of Section 4.1.
33. Repeat Problem 31, except use the electrical network of Problem 28 of Section 4.1. Assume that $I_1(0) = 2$ and $Q(0) = 0$, so that at time $t = 0$ there is no charge on the capacitor.
34. Three 100-gal brine tanks are connected as indicated in Fig. 4.1.13 of Section 4.1. Assume that the first tank initially contains 100 lb of salt, whereas the other two are filled with fresh water. Find the amounts of salt in each of the three tanks at time t. (*Suggestion:* Examine the equations to be derived in Problem 26 of Section 4.1.)
35. From Problem 31 of Section 4.1, recall the equations of motion
$$mx'' = qBy', \quad my'' = -qBx'$$
for a particle of mass m and electrical charge q under the influence of the uniform magnetic field $\mathbf{B} = B\mathbf{k}$. Suppose that the initial conditions are $x(0) = r_0$, $y(0) = 0$,

$x'(0) = 0$, and $y'(0) = -\omega r_0$ where $\omega = qB/m$. Show that the trajectory of the particle is a circle of radius r_0.

36. If, in addition to the magnetic field $\mathbf{B} = B\mathbf{k}$, the charged particle of Problem 35 moves with velocity $\mathbf{v}$ under the influence of a uniform electric field $\mathbf{E} = E\mathbf{i}$, then the force acting on it is $\mathbf{F} = q(\mathbf{E} + \mathbf{v} \times \mathbf{B})$. Assume that the particle starts from rest at the origin. Show that its trajectory is the cycloid

$$x = a(1 - \cos \omega t), \quad y = -a(\omega t - \sin \omega t)$$

where $a = E/(\omega B)$ and $\omega = qB/m$. The graph of such a cycloid is shown in Fig. 4.2.5.

FIGURE 4.2.5. The cycloidal path of the particle of Problem 36.

37. In the mass-and-spring system of Example 3, suppose instead that $m_1 = 2$, $m_2 = 0.5$, $k_1 = 75$, and $k_2 = 25$. **(a)** Find the general solution of the equations of motion of the system. In particular, show that its natural frequencies are $\omega_1 = 5$ and $\omega_2 = 5\sqrt{3}$. **(b)** Describe the natural modes of oscillation of the system.

38. Consider the system of two masses and three springs shown in Fig. 4.2.6. Derive the equations of motion

$$m_1 x'' = -(k_1 + k_2)x + \quad k_2 y,$$
$$m_2 y'' = \quad k_2 x - (k_2 + k_3)y.$$

Equilibrium positions

FIGURE 4.2.6. The mechanical system of Problem 38.

In Problems 39 through 46, find the general solution of the system in Problem 38 with the given masses and spring constants. Find the natural frequencies of the mass-and-spring system and describe its natural modes of oscillation. Use a computer system or graphing calculator to illustrate the two natural modes graphically (as in Figs. 4.2.3 and 4.2.4).

39. $m_1 = 4$, $m_2 = 2$, $k_1 = 8$, $k_2 = 4$, $k_3 = 0$
40. $m_1 = 2$, $m_2 = 1$, $k_1 = 100$, $k_2 = 50$, $k_3 = 0$
41. $m_1 = 1$, $m_2 = 1$, $k_1 = 1$, $k_2 = 4$, $k_3 = 1$
42. $m_1 = 1$, $m_2 = 2$, $k_1 = 1$, $k_2 = 2$, $k_3 = 2$
43. $m_1 = 1$, $m_2 = 1$, $k_1 = 1$, $k_2 = 2$, $k_3 = 1$

44. $m_1 = 1$, $m_2 = 1$, $k_1 = 2$, $k_2 = 1$, $k_3 = 2$
45. $m_1 = 1$, $m_2 = 2$, $k_1 = 2$, $k_2 = 4$, $k_3 = 4$
46. $m_1 = 1$, $m_2 = 1$, $k_1 = 4$, $k_2 = 6$, $k_3 = 4$
47. **(a)** For the system shown in Fig. 4.2.7, derive the equations of motion

$$mx'' = -2kx + \quad ky,$$
$$my'' = \quad kx - 2ky + \quad kz,$$
$$mz'' = \quad\quad\quad ky - 2kz.$$

(b) Assume that $m = k = 1$. Show that the natural frequencies of oscillation of the system are

$$\omega_1 = \sqrt{2}, \quad \omega_2 = \sqrt{2 - \sqrt{2}}, \quad \text{and} \quad \omega_3 = \sqrt{2 + \sqrt{2}}.$$

FIGURE 4.2.7. The mechanical system of Problem 47.

48. Suppose that the trajectory $(x(t), y(t))$ of a particle moving in the plane satisfies the initial value problem

$$x'' - 2y' + 3x = 0,$$
$$y'' + 2x' + 3y = 0;$$
$$x(0) = 4, \quad y(0) = x'(0) = y'(0) = 0.$$

Solve this problem. You should obtain

$$x(t) = 3\cos t + \cos 3t,$$
$$y(t) = 3\sin t - \sin 3t.$$

Verify that these equations describe the *hypocycloid* traced by a point $P(x, y)$ fixed on the circumference of a circle of radius $b = 1$ that rolls around inside a circle of radius $a = 4$. If P begins at $A(a, 0)$ when $t = 0$, then the parameter t represents the angle AOC shown in Fig. 4.2.8.

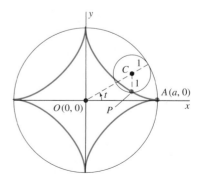

FIGURE 4.2.8. The hypocycloid of Problem 48.

4.2 Application   Computer Algebra Solution of Systems

Computer algebra systems can be used to solve systems as well as single differential equations. For instance, consider the system

$$\frac{dx}{dt} = 4x - 3y, \quad \frac{dy}{dt} = 6x - 7y \tag{1}$$

of Example 1. The *Maple* command

```
dsolve({diff(x(t),t) = 4*x(t) - 3*y(t),
        diff(y(t),t) = 6*x(t) - 7*y(t)}, {x(t),y(t)});
```

yields

$$x(t) = \tfrac{1}{7}(3a_1 - 2a_2)e^{-5t} + \tfrac{1}{7}(-3a_1 + 9a_2)e^{2t},$$
$$y(t) = \tfrac{1}{7}(9a_1 - 6a_2)e^{-5t} + \tfrac{1}{7}(-2a_1 + 6a_2)e^{2t} \tag{2}$$

(after a bit of simplification), and the *Mathematica* command

```
DSolve[ {x'[t]  == 4 x[t] - 3 y[t],
         y'[t]  == 6 x[t] - 7 y[t]}, {x[t],y[t]}, t ]
```

yields

$$x(t) = b_1 e^{-5t} + 3b_2 e^{2t}, \quad y(t) = 3b_1 e^{-5t} + 2b_2 e^{2t}. \tag{3}$$

Is it clear that the general solutions in (2) and (3) are equivalent to each other and to the general solution

$$x(t) = \tfrac{3}{2}c_1 e^{2t} + \tfrac{1}{3}c_2 e^{-5t}, \quad y(t) = c_1 e^{2t} + c_2 e^{-5t} \tag{4}$$

found in the text? What is the relation between the constants a_1, a_2 in (2), the constants b_1, b_2 in (3), and the constants c_1, c_2 in (4)?

Now consider the initial value problem

$$\begin{aligned} x'' &= -3x + y, & x(0) &= 0, & x'(0) &= 6, \\ y'' &= 2x - 2y, & y(0) &= 0, & y'(0) &= 6 \end{aligned} \tag{5}$$

for the mass-and-spring system of Example 3 in the text. Then the *Maple* command

```
dsolve({diff(x(t),t,t) = -3*x(t) + y(t),
        diff(y(t),t,t) = 2*x(t) - 2*y(t),
        x(0) = 0, y(0) = 0, D(x)(0) = 6, D(y)(0) = 6},
        {x(t),y(t)});
```

and the *Mathematica* command

```
DSolve[{x''[t]  == -3 x[t] + y[t],
        y''[t]  == 2 x[t] - 2 y[t],
        x[0] == 0, y[0] == 0, x'[0] == 6, y'[0] == 6},
        {x[t], y[t]}, t ] // ExpToTrig // Simplify
```

both yield the solution

$$x(t) = 4\sin t + \sin 2t, \quad y(t) = 8\sin t - \sin 2t \tag{6}$$

where we see a linear combination of

- an oscillation with frequency 1 in which the two masses move synchronously with the amplitude of motion of the second mass twice that of the first, and
- an oscillation of frequency 2 in which the two masses move in opposite directions with the same amplitude of motion.

You can apply similarly an available computer algebra system to solve Problems 1 through 20 and 39 through 46 in this section (supplying initial conditions for the latter ones if you like).

4.3 Numerical Methods for Systems

We now discuss the numerical approximation of solutions of systems of differential equations. Our goal is to apply the methods of Sections 2.4 through 2.6 to the initial value problem

$$\mathbf{x}' = \mathbf{f}(t, \mathbf{x}), \quad \mathbf{x}(t_0) = \mathbf{x}_0 \tag{1}$$

for a system of m first-order differential equations. In (1) the independent variable is the scalar t, and

$$\mathbf{x} = (x_1, x_2, \ldots, x_m) \quad \text{and} \quad \mathbf{f} = (f_1, f_2, \ldots, f_m)$$

are vector-valued functions. If the component functions of $\mathbf{f}$ and their first-order partial derivatives are all continuous in a neighborhood of the point $(t_0, \mathbf{x}_0)$, then Theorems 3 and 4 of the Appendix guarantee the existence and uniqueness of a solution $\mathbf{x} = \mathbf{x}(t)$ of (1) on some subinterval [of the t-axis] containing t_0. With this assurance we can proceed to discuss the numerical approximation of this solution.

Beginning with step size h, we want to approximate the values of $\mathbf{x}(t)$ at the points $t_1, t_2, t_3, \ldots$, where $t_{n+1} = t_n + h$ for $n \geq 0$. Suppose that we have already computed the *approximations*

$$\mathbf{x}_1, \quad \mathbf{x}_2, \quad \mathbf{x}_3, \quad \ldots, \quad \mathbf{x}_n$$

to the *actual values*

$$\mathbf{x}(t_1), \quad \mathbf{x}(t_2), \quad \mathbf{x}(t_3), \quad \ldots, \quad \mathbf{x}(t_n)$$

of the exact solution of the system in (1). We can then make the step from $\mathbf{x}_n$ to the next approximation $\mathbf{x}_{n+1} \approx \mathbf{x}(t_{n+1})$ by any one of the methods of Sections 2.4 through 2.6. Essentially all that is required is to write the iterative formula of the selected method in the vector notation of the present discussion.

Euler Methods for Systems

For example, the iterative formula of Euler's method for systems is

$$\mathbf{x}_{n+1} = \mathbf{x}_n + h\mathbf{f}(t, \mathbf{x}_n). \tag{2}$$

To examine the case $m = 2$ of a pair of first-order differential equations, let us write

$$\mathbf{x} = \begin{bmatrix} x \\ y \end{bmatrix} \quad \text{and} \quad \mathbf{f} = \begin{bmatrix} f \\ g \end{bmatrix}.$$

Then the initial value problem in (1) is

$$x' = f(t, x, y), \qquad x(t_0) = x_0,$$
$$y' = g(t, x, y), \qquad y(t_0) = y_0, \tag{3}$$

and the scalar components of the vector formula in (2) are

$$x_{n+1} = x_n + hf(t_n, x_n, y_n),$$
$$y_{n+1} = y_n + hg(t_n, x_n, y_n). \tag{4}$$

Note that each iterative formula in (4) has the form of a single Euler iteration, but with y_n inserted like a parameter in the first formula (for x_{n+1}) and with x_n inserted like a parameter in the second formula (for y_{n+1}). The generalization to the system in (3) of each of the other methods in Sections 2.4 through 2.6 follows a similar pattern.

The improved Euler method for systems consists at each step of calculating first the predictor

$$\mathbf{u}_{n+1} = \mathbf{x}_n + h\mathbf{f}(t_n, \mathbf{x}_n) \tag{5}$$

and then the corrector

$$\mathbf{x}_{n+1} = \mathbf{x}_n + \frac{h}{2}[\mathbf{f}(t_n, \mathbf{x}_n) + \mathbf{f}(t_{n+1}, \mathbf{u}_{n+1})]. \tag{6}$$

For the case of the two-dimensional initial value problem in (3), the scalar components of the formulas in (5) and (6) are

$$u_{n+1} = x_n + hf(t_n, x_n, y_n),$$
$$v_{n+1} = y_n + hg(t_n, x_n, y_n) \tag{7}$$

and

$$x_{n+1} = x_n + \frac{h}{2}[f(t_n, x_n, y_n) + f(t_{n+1}, u_{n+1}, v_{n+1})],$$
$$y_{n+1} = y_n + \frac{h}{2}[g(t_n, x_n, y_n) + g(t_{n+1}, u_{n+1}, v_{n+1})]. \tag{8}$$

Example 1 Consider the initial value problem

$$x' = 3x - 2y, \qquad x(0) = 3;$$
$$y' = 5x - 4y, \qquad y(0) = 6. \tag{9}$$

The exact solution of the system in (9) is

$$x(t) = 2e^{-2t} + e^t, \qquad y(t) = 5e^{-2t} + e^t. \tag{10}$$

Here we have $f(x, y) = 3x - 2y$ and $g(x, y) = 5x - 4y$ in (3), so the Euler iterative formulas in (4) are

$$x_{n+1} = x_n + h \cdot (3x_n - 2y_n), \qquad y_{n+1} = y_n + h \cdot (5x_n - 4y_n).$$

With step size $h = 0.1$ we calculate

$$x_1 = 3 + (0.1) \cdot [3 \cdot 3 - 2 \cdot 6] = 2.7,$$
$$y_1 = 6 + (0.1) \cdot [5 \cdot 3 - 4 \cdot 6] = 5.1$$

and

$$x_2 = 2.7 + (0.1) \cdot [3 \cdot (2.7) - 2 \cdot (5.1)] = 2.49,$$
$$y_2 = 5.1 + (0.1) \cdot [5 \cdot (2.7) - 4 \cdot (5.1)] = 4.41.$$

The actual values at $t_2 = 0.2$ given by (10) are $x(0.2) \approx 2.562$ and $y(0.2) \approx 4.573$.

To compute the improved Euler approximations to $x(0.2)$ and $y(0.2)$ with a single step of size $h = 0.2$, we first calculate the predictors

$$u_1 = 3 + (0.2) \cdot [3 \cdot 3 - 2 \cdot 6] = 2.4,$$
$$v_1 = 6 + (0.2) \cdot [5 \cdot 3 - 4 \cdot 6] = 4.2.$$

Then the corrector formulas in (8) yield

$$x_1 = 3 + (0.1) \cdot ([3 \cdot 3 - 2 \cdot 6] + [3 \cdot (2.4) - 2 \cdot (4.2)]) = 2.58,$$
$$y_1 = 6 + (0.1) \cdot ([5 \cdot 3 - 4 \cdot 6] + [5 \cdot (2.4) - 4 \cdot (4.2)]) = 4.62.$$

As we would expect, a single improved Euler step gives better accuracy than two ordinary Euler steps. ∎

The Runge–Kutta Method and Second-Order Equations

The vector version of the iterative formula for the Runge–Kutta method is

$$\mathbf{x}_{n+1} = \mathbf{x}_n + \frac{h}{6}(\mathbf{k}_1 + 2\mathbf{k}_2 + 2\mathbf{k}_3 + \mathbf{k}_4) \tag{11}$$

where the vectors $\mathbf{k}_1$, $\mathbf{k}_2$, $\mathbf{k}_3$, and $\mathbf{k}_4$ are defined (by analogy with Eqs. (5a)–(5d) of Section 2.6) as follows:

$$\begin{aligned}
\mathbf{k}_1 &= \mathbf{f}(t_n, \mathbf{x}_n), \\
\mathbf{k}_2 &= \mathbf{f}\left(t_n + \tfrac{1}{2}h, \mathbf{x}_n + \tfrac{1}{2}h\mathbf{k}_1\right), \\
\mathbf{k}_3 &= \mathbf{f}\left(t_n + \tfrac{1}{2}h, \mathbf{x}_n + \tfrac{1}{2}h\mathbf{k}_2\right), \\
\mathbf{k}_4 &= \mathbf{f}(t_n + h, \mathbf{x}_n + h\mathbf{k}_3).
\end{aligned} \tag{12}$$

To describe in scalar notation the Runge–Kutta method for the two-dimensional initial value problem

$$\begin{aligned}
x' &= f(t, x, y), & x(t_0) &= x_0, \\
y' &= g(t, x, y), & y(t_0) &= y_0,
\end{aligned} \tag{3}$$

let us write

$$\mathbf{x} = \begin{bmatrix} x \\ y \end{bmatrix}, \quad \mathbf{f} = \begin{bmatrix} f \\ g \end{bmatrix}, \quad \text{and} \quad \mathbf{k}_i = \begin{bmatrix} F_i \\ G_i \end{bmatrix}.$$

Then the Runge–Kutta iterative formulas for the step from (x_n, y_n) to the next approximation $(x_{n+1}, y_{n+1}) \approx (x(t_{n+1}), y(t_{n+1}))$ are

$$x_{n+1} = x_n + \frac{h}{6}(F_1 + 2F_2 + 2F_3 + F_4),$$

$$y_{n+1} = y_n + \frac{h}{6}(G_1 + 2G_2 + 2G_3 + G_4), \tag{13}$$

where the values F_1, F_2, F_3, and F_4 of the function f are

$$\begin{aligned}
F_1 &= f(t_n, x_n, y_n), \\
F_2 &= f\left(t_n + \tfrac{1}{2}h, x_n + \tfrac{1}{2}hF_1, y_n + \tfrac{1}{2}hG_1\right), \\
F_3 &= f\left(t_n + \tfrac{1}{2}h, x_n + \tfrac{1}{2}hF_2, y_n + \tfrac{1}{2}hG_2\right), \\
F_4 &= f(t_n + h, x_n + hF_3, y_n + hG_3);
\end{aligned} \tag{14}$$

G_1, G_2, G_3, and G_4 are the similarly defined values of the function g.

Perhaps the most common application of the two-dimensional Runge–Kutta method is to the numerical solution of second-order initial value problems of the form

$$\begin{aligned}
x'' &= g(t, x, x'), \\
x(t_0) &= x_0, \quad x'(t_0) = y_0.
\end{aligned} \tag{15}$$

If we introduce the auxiliary variable $y = x'$, then the problem in (15) translates into the two-dimensional first-order problem

$$\begin{aligned}
x' &= y, & x(t_0) &= x_0, \\
y' &= g(t, x, y), & y(t_0) &= y_0.
\end{aligned} \tag{16}$$

This is a problem of the form in (3) with $f(t, x, y) = y$.

If the functions f and g are not too complicated, then it is feasible to carry out manually a reasonable number of steps of the two-dimensional Runge–Kutta method described here. But the first operating electronic computers were constructed (during World War II) specifically to implement methods similar to the Runge–Kutta method for the numerical computation of trajectories of artillery projectiles. The application material for this section lists TI-85 and BASIC versions of Program RK2DIM that can be used with two-dimensional systems.

t	$x = \sin t$	$y = \cos t$
0.5	+0.47943	+0.87758
1.0	+0.84147	+0.54030
1.5	+0.99749	+0.07074
2.0	+0.90930	−0.41615
2.5	+0.59847	−0.80114
3.0	+0.14112	−0.98999
3.5	−0.35078	−0.93646
4.0	−0.75680	−0.65364
4.5	−0.97753	−0.21080
5.0	−0.95892	+0.28366

FIGURE 4.3.1. Runge–Kutta values (with $h = 0.05$) for the problem in Eq. (18).

Example 2 The exact solution of the initial value problem

$$x'' = -x; \quad x(0) = 0, \quad x'(0) = 1 \tag{17}$$

is $x(t) = \sin t$. The substitution $y = x'$ translates (17) into the two-dimensional problem

$$\begin{aligned}
x' &= y, & x(0) &= 0; \\
y' &= -x, & y(0) &= 1,
\end{aligned} \tag{18}$$

which has the form in (3) with $f(t, x, y) = y$ and $g(t, x, y) = -x$. The table in Fig. 4.3.1 shows the results produced for $0 \leq t \leq 5$ (radians) using Program RK2DIM with step size $h = 0.05$. The values shown for $x = \sin t$ and $y = \cos t$ are all accurate to five decimal places. ∎

Example 3	In Example 4 of Section 2.3 we considered a lunar lander that initially is falling freely toward the surface of the moon. Its retrorockets, when fired, provide a deceleration of $T = 4$ m/s^2. We found that a soft touchdown at the lunar surface is achieved by igniting these retrorockets when the lander is at a height of 41,870 meters (just over 26 miles) above the surface and is then descending at the rate of 450 m/s.

Now we want to compute the *descent time* of the lunar lander. Let the distance $x(t)$ of the lander from the center of the moon be measured in meters and measure time t in seconds. According to the analysis in Section 2.3 (where we used $r(t)$ instead of $x(t)$), $x(t)$ satisfies the initial value problem

$$\frac{d^2x}{dt^2} = T - \frac{GM}{x^2} = 4 - \frac{4.9044 \times 10^{12}}{x^2},$$

$$x(0) = R + 41870 = 1{,}781{,}870, \quad x'(0) = -450 \tag{19}$$

where $G \approx 6.6726 \times 10^{-11}$ N·(m/kg)^2 is the universal gravitational constant and $M = 7.35 \times 10^{22}$ kg and $R = 1.74 \times 10^6$ m are the mass and radius of the moon. We seek the value of t when $x(t) = R = 1{,}740{,}000$.

The problem in (19) is equivalent to the first-order system

$$\frac{dx}{dt} = y, \quad x(0) = 1{,}781{,}870;$$

$$\frac{dy}{dx} = 4 - \frac{4.9044 \times 10^{12}}{x^2}, \quad y(0) = -450. \tag{20}$$

The table in Fig. 4.3.2 shows the result of a Runge–Kutta approximation with step size $h = 1$ (the indicated data agreeing with those obtained with step size $h = 2$). Evidently, touchdown on the lunar surface ($x = 1{,}740{,}000$) occurs at some time between $t = 180$ and $t = 190$ seconds. The table in Fig. 4.3.3 shows a second Runge–Kutta approximation with $t(0) = 180$, $x(0) = 1{,}740{,}059$, $y(0) = -16.83$, and $h = 0.1$. Now it is apparent that the lander's time of descent to the lunar surface is very close to 187 seconds; that is, 3 min 7 s. (The final velocity terms in these two tables are positive because the lander would begin to ascend if its retrorockets were not turned off at touchdown.) ∎

t (s)	x (m)	v (m/s)		t (s)	x (m)	v (m/s)
0	1,781,870	−450.00		180	1,740,059	−16.83
20	1,773,360	−401.04		181	1,740,044	−14.45
40	1,765,826	−352.37		182	1,740,030	−12.07
60	1,759,264	−303.95		183	1,740,019	−9.69
80	1,753,667	−255.74		184	1,740,011	−7.31
100	1,749,033	−207.73		185	1,740,005	−4.93
120	1,745,357	−159.86		186	1,740,001	−2.55
140	1,742,637	−112.11		187	1,740,000	−0.17
160	1,740,872	−64.45		188	1,740,001	2.21
180	1,740,059	−16.83		189	1,740,004	4.59
200	1,740,199	30.77		190	1,740,010	6.97

FIGURE 4.3.2. The lander's descent to the lunar surface.

FIGURE 4.3.3. Focusing on the lunar lander's soft touchdown.

Higher-Order Systems

As we saw in Section 4.1, any system of higher-order differential equations can be replaced with an equivalent system of first-order differential equations. For example, consider the system

$$x'' = F(t, x, y, x', y'),$$
$$y'' = G(t, x, y, x', y') \tag{21}$$

of second-order equations. If we substitute

$$x = x_1, \quad y = x_2, \quad x' = x_3 = x_1', \quad y' = x_4 = x_2',$$

then we get the equivalent system

$$x_1' = x_3,$$
$$x_2' = x_4,$$
$$x_3' = F(t, x_1, x_2, x_3, x_4), \tag{22}$$
$$x_4' = G(t, x_1, x_2, x_3, x_4)$$

of four first-order equations in the unknown functions $x_1(t) = x(t)$, $x_2(t) = y(t)$, $x_3(t)$, and $x_4(t)$. It would be a routine (if slightly tedious) matter to write a four-dimensional version of program RK2DIM for the purpose of solving such a system. But in a programming language that accommodates vectors, an n-dimensional Runge–Kutta program is scarcely more complicated than a one-dimensional program. For instance, the application material for this section lists the n-dimensional MATLAB program **rkn** that closely resembles the one-dimensional program **rk** of Fig. 2.6.11.

Example 4 Suppose that a batted ball starts at $x_0 = 0$, $y_0 = 0$ with initial velocity $v_0 = 160$ ft/s and with initial angle of inclination $\theta = 30°$. If air resistance is ignored, we find by the elementary methods of Section 1.2 that the baseball travels a [horizontal] distance of $400\sqrt{3}$ ft (approximately 693 ft) in 5 s before striking the ground. Now suppose that in addition to a downward gravitational acceleration ($g = 32$ ft/s^2), the baseball experiences an acceleration due to air resistance of $(0.0025)v^2$ feet per second per second, directed opposite to its instantaneous direction of motion. Determine how far the baseball will travel horizontally under these conditions.

Solution According to Problem 30 of Section 4.1, the equations of motion of the baseball are

$$\frac{d^2x}{dt^2} = -cv\frac{dx}{dt}, \quad \frac{d^2y}{dt^2} = -cv\frac{dy}{dt} - g \tag{23}$$

where $v = \sqrt{(x')^2 + (y')^2}$ is the speed of the ball, and where $c = 0.0025$ and $g = 32$ in fps units. We convert to a first-order system as in (22) and thereby obtain the system

$$x_1' = x_3,$$
$$x_2' = x_4,$$
$$x_3' = -cx_3\sqrt{x_3^2 + x_4^2}, \tag{24}$$
$$x_4' = -cx_4\sqrt{x_3^2 + x_4^2} - g$$

of four first-order differential equations with

$$x_1(0) = x_2(0) = 0,$$
$$x_3(0) = 80\sqrt{3}, \quad x_4(0) = 80. \tag{25}$$

Note that $x_3(t)$ and $x_4(t)$ are simply the x- and y-components of the baseball's velocity vector, so $v = \sqrt{x_3^2 + x_4^2}$. We proceed to apply the Runge–Kutta method to investigate the motion of the batted baseball described by the initial value problem in (24) and (25), first taking $c = 0$ to ignore air resistance and then using $c = 0.0025$ to take air resistance into account.

WITHOUT AIR RESISTANCE: Figure 4.3.4 shows the numerical results obtained when a Runge–Kutta program such as **rkn** is applied with step size $h = 0.1$ and with $c = 0$ (no air resistance). For convenience in interpreting the results, the printed output at each selected step consists of the horizontal and vertical coordinates x and y of the baseball, its velocity v, and the angle of inclination α of its velocity vector (in degrees measured from the horizontal). These results agree with the exact solution when $c = 0$. The ball travels a horizontal distance of $400\sqrt{3} \approx 692.82$ ft in exactly 5 s, having reached a maximum height of 100 ft after 2.5 s. Note also that the ball strikes the ground at the same angle and with the same speed as its initial angle and speed.

t	x	y	v	α
0.0	0.00	0.00	160.00	+30
0.5	69.28	36.00	152.63	+25
1.0	138.56	64.00	146.64	+19
1.5	207.85	84.00	142.21	+13
2.0	277.13	96.00	139.48	+7
2.5	346.41	100.00	138.56	+0
3.0	415.69	96.00	139.48	−7
3.5	484.97	84.00	142.21	−13
4.0	554.26	64.00	146.64	−19
4.5	623.54	36.00	152.63	−25
5.0	692.82	0.00	160.00	−30

FIGURE 4.3.4. The batted baseball with no air resistance ($c = 0$).

t	x	y	v	α
0.0	0.00	0.00	160.00	+30
0.5	63.25	32.74	127.18	+24
1.0	117.11	53.20	104.86	+17
1.5	164.32	63.60	89.72	+8
2.0	206.48	65.30	80.17	−3
2.5	244.61	59.22	75.22	−15
3.0	279.29	46.05	73.99	−27
3.5	310.91	26.41	75.47	−37
4.0	339.67	0.91	78.66	−46

FIGURE 4.3.5. The batted baseball with air resistance ($c = 0.0025$).

WITH AIR RESISTANCE: Figure 4.3.5 shows the results obtained with the fairly realistic value of $c = 0.0025$ for the air resistance for a batted baseball. To within a hundredth of a foot in either direction, the same results are obtained with step sizes $h = 0.05$ and $h = 0.025$. We now see that with air resistance the ball travels a distance well under 400 ft in just over 4 s. The more refined data in Fig. 4.3.6 show that the ball travels horizontally only about 340 ft and that its maximum height is only about 66 ft. As illustrated in Fig. 4.3.7, air resistance has converted a massive home run into a routine fly ball (if hit straightaway to center field). Note also that when the ball strikes the ground, it has slightly under *half* its initial speed (only about 79 ft/s) and is falling at a steeper angle (about 46°). Every baseball fan has observed empirically these aspects of the trajectory of a fly ball.

t	x	y	v	α	
1.5	164.32	63.60	89.72	+8	
1.6	173.11	64.60	87.40	+5	
1.7	181.72	65.26	85.29	+3	
1.8	190.15	65.60	83.39	+1	← Apex
1.9	198.40	65.61	81.68	−1	
2.0	206.48	65.30	80.17	−3	
⋮	⋮	⋮	⋮	⋮	
3.8	328.50	11.77	77.24	−42	
3.9	334.14	6.45	77.93	−44	
4.0	339.67	0.91	78.66	−46	
4.1	345.10	−4.84	79.43	−47	← Impact
4.2	350.41	−10.79	80.22	−49	

FIGURE 4.3.6. The batted ball's apex and its impact with the ground.

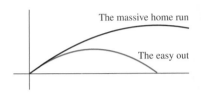

FIGURE 4.3.7. An "easy out" or a home run?

Variable Step Size Methods

The Runge–Kutta method for a large system requires an appreciable amount of computational labor, even when a computer is employed. Therefore, just as the step size h should not be so large that the resulting error in the solution is unacceptable, h ought not to be so small that too many steps are needed, hence requiring an unacceptable amount of computation. Thus the practical numerical solution of differential equations involves a tradeoff between accuracy and efficiency.

To facilitate this tradeoff, modern *variable step size methods* vary the step size h as the solution process proceeds. Large steps are taken in regions where the dependent variables are changing slowly; smaller steps are taken when these variables are changing rapidly, in order to prevent large errors.

An *adaptable* or *variable step size* Runge–Kutta method employs both a pre-assigned minimum error tolerance *MinTol* and a maximum error tolerance *MaxTol* to attempt to ensure that the error made in the typical step from $\mathbf{x}_n$ to $\mathbf{x}_{n+1}$ is neither too large (and hence inaccurate) nor too small (and hence inefficient). A fairly simple scheme for doing this may be outlined as follows:

- Having reached $\mathbf{x}_n$ with a Runge–Kutta step of length $t_n - t_{n-1} = h$, let $\mathbf{x}^{(1)}$ denote the result of a further Runge–Kutta step of length h and let $\mathbf{x}^{(2)}$ denote the result of *two* successive Runge–Kutta steps each of length $h/2$.
- On the grounds that $\mathbf{x}^{(2)}$ should be a more accurate approximation to $\mathbf{x}(t_n + h)$ than is $\mathbf{x}^{(1)}$, take

$$Err = |\mathbf{x}^{(1)} - \mathbf{x}^{(2)}|$$

  as an estimate of the error in $\mathbf{x}^{(1)}$.
- If $MinTol \leq Err \leq MaxTol$, then let $\mathbf{x}_{n+1} = \mathbf{x}^{(1)}$, $t_{n+1} = t_n + h$, and proceed to the next step.
- If $Err < MinTol$, then the error is too small! Hence let $\mathbf{x}_{n+1} = \mathbf{x}^{(1)}$, $t_{n+1} = t_n + h$, but *double* the step size to $2h$ before making the next step.
- If $Err > MaxTol$, then the error is too large. Hence reject $\mathbf{x}^{(1)}$ and start afresh at $\mathbf{x}_n$ with the *halved* step size $h/2$.

The detailed implementation of such a scheme can be complicated. For a much more complete but readable discussion of adaptive Runge–Kutta methods, see Section 15.2 of William H. Press et al., *Numerical Recipes: The Art of Scientific Computing* (New York: Cambridge University Press, 1986).

Several widely available scientific computing packages (such as *Maple, Mathematica*, and MATLAB) include sophisticated variable step size programs that will accommodate an essentially arbitrary number of simultaneous differential equations. Such a general-purpose program might be used, for example, to model numerically the major components of the solar system: the sun and the nine (known) major planets. If m_i denotes the mass and $\mathbf{r}_i = (x_i, y_i, z_i)$ denotes the position vector of the ith one of these 10 bodies, then—by Newton's laws—the equation of motion of m_i is

$$m_i \mathbf{r}_i'' = \sum_{j \neq i} \frac{G m_i m_j}{(r_{ij})^3} (\mathbf{r}_j - \mathbf{r}_i), \tag{26}$$

where $r_{ij} = |\mathbf{r}_j - \mathbf{r}_i|$ denotes the distance between m_i and m_j. For each $i = 1$, $2, \ldots, 10$, the summation in Eq. (26) is over all values of $j \neq i$ from 1 to 10. The 10 vector equations in (26) constitute a system of 30 second-order scalar equations, and the equivalent first-order system consists of 60 differential equations in the coordinates and velocity components of the 10 major bodies in the solar system. Mathematical models that involve this many (or more) differential equations—and that require sophisticated software and hardware for their numerical analysis—are quite common in science, engineering, and applied technology.

Earth–Moon Satellite Orbits

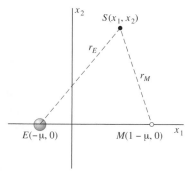

FIGURE 4.3.8. The Earth–Moon center-of-mass coordinate system.

For an example of a program whose efficient solution requires adaptive step size methods, we consider an Apollo satellite in orbit about the Earth E and Moon M. Figure 4.3.8 shows an $x_1 x_2$-coordinate system whose origin lies at the center of mass of the Earth and the Moon and which rotates at the rate of one revolution per "moon month" of approximately $\tau = 27.32$ days, so the Earth and Moon remain fixed in their positions on the x_1-axis. If we take as unit distance the distance (about 384,000 kilometers, assumed constant) between the Earth and Moon centers, then their coordinates are $E(-\mu, 0)$ and $M(1 - \mu, 0)$, where $\mu = m_M / (m_E + m_M)$ in terms of the Earth mass m_E and Moon mass m_M. If we take the total mass $m_E + m_M$ as the unit of mass and $\tau/(2\pi) \approx 4.35$ days as the unit of time, then the gravitational constant is $G = 1$ in Eq. (26), and the equations of motion of the satellite position $S(x_1, x_2)$ are

$$x_1'' = x_1 + 2x_2' - \frac{(1 - \mu)(x_1 + \mu)}{(r_E)^3} - \frac{\mu(x_1 - 1 + \mu)}{(r_M)^3},$$

$$x_2'' = x_2 - 2x_1' - \frac{(1 - \mu)x_2}{(r_E)^3} - \frac{\mu x_2}{(r_M)^3}, \tag{27}$$

where r_E and r_M denote the satellite's distance to the Earth and Moon (indicated in Fig. 4.3.8). The initial two terms on the right-hand side of each equation result from the rotation of the coordinate system. In the system of units described here, the lunar mass is approximately $m_M = 0.012277471$. The second-order system in (27) can be converted to an equivalent first-order system (of four differential equations) by substituting

$$x_1' = x_3, \quad x_2' = x_4, \quad \text{so that} \quad x_1'' = x_3', \quad x_2'' = x_4'.$$

Suppose that the satellite initially is in a clockwise circular orbit of radius about 2400 kilometers about the Moon. At its farthest point from the Earth ($x_1 = 0.994$) it is "launched" into Earth–Moon orbit with initial velocity v_0. The corresponding initial conditions are

$$x_1(0) = 0.994, \quad x_2(0) = 0, \quad x_3(0) = 0, \quad x_4(0) = -v_0.$$

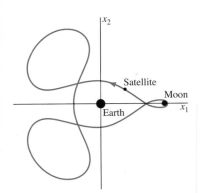

FIGURE 4.3.9. Apollo Moon–Earth bus orbit with insertion velocity $v_0 = 7476$ km/h.

An adaptive step size method (**ode45**) in the MATLAB software system was used to solve numerically the system in (27). The orbits in Figs. 4.3.9 and 4.3.10 were obtained with

$$v_0 = 2.031732629557 \quad \text{and} \quad v_0 = 2.001585106379,$$

respectively. [In the system of units used here, the unit of velocity is approximately 3680 km/h.] In each case a closed but multilooped periodic trajectory about the Earth and the Moon—a so-called bus orbit—is obtained, but a relatively small change in the initial velocity changes the number of loops! For more information, see NASA Contractor Report CR-61139, "Study of the Methods for the Numerical Solution of Ordinary Differential Equations," prepared by O. B. Francis, Jr. et al. for the NASA–George C. Marshall Space Flight Center, June 7, 1966.

So-called Moon–Earth "bus orbits" are periodic—that is, are closed trajectories traversed repeatedly by the satellite—only in a rotating $x_1 x_2$-coordinate system as discussed above. The satellite of Fig. 4.3.9 traverses its closed orbit and returns to rendezvous with the Moon about 48.4 days after its insertion into orbit. Figures 4.3.11 and 4.3.12 illustrate the motion of the same satellite—but in an ordinary nonrotating xy-coordinate system centered at the Earth, in which the Moon encircles the Earth counterclockwise in a near-circular orbit, completing one revolution in about 27.3 days. The Moon starts at point S, and after 48.4 days it has completed a bit over 1.75 revolutions about the Earth and reaches the point R at which its rendezvous with the satellite occurs. Figure 4.3.11 shows the positions of Moon and satellite a day and a half after the satellite's insertion into its orbit, each traveling in a generally counterclockwise direction around the Earth. Figure 4.3.12 shows their positions a day and a half before their rendezvous at point R, the satellite meanwhile having encircled the Earth about 2.5 times in an orbit that (in the indicated xy-coordinate system) appears to resemble a slowly varying ellipse.

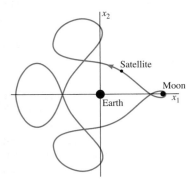

FIGURE 4.3.10. Apollo Moon–Earth bus orbit with insertion velocity $v_0 = 7365$ km/h.

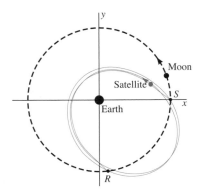

FIGURE 4.3.11. The moon and satellite in a nonrotating coordinate system, 1.5 days after orbital insertion of the satellite at starting point S.

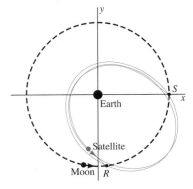

FIGURE 4.3.12. The moon and satellite in a nonrotating coordinate system, 1.5 days before their rendezvous at point R.

4.3 Problems

A hand-held calculator will suffice for Problems 1 through 8. In each problem an initial value problem and its exact solution are given. Approximate the values of $x(0.2)$ and $y(0.2)$ in three ways: (a) by the Euler method with two steps of size $h = 0.1$; (b) by the improved Euler method with a single step of size $h = 0.2$; and (c) by the Runge–Kutta method with a single step of size $h = 0.2$. Compare the approximate values with the actual values $x(0.2)$ and $y(0.2)$.

1. $x' = x + 2y, x(0) = 0,$
   $y' = 2x + y, y(0) = 2;$
   $x(t) = e^{3t} - e^{-t}, y(t) = e^{3t} + e^{-t}$
2. $x' = 2x + 3y, x(0) = 1,$
   $y' = 2x + y, y(0) = -1;$
   $x(t) = e^{-t}, y(t) = -e^{-t}$
3. $x' = 3x + 4y, x(0) = 1,$
   $y' = 3x + 2y, y(0) = 1;$
   $x(t) = \frac{1}{7}(8e^{6t} - e^{-t}), y(t) = \frac{1}{7}(6e^{6t} + e^{-t})$
4. $x' = 9x + 5y, x(0) = 1,$
   $y' = -6x - 2y, y(0) = 0;$
   $x(t) = -5e^{3t} + 6e^{4t}, y(t) = 6e^{3t} - 6e^{4t}$
5. $x' = 2x - 5y, x(0) = 2,$
   $y' = 4x - 2y, y(0) = 3;$
   $x(t) = 2\cos 4t - \frac{11}{4}\sin 4t, y(t) = 3\cos 4t + \frac{1}{2}\sin 4t$
6. $x' = x - 2y, x(0) = 0,$
   $y' = 2x + y, y(0) = 4;$
   $x(t) = -4e^t \sin 2t, y(t) = 4e^t \cos 2t$
7. $x' = 3x - y, x(0) = 2,$
   $y' = x + y, y(0) = 1;$
   $x(t) = (t + 2)e^{2t}, y(t) = (t + 1)e^{2t}$
8. $x' = 5x - 9y, x(0) = 0,$
   $y' = 2x - y, y(0) = -1;$
   $x(t) = 3e^{2t} \sin 3t, y(t) = e^{2t}(\sin 3t - \cos 3t)$

A computer will be required for the remaining problems in this section. In Problems 9 through 12, an initial value problem and its exact solution are given. In each of these four problems, use the Runge–Kutta method with step sizes $h = 0.1$ and $h = 0.05$ to approximate to five decimal places the values $x(1)$ and $y(1)$. Compare the approximations with the actual values.

9. $x' = 2x - y, \quad x(0) = 1,$
   $y' = x + 2y, \quad y(0) = 0;$
   $x(t) = e^{2t} \cos t, \quad y(t) = e^{2t} \sin t$
10. $x' = x + 2y, \quad x(0) = 0,$
    $y' = x + e^{-t}, \quad y(0) = 0;$
    $x(t) = \frac{1}{9}(2e^{2t} - 2e^{-t} + 6te^{-t}),$
    $y(t) = \frac{1}{9}(e^{2t} - e^{-t} + 6te^{-t})$
11. $x' = -x - y - (1 + t^3)e^{-t}, \quad x(0) = 0,$
    $y' = -x - y - (t - 3t^2)e^{-t}, \quad y(0) = 1;$
    $x(t) = e^{-t}(\sin t - t), \quad y(t) = e^{-t}(\cos t + t^3)$
12. $x'' + x = \sin t, \quad x(0) = 0;$
    $x(t) = \frac{1}{2}(\sin t - t \cos t)$
13. Suppose that a crossbow bolt is shot straight upward with initial velocity 288 ft/s. If its deceleration due to air resistance is $(0.04)v$, then its height $x(t)$ satisfies the initial

value problem

$$x'' = -32 - (0.04)x'; \quad x(0) = 0, \quad x'(0) = 288.$$

Find the maximum height that the bolt attains and the time required for it to reach this height.

14. Repeat Problem 13, but assume instead that the deceleration of the bolt due to air resistance is $(0.0002)v^2$.
15. Suppose that a projectile is fired straight upward with initial velocity v_0 from the surface of the earth. If air resistance is not a factor, then its height $x(t)$ at time t satisfies the initial value problem

$$\frac{d^2x}{dt^2} = -\frac{gR^2}{(x + R)^2}; \quad x(0) = 0, \quad x'(0) = v_0.$$

Use the values $g = 32.15$ ft/s$^2 \approx 0.006089$ mi/s^2 for the gravitational acceleration of the earth at its surface and $R = 3960$ mi as the radius of the earth. If $v_0 = 1$ mi/s, find the maximum height attained by the projectile and its time of ascent to this height.

Problems 16 through 18 deal with the batted baseball of Example 4, having initial velocity 160 ft/s and air resistance coefficient $c = 0.0025$.

16. Find the *range*—the horizontal distance the ball travels before it hits the ground—and its total time of flight with initial inclination angles 40°, 45°, and 50°.
17. Find (to the nearest degree) the initial inclination that maximizes the range. If there were no air resistance it would be exactly 45°, but your answer should be less than 45°.
18. Find (to the nearest half degree) the initial inclination angle greater than 45° for which the range is 300 ft.
19. Find the initial velocity of a baseball hit by Babe Ruth (with $c = 0.0025$ and initial inclination 40°) if it hit the bleachers at a point 50 ft high and 500 horizontal feet from home plate.
20. Consider the crossbow bolt of Problem 14, fired with the same initial velocity of 288 ft/s and with the air resistance deceleration $(0.0002)v^2$ directed opposite its direction of motion. Suppose that this bolt is fired from ground level at an initial angle of 45°. Find how high vertically and how far horizontally it goes, and how long it remains in the air.
21. Suppose that an artillery projectile is fired from ground level with initial velocity 3000 ft/s and initial inclination angle 40°. Assume that its air resistance deceleration is $(0.0001)v^2$. (a) What is the range of the projectile and what is its total time of flight? What is its speed at impact with the ground? (b) What is the maximum altitude of the projectile, and when is that altitude attained? (c) You will find that the projectile is still losing speed at the apex of its trajectory. What is the *minimum* speed that it attains during its descent?

4.3 Application Comets and Spacecraft

Figure 4.3.13 lists TI-85 and BASIC versions of the two-dimensional Runge–Kutta program RK2DIM. You should note that it closely parallels the one-dimensional Runge–Kutta program listed in Fig. 2.6.11, with a single line there replaced (where appropriate) with two lines here to calculate a *pair* of x- and y-values or slopes. Note also that the notation used is essentially that of Eqs. (13) and (14) in this section. The first several lines define the functions and initial data needed for Example 1.

Figure 4.3.14 exhibits an n-dimensional MATLAB implementation of the Runge–Kutta method. The MATLAB function **f** defines the vector of right-hand sides of the differential equations in the system $\mathbf{x}' = \mathbf{f}(t, \mathbf{x})$ to be solved. The **rkn** function then takes as input the initial t-value **t**, the column vector **x** of initial x-values, the final t-value **t1**, and the desired number **n** of subintervals. As output it produces the resulting column vector **T** of t-values and the matrix **X** whose rows give the corresponding x-values. For instance, with **f** as indicated in the figure, the MATLAB command

```
[T,X] = rkn(0, [0;1], 5, 50)
```

then generates the data shown in the table of Fig. 4.3.1 (which lists only every fifth value of each variable).

You can use Examples 1 through 3 in this section to test your own implementation of the Runge–Kutta method. Then investigate the comet and spacecraft problems described next. Additional application material at the Web site **www.prenhall.com/edwards** describes additional numerical ODE investigations ranging from batted baseballs to the Apollo orbits shown in Figs. 4.3.9 and 4.3.10.

Your Spacecraft Landing

Your spacecraft is traveling at constant velocity V, approaching a distant earthlike planet with mass M and radius R. When activated, your deceleration system provides a constant thrust T until impact with the surface of the planet. During the period of deceleration, your distance $x(t)$ from the center of the planet satisfies the differential equation

$$\frac{d^2x}{dt^2} = T - \frac{GM}{x^2}, \tag{1}$$

where $G \approx 6.6726 \times 10^{-11}$ N·(m/kg)^2 as in Example 3. Your question is this: At what altitude above the surface should your deceleration system be activated in order to achieve a soft touchdown? For a reasonable problem, you can take

$$M = 5.97 \times 10^{24} \text{ (kg)},$$
$$R = 6.38 \times 10^6 \text{ (m)},$$
$$V = p \times 10^4 \text{ (km/h)},$$
$$T = g + q \text{ (m/s}^2\text{)}$$

where $g = GM/R^2$ is the surface gravitational acceleration of the planet. Choose p to be the smallest nonzero digit and q the next-to-smallest nonzero digit in your ID number. Find the "ignition altitude" accurate to the nearest meter and the resulting "descent time" accurate to the nearest tenth of a second.

TI-85	BASIC	Comment
PROGRAM:RK2DIM	Program RK2DIM	Program title
:F=Y	DEF FN F(T,X,Y) = Y	Define function f
:G=-X	DEF FN G(T,X,Y) = -X	Define function g
:50→N	N = 50	No. of steps
:0→T	T = 0	Initial t
:0→X	X = 0	Initial x
:1→Y	Y = 1	Initial y
:5→T1	T1 = 5	Final t
:(T1-T)/N→H	H = (T1-T)/N	Step size
:For(I,1,N)	FOR I=1 TO N	Begin loop
:T→T0	T0 = T	Save previous t
:X→X0	X0 = X	Save previous x
:Y→Y0	Y0 = Y	Save previous y
:F→F1	F1 = FNF(T,X,Y)	First f-slope
:G→G1	G1 = FNG(T,X,Y)	First g-slope
:T0+H/2→T	T = T0 + H/2	Midpoint t
:X0+H*F1/2→X	X = X0 + H*F1/2	Midpt x-predictor
:Y0+H*G1/2→Y	Y = Y0 + H*G1/2	Midpt y-predictor
:F→F2	F2 = FNF(T,X,Y)	Second f-slope
:G→G2	G2 = FNG(T,X,Y)	Second g-slope
:X0+H*F2/2→X	X = X0 + H*F2/2	Midpt x-predictor
:Y0+H*G2/2→Y	Y = Y0 + H*G2/2	Midpt y-predictor
:F→F3	F3 = FNF(T,X,Y)	Third f-slope
:G→G3	G3 = FNG(T,X,Y)	Third g-slope
:T0+H→T	T = T0 + H	New t
:X0+H*F3→X	X = X0 + H*F3	Endpt x-predictor
:Y0+H*G3→Y	Y = Y0 + H*G3	Endpt y-predictor
:F→F4	F4 = FNF(T,X,Y)	Fourth f-slope
:G→G4	G4 = FNG(T,X,Y)	Fourth g-slope

:(F1+2*F2+2*F3
  +F4)/6→FA
	FA = (F1+2*F2+2*F3
	     +F4)/6
		Average f-slope

:(G1+2*G2+2*G3
  +G4)/6→GA
	GA = (G1+2*G2+2*G3
	     +G4)/6
		Average g-slope

:X0+H*FA→X	X = Y0 + H*FA	x-corrector
:Y0+H*GA→Y	Y = Y0 + H*GA	y-corrector
:Disp T,X,Y	PRINT T,X,Y	Display results
:End	NEXT I	End loop

FIGURE 4.3.13. TI-85 and BASIC two-dimensional Runge–Kutta programs.

```
function xp = f(t,x)
xp = x;
xp(1) = x(2);
xp(2) = -x(1);

function [T,Y] = rkn(t,x,t1,n)
h = (t1 - t)/n;                          % step size
T = t;                                    % initial t
X = x';                                   % initial x-vector
for i = 1:n                               % begin loop
    k1 = f(t,x);                          % first k-vector
    k2 = f(t+h/2,x+h*k1/2);               % second k-vector
    k3 = f(t+h/2,x+h*k2/2);               % third k-vector
    k4 = f(t+h  ,x+h*k3  );               % fourth k-vector
    k  = (k1+2*k2+2*k3+k4)/6;             % average k-vector
    t  = t + h;                           % new t
    x  = x + h*k;                         % new x
    T = [T;t];                            % update t-column
    X = [X;x'];                           % update x-matrix
    end                                   % end loop
```

FIGURE 4.3.14. MATLAB implementation of the Runge–Kutta method.

Kepler's Law of Planetary (or Satellite) Motion

Consider a satellite in elliptical orbit around a planet of mass M, and suppose that physical units are so chosen that $GM = 1$ (where G is the gravitational constant). If the planet is located at the origin in the xy-plane, then the equations of motion of the satellite are

$$\frac{d^2x}{dt^2} = -\frac{x}{(x^2 + y^2)^{3/2}}, \quad \frac{d^2y}{dt^2} = -\frac{y}{(x^2 + y^2)^{3/2}}. \tag{2}$$

Let T denote the period of revolution of the satellite. Kepler's third law says that the *square* of T is proportional to the *cube* of the major semiaxis a of its elliptical orbit. In particular, if $GM = 1$, then

$$T^2 = 4\pi^2 a^3. \tag{3}$$

(For details, see Section 11.6 of Edwards and Penney, *Calculus: Early Transcendentals*, 7th ed. (Upper Saddle River, NJ: Prentice Hall, 2008).) If the satellite's x- and y-components of velocity, $x_3 = x' = x_1'$ and $x_4 = y' = x_2'$, are introduced, then the system in (2) translates into a system of four first-order differential equations having the form of those in Eq. (22) of this section.

(a) Solve this 4×4 system numerically with the initial conditions

$$x(0) = 1, \quad y(0) = 0, \quad x'(0) = 0, \quad y'(0) = 1$$

that correspond theoretically to a circular orbit of radius $a = 1$, so Eq. (3) gives $T = 2\pi$. Is this what you get?

(b) Now solve the system numerically with the initial conditions

$$x(0) = 1, \quad y(0) = 0, \quad x'(0) = 0, \quad y'(0) = \tfrac{1}{2}\sqrt{6}$$

that correspond theoretically to an elliptical orbit with major semiaxis $a = 2$, so Eq. (3) gives $T = 4\pi\sqrt{2}$. Is this what you get?

Halley's Comet

Halley's comet last reached perihelion (its point of closest approach to the sun at the origin) on February 9, 1986. Its position and velocity components at that time were

$$\mathbf{p}_0 = (0.325514, -0.459460, 0.166229) \qquad \text{and}$$
$$\mathbf{v}_0 = (-9.096111, -6.916686, -1.305721)$$

(respectively), with position in AU (astronomical units, in which the unit of distance is the major semiaxis of the earth's orbit) and time in years. In this system, the three-dimensional equations of motion of the comet are

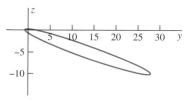

$$\frac{d^2 x}{dt^2} = -\frac{\mu x}{r^3}, \quad \frac{d^2 y}{dt^2} = -\frac{\mu y}{r^3}, \quad \frac{d^2 z}{dt^2} = -\frac{\mu z}{r^3} \qquad (4)$$

where

$$\mu = 4\pi^2 \quad \text{and} \quad r = \sqrt{x^2 + y^2 + z^2}.$$

FIGURE 4.3.15. yz-projection of the orbit of Halley's comet.

Solve the equations in (4) numerically to verify the appearance of the yz-projection of the orbit of Halley's comet shown in Fig. 4.3.15. Plot the xy- and xz-projections as well.

Figure 4.3.16 shows the graph of the distance $r(t)$ of Halley's comet from the sun. Inspection of this graph indicates that Halley's comet reaches a maximum distance (at aphelion) of about 35 AU in a bit less than 40 years and returns to perihelion after about three-quarters of a century. The closer look in Fig. 4.3.17 indicates that the period of revolution of Halley's comet is about 76 years. Use your numerical solution to refine these observations. What is your best estimate of the calendar date of the comet's next perihelion passage?

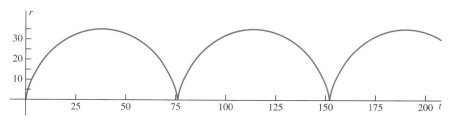

FIGURE 4.3.16. 200-year plot of the distance $r(t)$ of Halley's comet from the sun. Is there a cusp near $t = 75$?

Your Own Comet

The night before your birthday in 2007 you set up your telescope on a nearby mountaintop. It was a clear night, and you had a stroke of luck: At 12:30 A.M. you spotted a new comet. After repeating the observation on successive nights, you were able to calculate its solar system coordinates $\mathbf{p}_0 = (x_0, y_0, z_0)$ and its velocity vector $\mathbf{v}_0 = (v_{x0}, v_{y0}, v_{z0})$ on that first night. Using this information, determine the following:

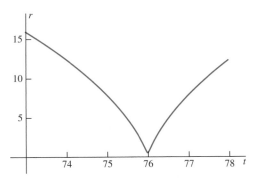

FIGURE 4.3.17. A closer look at Halley's perihelion passage after about 76 years.

- the comet's perihelion (point nearest the sun) and aphelion (point farthest from the sun),
- the comet's velocity at perihelion and at aphelion,
- the comet's period of revolution around the sun, and
- the comet's next two dates of perihelion passage.

Using units of length in AU and time in earth years, the equations of motion of your comet are given in (4). For your personal comet, begin with random initial position and velocity vectors with the same order of magnitude as those of Halley's comet. Repeat the random selection of initial position and velocity vectors, if necessary, until you get a plausible eccentric orbit that ranges well outside the earth's orbit (as most real comets do).

9 Fourier Series Methods

Periodic Functions and Trigonometric Series

$$\mathbf{A}\text{s motivation for the subject of Fourier series, we consider the differential equation}$$

$$\frac{d^2x}{dt^2} + \omega_0^2 x = f(t), \tag{1}$$

which models the behavior of a mass-and-spring system with natural (circular) frequency ω_0, moving under the influence of an external force of magnitude $f(t)$ per unit mass. As we saw in Section 3.6, a particular solution of Eq. (1) can easily be found by the method of undetermined coefficients if $f(t)$ is a simple harmonic function—a sine or cosine function. For instance, the equation

$$\frac{d^2x}{dt^2} + \omega_0^2 x = A \cos \omega t \tag{2}$$

with $\omega^2 \neq \omega_0^2$ has the particular solution

$$x_p(t) = \frac{A}{\omega_0^2 - \omega^2} \cos \omega t, \tag{3}$$

which is readily found by beginning with the trial solution $x_p(t) = a \cos \omega t$.

Now suppose, more generally, that the force function $f(t)$ in Eq. (1) is a linear combination of simple harmonic functions. Then, on the basis of Eq. (3) and the analogous formula with sine in place of cosine, we can apply the principle of superposition to construct a particular solution of Eq. (1). For example, consider the equation

$$\frac{d^2x}{dt^2} + \omega_0^2 x = \sum_{n=1}^{N} A_n \cos \omega_n t, \tag{4}$$

in which ω_0^2 is equal to none of the ω_n^2. Equation (4) has the particular solution

$$x_p(t) = \sum_{n=1}^{N} \frac{A_n}{\omega_0^2 - \omega_n^2} \cos \omega_n t, \tag{5}$$

obtained by adding the solutions given in Eq. (3) corresponding to the N terms on the right-hand side in Eq. (4).

Mechanical (and electrical) systems often involve periodic forcing functions that are not (simply) finite linear combinations of sines and cosines. Nevertheless, as we will soon see, any reasonably nice periodic function $f(t)$ has a representation as an *infinite series* of trigonometric terms. This fact opens the way toward solving Eq. (1) by superposition of trigonometric "building blocks," with the finite sum in Eq. (5) replaced with an infinite series.

DEFINITION Periodic Function

The function $f(t)$ defined for all t is said to be **periodic** provided that there exists a positive number p such that

$$➤ \qquad f(t + p) = f(t) \tag{6}$$

for all t. The number p is then called a **period** of the function f.

Note that the period of a periodic function is not unique; for example, if p is a period of $f(t)$, then so are the numbers $2p$, $3p$, and so on. Indeed, every positive number is a period of any constant function.

If there exists a smallest positive number P such that $f(t)$ is periodic with period P, then we call P *the* period of f. For instance, the period of the functions $g(t) = \cos nt$ and $h(t) = \sin nt$ (where n is a positive integer) is $2\pi/n$ because

$$\cos n \left(t + \frac{2\pi}{n} \right) = \cos(nt + 2\pi) = \cos nt$$

and $\tag{7}$

$$\sin n \left(t + \frac{2\pi}{n} \right) = \sin(nt + 2\pi) = \sin nt.$$

Moreover, 2π itself is a period of the functions $g(t)$ and $h(t)$. Ordinarily we will have no need to refer to the smallest period of a function $f(t)$ and will simply say that $f(t)$ has period p if p is any period of $f(t)$.

In Section 7.5 we saw several examples of piecewise continuous periodic functions. For instance, the square-wave function having the graph shown in Fig. 9.1.1 has period 2π.

Because $g(t) = \cos nt$ and $h(t) = \sin nt$ each have period 2π, any linear combination of sines and cosines of integral multiples of t, such as

$$f(t) = 3 + \cos t - \sin t + 5 \cos 2t + 17 \sin 3t,$$

has period 2π. But every such linear combination is continuous, so the square-wave function cannot be expressed in such manner. In his celebrated treatise *The Analytic Theory of Heat* (1822), the French scientist Joseph Fourier (1768–1830) made the

FIGURE 9.1.1. A square-wave function.

remarkable assertion that every function $f(t)$ with period 2π can be represented by an *infinite* trigonometric series of the form

$$\frac{a_0}{2} + \sum_{n=1}^{\infty}(a_n \cos nt + b_n \sin nt). \tag{8}$$

(The reason for writing $\frac{1}{2}a_0$ rather than a_0 here will appear shortly—when we see that a single formula for a_n thereby includes the case $n = 0$ as well as $n > 0$.) We will see in Section 9.2 that under rather mild restrictions on the function $f(t)$, this is so! An infinite series of the form in (8) is called a *Fourier series*, and the representation of functions by Fourier series is one of the most widely used techniques in applied mathematics, especially for the solution of partial differential equations (see Sections 9.5 through 9.7).

Fourier Series of Period 2π Functions

In this section we will confine our attention to functions of period 2π. We want to determine what the coefficients in the Fourier series in (8) must be if it is to converge to a given function $f(t)$ of period 2π. For this purpose we need the following integrals, in which m and n denote positive integers (Problems 27 through 29):

$$\int_{-\pi}^{\pi} \cos mt \cos nt \, dt = \begin{cases} 0 & \text{if } m \neq n, \\ \pi & \text{if } m = n. \end{cases} \tag{9}$$

$$\int_{-\pi}^{\pi} \sin mt \sin nt \, dt = \begin{cases} 0 & \text{if } m \neq n, \\ \pi & \text{if } m = n. \end{cases} \tag{10}$$

$$\int_{-\pi}^{\pi} \cos mt \sin nt \, dt = 0 \quad \text{for all } m \text{ and } n. \tag{11}$$

These formulas imply that the functions $\cos nt$ and $\sin nt$ for $n = 1, 2, 3, \ldots$ constitute a *mutually orthogonal* set of functions on the interval $[-\pi, \pi]$. Two real-valued functions $u(t)$ and $v(t)$ are said to be **orthogonal** on the interval $[a, b]$ provided that

$$\int_{a}^{b} u(t)v(t) \, dt = 0. \tag{12}$$

(The reason for the word "orthogonal" here is a certain interpretation of functions as vectors with infinitely many values or "components," in which the integral of the product of two functions plays the same role as the dot product of two ordinary vectors; recall that $\mathbf{u} \cdot \mathbf{v} = 0$ if and only if the two vectors are orthogonal.)

Suppose now that the piecewise continuous function $f(t)$ of period 2π has a Fourier series representation

➤
$$f(t) = \frac{a_0}{2} + \sum_{m=1}^{\infty}(a_m \cos mt + b_m \sin mt), \tag{13}$$

in the sense that the infinite series on the right converges to the value $f(t)$ for every t. We assume in addition that, when the infinite series in Eq. (13) is multiplied by any continuous function, the resulting series can be integrated term by term. Then the result of termwise integration of Eq. (13) itself from $t = -\pi$ to $t = \pi$ is

$$\int_{-\pi}^{\pi} f(t)\, dt = \frac{a_0}{2} \int_{-\pi}^{\pi} 1\, dt$$

$$+ \sum_{m=1}^{\infty} \left(a_m \int_{-\pi}^{\pi} \cos mt\, dt \right) + \sum_{m=1}^{\infty} \left(b_m \int_{-\pi}^{\pi} \sin mt\, dt \right) = \pi a_0$$

because all the trigonometric integrals vanish. Hence

$$a_0 = \frac{1}{\pi} \int_{-\pi}^{\pi} f(t)\, dt. \tag{14}$$

If we first multiply each side in Eq. (13) by $\cos nt$ and then integrate termwise, the result is

$$\int_{-\pi}^{\pi} f(t) \cos nt\, dt = \frac{a_0}{2} \int_{-\pi}^{\pi} \cos nt\, dt$$

$$+ \sum_{m=1}^{\infty} \left(a_m \int_{-\pi}^{\pi} \cos mt\, \cos nt\, dt \right) + \sum_{m=1}^{\infty} \left(b_m \int_{-\pi}^{\pi} \sin mt\, \cos nt\, dt \right);$$

it then follows from Eq. (11) that

$$\int_{-\pi}^{\pi} f(t) \cos nt\, dt = \sum_{m=1}^{\infty} a_m \left(\int_{-\pi}^{\pi} \cos mt\, \cos nt\, dt \right). \tag{15}$$

But Eq. (9) says that—of all the integrals (for $m = 1, 2, 3, \ldots$) on the right-hand side in (15)—only the one for which $m = n$ is nonzero. It follows that

$$\int_{-\pi}^{\pi} f(t) \cos nt\, dt = a_n \int_{-\pi}^{\pi} \cos^2 nt\, dt = \pi a_n,$$

so the value of the coefficient a_n is

$$a_n = \frac{1}{\pi} \int_{-\pi}^{\pi} f(t) \cos nt\, dt. \tag{16}$$

Note that with $n = 0$, the formula in (16) reduces to Eq. (14); this explains why we denote the constant term in the original Fourier series by $\frac{1}{2} a_0$ (rather than simply a_0). If we multiply each side in Eq. (13) by $\sin nt$ and then integrate termwise, we find in a similar way that

$$b_n = \frac{1}{\pi} \int_{-\pi}^{\pi} f(t) \sin nt\, dt \tag{17}$$

(Problem 31). In short, we have found that *if* the series in (13) converges to $f(t)$ and *if* the termwise integrations carried out here are valid, *then* the coefficients in the series must have the values given in Eqs. (16) and (17). This motivates us to *define* the Fourier series of a periodic function by means of these formulas, whether or not the resulting series converges to the function (or even converges at all).

DEFINITION   Fourier Series and Fourier Coefficients

Let $f(t)$ be a piecewise continuous function of period 2π that is defined for all t. Then the **Fourier series** of $f(t)$ is the series

$$\frac{a_0}{2} + \sum_{n=1}^{\infty}(a_n \cos nt + b_n \sin nt), \tag{18}$$

where the **Fourier coefficients** a_n and b_n are defined by means of the formulas

$$a_n = \frac{1}{\pi}\int_{-\pi}^{\pi} f(t)\cos nt\, dt \tag{16}$$

for $n = 0, 1, 2, 3, \ldots$ and

$$b_n = \frac{1}{\pi}\int_{-\pi}^{\pi} f(t)\sin nt\, dt \tag{17}$$

for $n = 1, 2, 3, \ldots$.

You may recall that the Taylor series of a function sometimes fails to converge everywhere to the function whence it came. It is still more common that the Fourier series of a given function sometimes fails to converge to its actual values at certain points in the domain of the function. We will therefore write

$$f(t) \sim \frac{a_0}{2} + \sum_{n=1}^{\infty}(a_n \cos nt + b_n \sin nt), \tag{19}$$

not using an equals sign between the function and its Fourier series until we have discussed convergence of Fourier series in Section 9.2.

Suppose that the piecewise continuous function $f(t)$ as given initially is defined only on the interval $[-\pi, \pi]$, and assume that $f(-\pi) = f(\pi)$. Then we can extend f so that its domain includes all real numbers by means of the periodicity condition $f(t + 2\pi) = f(t)$ for all t. We continue to denote this extension of the original function by f, and note that it automatically has period 2π. Its graph looks the same on every interval of the form

$$(2n - 1)\pi \leqq t \leqq (2n + 1)\pi$$

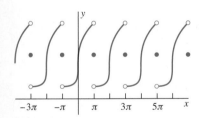

FIGURE 9.1.2. Extending a function to produce a periodic function.

where n is an integer (Fig. 9.1.2). For instance, the square-wave function of Fig. 9.1.1 can be described as the period 2π function such that

$$f(t) = \begin{cases} -1 & \text{if } -\pi < t < 0; \\ +1 & \text{if } 0 < t < \pi; \\ 0 & \text{if } t = -\pi, 0, \text{ or } \pi. \end{cases} \tag{20}$$

Thus the square-wave function is the period 2π function defined on one full period by means of Eq. (20).

We need to consider Fourier series of piecewise continuous functions because many functions that appear in applications are only piecewise continuous, not continuous. Note that the integrals in Eqs. (16) and (17) exist if $f(t)$ is piecewise continuous, so every piecewise continuous function has a Fourier series.

| Example 1 | Find the Fourier series of the square-wave function defined in Eq. (20).

Solution It is always a good idea to calculate a_0 separately, using Eq. (14). Thus

$$a_0 = \frac{1}{\pi} \int_{-\pi}^{\pi} f(t) \, dt = \frac{1}{\pi} \int_{-\pi}^{0} (-1) \, dt + \frac{1}{\pi} \int_{0}^{\pi} (+1) \, dt$$

$$= \frac{1}{\pi}(-\pi) + \frac{1}{\pi}(\pi) = 0.$$

We split the first integral into two integrals because $f(t)$ is defined by different formulas on the intervals $(-\pi, 0)$ and $(0, \pi)$; the values of $f(t)$ at the endpoints of these intervals do not affect the values of the integrals.

Equation (16) yields (for $n > 0$)

$$a_n = \frac{1}{\pi} \int_{-\pi}^{\pi} f(t) \cos nt \, dt = \frac{1}{\pi} \int_{-\pi}^{0} (-\cos nt) \, dt + \frac{1}{\pi} \int_{0}^{\pi} \cos nt \, dt$$

$$= \frac{1}{\pi} \left[-\frac{1}{n} \sin nt \right]_{-\pi}^{0} + \frac{1}{\pi} \left[\frac{1}{n} \sin nt \right]_{0}^{\pi} = 0.$$

And Eq. (17) yields

$$b_n = \frac{1}{\pi} \int_{-\pi}^{\pi} f(t) \sin nt \, dt = \frac{1}{\pi} \int_{-\pi}^{0} (-\sin nt) \, dt + \frac{1}{\pi} \int_{0}^{\pi} \sin nt \, dt$$

$$= \frac{1}{\pi} \left[\frac{1}{n} \cos nt \right]_{-\pi}^{0} + \frac{1}{\pi} \left[-\frac{1}{n} \cos nt \right]_{0}^{\pi}$$

$$= \frac{2}{n\pi} (1 - \cos n\pi) = \frac{2}{n\pi} [1 - (-1)^n].$$

Thus $a_n = 0$ for all $n \geq 0$, and

$$b_n = \begin{cases} \dfrac{4}{n\pi} & \text{for } n \text{ odd}; \\ 0 & \text{for } n \text{ even}. \end{cases}$$

The last result follows because $\cos(-n\pi) = \cos(n\pi) = (-1)^n$. With these values of the Fourier coefficients, we obtain the Fourier series

$$f(t) \sim \frac{4}{\pi} \sum_{n \text{ odd}} \frac{\sin nt}{n} = \frac{4}{\pi} \left(\sin t + \frac{1}{3} \sin 3t + \frac{1}{5} \sin 5t + \cdots \right). \qquad (21)$$

Here we have introduced the useful abbreviation

$$\sum_{n \text{ odd}} \quad \text{for} \quad \sum_{\substack{n=1 \\ n \text{ odd}}}^{\infty}$$

—for example,

$$\sum_{n \text{ odd}} \frac{1}{n} = 1 + \frac{1}{3} + \frac{1}{5} + \cdots.$$

Figure 9.1.3 shows the graphs of several of the partial sums

$$S_N(t) = \frac{4}{\pi} \sum_{n=1}^{N} \frac{\sin(2n-1)t}{2n-1}$$

of the Fourier series in (21). Note that as t approaches a discontinuity of $f(t)$ from either side, the value of $S_n(t)$ tends to overshoot the limiting value of $f(t)$—either $+1$ or -1 in this case. This behavior of a Fourier series near a point of discontinuity of its function is typical and is known as **Gibbs's phenomenon**. ■

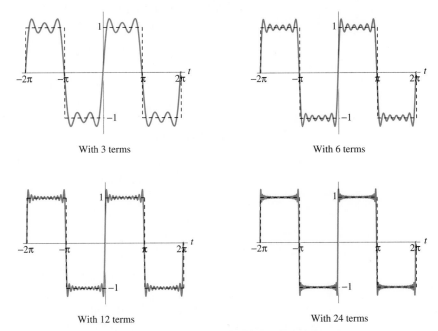

With 3 terms

With 6 terms

With 12 terms

With 24 terms

FIGURE 9.1.3. Graphs of partial sums of the Fourier series of the square-wave function (Example 1) with $N = 3, 6, 12$, and 24 terms.

The following integral formulas, easily derived by integration by parts, are useful in computing Fourier series of polynomial functions:

$$\int u \cos u \, du = \cos u + u \sin u + C; \tag{22}$$

$$\int u \sin u \, du = \sin u - u \cos u + C; \tag{23}$$

$$\int u^n \cos u \, du = u^n \sin u - n \int u^{n-1} \sin u \, du; \tag{24}$$

$$\int u^n \sin u \, du = -u^n \cos u + n \int u^{n-1} \cos u \, du. \tag{25}$$

Example 2 Find the Fourier series of the period 2π function that is defined in one period to be

$$f(t) = \begin{cases} 0 & \text{if } -\pi < t \leq 0; \\ t & \text{if } 0 \leq t < \pi; \\ \dfrac{\pi}{2} & \text{if } t = \pm\pi. \end{cases} \tag{26}$$

The graph of f is shown in Fig. 9.1.4.

Solution The values of $f(\pm\pi)$ are irrelevant because they have no effect on the values of the integrals that yield the Fourier coefficients. Because $f(t) \equiv 0$ on the interval $(-\pi, 0)$, each integral from $t = -\pi$ to $t = \pi$ may be replaced with an integral from $t = 0$ to $t = \pi$. Equations (14), (16), and (17) therefore give

FIGURE 9.1.4. The periodic function of Example 2.

$$a_0 = \frac{1}{\pi} \int_0^\pi t \, dt = \frac{1}{\pi} \left[\frac{1}{2} t^2 \right]_0^\pi = \frac{\pi}{2};$$

$$a_n = \frac{1}{\pi} \int_0^\pi t \cos nt \, dt = \frac{1}{n^2\pi} \int_0^{n\pi} u \cos u \, du \qquad \left(u = nt, \ t = \frac{u}{n} \right)$$

$$= \frac{1}{n^2\pi} \Big[\cos u + u \sin u \Big]_0^{n\pi} \qquad \text{(by Eq. (22))}$$

$$= \frac{1}{n^2\pi} [(-1)^n - 1].$$

Consequently, $a_n = 0$ if n is even and $n \geq 2$;

$$a_n = -\frac{2}{n^2\pi} \qquad \text{if } n \text{ is odd.}$$

Next,

$$b_n = \frac{1}{\pi} \int_0^\pi t \sin nt \, dt = \frac{1}{n^2\pi} \int_0^{n\pi} u \sin u \, du$$

$$= \frac{1}{n^2\pi} \Big[\sin u - u \cos u \Big]_0^{n\pi} \qquad \text{(by Eq. (20))}$$

$$= -\frac{1}{n} \cos n\pi.$$

Thus

$$b_n = \frac{(-1)^{n+1}}{n} \qquad \text{for all } n \geq 1.$$

Therefore, the Fourier series of $f(t)$ is

$$f(t) \sim \frac{\pi}{4} - \frac{2}{\pi} \sum_{n \text{ odd}} \frac{\cos nt}{n^2} + \sum_{n=1}^\infty \frac{(-1)^{n+1} \sin nt}{n}. \tag{27}$$

If $f(t)$ is a function of period 2π, it is readily verified (Problem 30) that

$$\int_{-\pi}^{\pi} f(t)\,dt = \int_{a}^{a+2\pi} f(t)\,dt \tag{28}$$

for all a. That is, the integral of $f(t)$ over one interval of length 2π is equal to its integral over any other such interval. In case $f(t)$ is given explicitly on the interval $[0, 2\pi]$ rather than on $[-\pi, \pi]$, it may be more convenient to compute its Fourier coefficients as

$$a_n = \frac{1}{\pi} \int_0^{2\pi} f(t) \cos nt\,dt \tag{29a}$$

and

$$b_n = \frac{1}{\pi} \int_0^{2\pi} f(t) \sin nt\,dt. \tag{29b}$$

9.1 Problems

In Problems 1 through 10, sketch the graph of the function f defined for all t by the given formula, and determine whether it is periodic. If so, find its smallest period.

1. $f(t) = \sin 3t$
2. $f(t) = \cos 2\pi t$
3. $f(t) = \cos \dfrac{3t}{2}$
4. $f(t) = \sin \dfrac{\pi t}{3}$
5. $f(t) = \tan t$
6. $f(t) = \cot 2\pi t$
7. $f(t) = \cosh 3t$
8. $f(t) = \sinh \pi t$
9. $f(t) = |\sin t|$
10. $f(t) = \cos^2 3t$

In Problems 11 through 26, the values of a period 2π function $f(t)$ in one full period are given. Sketch several periods of its graph and find its Fourier series.

11. $f(t) \equiv 1$, $-\pi \le t \le \pi$

12. $f(t) = \begin{cases} +3, & -\pi < t \le 0; \\ -3, & 0 < t \le \pi \end{cases}$

13. $f(t) = \begin{cases} 0, & -\pi < t \le 0; \\ 1, & 0 < t \le \pi \end{cases}$

14. $f(t) = \begin{cases} 3, & -\pi < t \le 0; \\ -2, & 0 < t \le \pi \end{cases}$

15. $f(t) = t, -\pi < t \le \pi$
16. $f(t) = t, 0 < t < 2\pi$
17. $f(t) = |t|, -\pi \le t \le \pi$

18. $f(t) = \begin{cases} \pi + t, & -\pi < t \le 0; \\ \pi - t, & 0 < t \le \pi \end{cases}$

19. $f(t) = \begin{cases} \pi + t, & -\pi \le t < 0; \\ 0, & 0 \le t \le \pi \end{cases}$

20. $f(t) = \begin{cases} 0, & -\pi \le t < -\pi/2; \\ 1, & -\pi/2 \le t \le \pi/2; \\ 0, & \pi/2 < t \le \pi \end{cases}$

21. $f(t) = t^2$, $-\pi \le t \le \pi$
22. $f(t) = t^2$, $0 \le t < 2\pi$

23. $f(t) = \begin{cases} 0, & -\pi \le t \le 0; \\ t^2, & 0 \le t < \pi \end{cases}$

24. $f(t) = |\sin t|$, $-\pi \le t \le \pi$
25. $f(t) = \cos^2 2t$, $-\pi \le t \le \pi$

26. $f(t) = \begin{cases} 0, & -\pi \le t \le 0; \\ \sin t, & 0 \le t \le \pi \end{cases}$

27. Verify Eq. (9). (*Suggestion*: Use the trigonometric identity

$$\cos A \cos B = \tfrac{1}{2}[\cos(A + B) + \cos(A - B)].)$$

28. Verify Eq. (10).
29. Verify Eq. (11).
30. Let $f(t)$ be a piecewise continuous function with period P. **(a)** Suppose that $0 \le a < P$. Substitute $u = t - P$ to show that

$$\int_P^{a+P} f(t)\,dt = \int_0^a f(t)\,dt.$$

Conclude that

$$\int_a^{a+P} f(t)\,dt = \int_0^P f(t)\,dt.$$

(b) Given A, choose n so that $A = nP + a$ with $0 \le a < P$. Then substitute $v = t - nP$ to show that

$$\int_A^{A+P} f(t)\,dt = \int_a^{a+P} f(t)\,dt = \int_0^P f(t)\,dt.$$

31. Multiply each side in Eq. (13) by $\sin nt$ and then integrate term by term to derive Eq. (17).

9.2 General Fourier Series and Convergence

In Section 9.1 we defined the Fourier series of a periodic function of period 2π. Now let $f(t)$ be a function that is piecewise continuous for all t and has arbitrary period $P > 0$. We write

$$P = 2L, \tag{1}$$

so L is the **half-period** of the function f. Let us define the function g as follows:

$$g(u) = f\left(\frac{Lu}{\pi}\right) \tag{2}$$

for all u. Then

$$g(u + 2\pi) = f\left(\frac{Lu}{\pi} + 2L\right) = f\left(\frac{Lu}{\pi}\right) = g(u),$$

and hence $g(u)$ is also periodic and has period 2π. Consequently, g has the Fourier series

$$g(u) \sim \frac{a_0}{2} + \sum_{n=1}^{\infty}(a_n \cos nu + b_n \sin nu) \tag{3}$$

with Fourier coefficients

$$a_n = \frac{1}{\pi}\int_{-\pi}^{\pi} g(u)\cos nu\, du \tag{4a}$$

and

$$b_n = \frac{1}{\pi}\int_{-\pi}^{\pi} g(u)\sin nu\, du. \tag{4b}$$

If we now write

$$t = \frac{Lu}{\pi}, \quad u = \frac{\pi t}{L}, \quad f(t) = g(u), \tag{5}$$

then

$$f(t) = g\left(\frac{\pi t}{L}\right) \sim \frac{a_0}{2} + \sum_{n=1}^{\infty}\left(a_n \cos\frac{n\pi t}{L} + b_n \frac{n\pi t}{L}\right), \tag{6}$$

and then substitution of (5) in (4) yields

$$a_n = \frac{1}{\pi}\int_{-\pi}^{\pi} g(u)\cos nu\, du \quad \left(u = \frac{\pi t}{L},\ du = \frac{\pi}{L}\, dt\right)$$

$$= \frac{1}{L}\int_{-L}^{L} g\left(\frac{\pi t}{L}\right)\cos\frac{n\pi t}{L}\, dt.$$

Therefore,

$$a_n = \frac{1}{L} \int_{-L}^{L} f(t) \cos \frac{n\pi t}{L} \, dt; \tag{7}$$

similarly,

$$b_n = \frac{1}{L} \int_{-L}^{L} f(t) \sin \frac{n\pi t}{L} \, dt. \tag{8}$$

This computation motivates the following definition of the Fourier series of a periodic function of period $2L$.

DEFINITION   Fourier Series and Fourier Coefficients

Let $f(t)$ be a piecewise continuous function of period $2L$ that is defined for all t. Then the **Fourier series** of $f(t)$ is the series

➤
$$f(t) \sim \frac{a_0}{2} + \sum_{n=1}^{\infty} \left(a_n \cos \frac{n\pi t}{L} + b_n \sin \frac{n\pi t}{L} \right), \tag{6}$$

where the **Fourier coefficients** $\{a_n\}_0^{\infty}$ and $\{b_n\}_1^{\infty}$ are defined to be

➤
$$a_n = \frac{1}{L} \int_{-L}^{L} f(t) \cos \frac{n\pi t}{L} \, dt \tag{7}$$

and

➤
$$b_n = \frac{1}{L} \int_{-L}^{L} f(t) \sin \frac{n\pi t}{L} \, dt. \tag{8}$$

With $n = 0$, Eq. (7) takes the simple form

$$a_0 = \frac{1}{L} \int_{-L}^{L} f(t) \, dt, \tag{9}$$

which demonstrates that the constant term $\frac{1}{2}a_0$ in the Fourier series of f is simply the average value of $f(t)$ on the interval $[-L, L]$.

As a consequence of Problem 30 of Section 9.1, we may evaluate the integrals in (7) and (8) over any other interval of length $2L$. For instance, if $f(t)$ is given by a single formula for $0 < t < 2L$, it may be more convenient to compute the integrals

$$a_n = \frac{1}{L} \int_0^{2L} f(t) \cos \frac{n\pi t}{L} \, dt \tag{10a}$$

and

$$b_n = \frac{1}{L} \int_0^{2L} f(t) \sin \frac{n\pi t}{L} \, dt. \tag{10b}$$

Example 1 Figure 9.2.1 shows the graph of a square-wave function with period 4. Find its Fourier series.

Solution Here, $L = 2$; also, $f(t) = -1$ if $-2 < t < 0$, while $f(t) = 1$ if $0 < t < 2$. Hence Eqs. (7), (8), and (9) yield

$$a_0 = \frac{1}{2} \int_{-2}^{2} f(t)\, dt = \frac{1}{2} \int_{-2}^{0} (-1)\, dt + \frac{1}{2} \int_{0}^{2} (+1)\, dt = 0,$$

$$a_n = \frac{1}{2} \int_{-2}^{0} (-1) \cos \frac{n\pi t}{2}\, dt + \frac{1}{2} \int_{0}^{2} (+1) \cos \frac{n\pi t}{2}\, dt$$

$$= \frac{1}{2} \left[-\frac{2}{n\pi} \sin \frac{n\pi t}{2} \right]_{-2}^{0} + \frac{1}{2} \left[\frac{2}{n\pi} \sin \frac{n\pi t}{2} \right]_{0}^{2} = 0,$$

FIGURE 9.2.1. The square-wave of Example 1.

and

$$b_n = \frac{1}{2} \int_{-2}^{0} (-1) \sin \frac{n\pi t}{2}\, dt + \frac{1}{2} \int_{0}^{2} (+1) \sin \frac{n\pi t}{2}\, dt$$

$$+ \frac{1}{2} \left[\frac{2}{n\pi} \cos \frac{n\pi t}{2} \right]_{-2}^{0} + \frac{1}{2} \left[-\frac{2}{n\pi} \cos \frac{n\pi t}{2} \right]_{0}^{2}$$

$$= \frac{2}{n\pi} \left[1 - (-1)^n \right] = \begin{cases} \dfrac{4}{n\pi} & \text{if } n \text{ is odd,} \\[2mm] 0 & \text{if } n \text{ is even.} \end{cases}$$

Thus the Fourier series is

$$f(t) \sim \frac{4}{\pi} \sum_{n \text{ odd}} \frac{1}{n} \sin \frac{n\pi t}{2} \tag{11a}$$

$$= \frac{4}{\pi} \left(\sin \frac{\pi t}{2} + \frac{1}{3} \sin \frac{3\pi t}{2} + \frac{1}{5} \sin \frac{5\pi t}{2} + \cdots \right). \tag{11b}$$

∎

The Convergence Theorem

We want to impose conditions on the periodic function f that are enough to guarantee that its Fourier series actually converges to $f(t)$ at least at those values of t at which f is continuous. Recall that the function f is said to be *piecewise continuous* on the interval $[a, b]$ provided that there is a finite partition of $[a, b]$ with endpoints

$$a = t_0 < t_1 < t_2 < \cdots < t_{n-1} < t_n = b$$

such that

1. f is continuous on each open interval $t_{i-1} < t < t_i$; and
2. At each endpoint t_i of such a subinterval the limit of $f(t)$, as t approaches t_i from within the subinterval, exists and is finite.

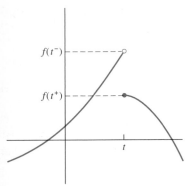

FIGURE 9.2.2. A finite jump discontinuity.

The function f is called *piecewise continuous* for all t if it is piecewise continuous on every bounded interval. It follows that a piecewise continuous function is continuous except possibly at isolated points, and that at each such point of discontinuity, the one-sided limits

$$f(t+) = \lim_{u \to t^+} f(u) \quad \text{and} \quad f(t-) = \lim_{u \to t^-} f(u) \tag{12}$$

both exist and are finite. Thus a piecewise continuous function has only isolated "finite jump" discontinuities like the one shown in Fig. 9.2.2.

The square-wave and sawtooth functions that we saw in Chapter 7 are typical examples of periodic piecewise continuous functions. The function $f(t) = \tan t$ is a periodic function (of period π) that is not piecewise continuous because it has infinite discontinuities. The function $g(t) = \sin(1/t)$ is not piecewise continuous on $[-1, 1]$ because its one-sided limits at $t = 0$ do not exist. The function

$$h(t) = \begin{cases} t & \text{if } t = \dfrac{1}{n} \quad (n \text{ an integer}), \\ 0 & \text{otherwise} \end{cases}$$

on $[-1, 1]$ has one-sided limits everywhere, but is not piecewise continuous because its discontinuities are not isolated—it has the infinite sequence $\{1/n\}_1^\infty$ of discontinuities; a piecewise continuous function can have only finitely many discontinuities in any bounded interval.

Note that a piecewise continuous function need not be defined at its isolated points of discontinuity. Alternatively, it can be defined arbitrarily at such points. For instance, the square wave function f of Fig. 9.2.1 is piecewise continuous no matter what its values might be at the points $\ldots, -4, -2, 0, 2, 4, 6, \ldots$ at which it is discontinuous. Its derivative f' is also piecewise continuous; $f'(t) = 0$ unless t is an even integer, in which case $f'(t)$ is undefined.

The piecewise continuous function f is said to be **piecewise smooth** provided that its derivative f' is piecewise continuous. Theorem 1 (next) tells us that the Fourier series of a piecewise smooth function converges everywhere. More general Fourier convergence theorems—with weaker hypotheses on the periodic function f—are known. But the hypothesis that f is piecewise smooth is easy to check and is satisfied by most functions encountered in practical applications. A proof of the following theorem may be found in G. P. Tolstov, *Fourier Series* (New York: Dover, 1976).

THEOREM 1   Convergence of Fourier Series

Suppose that the periodic function f is piecewise smooth. Then its Fourier series in (6) converges

(a) to the value $f(t)$ at each point where f is continuous, and

(b) to the value $\frac{1}{2}[f(t+) + f(t-)]$ at each point where f is discontinuous.

Note that $\frac{1}{2}[f(t+) + f(t-)]$ is the *average* of the right-hand and left-hand limits of f at the point t. If f is continuous at t, then $f(t) = f(t+) = f(t-)$, so

$$f(t) = \frac{f(t+) + f(t-)}{2}. \tag{13}$$

Hence Theorem 1 could be rephrased as follows: The Fourier series of a piecewise smooth function f converges for *every* t to the average value in (13). For this reason it is customary to write

$$f(t) = \frac{a_0}{2} + \sum_{n=1}^{\infty} \left(a_n \cos \frac{n\pi t}{L} + b_n \sin \frac{n\pi t}{L} \right), \tag{14}$$

with the understanding that the piecewise smooth function f has been redefined (if necessary) at each of its points of discontinuity in order to satisfy the average value condition in (13).

Example 1

Continued

Figure 9.2.1 shows us at a glance that if t_0 is an even integer, then

$$\lim_{t \to t_0^+} f(t) = +1 \quad \text{and} \quad \lim_{t \to t_0^-} f(t) = -1.$$

Hence

$$\frac{f(t_0+) + f(t_0-)}{2} = 0.$$

Note that, in accord with Theorem 1, the Fourier series of $f(t)$ in (11) clearly converges to zero if n is an even integer (because $\sin n\pi = 0$). ∎

Example 2

Let $f(t)$ be a function of period 2 with $f(t) = t^2$ if $0 < t < 2$. We define $f(t)$ for t an even integer by the average value condition in (13); consequently, $f(t) = 2$ if t is an even integer. The graph of the function f appears in Fig. 9.2.3. Find its Fourier series.

Solution

Here $L = 1$, and it is most convenient to integrate from $t = 0$ to $t = 2$. Then

$$a_0 = \frac{1}{1} \int_0^2 t^2 \, dt = \left[\frac{1}{3} t^3 \right]_0^2 = \frac{8}{3}.$$

With the aid of the integral formulas in Eqs. (22) through (25) of Section 9.1, we obtain

FIGURE 9.2.3. The period 2 function of Example 2.

$$a_n = \int_0^2 t^2 \cos n\pi t \, dt$$

$$= \frac{1}{n^3 \pi^3} \int_0^{2n\pi} u^2 \cos u \, du \qquad \left(u = n\pi t, \; t = \frac{u}{n\pi} \right)$$

$$= \frac{1}{n^3 \pi^3} \left[u^2 \sin u - 2 \sin u + 2u \cos u \right]_0^{2n\pi} = \frac{4}{n^2 \pi^2};$$

$$b_n = \int_0^2 t^2 \sin n\pi t \, dt = \frac{1}{n^3 \pi^3} \int_0^{2n\pi} u^2 \sin u \, du$$

$$= \frac{1}{n^3 \pi^3} \left[-u^2 \cos u + 2 \cos u + 2u \sin u \right]_0^{2n\pi} = -\frac{4}{n\pi}.$$

Hence the Fourier series of f is

$$f(t) = \frac{4}{3} + \frac{4}{\pi^2} \sum_{n=1}^{\infty} \frac{\cos n\pi t}{n^2} - \frac{4}{\pi} \sum_{n=1}^{\infty} \frac{\sin n\pi t}{n}, \tag{15}$$

and Theorem 1 assures us that this series converges to $f(t)$ for all t.   ■

We can draw some interesting consequences from the Fourier series in (15). If we substitute $t = 0$ on each side, we find that

$$f(0) = 2 = \frac{4}{3} + \frac{4}{\pi^2} \sum_{n=1}^{\infty} \frac{1}{n^2}.$$

On solving for the series, we obtain the lovely summation

$$\blacktriangleright \qquad \sum_{n=1}^{\infty} \frac{1}{n^2} = 1 + \frac{1}{2^2} + \frac{1}{3^2} + \frac{1}{4^2} + \cdots = \frac{\pi^2}{6} \tag{16}$$

that was discovered by Euler. If we substitute $t = 1$ in Eq. (15), we get

$$f(1) = 1 = \frac{4}{3} + \frac{4}{\pi^2} \sum_{n=1}^{\infty} \frac{(-1)^n}{n^2},$$

which yields

$$\sum_{n=1}^{\infty} \frac{(-1)^{n+1}}{n^2} = 1 - \frac{1}{2^2} + \frac{1}{3^2} - \frac{1}{4^2} + \cdots = \frac{\pi^2}{12}. \tag{17}$$

If we add the series in Eqs. (16) and (17) and then divide by 2, the "even" terms cancel and the result is

$$\sum_{n \text{ odd}} \frac{1}{n^2} = 1 + \frac{1}{3^2} + \frac{1}{5^2} + \frac{1}{7^2} + \cdots = \frac{\pi^2}{8}. \tag{18}$$

9.2 Problems

In Problems 1 through 14, the values of a periodic function $f(t)$ in one full period are given; at each discontinuity the value of $f(t)$ is that given by the average value condition in (13). Sketch the graph of f and find its Fourier series.

1. $f(t) = \begin{cases} -2, & -3 < t < 0; \\ 2, & 0 < t < 3 \end{cases}$

2. $f(t) = \begin{cases} 0, & -5 < t < 0; \\ 1, & 0 < t < 5 \end{cases}$

3. $f(t) = \begin{cases} 2, & -2\pi < t < 0; \\ -1, & 0 < t < 2\pi \end{cases}$

4. $f(t) = t, \ -2 < t < 2$

5. $f(t) = t, \ -2\pi < t < 2\pi$

6. $f(t) = t, \ 0 < t < 3$

7. $f(t) = |t|, \ -1 < t < 1$

8. $f(t) = \begin{cases} 0, & 0 < t < 1; \\ 1, & 1 < t < 2; \\ 0, & 2 < t < 3 \end{cases}$

9. $f(t) = t^2, \ -1 < t < 1$

10. $f(t) = \begin{cases} 0, & -2 < t < 0; \\ t^2, & 0 < t < 2 \end{cases}$

11. $f(t) = \cos \dfrac{\pi t}{2}, \ -1 < t < 1$

12. $f(t) = \sin \pi t, \ 0 < t < 1$

13. $f(t) = \begin{cases} 0, & -1 < t < 0; \\ \sin \pi t, & 0 < t < 1 \end{cases}$

14. $f(t) = \begin{cases} 0, & -2\pi < t < 0; \\ \sin t, & 0 < t < 2\pi \end{cases}$

15. (a) Suppose that f is a function of period 2π with $f(t) = t^2$ for $0 < t < 2\pi$. Show that

$$f(t) = \frac{4\pi^2}{3} + 4 \sum_{n=1}^{\infty} \frac{\cos nt}{n^2} - 4\pi \sum_{n=1}^{\infty} \frac{\sin nt}{n}$$

and sketch the graph of f, indicating the value at each discontinuity. **(b)** Deduce the series summations in Eqs. (16) and (17) from the Fourier series in part (a).

16. (a) Suppose that f is a function of period 2 such that $f(t) = 0$ if $-1 < t < 0$ and $f(t) = t$ if $0 < t < 1$. Show that

$$f(t) = \frac{1}{4} - \frac{2}{\pi^2} \sum_{n \text{ odd}} \frac{\cos n\pi t}{n^2} + \frac{1}{\pi} \sum_{n=1}^{\infty} \frac{(-1)^{n+1} \sin n\pi t}{n}$$

and sketch the graph of f, indicating the value at each discontinuity. **(b)** Deduce the series summation in Eq. (18) from the Fourier series in part (a).

17. (a) Suppose that f is a function of period 2 with $f(t) = t$ for $0 < t < 2$. Show that

$$f(t) = 1 - \frac{2}{\pi} \sum_{n=1}^{\infty} \frac{\sin n\pi t}{n}$$

and sketch the graph of f, indicating the value at each discontinuity. **(b)** Substitute an appropriate value of t to deduce **Leibniz's series**

$$1 - \frac{1}{3} + \frac{1}{5} - \frac{1}{7} + \cdots = \frac{\pi}{4}.$$

Derive the Fourier series listed in Problems 18 through 21, and graph the period 2π function to which each series converges.

18. $\displaystyle\sum_{n=1}^{\infty} \frac{\sin nt}{n} = \frac{\pi - t}{2} \quad (0 < t < 2\pi)$

19. $\displaystyle\sum_{n=1}^{\infty} \frac{(-1)^{n+1} \sin nt}{n} = \frac{t}{2} \quad (-\pi < t < \pi)$

20. $\displaystyle\sum_{n=1}^{\infty} \frac{\cos nt}{n^2} = \frac{3t^2 - 6\pi t + 2\pi^2}{12} \quad (0 < t < 2\pi)$

21. $\displaystyle\sum_{n=1}^{\infty} \frac{(-1)^{n+1} \cos nt}{n^2} = \frac{\pi^2 - 3t^2}{12} \quad (-\pi < t < \pi)$

22. Suppose that $p(t)$ is a polynomial of degree n. Show by repeated integration by parts that

$$\int p(t)g(t) \, dt = p(t)G_1(t) - p'(t)G_2(t)$$
$$+ p''(t)G_3(t) - \cdots + (-1)^n p^{(n)}(t)G_{n+1}(t)$$

where $G_k(t)$ denotes the kth iterated antiderivative $G_k(t) = (D^{-1})^k g(t)$. This formula is useful in computing Fourier coefficients of polynomials.

23. Apply the integral formula of Problem 22 to show that

$$\int t^4 \cos t \, dt = t^4 \sin t + 4t^3 \cos t$$
$$- 12t^2 \sin t - 24t \cos t + 24 \sin t + C$$

and that

$$\int t^4 \sin t \, dt = -t^4 \cos t + 4t^3 \sin t$$
$$+ 12t^2 \cos t - 24t \sin t - 24 \cos t + C.$$

24. (a) Show that for $0 < t < 2\pi$,

$$t^4 = \frac{16\pi^4}{5} + 16 \sum_{n=1}^{\infty} \left(\frac{2\pi^2}{n^2} - \frac{3}{n^4} \right) \cos nt$$
$$+ 16\pi \sum_{n=1}^{\infty} \left(\frac{3}{n^3} - \frac{\pi^2}{n} \right) \sin nt$$

and sketch the graph of f, indicating the value at each discontinuity. **(b)** From the Fourier series in part (a), deduce the summations

$$\sum_{n=1}^{\infty} \frac{1}{n^4} = \frac{\pi^4}{90}, \qquad \sum_{n=1}^{\infty} \frac{(-1)^{n+1}}{n^4} = \frac{7\pi^4}{720},$$

and

$$\sum_{n \text{ odd}} \frac{1}{n^4} = \frac{\pi^4}{96}.$$

25. (a) Find the Fourier series of the period 2π function f with $f(t) = t^3$ if $-\pi < t < \pi$. **(b)** Use the series of part (a) to derive the summation

$$1 - \frac{1}{3^3} + \frac{1}{5^3} - \frac{1}{7^3} + \cdots = \frac{\pi^3}{32}$$

and sketch the graph of f, indicating the value at each discontinuity. **(c)** *Attempt* to evaluate the series

$$\sum_{n=1}^{\infty} \frac{1}{n^3} = 1 + \frac{1}{2^3} + \frac{1}{3^3} + \frac{1}{4^3} + \cdots$$

by substituting an appropriate value of t in the Fourier series of part (a). Is your attempt successful? Explain. *Remark:* If you succeed in expressing the sum of this inverse-cube series in terms of familiar numbers—for instance, as a rational multiple of π^3 similar to Euler's sum in part (a)—you will win great fame for yourself, for many have tried without success over the last two centuries since Euler. Indeed, it was not until 1979 that the sum of the inverse-cube series was proved to be an irrational number (as long suspected).

9.2 Application Computer Algebra Calculation of Fourier Coefficients

A computer algebra system can greatly ease the burden of calculation of the Fourier coefficients of a given function $f(t)$. In the case of a function that is defined "piecewise," we must take care to "split" the integral according to the different intervals of definition of the function. We illustrate the method by deriving the Fourier series of the period 2π square-wave function defined on $(-\pi, \pi)$ by

$$f(t) = \begin{cases} -1 & \text{if } -\pi < t < 0, \\ +1 & \text{if } 0 < t < \pi. \end{cases} \tag{1}$$

In this case the function is defined by different formulas on two different intervals, so each Fourier coefficient integral from $-\pi$ to π must be calculated as the sum of two integrals:

$$a_n = \frac{1}{\pi} \int_{-\pi}^{0} (-1) \cos nt \, dt + \frac{1}{\pi} \int_{0}^{\pi} (+1) \cos nt \, dt,$$
$$b_n = \frac{1}{\pi} \int_{-\pi}^{0} (-1) \sin nt \, dt + \frac{1}{\pi} \int_{0}^{\pi} (+1) \sin nt \, dt. \tag{2}$$

We can define the coefficients in (2) as functions of n by the *Maple* commands

```
a := n -> (1/Pi)*(int(-cos(n*t), t=-Pi..0) +
                  int(+cos(n*t), t=0..Pi)):
b := n -> (1/Pi)*(int(-sin(n*t), t=-Pi..0) +
                  int(+sin(n*t), t=0..Pi)):
```

or by the *Mathematica* commands

```
a[n_] := (1/Pi)*(Integrate[-Cos[n*t], {t, -Pi, 0}] +
                 Integrate[+Cos[n*t], {t, 0, Pi}])
b[n_] := (1/Pi)*(Integrate[-Sin[n*t], {t, -Pi, 0}] +
                 Integrate[+Sin[n*t], {t, 0, Pi}])
```

Because the function $f(t)$ in Eq. (1) is odd, we naturally find that $a_n \equiv 0$. Hence the *Maple* commands

```
fourierSum := sum(b(n)*sin(n*t), n=1..9);
plot(fourierSum, t=-2*Pi..4*Pi);
```

or the *Mathematica* commands

```
fourierSum = Sum[b[n]*Sin[n*t], {n,1,9}]
Plot[fourierSum, {t, -2*Pi, 4*Pi}];
```

yield the partial sum

$$\sum_{n=1}^{9} b_n \sin nt = \frac{4}{\pi} \left(\sin t + \frac{\sin 3t}{3} + \frac{\sin 5t}{5} + \frac{\sin 7t}{7} + \frac{\sin 9t}{9} \right)$$

and generate a graph like one of those in Fig. 9.1.3. The corresponding MATLAB commands are entirely analogous and can be found in the applications manual that accompanies this text.

To practice the symbolic derivation of Fourier series in this manner, you can begin by verifying the Fourier series calculated manually in Examples 1 and 2 of this section. Then Problems 1 through 21 are fair game. Finally, the period 2π triangular wave and trapezoidal wave functions illustrated in Figs. 9.2.4 and 9.2.5 have especially interesting Fourier series that we invite you to discover for yourself.

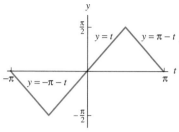

FIGURE 9.2.4. The triangular wave.

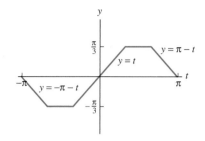

FIGURE 9.2.5. The trapezoidal wave.

9.3 Fourier Sine and Cosine Series

Certain properties of functions are reflected prominently in their Fourier series. The function f defined for all t is said to be **even** if

$$f(-t) = f(t) \tag{1}$$

for all t; f is **odd** if

$$f(-t) = -f(t) \tag{2}$$

for all t. The first condition implies that the graph of $y = f(t)$ is symmetric with respect to the y-axis, whereas the condition in (2) implies that the graph of an odd function is symmetric with respect to the origin (see Fig. 9.3.1). The functions $f(t) = t^{2n}$ (with n an integer) and $g(t) = \cos t$ are even functions, whereas the functions $f(t) = t^{2n+1}$ and $g(t) = \sin t$ are odd. We will see that the Fourier series of an even periodic function has only cosine terms and that the Fourier series of an odd periodic function has only sine terms.

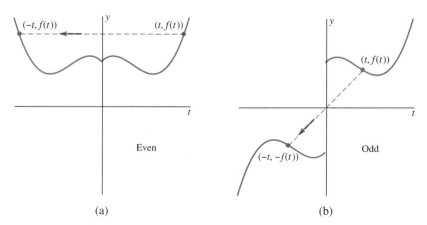

FIGURE 9.3.1. (a) An even function; (b) an odd function.

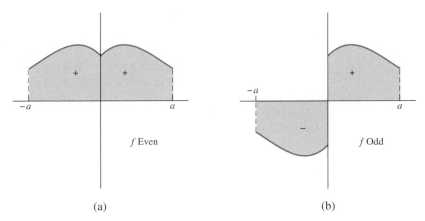

FIGURE 9.3.2. Area under the graph of (a) an even function and (b) an odd.

Addition and cancellation of areas as indicated in Fig. 9.3.2 reminds us of the following basic facts about integrals of even and odd functions over an interval $[-a, a]$ that is symmetric around the origin.

$$\text{If } f \text{ is even:} \qquad \int_{-a}^{a} f(t)\, dt = 2 \int_{0}^{a} f(t)\, dt. \qquad (3)$$

$$\text{If } f \text{ is odd:} \qquad \int_{-a}^{a} f(t)\, dt = 0. \qquad (4)$$

These facts are easy to verify analytically (Problem 17).

It follows immediately from Eqs. (1) and (2) that the product of two even functions is even, as is the product of two odd functions; the product of an even function and an odd function is odd. In particular, if $f(t)$ is an *even* periodic function of period $2L$, then $f(t) \cos(n\pi t/L)$ is even, whereas $f(t) \sin(n\pi t/L)$ is odd, because the cosine function is even and the sine function is odd. When we compute the Fourier coefficients of f, we therefore get

$$a_n = \frac{1}{L} \int_{-L}^{L} f(t) \cos \frac{n\pi t}{L}\, dt = \frac{2}{L} \int_{0}^{L} f(t) \cos \frac{n\pi t}{L}\, dt \qquad (5a)$$

and

$$b_n = \frac{1}{L} \int_{-L}^{L} f(t) \sin \frac{n\pi t}{L}\, dt = 0 \qquad (5b)$$

because of (3) and (4). Hence the Fourier series of the *even* function f of period $2L$ has only *cosine* terms:

$$f(t) = \frac{a_0}{2} + \sum_{n=1}^{\infty} a_n \cos \frac{n\pi t}{L} \qquad (f \text{ even}) \qquad (6)$$

with the values of a_n given by Eq. (5a). If $f(t)$ is *odd*, then $f(t) \cos(n\pi t/L)$ is odd, whereas $f(t) \sin(n\pi t/L)$ is even, so

$$a_n = \frac{1}{L} \int_{-L}^{L} f(t) \cos \frac{n\pi t}{L}\, dt = 0 \qquad (7a)$$

and

$$b_n = \frac{1}{L} \int_{-L}^{L} f(t) \sin \frac{n\pi t}{L} \, dt = \frac{2}{L} \int_{0}^{L} f(t) \sin \frac{n\pi t}{L} \, dt. \tag{7b}$$

Hence the Fourier series of the *odd* function f of period $2L$ has only *sine* terms:

$$f(t) = \sum_{n=1}^{\infty} b_n \sin \frac{n\pi t}{L} \qquad (f \text{ odd}) \tag{8}$$

with the coefficients b_n given in Eq. (7b).

Even and Odd Extensions

In all our earlier discussion and examples, we began with a periodic function de-fined *for all* t; the Fourier series of such a function is uniquely determined by the Fourier coefficient formulas. In many practical situations, however, we begin with a function f defined only on an interval of the form $0 < t < L$, and we want to represent its values on this interval by a Fourier series of period $2L$. The first step is the necessary extension of f to the interval $-L < t < 0$. Granted this, we may extend f to the entire real line by the periodicity condition $f(t + 2L) = f(t)$ (and use the average value property should any discontinuities arise). But *how* we define f for $-L < t < 0$ is our choice, and the Fourier series representation for $f(t)$ on $(0, L)$ that we obtain will depend on that choice. Specifically, different choices of the extension of f to the interval $(-L, 0)$ will yield different Fourier series that converge to the same function $f(t)$ in the original interval $0 < t < L$, but converge to the different extensions of f on the interval $-L < t < 0$.

In practice, given $f(t)$ defined for $0 < t < L$, we generally make one of two natural choices—we extend f in such a way as to obtain either an *even function* or an *odd function* on the whole real line. The **even period 2L extension** of f is the function f_E defined as

$$f_E(t) = \begin{cases} f(t) & \text{if } 0 < t < L, \\ f(-t) & \text{if } -L < t < 0 \end{cases} \tag{9}$$

and by $f_E(t + 2L) = f_E(t)$ for all t. The **odd period 2L extension** of f is the function f_O defined as

$$f_O(t) = \begin{cases} f(t) & \text{if } 0 < t < L, \\ -f(-t) & \text{if } -L < t < 0 \end{cases} \tag{10}$$

and by $f_O(t + 2L) = f_O(t)$ for all t. The values of f_E or f_O for t an integral multiple of L can be defined in any convenient way we wish, because these isolated values cannot affect the Fourier series of the extensions we get. As suggested by Fig. 9.3.1, it frequently suffices simply to visualize the graph of f_E on $(-L, 0)$ as the reflection in the vertical axis of the original graph of f on $(0, L)$, and the graph of f_O on $(-L, 0)$ as the reflection in the origin of the original graph.

For instance, if $f(t) = 2t - t^2$ on the interval $0 < t < 2$ (so $L = 2$), then (9) and (10) yield

$$f_E(t) = 2(-t) - (-t)^2 = -2t - t^2$$

and

$$f_O(t) = -\left[2(-t) - (-t)^2\right] = 2t + t^2$$

FIGURE 9.3.3. (a) The period 4 even extension of $f(t) = 2t - t^2$ for $0 < t < 2$. (b) Graph of the period 4 odd extension of $f(t) = 2t - t^2$ for $0 < t < 2$.

for the values of these two extensions on the interval $-2 < t < 0$. The graphs of the corresponding two periodic extensions of f are shown in Fig. 9.3.3.

The Fourier series of the even extension f_E of the function f, given by Eqs. (5) and (6), will contain only cosine terms and is called the *Fourier cosine series* of the original function f. The Fourier series of the odd extension f_O, given by Eqs. (7) and (8), will contain only sine terms and is called the *Fourier sine series* of f.

DEFINITION   Fourier Cosine and Sine Series

Suppose that the function $f(t)$ is piecewise continuous on the interval $[0, L]$. Then the **Fourier cosine series** of f is the series

$$f(t) = \frac{a_0}{2} + \sum_{n=1}^{\infty} a_n \cos \frac{n\pi t}{L} \tag{11}$$

with

$$a_n = \frac{2}{L} \int_0^L f(t) \cos \frac{n\pi t}{L}\, dt. \tag{12}$$

The **Fourier sine series** of f is the series

$$f(t) = \sum_{n=1}^{\infty} b_n \sin \frac{n\pi t}{L} \tag{13}$$

with

$$b_n = \frac{2}{L} \int_0^L f(t) \sin \frac{n\pi t}{L}\, dt. \tag{14}$$

Assuming that f is piecewise smooth and satisfies the average value condition $f(t) = \frac{1}{2}[f(t+) + f(t-)]$ at each of its isolated discontinuities, Theorem 1 of Section 9.2 implies that each of the two series in (11) and (13) converges to $f(t)$ for all t in the interval $0 < t < L$. Outside this interval, the cosine series in (11) converges to the even period $2L$ extension of f, whereas the sine series in (13) converges to the odd period $2L$ extension of f. In many cases of interest we have no concern with the values of f outside the original interval $(0, L)$, and therefore the choice between (11) and (12) or (13) and (14) is determined by whether we prefer to represent $f(t)$ in the interval $(0, L)$ by a cosine series or a sine series. (See Example 2 for a situation that dictates our choice between a Fourier cosine series and a Fourier sine series to represent a given function.)

Example 1   Suppose that $f(t) = t$ for $0 < t < L$. Find both the Fourier cosine series and the Fourier sine series for f.

Solution   Equation (12) gives

$$a_0 = \frac{2}{L} \int_0^L t\, dt = \frac{2}{L} \left[\frac{1}{2} t^2 \right]_0^L = L$$

and

$$a_n = \frac{2}{L} \int_0^L t \cos \frac{n\pi t}{L} \, dt = \frac{2L}{n^2 \pi^2} \int_0^{n\pi} u \cos u \, du$$

$$= \frac{2L}{n^2 \pi^2} \Big[u \sin u + \cos u \Big]_0^{n\pi} = \begin{cases} -\dfrac{4L}{n^2 \pi^2} & \text{for } n \text{ odd;} \\ 0 & \text{for } n \text{ even.} \end{cases}$$

Thus the Fourier cosine series of f is

$$t = \frac{L}{2} - \frac{4L}{\pi^2} \left(\cos \frac{\pi t}{L} + \frac{1}{3^2} \cos \frac{3\pi t}{L} + \frac{1}{5^2} \cos \frac{5\pi t}{L} + \cdots \right) \tag{15}$$

for $0 < t < L$. Next, Eq. (14) gives

$$b_n = \frac{2}{L} \int_0^L t \sin \frac{n\pi t}{L} \, dt = \frac{2L}{n^2 \pi^2} \int_0^{n\pi} u \sin u \, du$$

$$= \frac{2L}{n^2 \pi^2} \Big[-u \cos u + \sin u \Big]_0^{n\pi} = \frac{2L}{n\pi} (-1)^{n+1}.$$

Thus the Fourier sine series of f is

$$t = \frac{2L}{\pi} \left(\sin \frac{\pi t}{L} - \frac{1}{2} \sin \frac{2\pi t}{L} + \frac{1}{3} \sin \frac{3\pi t}{L} - \cdots \right) \tag{16}$$

for $0 < t < L$. The series in Eq. (15) converges to the even period $2L$ extension of f shown in Fig. 9.3.4; the series in Eq. (16) converges to the odd period $2L$ extension shown in Fig. 9.3.5. ∎

FIGURE 9.3.4. The even period $2L$ extension of f.

FIGURE 9.3.5. The odd period $2L$ extension of f.

Termwise Differentiation of Fourier Series

In this and in subsequent sections, we want to consider Fourier series as possible solutions of differential equations. In order to substitute a Fourier series for the unknown dependent variable in a differential equation to check whether it is a solution, we first need to differentiate the series in order to compute the derivatives that appear in the equation. Care is required here; term-by-term differentiation of an infinite series of variable terms is not always valid. Theorem 1 gives sufficient conditions for the validity of termwise differentiation of a Fourier series.

THEOREM 1 Termwise Differentiation of Fourier Series

Suppose that the function f is continuous for all t, periodic with period $2L$, and that its derivative f' is piecewise smooth for all t. Then the Fourier series of f' is the series

$$f'(t) = \sum_{n=1}^{\infty} \left(-\frac{n\pi}{L} a_n \sin \frac{n\pi t}{L} + \frac{n\pi}{L} b_n \cos \frac{n\pi t}{L} \right) \tag{17}$$

obtained by termwise differentiation of the Fourier series

$$f(t) = \frac{a_0}{2} + \sum_{n=1}^{\infty} \left(a_n \cos \frac{n\pi t}{L} + b_n \sin \frac{n\pi t}{L} \right). \tag{18}$$

Proof: The point of the theorem is that the differentiated series in Eq. (17) actually converges to $f'(t)$ (with the usual proviso about average values). But because f' is periodic and piecewise smooth, we know from Theorem 1 of Section 9.2 that the Fourier series of f' converges to $f'(t)$:

$$f'(t) = \frac{\alpha_0}{2} + \sum_{n=1}^{\infty} \left(\alpha_n \cos \frac{n\pi t}{L} + \beta_n \sin \frac{n\pi t}{L} \right). \tag{19}$$

In order to prove Theorem 1, it therefore suffices to show that the series in Eqs. (17) and (19) are identical. We will do so under the additional hypothesis that f' is continuous everywhere. Then

$$\alpha_0 = \frac{1}{L} \int_{-L}^{L} f'(t)\, dt = \frac{1}{L} \Big[f(t) \Big]_{-L}^{L} = 0$$

because $f(L) = f(-L)$ by periodicity, and

$$\alpha_n = \frac{1}{L} \int_{-L}^{L} f'(t) \cos \frac{n\pi t}{L}\, dt$$

$$= \frac{1}{L} \left[f(t) \cos \frac{n\pi t}{L} \right]_{-L}^{L} + \frac{n\pi}{L} \cdot \frac{1}{L} \int_{-L}^{L} f(t) \sin \frac{n\pi t}{L}\, dt$$

—integration by parts. It follows that

$$\alpha_n = \frac{n\pi}{L} b_n.$$

Similarly, we find that

$$\beta_n = -\frac{n\pi}{L} a_n,$$

and therefore the series in Eqs. (17) and (19) are, indeed, identical. ▲

Whereas the assumption that the derivative f' is continuous is merely a convenience—the proof of Theorem 1 can be strengthened to allow isolated discontinuities in f'—it is important to note that the conclusion of Theorem 1 generally fails when f itself is discontinuous. For example, consider the Fourier series

$$t = \frac{2L}{\pi} \left(\sin \frac{\pi t}{L} - \frac{1}{2} \sin \frac{2\pi t}{L} + \frac{1}{3} \sin \frac{3\pi t}{L} - \cdots \right), \tag{16}$$

$-L < t < L$, of the discontinuous sawtooth function having the graph shown in Fig. 9.3.5. All the hypotheses of Theorem 1 are satisfied apart from the continuity of f, and f has only isolated jump discontinuities. But the series

$$2 \left(\cos \frac{\pi t}{L} - \cos \frac{2\pi t}{L} + \cos \frac{3\pi t}{L} - \cdots \right) \tag{20}$$

obtained by differentiating the series in Eq. (16) term by term diverges (for instance, when $t = 0$ and when $t = L$), and therefore termwise differentiation of the series in Eq. (16) is not valid.

By contrast, consider the (continuous) triangular wave function $f(t)$ having the graph shown in Fig. 9.3.4, with $f(t) = |t|$ for $-L < t < L$. This function satisfies all the hypotheses of Theorem 1, so its Fourier series

$$f(t) = \frac{L}{2} - \frac{4L}{\pi^2}\left(\cos\frac{\pi t}{L} + \frac{1}{3^2}\cos\frac{3\pi t}{L} + \frac{1}{5^2}\cos\frac{5\pi t}{L} + \cdots\right) \qquad (15)$$

can be differentiated termwise. The result is

$$f'(t) = \frac{4}{\pi}\left(\sin\frac{\pi t}{L} + \frac{1}{3}\sin\frac{3\pi t}{L} + \frac{1}{5}\sin\frac{5\pi t}{L} + \cdots\right), \qquad (21)$$

which is the Fourier series of the period $2L$ square wave function that takes the value -1 for $-L < t < 0$ and $+1$ for $0 < t < L$.

Fourier Series Solutions of Differential Equations

In the remainder of this chapter and in Chapter 10, we will frequently need to solve endpoint value problems of the general form

$$ax'' + bx' + cx = f(t) \quad (0 < t < L); \qquad (22)$$
$$x(0) = x(L) = 0, \qquad (23)$$

where the function $f(t)$ is given. Of course, we might consider applying the techniques of Chapter 3, solving the problem by

1. First finding the general solution $x_c = c_1 x_1 + c_2 x_2$ of the associated homogeneous differential equation;
2. Then finding a single particular solution x_p of the nonhomogeneous equation in (22); and
3. Finally, determining the constants c_1 and c_2 so that $x = x_c + x_p$ satisfies the endpoint conditions in (23).

In many problems, however, the following Fourier series method is more convenient and more useful. We first extend the definition of the function $f(t)$ to the interval $-L < t < 0$ in an appropriate way, and then to the entire real line by the periodicity conditions $f(t+2L) = f(t)$. Then the function f, if piecewise smooth, has a Fourier series

$$f(t) = \frac{A_0}{2} + \sum_{n=1}^{\infty}\left(A_n\cos\frac{n\pi t}{L} + B_n\sin\frac{n\pi t}{L}\right), \qquad (24)$$

which has coefficients $\{A_n\}$ and $\{B_n\}$ that we can and do compute. We then assume that the differential equation in (22) has a solution $x(t)$ with a Fourier series

$$x(t) = \frac{a_0}{2} + \sum_{n=1}^{\infty}\left(a_n\cos\frac{n\pi t}{L} + b_n\sin\frac{n\pi t}{L}\right) \qquad (25)$$

that may validly be differentiated twice termwise. We attempt to determine the coefficients in Eq. (25) by first substituting the series in Eqs. (24) and (25) into the differential equation in (22) and then equating coefficients of like terms—much as in the ordinary method of undetermined coefficients (Section 3.5), except that now we have infinitely many coefficients to determine. If this procedure is carried out in such a way that the resulting series in Eq. (25) also satisfies the endpoint conditions in (23), then we have a "formal Fourier series solution" of the original endpoint value problem; that is, a solution subject to verification of the assumed termwise differentiability. Example 2 illustrates this process.

Example 2   Find a formal Fourier series solution of the endpoint value problem

$$x'' + 4x = 4t, \tag{26}$$

$$x(0) = x(1) = 0. \tag{27}$$

Solution   Here $f(t) = 4t$ for $0 < t < 1$. A crucial first step—which we did not make explicit in the preceding outline—is to choose a periodic extension $f(t)$ so that each term in its Fourier series satisfies the endpoint conditions in (27). For this purpose we choose the odd period 2 extension, because each term of the form $\sin n\pi t$ satisfies (27). Then from the series in Eq. (16) with $L = 1$, we get the Fourier series

$$4t = \frac{8}{\pi} \sum_{n=1}^{\infty} \frac{(-1)^{n+1}}{n} \sin n\pi t \tag{28}$$

for $0 < t < 1$. We therefore anticipate a sine series solution

$$x(t) = \sum_{n=1}^{\infty} b_n \sin n\pi t, \tag{29}$$

noting that any such series will satisfy the endpoint conditions in (27). When we substitute the series in (28) and (29) in Eq. (26), the result is

$$\sum_{n=1}^{\infty}(-n^2\pi^2 + 4)b_n \sin n\pi t = \frac{8}{\pi} \sum_{n=1}^{\infty} \frac{(-1)^{n+1}}{n} \sin n\pi t. \tag{30}$$

We next equate coefficients of like terms in Eq. (30). This yields

$$b_n = \frac{8 \cdot (-1)^{n+1}}{n\pi(4 - n^2\pi^2)},$$

so our formal Fourier series solution is

$$x(t) = \frac{8}{\pi} \sum_{n=1}^{\infty} \frac{(-1)^{n+1} \sin n\pi t}{n(4 - n^2\pi^2)}. \tag{31}$$

In Problem 16 we ask you to derive the exact solution

$$x(t) = t - \frac{\sin 2t}{\sin 2} \qquad (0 \leq t \leq 1), \tag{32}$$

and to verify that (31) is the Fourier series of the odd period 2 extension of this solution.

The dashed curve in Fig. 9.3.6 was plotted by summing 10 terms of the Fourier series in (31). The solid curve for $0 \leq t \leq 2$ is the graph of the exact solution in (32).

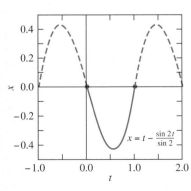

$x = t - \frac{\sin 2t}{\sin 2}$

FIGURE 9.3.6.   Graph of the solution in Example 2.

Termwise Integration of Fourier Series

Theorem 2 guarantees that the Fourier series of a piecewise continuous periodic function can always be integrated term by term, whether or not it converges! A proof is outlined in Problem 25.

THEOREM 2   Termwise Integration of Fourier Series

Suppose that f is a piecewise continuous periodic function with period $2L$ and Fourier series

$$f(t) \sim \frac{a_0}{2} + \sum_{n=1}^{\infty} \left(a_n \cos \frac{n\pi t}{L} + b_n \sin \frac{n\pi t}{L} \right), \tag{33}$$

which may not converge. Then

$$\int_0^t f(s)\,ds = \frac{a_0 t}{2} + \sum_{n=1}^{\infty} \frac{L}{n\pi} \left[a_n \sin \frac{n\pi t}{L} - b_n \left(\cos \frac{n\pi t}{L} - 1 \right) \right], \tag{34}$$

with the series on the right-hand side convergent for all t. Note that the series in Eq. (34) is the result of term-by-term integration of the series in (33), but if $a_0 \neq 0$ it is not a Fourier series because of its linear initial term $\frac{1}{2} a_0 t$.

Example 3

Let us attempt to verify the conclusion of Theorem 2 in the case that $f(t)$ is the period 2π function such that

$$f(t) = \begin{cases} -1, & -\pi < t < 0; \\ +1, & 0 < t < \pi. \end{cases} \tag{35}$$

By Example 1 of Section 9.1, the Fourier series of f is

$$f(t) = \frac{4}{\pi} \left(\sin t + \frac{1}{3} \sin 3t + \frac{1}{5} \sin 5t + \cdots \right). \tag{36}$$

Theorem 2 then implies that

$$F(t) = \int_0^t f(s)\,ds$$

$$= \int_0^t \frac{4}{\pi} \left(\sin s + \frac{1}{3} \sin 3s + \frac{1}{5} \sin 5s + \cdots \right) ds$$

$$= \frac{4}{\pi} \left[(1 - \cos t) + \frac{1}{3^2}(1 - \cos 3t) + \frac{1}{5^2}(1 - \cos 5t) + \cdots \right].$$

Thus

$$F(t) = \frac{4}{\pi} \left(1 + \frac{1}{3^2} + \frac{1}{5^2} + \cdots \right)$$

$$- \frac{4}{\pi} \left(\cos t + \frac{1}{3^2} \cos 3t + \frac{1}{5^2} \cos 5t + \cdots \right). \tag{37}$$

On the other hand, direct integration of (35) yields

$$F(t) = \int_0^t f(s)\,ds = |t| = \begin{cases} -t, & -\pi < t < 0, \\ t, & 0 < t < \pi. \end{cases}$$

We know from Example 1 in this section (with $L = \pi$) that

$$|t| = \frac{\pi}{2} - \frac{4}{\pi}\left(\cos t + \frac{1}{3^2}\cos 3t + \frac{1}{5^2}\cos 5t + \cdots\right). \tag{38}$$

We also know from Eq. (18) of Section 9.2 that

$$1 + \frac{1}{3^2} + \frac{1}{5^2} + \frac{1}{7^2} + \cdots = \frac{\pi^2}{8},$$

so it follows that the two series in Eqs. (37) and (38) are indeed identical. ∎

9.3 Problems

In Problems 1 through 10, a function $f(t)$ defined on an interval $0 < t < L$ is given. Find the Fourier cosine and sine series of f and sketch the graphs of the two extensions of f to which these two series converge.

1. $f(t) = 1, 0 < t < \pi$
2. $f(t) = 1 - t, 0 < t < 1$
3. $f(t) = 1 - t, 0 < t < 2$
4. $f(t) = \begin{cases} t, & 0 < t \leq 1; \\ 2 - t, & 1 \leq t < 2 \end{cases}$
5. $f(t) = \begin{cases} 0, & 0 < t < 1; \\ 1, & 1 < t < 2; \\ 0, & 2 < t < 3 \end{cases}$
6. $f(t) = t^2, 0 < t < \pi$
7. $f(t) = t(\pi - t), 0 < t < \pi$
8. $f(t) = t - t^2, 0 < t < 1$
9. $f(t) = \sin t, 0 < t < \pi$
10. $f(t) = \begin{cases} \sin t, & 0 < t \leq \pi \\ 0, & \pi \leq t < 2\pi \end{cases}$

Find formal Fourier series solutions of the endpoint value problems in Problems 11 through 14.

11. $x'' + 2x = 1, x(0) = x(\pi) = 0$
12. $x'' - 4x = 1, x(0) = x(\pi) = 0$
13. $x'' + x = t, x(0) = x(1) = 0$
14. $x'' + 2x = t, x(0) = x(2) = 0$
15. Find a formal Fourier series solution of the endpoint value problem

$$x'' + 2x = t, \quad x'(0) = x'(\pi) = 0.$$

(*Suggestion*: Use a Fourier cosine series in which each term satisfies the endpoint conditions.)

16. (a) Derive the solution $x(t) = t - (\sin 2t)/(\sin 2)$ of the endpoint value problem

$$x'' + 4x = 4t, \quad x(0) = x(1) = 0.$$

(b) Show that the series in Eq. (31) is the Fourier sine series of the solution in part (a).
17. (a) Suppose that f is an even function. Show that

$$\int_{-a}^0 f(t)\,dt = \int_0^a f(t)\,dt.$$

(b) Suppose that f is an odd function. Show that

$$\int_{-a}^0 f(t)\,dt = -\int_0^a f(t)\,dt.$$

18. By Example 2 of Section 9.2, the Fourier series of the period 2 function f with $f(t) = t^2$ for $0 < t < 2$ is

$$f(t) = \frac{4}{3} + \frac{4}{\pi^2}\sum_{n=1}^\infty \frac{\cos n\pi t}{n^2} - \frac{4}{\pi}\sum_{n=1}^\infty \frac{\sin n\pi t}{n}.$$

Show that the termwise derivative of this series does not converge to $f'(t)$.
19. Begin with the Fourier series

$$t = 2\sum_{n=1}^\infty \frac{(-1)^{n+1}}{n}\sin nt, \quad -\pi < t < \pi,$$

and integrate termwise three times in succession to obtain the series

$$\frac{1}{24}t^4 = \frac{\pi^2 t^2}{12} - 2\sum_{n=1}^\infty \frac{(-1)^n}{n^4}\cos nt + 2\sum_{n=1}^\infty \frac{(-1)^n}{n^4}.$$

20. Substitute $t = \pi/2$ and $t = \pi$ in the series of Problem 19 to obtain the summations

$$\sum_{n=1}^{\infty} \frac{1}{n^4} = \frac{\pi^4}{90}, \quad \sum_{n=1}^{\infty} \frac{(-1)^{n+1}}{n^4} = \frac{7\pi^4}{720},$$

and

$$1 + \frac{1}{3^4} + \frac{1}{5^4} + \frac{1}{7^4} + \cdots = \frac{\pi^4}{96}.$$

21. (*Odd half-multiple sine series*) Let $f(t)$ be given for $0 < t < L$, and define $F(t)$ for $0 < t < 2L$ as follows:

$$F(t) = \begin{cases} f(t), & 0 < t < L; \\ f(2L - t), & L < t < 2L. \end{cases}$$

Thus the graph of $F(t)$ is symmetric around the line $t = L$ (Fig. 9.3.7). Then the period $4L$ Fourier sine series of F is

$$F(t) = \sum_{n=1}^{\infty} b_n \sin \frac{n\pi t}{2L},$$

where

$$b_n = \frac{1}{L} \int_0^L f(t) \sin \frac{n\pi t}{2L} \, dt$$

$$+ \frac{1}{L} \int_L^{2L} f(2L - t) \sin \frac{n\pi t}{2L} \, dt.$$

Substitute $s = 2L - t$ in the second integral to derive the series (for $0 < t < L$)

$$f(t) = \sum_{n \text{ odd}} b_n \sin \frac{n\pi t}{2L},$$

where

$$b_n = \frac{2}{L} \int_0^L f(t) \sin \frac{n\pi t}{2L} \, dt \quad (n \text{ odd}).$$

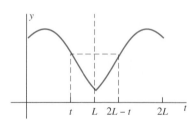

FIGURE 9.3.7. Construction of F from f in Problem 21.

22. (*Odd half-multiple cosine series*) Let $f(t)$ be given for $0 < t < L$, and define $G(t)$ for $0 < t < 2L$ as follows:

$$G(t) = \begin{cases} f(t), & 0 < t < L; \\ -f(2L - t), & L < t < 2L. \end{cases}$$

Use the period $4L$ Fourier cosine series of $G(t)$ to derive the series (for $0 < t < L$)

$$f(t) = \sum_{n \text{ odd}} a_n \cos \frac{n\pi t}{2L},$$

where

$$a_n = \frac{2}{L} \int_0^L f(t) \cos \frac{n\pi t}{2L} \, dt \quad (n \text{ odd}).$$

23. Given: $f(t) = t$, $0 < t < \pi$. Derive the odd half-multiple sine series (Problem 21)

$$f(t) = \frac{8}{\pi} \sum_{n \text{ odd}} \frac{(-1)^{(n-1)/2}}{n^2} \sin \frac{nt}{2}.$$

24. Given the endpoint value problem

$$x'' - x = t, \quad x(0) = 0, \quad x'(\pi) = 0,$$

note that any constant multiple of $\sin(nt/2)$ with n odd satisfies the endpoint conditions. Hence use the odd half-multiple sine series of Problem 23 to derive the formal Fourier series solution

$$x(t) = \frac{32}{\pi} \sum_{n \text{ odd}} \frac{(-1)^{(n+1)/2}}{n^2(n^2 + 4)} \sin \frac{nt}{2}.$$

25. In this problem we outline the proof of Theorem 2. Suppose that $f(t)$ is a piecewise continuous period $2L$ function. Define

$$F(t) = \int_0^t \left[f(s) - \tfrac{1}{2} a_0 \right] ds,$$

where $\{a_n\}$ and $\{b_n\}$ denote the Fourier coefficients of $f(t)$. **(a)** Show directly that $F(t + 2L) = F(t)$, so that F is a continuous period $2L$ function and therefore has a convergent Fourier series

$$F(t) = \frac{A_0}{2} + \sum_{n=1}^{\infty} \left(A_n \cos \frac{n\pi t}{L} + B_n \sin \frac{n\pi t}{L} \right).$$

(b) Suppose that $n \geq 1$. Show by direct computation that

$$A_n = -\frac{L}{n\pi} b_n \quad \text{and} \quad B_n = \frac{L}{n\pi} a_n.$$

(c) Thus

$$\int_0^t f(s) \, ds = \frac{t}{2} a_0 + \frac{1}{2} A_0$$

$$+ \sum_{n=1}^{\infty} \frac{L}{n\pi} \left(a_n \sin \frac{n\pi t}{L} - b_n \cos \frac{n\pi t}{L} \right).$$

Finally, substitute $t = 0$ to see that

$$\frac{1}{2} A_0 = \sum_{n=1}^{\infty} \frac{L}{n\pi} b_n.$$

9.3 Application Fourier Series of Piecewise Smooth Functions

Most computer algebra systems permit the use of unit step functions for the efficient derivation of Fourier series of "piecewise-defined" functions. Here we illustrate the use of *Maple* for this purpose. *Mathematica* and MATLAB versions can be found in the applications manual that accompanies this text.

Let the "unit function" unit(t, a, b) have the value 1 on the interval $a \leqq t < b$ and the value 0 otherwise. Then we can define a given piecewise smooth function $f(t)$ as a "linear combination" of different unit functions corresponding to the separate intervals on which the function is smooth, with the unit function for each interval multiplied by the formula defining $f(t)$ on that interval. For example, consider the even period 2π function whose graph is shown in Fig. 9.3.8. This "trapezoidal wave function" is defined for $0 < t < \pi$ by

$$f(t) = \frac{\pi}{3}\text{unit}\left(t, 0, \frac{\pi}{6}\right)$$

$$+ \left(\frac{\pi}{2} - t\right)\text{unit}\left(t, \frac{\pi}{6}, \frac{5\pi}{6}\right) + \left(-\frac{\pi}{3}\right)\text{unit}\left(t, \frac{5\pi}{6}, \pi\right). \qquad (1)$$

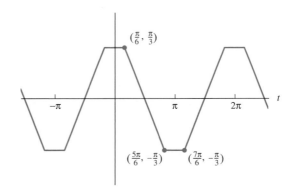

FIGURE 9.3.8. Even period 2π trapezoidal-wave function.

The unit step function (with values 0 for $t < 0$ and 1 for $t > 0$) is available in *Maple* as the "Heaviside function." For instance, Heaviside(-2) = 0 and Heaviside(3) = 1. The unit function on the interval $[a, b]$ can be defined by

```
unit := (t,a,b) -> Heaviside(t-a) - Heaviside(t-b):
```

Then the trapezoidal-wave function in Eq. (1) is defined for $0 \leqq t \leqq \pi$ by

```
f := t -> (Pi/3)*unit(t, 0, Pi/6) +
          (Pi/2 - t)*unit(t, Pi/6, 5*Pi/6) +
          (-Pi/3)*unit(t, 5*Pi/6, Pi):
```

We can now calculate the Fourier coefficients in the cosine series $f(t) = \frac{1}{2}a_0 + \sum a_n \cos nt$.

```
a := n -> (2/Pi)*int(f(t)*cos(n*t), t=0..Pi);
```

We then find that a typical partial sum of the series is given by

```
fourierSum := a(0)/2 + sum(a(n)*cos(n*t), n=1..25);
```

$$fourierSum := 2\frac{\sqrt{3}\,\cos(t)}{\pi} - \frac{2}{25}\frac{\sqrt{3}\,\cos(5t)}{\pi} - \frac{2}{49}\frac{\sqrt{3}\,\cos(7t)}{\pi}$$

$$+\frac{2}{121}\frac{\sqrt{3}\,\cos(11t)}{\pi} + \frac{2}{169}\frac{\sqrt{3}\,\cos(13t)}{\pi} - \frac{2}{289}\frac{\sqrt{3}\,\cos(17t)}{\pi}$$

$$-\frac{2}{361}\frac{\sqrt{3}\,\cos(19t)}{\pi} + \frac{2}{529}\frac{\sqrt{3}\,\cos(23t)}{\pi} + \frac{2}{625}\frac{\sqrt{3}\,\cos(25t)}{\pi}$$

Thus we discover the lovely Fourier series

$$f(t) = \frac{2\sqrt{3}}{\pi}\sum \frac{(\pm)\cos nt}{n^2} \tag{2}$$

with a $+--++--++$ pattern of signs, and where the summation is taken over all odd positive integers n that are *not* multiples of 3. You can enter the command

```
plot(fourierSum, t=-2*Pi..3*Pi);
```

to verify that this Fourier series is consistent with Fig. 9.3.8.

You can then apply this method to find the Fourier series of the following period 2π functions.

1. The even square-wave function whose graph is shown in Fig. 9.3.9.
2. The even and odd triangular-wave functions whose graphs are shown in Figs. 9.2.4 and 9.3.10.
3. The odd trapezoidal-wave function whose graph is shown in Fig. 9.2.5.

Then find similarly the Fourier series of some piecewise smooth functions of your own choice, perhaps ones that have periods other than 2π and are neither even nor odd.

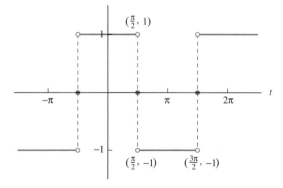

FIGURE 9.3.9. Even period 2π square-wave function.

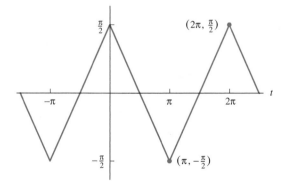

FIGURE 9.3.10. Even period 2π triangular-wave function.

9.4 Applications of Fourier Series

We consider first the undamped motion of a mass m on a spring with Hooke's constant k under the influence of a *periodic* external force $F(t)$, as indicated in Fig. 9.4.1. Its displacement $x(t)$ from equilibrium satisfies the familiar equation

$$mx'' + kx = F(t). \tag{1}$$

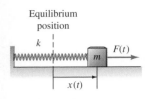

FIGURE 9.4.1. A mass-and-spring system with external force.

The general solution of Eq. (1) is of the form

$$x(t) = c_1 \cos \omega_0 t + c_2 \sin \omega_0 t + x_p(t), \tag{2}$$

where $\omega_0 = \sqrt{k/m}$ is the natural frequency of the system and $x_p(t)$ is a particular solution of Eq. (1). The values c_1 and c_2 would be determined by the initial conditions. Here we want to use Fourier series to find a *periodic* particular solution of Eq. (1). We will denote it by $x_{sp}(t)$ and call it a **steady periodic solution.**

We assume for simplicity that $F(t)$ is an odd function with period $2L$, so its Fourier series has the form

$$F(t) = \sum_{n=1}^{\infty} B_n \sin \frac{n\pi t}{L}. \tag{3}$$

If $n\pi/L$ is not equal to ω_0 for any positive integer n, we can determine a steady periodic solution of the form

$$x_{sp}(t) = \sum_{n=1}^{\infty} b_n \sin \frac{n\pi t}{L} \tag{4}$$

by substituting the series in Eqs. (3) and (4) in Eq. (1) to find the coefficients in Eq. (4). Example 1 illustrates this procedure.

Example 1 Suppose that $m = 2$ kg, $k = 32$ N/m, and that $F(t)$ is an odd periodic force with a period of 2 s given in one period by

$$F(t) = \begin{cases} +10\,\text{N} & \text{if } 0 < t < 1; \\ -10\,\text{N} & \text{if } 1 < t < 2. \end{cases} \tag{5}$$

Find the steady periodic motion $x_{sp}(t)$.

Solution The graph of the periodic forcing function $F(t)$ is shown in Fig. 9.4.2. By essentially the same computation as in Example 1 of Section 9.1, the Fourier series of $F(t)$ is

$$F(t) = \frac{40}{\pi} \sum_{n \text{ odd}} \frac{\sin n\pi t}{n}; \tag{6}$$

note that it contains only terms corresponding to n odd. When we substitute this series and

$$x_{sp}(t) = \sum_{n \text{ odd}} b_n \sin n\pi t, \tag{7}$$

a trial solution likewise containing only odd terms, into Eq. (1) with $m = 2$ and $k = 32$, we get

$$\sum_{n \text{ odd}} b_n(-2n^2\pi^2 + 32) \sin n\pi t = \frac{40}{\pi} \sum_{n \text{ odd}} \frac{\sin n\pi t}{n}.$$

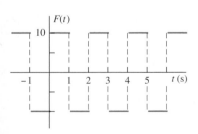

FIGURE 9.4.2. The graph of the forcing function of Example 1.

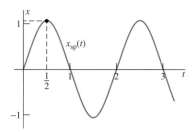

FIGURE 9.4.3. The graph of the steady periodic solution $x_{sp}(t)$.

We equate coefficients of like terms; the result is that

$$b_n = \frac{20}{n\pi(16 - n^2\pi^2)} \qquad \text{for } n \text{ odd.}$$

Hence

$$x_{sp}(t) = \frac{20}{\pi} \sum_{n \text{ odd}} \frac{\sin n\pi t}{n(16 - n^2\pi^2)}. \tag{8}$$

The fact that each term in Eq. (8) is symmetric around $t = \frac{1}{2}$ suggests that $x_{sp}(t)$ is maximal when $t = \frac{1}{2}$, as does the graph in Fig. 9.4.3. Assuming this, we find the amplitude of the steady periodic motion to be

$$x_{sp}\left(\tfrac{1}{2}\right) = \frac{20}{\pi} \sum_{n \text{ odd}} \frac{1}{n(16 - n^2\pi^2)} \sin\frac{n\pi}{2}.$$

The first 100 terms yield the correct four-place value $x\left(\frac{1}{2}\right) \approx 1.0634$ m. ∎

FIGURE 9.4.4. The steady periodic solution $x_{sp}(t)$ and the nonperiodic solution $x(t)$.

The periodic solution $x_{sp}(t)$ is a single particular solution of the nonhomogeneous differential equation $2x'' + 32x = F(t)$ that has associated homogeneous equation $x'' + 16x = 0$. Hence the general solution is of the form

$$x(t) = A\cos 4t + B\sin 4t + x_{sp}(t)$$

and thus is a sum of periodic functions with periods 2 and $2\pi/4 = \pi/2$ unless $A = B = 0$. Because numerical calculation gives $x_{sp}(0) = 0$ and $x_{sp}'(0) \approx 2.7314$, the two period $\pi/2$ terms both drop out—leaving the period 2 solution $x_{sp}(t)$—only with these particular initial values of $x(0)$ and $x'(0)$. With any other initial conditions, either A or B (or both) is nonzero, and the corresponding solution is a superposition of two oscillations whose periods have an irrational ratio (see Problems 19 and 20). For instance, Fig. 9.4.4 shows the graphs of the periodic solution $x_{sp}(t)$ and the solution $x(t)$ that satisfies the initial conditions $x(0) = 2$ and $x'(0) = 0$ and appears to be nonperiodic.

Pure Resonance

If there is a nonzero term $B_N \sin(N\pi t/L)$ in the Fourier series solution of the force function $F(t)$ in Eq. (1) for which $N\pi/L = \omega_0$, then this term causes **pure resonance**. The reason is that the equation

$$mx'' + kx = B_N \sin\omega_0 t$$

has the resonance solution

$$x(t) = -\frac{B_N}{2m\omega_0} t \cos\omega_0 t$$

if $\omega_0 = \sqrt{k/m}$. The solution corresponding to Eq. (4) in this case is then

$$x(t) = -\frac{B_N}{2m\omega_0} t \cos\omega_0 t + \sum_{n \neq N} \frac{B_N}{m(\omega_0^2 - n^2\pi^2/L^2)} \sin\frac{n\pi t}{L}. \tag{9}$$

Example 2   Suppose that $m = 2$ kg and $k = 32$ N/m as in Example 1. Determine whether pure resonance will occur if $F(t)$ is the odd periodic function defined in one period to be

(a) $F(t) = \begin{cases} +10, & 0 < t < \pi; \\ -10, & \pi < t < 2\pi. \end{cases}$

(b) $F(t) = 10t, \quad -\pi < t < \pi.$

Solution   (a) The natural frequency is $\omega_0 = 4$, and the Fourier series of $F(t)$ is

$$F(t) = \frac{40}{\pi} \left(\sin t + \frac{1}{3} \sin 3t + \frac{1}{5} \sin 5t + \cdots \right).$$

Because this series contains no $\sin 4t$ term, no resonance occurs.

(b) In this case the Fourier series is

$$F(t) = 20 \sum_{n=1}^{\infty} \frac{(-1)^{n+1}}{n} \sin nt.$$

Pure resonance occurs because of the presence of the term containing the factor $\sin 4t$.   ∎

Example 3 illustrates the *near resonance* that can occur when a single term in the solution is magnified because its frequency is close to the natural frequency ω_0.

Example 3   Find a steady periodic solution of

$$x'' + 10x = F(t), \tag{10}$$

where $F(t)$ is the period 4 function with $F(t) = 5t$ for $-2 < t < 2$ and Fourier series

$$F(t) = \frac{20}{\pi} \sum_{n=1}^{\infty} \frac{(-1)^{n+1}}{n} \sin \frac{n\pi t}{2}. \tag{11}$$

Solution   When we substitute Eq. (11) and

$$x_{\text{sp}}(t) = \sum_{n=1}^{\infty} b_n \sin \frac{n\pi t}{2}$$

in (10), we obtain

$$\sum_{n=1}^{\infty} b_n \left(-\frac{n^2\pi^2}{4} + 10 \right) \sin \frac{n\pi t}{2} = \frac{20}{\pi} \sum_{n=1}^{\infty} \frac{(-1)^{n+1}}{n} \sin \frac{n\pi t}{2}.$$

We equate coefficients of like terms and then solve for b_n to get the steady periodic solution

$$x_{\text{sp}}(t) = \frac{80}{\pi} \sum_{n=1}^{\infty} \frac{(-1)^{n+1}}{n(40 - n^2\pi^2)} \sin \frac{n\pi t}{2}$$

$$\approx (0.8452) \sin \frac{\pi t}{2} - (24.4111) \sin \frac{2\pi t}{2} - (0.1738) \sin \frac{3\pi t}{2} + \cdots .$$

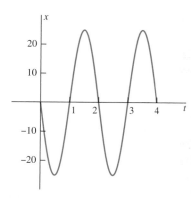

FIGURE 9.4.5. The graph of $x_{sp}(t)$.

The very large magnitude of the second term results from the fact that $\omega_0 = \sqrt{10} \approx \pi = 2\pi/2$. Thus the dominant motion of a spring with the differential equation in (10) would be an oscillation with frequency π radians per second, period 2 s, and amplitude about 24, consistent with the graph of $x_{sp}(t)$ shown in Fig. 9.4.5. ∎

Damped Forced Oscillations

Now we consider the motion of a mass m attached both to a spring with Hooke's constant k and to a dashpot with damping constant c, under the influence of a *periodic* external force $F(t)$ (Fig. 9.4.6). The displacement $x(t)$ of the mass from equilibrium satisfies the equation

$$mx'' + cx' + kx = F(t). \tag{12}$$

We recall from Problem 25 of Section 3.6 that the steady periodic solution of Eq. (12) with $F(t) = F_0 \sin \omega t$ is

FIGURE 9.4.6. A damped mass–and–spring system with external force.

$$x(t) = \frac{F_0}{\sqrt{(k - m\omega^2)^2 + (c\omega)^2}} \sin(\omega t - \alpha), \tag{13}$$

where

$$\alpha = \tan^{-1} \frac{c\omega}{k - m\omega^2}, \quad 0 \leq \alpha \leq \pi. \tag{14}$$

If $F(t)$ is an odd period $2L$ function with Fourier series

$$F(t) = \sum_{n=1}^{\infty} B_n \sin \frac{n\pi t}{L}, \tag{15}$$

then the preceding formulas yield, by superposition, the steady periodic solution

$$x_{sp}(t) = \sum_{n=1}^{\infty} \frac{B_n \sin(\omega_n t - \alpha_n)}{\sqrt{(k - m\omega_n^2)^2 + (c\omega_n)^2}}, \tag{16}$$

where $\omega_n = n\pi/L$ and α_n is the angle determined by Eq. (14) with this value of ω. Example 4 illustrates the interesting fact that the dominant frequency of the steady periodic solution can be an *integral multiple* of the frequency of the force $F(t)$.

Example 4 Suppose that $m = 3$ kg, $c = 0.02$ N/m/s, $k = 27$ N/m, and $F(t)$ is the odd period 2π function with $F(t) = \pi t - t^2$ if $0 < t < \pi$. Find the steady periodic motion $x_{sp}(t)$.

Solution We find that the Fourier series of $F(t)$ is

$$F(t) = \frac{8}{\pi} \left(\sin t + \frac{1}{3^3} \sin 3t + \frac{1}{5^3} \sin 5t + \cdots \right). \tag{17}$$

Thus $B_n = 0$ for n even, $B_n = 8/(\pi n^3)$ for n odd, and $\omega_n = n$. Equation (16) gives

$$x_{sp}(t) = \frac{8}{\pi} \sum_{n \text{ odd}} \frac{\sin(nt - \alpha_n)}{n^3 \sqrt{(27 - 3n^2)^2 + (0.02n)^2}} \tag{18}$$

with

$$\alpha_n = \tan^{-1}\frac{(0.02)n}{27 - 3n^2}, \quad 0 \leqq \alpha_n \leqq \pi. \tag{19}$$

With the aid of a programmable calculator, we find that

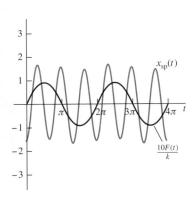

$$x_{\text{sp}}(t) \approx (0.1061)\sin(t - 0.0008) + (1.5719)\sin\left(3t - \tfrac{1}{2}\pi\right)$$
$$+ (0.0004)\sin(5t - 3.1437) + (0.0001)\sin(7t - 3.1428) + \cdots. \tag{20}$$

FIGURE 9.4.7. The imposed force and the resulting steady periodic motion in Example 4.

Because the coefficient corresponding to $n = 3$ is much larger than the others, the response of this system is approximately a sinusoidal motion with frequency *three times* that of the input force. Figure 9.4.7 shows $x_{\text{sp}}(t)$ in comparison with the scaled force $10F(t)/k$ that has the appropriate dimension of distance.

What is happening here is this: The mass $m = 3$ on a spring with $k = 27$ has (if we ignore the small effect of the dashpot) a natural frequency $\omega_0 = \sqrt{k/m} = 3$ rad/s. The imposed external force $F(t)$ has a (smallest) period of 2π s and hence a fundamental frequency of 1 rad/s. Consequently, the term corresponding to $n = 3$ in the Fourier series of $F(t)$ (in Eq. (17)) has the same frequency as the natural frequency of the system. Thus near resonance vibrations occur, with the mass completing essentially *three* oscillations for every single oscillation of the external force. This is the physical effect of the dominant $n = 3$ term on the right-hand side in Eq. (20). For instance, you can push a friend in a swing quite high even if you push the swing only every *third* time it returns to you. This also explains why some transformers "hum" at a frequency much higher than 60 Hz.

This is a general phenomenon that must be taken into account in the design of mechanical systems. To avoid the occurrence of abnormally large and potentially destructive near resonance vibrations, the system must be so designed that it is not subject to any external periodic force, some *integral multiple* of whose fundamental frequency is close to a natural frequency of vibration. ∎

Example 1

Continued

Finally, let us add to the mass–spring system of Example 1 a dashpot with damping constant $c = 3$ N/m/s. Then, since $m = 2$ and $k = 32$, the differential equation satisfied by the mass's displacement function $x(t)$ is now

$$2x'' + 3x' + 32x = F(t), \tag{21}$$

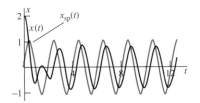

FIGURE 9.4.8. The steady periodic solution $x_{\text{sp}}(t)$ and the damped solution $x(t)$.

where $F(t)$ is the periodic force function defined in Eq. (5). Figure 9.4.8 shows graphs of both the steady periodic solution $x_{\text{sp}}(t)$ for the original undamped system of Example 1 and a numerically calculated solution of Eq. (21) with initial conditions $x(0) = 2$ and $x'(0) = 1$. As an initial transient solution determined by the initial conditions dies out, it appears that the damped solution $x(t)$ converges to a steady periodic solution of (21). However, we observe two evident effects of the damping—the amplitude of the steady periodic oscillation is decreased, and the damped steady oscillations lag behind the undamped steady oscillations. ∎

Find the steady periodic solution $x_{sp}(t)$ of each of the differential equations in 1 through 6. Use a computer algebra system to plot enough terms of the series to determine the visual appearance of the graph of $x_{sp}(t)$.

1. $x'' + 5x = F(t)$, where $F(t)$ is the function of period 2π such that $F(t) = 3$ if $0 < t < \pi$, $F(t) = -3$ if $\pi < t < 2\pi$.

2. $x'' + 10x = F(t)$, where $F(t)$ is the even function of period 4 such that $F(t) = 3$ if $0 < t < 1$, $F(t) = -3$ if $1 < t < 2$.

3. $x'' + 3x = F(t)$, where $F(t)$ is the odd function of period 2π such that $F(t) = 2t$ if $0 < t < \pi$.

4. $x'' + 4x = F(t)$, where $F(t)$ is the even function of period 4 such that $F(t) = 2t$ if $0 < t < 2$.

5. $x'' + 10x = F(t)$, where $F(t)$ is the odd function of period 2 such that $F(t) = t - t^2$ if $0 < t < 1$.

6. $x'' + 2x = F(t)$, where $F(t)$ is the even function of period 2π such that $F(t) = \sin t$ if $0 < t < \pi$.

In each of Problems 7 through 12, the mass m and Hooke's constant k for a mass-and-spring system are given. Determine whether or not pure resonance will occur under the influence of the given external periodic force $F(t)$.

7. $m = 1$, $k = 9$; $F(t)$ is the odd function of period 2π with $F(t) = 1$ for $0 < t < \pi$.

8. $m = 2$, $k = 10$; $F(t)$ is the odd function of period 2 with $F(t) = 1$ for $0 < t < 1$.

9. $m = 3$, $k = 12$; $F(t)$ is the odd function of period 2π with $F(t) = 3$ for $0 < t < \pi$.

10. $m = 1$, $k = 4\pi^2$; $F(t)$ is the odd function of period 2 with $F(t) = 2t$ for $0 < t < 1$.

11. $m = 3$, $k = 48$; $F(t)$ is the even function of period 2π with $F(t) = t$ for $0 < t < \pi$.

12. $m = 2$, $k = 50$; $F(t)$ is the odd function of period 2π with $F(t) = \pi t - t^2$ for $0 < t < \pi$.

In each of Problems 13 through 16, the values of m, c, and k for a damped mass-and-spring system are given. Find the steady periodic motion—in the form of Eq. (16)—of the mass under the influence of the given external force $F(t)$. Compute the coefficients and phase angles for the first three nonzero terms in the series for $x_{sp}(t)$.

13. $m = 1$, $c = 0.1$, $k = 4$; $F(t)$ is the force of Problem 1.

14. $m = 2$, $c = 0.1$, $k = 18$; $F(t)$ is the force of Problem 3.

15. $m = 3$, $c = 1$, $k = 30$; $F(t)$ is the force of Problem 5.

16. $m = 1$, $c = 0.01$, $k = 4$; $F(t)$ is the force of Problem 4.

17. Consider a forced damped mass-and-spring system with $m = \frac{1}{4}$ slug, $c = 0.6$ lb/ft/s, $k = 36$ lb/ft. The force $F(t)$ is the period 2 (s) function with $F(t) = 15$ if $0 < t < 1$, $F(t) = -15$ if $1 < t < 2$. **(a)** Find the steady periodic solution in the form

$$x_{sp}(t) = \sum_{n=1}^{\infty} b_n \sin(n\pi t - \alpha_n).$$

(b) Find the location—to the nearest tenth of an inch—of the mass when $t = 5$ s.

18. Consider a forced damped mass-and-spring system with $m = 1$, $c = 0.01$, and $k = 25$. The force $F(t)$ is the odd function of period 2π with $F(t) = t$ if $0 < t < \pi/2$, $F(t) = \pi - t$ if $\pi/2 < t < \pi$. Find the steady periodic motion; compute enough terms of its series to see that the dominant frequency of the motion is *five* times that of the external force.

19. Suppose the functions $f(t)$ and $g(t)$ are periodic with periods P and Q, respectively. If the ratio P/Q of their periods is a rational number, show that the sum $f(t) + g(t)$ is a periodic function.

20. If p/q is irrational, prove that the function $f(t) = \cos pt + \cos qt$ is not a periodic function. *Suggestion*: Show that the assumption $f(t+L) = f(t)$ would (upon substituting $t = 0$) imply that p/q is rational.

9.5 Heat Conduction and Separation of Variables

The most important applications of Fourier series are to the solution of partial differential equations by means of the method of separation of variables that we introduce in this section. Recall that a *partial differential equation* is one containing one or more *partial* derivatives of a dependent variable that is a function of at least two independent variables. An example is the **one-dimensional heat equation**

$$\frac{\partial u}{\partial t} = k \frac{\partial^2 u}{\partial x^2}, \tag{1}$$

in which the dependent variable u is an unknown function of x and t, and k is a given positive constant.

The Heated Rod

Equation (1) models the variation of temperature u with position x and time t in a heated rod that extends along the x-axis. We assume that the rod has uniform cross section with area A perpendicular to the axis and that it is made of a homogeneous material. We assume further that the cross section of the rod is so small that u is constant on each cross section, and that the lateral surface of the rod is insulated so that no heat can pass through it. Then u will, indeed, be a function of x and t, and heat will flow along the rod in only the x-direction. In general, we envision heat as flowing like a fluid from the warmer to the cooler parts of a body.

The **heat flux** $\phi(x, t)$ in the rod is the *rate of flow of heat* (in the positive x-direction) at time t across a unit area of the rod's cross section at x. Typical units for ϕ are calories (of heat) per second per square centimeter (of area). The derivation of Eq. (1) is based on the empirical principle that

$$\phi = -K\frac{\partial u}{\partial x}, \tag{2}$$

where the positive proportionality constant K is called the **thermal conductivity** of the material of the rod. Note that if $u_x > 0$, then $\phi < 0$, meaning that heat is flowing in the negative x-direction, while if $u_x < 0$, then $\phi > 0$, so heat is flowing in the positive x-direction. Thus the *rate* of heat flow is proportional to $|u_x|$, and the *direction* of heat flow is in the direction along the rod in which the temperature u is decreasing. In short, heat flows from a warm place to a cool place, not vice versa.

Now consider a small segment of the rod corresponding to the interval $[x, x + \Delta x]$, as shown in Fig. 9.5.1. The rate of flow R (in calories per second) of heat *into* this segment through its two ends is

$$R = A\phi(x, t) - A\phi(x + \Delta x, t) = KA[u_x(x + \Delta x, t) - u_x(x, t)]. \tag{3}$$

FIGURE 9.5.1. Net flow of heat into a short segment of the rod.

The resulting time rate of change u_t of the temperature in the segment depends on its density δ (grams per cubic centimeter) and specific heat c (both assumed constant). The **specific heat** c is the amount of heat (in calories) required to raise by $1°$ (Celsius) the temperature of 1 g of material. Consequently $c\delta u$ calories of heat are required to raise 1 cm^3 of the material from temperature zero to temperature u. A short slice of the rod of length dx has volume $A\,dx$, so $c\delta u A\,dx$ calories of heat are required to raise the temperature of this slice from 0 to u. The **heat content**

$$Q(t) = \int_x^{x+\Delta x} c\delta A u(x, t)\,dx \tag{4}$$

of the segment $[x, x + \Delta x]$ of the rod is the amount of heat needed to raise it from zero temperature to the given temperature $u(x, t)$. Because heat enters and leaves the segment only through its ends, we see from Eq. (3) that

$$Q'(t) = KA[u_x(x + \Delta x, t) - u_x(x, t)], \tag{5}$$

because $R = dQ/dt$. Thus by differentiating Eq. (4) within the integral and applying the mean value theorem for integrals, we see that

$$Q'(t) = \int_x^{x+\Delta x} c\delta A u_t(x, t)\,dx = c\delta A u_t(\overline{x}, t)\,\Delta x \tag{6}$$

for some $\bar{x}$ in $(x, x + \Delta x)$. Upon equating the values in Eqs. (5) and (6), we get

$$c\delta A u_t(\bar{x}, t)\,\Delta x = KA[u_x(x + \Delta x, t) - u_x(x, t)], \tag{7}$$

so

$$u_t(\bar{x}, t) = k\frac{u_x(x + \Delta x, t) - u_x(x, t)}{\Delta x}, \tag{8}$$

where

$$k = \frac{K}{c\delta} \tag{9}$$

is the **thermal diffusivity** of the material. We now take the limit as $\Delta x \to 0$, so $\bar{x} \to x$ (because $\bar{x}$ lies in the interval $[x, x + \Delta x]$ with fixed left endpoint x). Then the two sides of the equation in (8) approach the two sides of the one-dimensional heat equation

$$\frac{\partial u}{\partial t} = k\frac{\partial^2 u}{\partial x^2}. \tag{1}$$

Thus the temperature $u(x, t)$ in the thin rod with insulated sides must satisfy this partial differential equation.

Boundary Conditions

Now suppose that the rod has finite length L, extending from $x = 0$ to $x = L$. Its temperature function $u(x, t)$ will be determined among all possible solutions of Eq. (1) by appropriate subsidiary conditions. In fact, whereas a solution of an ordinary differential equation involves arbitrary *constants*, a solution of a partial differential equation generally involves arbitrary *functions*. In the case of the heated rod, we can specify its temperature function $f(x)$ at time $t = 0$. This gives the *initial condition*

$$u(x, 0) = f(x). \tag{10}$$

We may also specify fixed temperatures at the two ends of the rod. For instance, if each end were clamped against a large block of ice at temperature zero, we would have the *endpoint conditions*

$$u(0, t) = u(L, t) = 0 \qquad \text{(for all } t > 0\text{)}. \tag{11}$$

Combining all this, we get the **boundary value problem**

$$\frac{\partial u}{\partial t} = k\frac{\partial^2 u}{\partial x^2} \qquad (0 < x < L, \ t > 0); \tag{12a}$$

$$u(0, t) = u(L, t) = 0, \qquad (t > 0), \tag{12b}$$

$$u(x, 0) = f(x) \qquad (0 < x < L). \tag{12c}$$

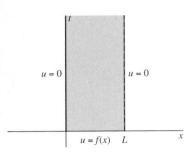

FIGURE 9.5.2. A geometric interpretation of the boundary value problem in Eqs. (12a)–(12c).

Figure 9.5.2 gives a geometric interpretation of the boundary value problem in (12): We are to find a function $u(x, t)$ that is continuous on the unbounded strip (including its boundary) shaded in the xt-plane. This function must satisfy the differential equation in (12a) at each interior point of the strip, and on the boundary of the strip must have the values prescribed by the *boundary conditions* in (12b) and (12c). Physical intuition suggests that if $f(x)$ is a reasonable function, then there will exist one and only one such function $u(x, t)$.

Instead of having fixed temperatures, the two ends of the rod might be insulated. In this case no heat would flow through either end, so we see from Eq. (2) that the conditions in (12b) would be replaced in the boundary value problem by the endpoint conditions

$$u_x(0, t) = u_x(L, t) = 0 \tag{13}$$

(for all t). Alternatively, the rod could be insulated at one end and have a fixed temperature at the other. This and other endpoint possibilities are discussed in the Problems.

Superposition of Solutions

Note that the heat equation in (12a) is *linear*. That is, any linear combination $u = c_1 u_1 + c_2 u_2$ of two solutions of (12a) is also a solution of (12a); this follows immediately from the linearity of partial differentiation. It is also true that if u_1 and u_2 each satisfy the conditions in (12b), then so does any linear combination $u = c_1 u_1 + c_2 u_2$. The conditions in (12b) are therefore called **homogeneous** boundary conditions (though a more descriptive term might be *linear* boundary conditions). By contrast, the final boundary condition in (12c) is not homogeneous; it is a **nonhomogeneous** boundary condition.

Our overall strategy for solving the boundary value problem in (12) will be to find functions u_1, u_2, u_3, ... that satisfy both the partial differential equation in (12a) and the homogeneous boundary conditions in (12b), and then attempt to combine these functions by superposition, as if they were building blocks, in the hope of obtaining a solution $u = c_1 u_1 + c_2 u_2 + \cdots$ that satisfies the nonhomogeneous condition in (12c) as well. Example 1 illustrates this approach.

Example 1 It is easy to verify by direct substitution that each of the functions

$$u_1(x, t) = e^{-t} \sin x, \quad u_2(x, t) = e^{-4t} \sin 2x, \quad \text{and} \quad u_3(x, t) = e^{-9t} \sin 3x$$

satisfies the equation $u_t = u_{xx}$. Use these functions to construct a solution of the boundary value problem

$$\frac{\partial u}{\partial t} = \frac{\partial^2 u}{\partial x^2} \quad (0 < x < \pi, \quad t > 0); \tag{14a}$$

$$u(0, t) = u(\pi, t) = 0, \tag{14b}$$

$$u(x, 0) = 80 \sin^3 x = 60 \sin x - 20 \sin 3x. \tag{14c}$$

Solution Any linear combination of the form

$$u(x, t) = c_1 u_1(x, t) + c_2 u_2(x, t) + c_3 u_3(x, t)$$
$$= c_1 e^{-t} \sin x + c_2 e^{-4t} \sin 2x + c_3 e^{-9t} \sin 3x$$

satisfies both the differential equation in (14a) and the homogeneous conditions in (14b). Because

$$u(x, 0) = c_1 \sin x + c_2 \sin 2x + c_3 \sin 3x,$$

we see that we can also satisfy the nonhomogeneous condition in (14c) simply by choosing $c_1 = 60$, $c_2 = 0$, and $c_3 = -20$. Thus a solution of the given boundary value problem is

$$u(x, t) = 60e^{-t} \sin x - 20e^{-9t} \sin 3x.$$ ■

The boundary value problem in Example 1 is exceptionally simple in that only a finite number of homogeneous solutions are needed to satisfy by superposition the nonhomogeneous boundary condition. It is more usual that an infinite sequence u_1, u_2, u_3, ... of functions satisfying (12a) and (12b) is required. If so, we write the infinite series

➤
$$u(x, t) = \sum_{n=1}^{\infty} c_n u_n(x, t) \tag{15}$$

and then attempt to determine the coefficients $c_1, c_2, c_3, \ldots$ in order to satisfy (12c) as well. The following principle summarizes the properties of this infinite series that must be verified to ensure that we have a solution of the boundary value problem in (12).

PRINCIPLE   Superposition of Solutions

Suppose that each of the functions u_1, u_2, u_3, ... satisfies both the differential equation in (12a) (for $0 < x < L$ and $t > 0$) and the homogeneous conditions in (12b). Suppose also that the coefficients in Eq. (15) are chosen to meet the following three criteria:

1. For $0 < x < L$ and $t > 0$, the function determined by the series in (15) is continuous and termwise differentiable (once with respect to t and twice with respect to x).

2. $\sum_{n=1}^{\infty} c_n u_n(x, 0) = f(x)$ for $0 < x < L$.

3. The function $u(x, t)$ determined by Eq. (15) interior to the strip $0 \leqq x \leqq L$ and $t \geqq 0$, and by the boundary conditions in (12b) and (12c) on its boundary, is continuous.

Then $u(x, t)$ is a solution of the boundary value problem in (12).

In the method of separation of variables described next, we concentrate on finding the solutions u_1, u_2, u_3, ... satisfying the homogeneous conditions and on determining the coefficients so that the series in Eq. (15) satisfies the nonhomogeneous conditions upon substitution of $t = 0$. At this point we have only a *formal* series solution of the boundary value problem—one that is subject to verification of the continuity and differentiability conditions given in part (1) of the superposition principle stated here. If the function $f(x)$ in (12c) is piecewise smooth, it can be proved that a formal series solution always satisfies the restrictions and, moreover, is the unique solution of the boundary value problem. For a proof, see Chapter 6 of R. V. Churchill and J. W. Brown, *Fourier Series and Boundary Value Problems*, 3rd ed. (New York: McGraw-Hill, 1978).

Separation of Variables

This method of solving the boundary value problem in (12) for the heated rod was introduced by Fourier in his study of heat cited in Section 9.1. We first search for the *building block* functions u_1, u_2, u_3, ... that satisfy the differential equation $u_t = ku_{xx}$ and the homogeneous conditions $u(0, t) = u(L, t) = 0$, with each of these functions being of the special form

$$u(x, t) = X(x)T(t) \tag{16}$$

in which the variables are "separated"—that is, each of the building-block functions is a product of a function of position x (only) and a function of time t (only). Substitution of (16) in $u_t = ku_{xx}$ yields $XT' = kX''T$, where for brevity we write T' for $T'(t)$ and X'' for $X''(x)$. Division of both sides by kXT then gives

$$\frac{X''}{X} = \frac{T'}{kT}. \tag{17}$$

The left-hand side of Eq. (17) is a function of x alone, but the right-hand side is a function of t alone. If t is held constant on the right-hand side, then the left-hand side X''/X must remain constant as x varies. Similarly, if x is held constant on the left-hand side, then the right-hand side T'/kT must remain constant as t varies. Consequently, equality can hold only if each of these two expressions is the same *constant*, which for convenience we denote by $-\lambda$. Thus Eq. (17) becomes

$$\frac{X''}{X} = \frac{T'}{kT} = -\lambda, \tag{18}$$

which consists of the two equations

$$X''(x) + \lambda X(x) = 0, \tag{19}$$
$$T'(t) + \lambda kT(t) = 0. \tag{20}$$

It follows that the product function $u(x, t) = X(x)T(t)$ satisfies the partial differential equation $u_t = ku_{xx}$ if $X(x)$ and $T(t)$ separately satisfy the ordinary differential equations in (19) and (20) for some (common) value of the constant λ.

We focus first on $X(x)$. The homogeneous endpoint conditions are

$$u(x, 0) = X(0)T(t) = 0, \qquad u(L, t) = X(L)T(t) = 0. \tag{21}$$

If $T(t)$ is to be a nontrivial function of t, then (21) can hold only if $X(0) = X(L) = 0$. Thus $X(x)$ must satisfy the endpoint value problem

$$X'' + \lambda X = 0, \atop X(0) = 0, \quad X(L) = 0. \tag{22}$$

This is actually an eigenvalue problem of the type we discussed in Section 3.8. Indeed, we saw in Example 3 of that section that (22) has a nontrivial solution if and only if λ is one of the eigenvalues

$$\lambda_n = \frac{n^2\pi^2}{L^2}, \qquad n = 1, 2, 3, \ldots, \tag{23}$$

and that an eigenfunction associated with λ_n is

$$X_n(x) = \sin \frac{n\pi x}{L}, \qquad n = 1, 2, 3, \ldots. \tag{24}$$

Recall that the reasoning behind (23) and (24) is as follows. If $\lambda = 0$, then (22) obviously implies that $X(x) \equiv 0$. If $\lambda = -\alpha^2 < 0$, then

$$X(x) = A \cosh \alpha x + B \sinh \alpha x,$$

and then the conditions $X(0) = 0 = X(L)$ imply that $A = B = 0$. Hence the only possibility for a nontrivial eigenfunction is that $\lambda = \alpha^2 > 0$. Then

$$X(x) = A \cos \alpha x + B \sin \alpha x,$$

and the conditions $X(0) = 0 = X(L)$ then imply that $A = 0$ and that $\alpha = n\pi/L$ for some positive integer n. (Whenever separation of variables leads to an unfamiliar eigenvalue problem, we generally must consider separately the cases $\lambda = 0$, $\lambda = -\alpha^2 < 0$, and $\lambda = \alpha^2 > 0$.)

Now we turn our attention to Eq. (20), knowing that the constant λ must be one of the eigenvalues listed in (23). For the nth of these possibilities we write Eq. (20) as

$$T_n' + \frac{n^2\pi^2 k}{L^2} T_n = 0, \tag{25}$$

in anticipation of a different solution $T_n(t)$ for each different positive integer n. A nontrivial solution of this equation is

$$T_n(t) = \exp\left(-n^2\pi^2 kt/L^2\right). \tag{26}$$

We omit the arbitrary constant of integration because it will (in effect) be inserted later.

To summarize our progress, we have discovered the two associated sequences $\{X_n\}_1^\infty$ and $\{T_n\}_1^\infty$ of functions given in (24) and (26). Together they yield the sequence of building-block product functions

$$u_n(x, t) = X_n(x)T_n(t) = \exp\left(-n^2\pi^2 kt/L^2\right) \sin \frac{n\pi x}{L}, \tag{27}$$

$n = 1, 2, 3, \ldots$. Each of these functions satisfies both the heat equation $u_t = ku_{xx}$ and the homogeneous conditions $u(0, t) = u(L, t) = 0$. Now we combine these functions (*superposition*) to attempt to satisfy the nonhomogeneous condition $u(x, 0) = f(x)$ as well. We therefore form the infinite series

$$u(x, t) = \sum_{n=1}^\infty c_n u_n(x, t) = \sum_{n=1}^\infty c_n \exp\left(-n^2\pi^2 kt/L^2\right) \sin \frac{n\pi x}{L}. \tag{28}$$

It remains only to determine the constant coefficients $\{c_n\}_1^\infty$ so that

$$u(x, 0) = \sum_{n=1}^\infty c_n \sin \frac{n\pi x}{L} = f(x) \tag{29}$$

for $0 < x < L$. But this will be the Fourier series of $f(x)$ on $[0, L]$ provided that we choose

$$c_n = b_n = \frac{2}{L} \int_0^L f(x) \sin \frac{n\pi x}{L}\, dx \tag{30}$$

for each $n = 1, 2, 3, \ldots$. Thus we have the following result.

THEOREM 1   The Heated Rod with Zero Endpoint Temperatures

The boundary value problem in (12) for a heated rod with zero endpoint temperatures has the formal series solution

$$u(x, t) = \sum_{n=1}^{\infty} b_n \exp\left(-n^2\pi^2 kt/L^2\right) \sin\frac{n\pi x}{L}, \tag{31}$$

where the $\{b_n\}$ are the Fourier sine coefficients in Eq. (30) of the rod's initial temperature function $f(x) = u(x, 0)$.

Material	k (cm^2/s)
Silver	1.70
Copper	1.15
Aluminum	0.85
Iron	0.15
Concrete	0.005

FIGURE 9.5.3.   Some thermal diffusivity constants.

Remark: By taking the limit in (31) termwise as $t \to \infty$, we get $u(x, \infty) \equiv 0$, as we expect because the two ends of the rod are held at temperature zero.   ■

The series solution in Eq. (31) usually converges quite rapidly, unless t is very small, because of the presence of the negative exponential factors. Therefore it is practical for numerical computations. For use in problems and examples, values of the thermal diffusivity constant k for some common materials are listed in the table in Fig. 9.5.3.

Example 2   Suppose that a rod of length $L = 50$ cm is immersed in steam until its temperature is $u_0 = 100°$C throughout. At time $t = 0$, its lateral surface is insulated and its two ends are imbedded in ice at $0°$C. Calculate the rod's temperature at its midpoint after half an hour if it is made of (a) iron; (b) concrete.

Solution   The boundary value problem for this rod's temperature function $u(x, t)$ is

$$u_t = ku_{xx},$$
$$u(0, t) = u(L, t) = 0;$$
$$u(x, 0) = u_0.$$

Recall the square-wave series

$$f(t) = \frac{4}{\pi} \sum_{n \text{ odd}} \frac{1}{n} \sin\frac{n\pi t}{L} = \begin{cases} +1 & \text{if } 0 < t < L, \\ -1 & \text{if } -L < t < 0 \end{cases}$$

that we derived in Example 1 of Section 9.2. It follows that the Fourier sine series of $f(x) \equiv u_0$ is

$$f(x) = \frac{4u_0}{\pi} \sum_{n \text{ odd}} \frac{1}{n} \sin\frac{n\pi x}{L}$$

for $0 < x < L$. Hence the Fourier coefficients in Eq. (31) are given by

$$b_n = \begin{cases} \dfrac{4u_0}{n\pi} & \text{for } n \text{ odd}, \\[2mm] 0 & \text{for } n \text{ even}, \end{cases}$$

and therefore the rod's temperature function is given by

$$u(x, t) = \frac{4u_0}{\pi} \sum_{n \text{ odd}} \frac{1}{n} \exp\left(-\frac{n^2\pi^2 kt}{L^2}\right) \sin\frac{n\pi x}{L}.$$

Figure 9.5.4 shows a graph $u = u(x, t)$ with $u_0 = 100$ and $L = 50$. As t increases, we see the maximum temperature of the rod (evidently at its midpoint) steadily decreasing. The temperature at the midpoint $x = 25$ after $t = 1800$ seconds is

$$u(25, 1800) = \frac{400}{\pi} \sum_{n \text{ odd}} \frac{(-1)^{n+1}}{n} \exp\left(-\frac{18n^2\pi^2 k}{25}\right).$$

(a) With the value $k = 0.15$ that was used in Fig. 9.5.4, this series gives

$$u(25, 1800) \approx 43.8519 - 0.0029 + 0.0000 - \cdots \approx 43.85^\circ\text{C}.$$

This value $u(25, 1800) \approx 43.85$ is the maximum height (at its midpoint $x = 25$) of the vertical sectional curve $u = u(x, 1800)$ that we see at one "end" of the temperature surface shown in Fig. 9.5.4.

(b) With $k = 0.005$ for concrete, it gives

$$\begin{aligned}
u(25, 1800) \approx{}& 122.8795 - 30.8257 + 10.4754 - 3.1894 \\
& + 0.7958 - 0.1572 + 0.0242 - 0.0029 \\
& + 0.0003 - 0.0000 + \cdots \approx 100.00^\circ\text{C}.
\end{aligned}$$

Thus concrete is a very effective insulator. ∎

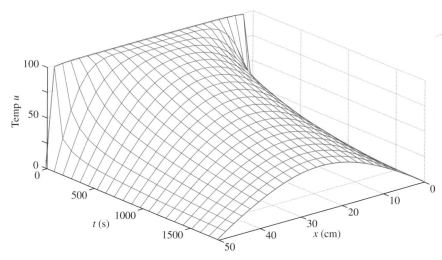

FIGURE 9.5.4.   The graph of the temperature function $u(x, t)$ in Example 2.

Insulated Endpoint Conditions

We now consider the boundary value problem

$$\frac{\partial u}{\partial t} = k\frac{\partial^2 u}{\partial x^2} \qquad (0 < x < L, \ t > 0); \tag{32a}$$

$$u_x(0, t) = u_x(L, t) = 0, \tag{32b}$$

$$u(x, 0) = f(x), \tag{32c}$$

which corresponds to a rod of length L with initial temperature $f(x)$, but with its two ends insulated. The separation of variables $u(x, t) = X(x)T(t)$ proceeds as in

Eqs. (16) through (20) without change. But the homogeneous endpoint conditions in (32b) yield $X'(0) = X'(L) = 0$. Thus $X(x)$ must satisfy the endpoint value problem

$$X'' + \lambda X = 0;$$
$$X'(0) = 0, \quad X'(L) = 0. \tag{33}$$

We must again consider separately the possibilities $\lambda = 0$, $\lambda = -\alpha^2 < 0$, and $\lambda = \alpha^2 > 0$ for the eigenvalues.

With $\lambda = 0$, the general solution of $X'' = 0$ is $X(x) = Ax + B$, so $X'(x) = A$. Hence the endpoint conditions in (33) require $A = 0$, but B may be nonzero. Because a constant multiple of an eigenfunction is an eigenfunction, we can choose any constant value we wish for B. Thus, with $B = 1$, we have the zero eigenvalue and associated eigenfunction

$$\lambda_0 = 0, \quad X_0(x) \equiv 1. \tag{34}$$

With $\lambda = 0$ in Eq. (20), we get $T'(t) = 0$, so we may take $T_0(t) \equiv 1$ as well.

With $\lambda = -\alpha^2 < 0$, the general solution of the equation $X'' - \alpha^2 X = 0$ is

$$X(x) = A \cosh \alpha x + B \sinh \alpha x,$$

and we readily verify that $X'(0) = X'(L) = 0$ only if $A = B = 0$. Thus there are no negative eigenvalues.

With $\lambda = \alpha^2 > 0$, the general solution of $X'' + \alpha^2 X = 0$ is

$$X(x) = A \cos \alpha x + B \sin \alpha x,$$
$$X'(x) = -A\alpha \sin \alpha x + B\alpha \cos \alpha x.$$

Hence $X'(0) = 0$ implies that $B = 0$, and then

$$X'(L) = -A\alpha \sin \alpha L = 0$$

requires that αL be an integral multiple of π, because $\alpha \neq 0$ and $A \neq 0$ if we are to have a nontrivial solution. Thus we have the infinite sequence of eigenvalues and associated eigenfunctions

$$\lambda_n = \alpha_n^2 = \frac{n^2 \pi^2}{L^2}, \quad X_n(x) = \cos \frac{n\pi x}{L} \tag{35}$$

for $n = 1, 2, 3, \ldots$. Just as before, the solution of Eq. (20) with $\lambda = n^2\pi^2/L^2$ is $T_n(t) = \exp\left(-n^2\pi^2 kt/L^2\right)$.

Therefore, the product functions satisfying the homogeneous conditions are

$$u_0(x, t) \equiv 1; \quad u_n(x, t) = \exp\left(n^2\pi^2 kt/L^2\right) \cos \frac{n\pi x}{L} \tag{36}$$

for $n = 1, 2, 3, \ldots$. Hence the trial solution is

$$u(x, t) = c_0 + \sum_{n=1}^{\infty} c_n \exp\left(-n^2\pi^2 kt/L^2\right) \cos \frac{n\pi x}{L}. \tag{37}$$

To satisfy the nonhomogeneous condition $u(x, 0) = f(x)$, we obviously want Eq. (37) to reduce when $t = 0$ to the Fourier cosine series

$$f(x) = \frac{a_0}{2} + \sum_{n=1}^{\infty} a_n \cos \frac{n \pi x}{L}, \tag{38}$$

where

$$\blacktriangleright \qquad a_n = \frac{2}{L} \int_0^L f(x) \cos \frac{n \pi x}{L} dx \tag{39}$$

for $n = 0, 1, 2, \ldots$. Thus we have the following result.

THEOREM 2 Heated Rod with Insulated Ends

The boundary value problem in (32) for a heated rod with insulated ends has the formal series solution

$$\blacktriangleright \qquad u(x, t) = \frac{a_0}{2} + \sum_{n=1}^{\infty} a_n \exp\left(-n^2 \pi^2 kt/L^2\right) \cos \frac{n \pi x}{L} \tag{40}$$

where the $\{a_n\}$ are the Fourier cosine coefficients in (39) of the rod's initial temperature function $f(x) = u(x, 0)$.

Remark: Note that

$$\lim_{t \to \infty} u(x, t) = \frac{a_0}{2} = \frac{1}{L} \int_0^L f(x) \, dx, \tag{41}$$

the average value of the initial temperature. With both the lateral surface and the ends of the rod insulated, its original heat content ultimately distributes itself uniformly throughout the rod. ∎

Example 3

We consider the same 50-cm rod as in Example 2, but now suppose that its initial temperature is given by the "triangular function" graphed in Fig. 9.5.5. At time $t = 0$, the rod's lateral surface *and* its two ends are insulated. Then its temperature function $u(x, t)$ satisfies the boundary value problem

$$u_t = k u_{xx},$$
$$u_x(0, t) = u_x(50, t) = 0,$$
$$u(x, 0) = f(x).$$

Now substitution of $L = 25$ in the even triangular-wave series of Eq. (15) in Section 9.3 (where the length of the interval is denoted by $2L$), followed by multiplication by 4, yields the Fourier cosine series

$$f(x) = 50 - \frac{400}{\pi^2} \sum_{n \text{ odd}} \frac{1}{n^2} \cos \frac{n \pi x}{25}$$

(for $0 < x < 50$) of our initial temperature function. But in order to match terms with the series in (40) with $L = 50$, we need to exhibit terms of the form

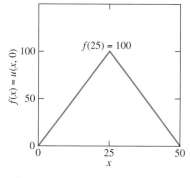

FIGURE 9.5.5. The graph of the initial temperature function $u(x, 0) = f(x)$ in Example 3.

$\cos(n\pi x/50)$ rather than terms of the form $\cos(n\pi x/25)$. Hence we replace n with $n/2$ throughout and thereby rewrite the series in the form

$$f(x) = 50 - \frac{1600}{\pi^2} \sum_{n=2,6,10,\ldots} \frac{1}{n^2} \cos\frac{n\pi x}{50};$$

note that the summation runs through all positive integers of the form $4m - 2$. Then Theorem 2 implies that the rod's temperature function is given by

$$u(x, t) = 50 - \frac{1600}{n^2} \sum_{n=2,6,10,\ldots} \frac{1}{n^2} \exp\left(-\frac{n^2\pi^2 kt}{2500}\right) \cos\frac{n\pi x}{50}.$$

Figure 9.5.6 shows the graph $u = u(x, t)$ for the first 1200 seconds, and we see the temperature in the rod beginning with a sharp maximum at the midpoint $x = 25$, but rapidly "averaging out" as the heat in the rod is redistributed with increasing t. ∎

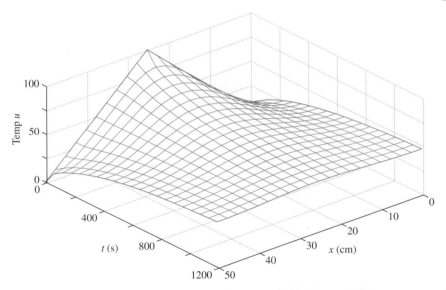

FIGURE 9.5.6. The graph of the temperature function $u(x, t)$ in Example 3.

Finally, we point out that, although we set up the boundary value problems in (12) and (32) for a rod of length L, they also model the temperature $u(x, t)$ within the infinite slab $0 \leq x \leq L$ in three-dimensional space if its initial temperature $f(x)$ depends only on x and its two faces $x = 0$ and $x = L$ are either both insulated or both held at temperature zero.

9.5 Problems

Solve the boundary value problems in Problems 1 through 12.

1. $u_t = 3u_{xx}$, $0 < x < \pi$, $t > 0$; $u(0, t) = u(\pi, t) = 0$,
   $u(x, 0) = 4\sin 2x$

2. $u_t = 10u_{xx}$, $0 < x < 5$, $t > 0$; $u_x(0, t) = u_x(5, t) = 0$,
   $u(x, 0) = 7$

3. $u_t = 2u_{xx}$, $0 < x < 1$, $t > 0$; $u(0, t) = u(1, t) = 0$,
   $u(x, 0) = 5\sin\pi x - \frac{1}{5}\sin 3\pi x$

4. $u_t = u_{xx}$, $0 < x < \pi$, $t > 0$; $u(0, t) = u(\pi, t) = 0$,
   $u(x, 0) = 4\sin 4x \cos 2x$

5. $u_t = 2u_{xx}$, $0 < x < 3$, $t > 0$; $u_x(0, t) = u_x(3, t) = 0$,
   $u(x, 0) = 4\cos\frac{2}{3}\pi x - 2\cos\frac{4}{3}\pi x$

6. $2u_t = u_{xx}$, $0 < x < 1$, $t > 0$; $u(0, t) = u(1, t) = 0$,
   $u(x, 0) = 4\sin\pi x \cos^3\pi x$

7. $3u_t = u_{xx}$, $0 < x < 2$, $t > 0$; $u_x(0, t) = u_x(2, t) = 0$,
$u(x, 0) = \cos^2 2\pi x$

8. $u_t = u_{xx}$, $0 < x < 2$, $t > 0$; $u_x(0, t) = u_x(2, t) = 0$,
$u(x, 0) = 10 \cos \pi x \cos 3\pi x$

9. $10u_t = u_{xx}$, $0 < x < 5$, $t > 0$; $u(0, t) = u(5, t) = 0$,
$u(x, 0) = 25$

10. $5u_t = u_{xx}$, $0 < x < 10$, $t > 0$; $u(0, t) = u(10, t) = 0$,
$u(x, 0) = 4x$

11. $5u_t = u_{xx}$, $0 < x < 10$, $t > 0$; $u_x(0, t) = u_x(10, t) = 0$,
$u(x, 0) = 4x$

12. $u_t = u_{xx}$, $0 < x < 100$, $t > 0$; $u(0, t) = u(100, t) = 0$,
$u(x, 0) = x(100 - x)$

13. Suppose that a rod 40 cm long with insulated lateral surface is heated to a uniform temperature of $100°$C, and that at time $t = 0$ its two ends are embedded in ice at $0°$C. **(a)** Find the formal series solution for the temperature $u(x, t)$ of the rod. **(b)** In the case the rod is made of copper, show that after 5 min the temperature at its midpoint is about $15°$C. **(c)** In the case the rod is made of concrete, use the first term of the series to find the time required for its midpoint to cool to $15°$C.

14. A copper rod 50 cm long with insulated lateral surface has initial temperature $u(x, 0) = 2x$, and at time $t = 0$ its two ends are insulated. **(a)** Find $u(x, t)$. **(b)** What will its temperature be at $x = 10$ after 1 min? **(c)** After approximately how long will its temperature at $x = 10$ be $45°$C?

15. The two faces of the slab $0 \leq x \leq L$ are kept at temperature zero, and the initial temperature of the slab is given by $u(x, 0) = A$ (a constant) for $0 < x < L/2$, $u(x, 0) = 0$ for $L/2 < x < L$. Derive the formal series solution

$$u(x, t) = \frac{4A}{\pi} \sum_{n=1}^{\infty} \frac{\sin^2(n\pi/4)}{n} \exp\left(-n^2\pi^2 kt/L^2\right) \sin \frac{n\pi x}{L}.$$

16. Two iron slabs are each 25 cm thick. Initially one is at temperature $100°$C throughout and the other is at temperature $0°$C. At time $t = 0$ they are placed face to face, and their outer faces are kept at $0°$C. **(a)** Use the result of Problem 15 to verify that after a half hour the temperature of their common face is approximately $22°$C. **(b)** Suppose that the two slabs are instead made of concrete. How long will it be until their common face reaches a temperature of $22°$C?

17. (Steady-state and transient temperatures) Let a laterally insulated rod with initial temperature $u(x, 0) = f(x)$ have fixed endpoint temperatures $u(0, t) = A$ and $u(L, t) = B$. **(a)** It is observed empirically that as $t \to +\infty$, $u(x, t)$ approaches a **steady-state temperature** $u_{ss}(x)$ that corresponds to setting $u_t = 0$ in the boundary value problem. Thus $u_{ss}(x)$ is the solution of the endpoint value problem

$$\frac{\partial^2 u_{ss}}{\partial x^2} = 0; \quad u_{ss}(0) = A, \quad u_{ss}(L) = B.$$

Find $u_{ss}(x)$. **(b)** The **transient temperature** $u_{tr}(x, t)$ is defined to be

$$u_{tr}(x, t) = u(x, t) - u_{ss}(x).$$

Show that u_{tr} satisfies the boundary value problem

$$\frac{\partial u_{tr}}{\partial t} = k \frac{\partial^2 u_{tr}}{\partial x^2};$$

$$u_{tr}(0, t) = u_{tr}(L, t) = 0,$$

$$u_{tr}(x, 0) = g(x) = f(x) - u_{ss}(x).$$

(c) Conclude from the formulas in (30) and (31) that

$$u(x, t) = u_{ss}(x) + u_{tr}(x, t)$$

$$= u_{ss}(x) + \sum_{n=1}^{\infty} c_n \exp\left(-n^2\pi^2 kt/L^2\right) \sin \frac{n\pi x}{L},$$

where

$$c_n = \frac{2}{L} \int_0^L [f(x) - u_{ss}(x)] \sin \frac{n\pi x}{L} \, dx.$$

18. Suppose that a laterally insulated rod with length $L = 50$ and thermal diffusivity $k = 1$ has initial temperature $u(x, 0) = 0$ and endpoint temperatures $u(0, t) = 0$, $u(50, t) = 100$. Apply the result of Problem 17 to show that

$$u(x, t) =$$

$$2x - \frac{200}{\pi} \sum_{n=1}^{\infty} \frac{(-1)^{n+1}}{n} \exp\left(-n^2\pi^2 kt/2500\right) \sin \frac{n\pi x}{50}.$$

19. Suppose that heat is generated within a laterally insulated rod at the rate of $q(x, t)$ calories per second per cubic centimeter. Extend the derivation of the heat equation in this section to derive the equation

$$\frac{\partial u}{\partial t} = k \frac{\partial^2 u}{\partial x^2} + \frac{q(x, t)}{c\delta}.$$

20. Suppose that current flowing through a laterally insulated rod generates heat at a constant rate; then Problem 19 yields the equation

$$\frac{\partial u}{\partial t} = k \frac{\partial^2 u}{\partial x^2} + C.$$

Assume the boundary conditions $u(0, t) = u(L, t) = 0$ and $u(x, 0) = f(x)$. **(a)** Find the steady-state temperature $u_{ss}(x)$ determined by

$$0 = k \frac{d^2 u_{ss}}{dx^2} + C, \quad u_{ss}(0) = u_{ss}(L) = 0.$$

(b) Show that the transient temperature

$$u_{tr}(x, t) = u(x, t) - u_{ss}(x)$$

satisfies the boundary value problem

$$\frac{\partial u_{tr}}{\partial t} = k \frac{\partial^2 u_{tr}}{\partial x^2};$$

$$u_{tr}(0, t) = u_{tr}(L, t) = 0,$$

$$u_{tr}(x, 0) = g(x) = f(x) - u_{ss}(x).$$

Hence conclude from the formulas in (34) and (35) that

$$u(x, t) = u_{ss}(x) + \sum_{n=1}^{\infty} c_n \exp\left(-n^2\pi^2 kt/L^2\right) \sin\frac{n\pi x}{L},$$

where

$$c_n = \frac{2}{L} \int_0^L [f(x) - u_{ss}(x)] \sin\frac{n\pi x}{L} dx.$$

21. The answer to part (a) of Problem 20 is $u_{ss}(x) = Cx(L - x)/2k$. If $f(x) \equiv 0$ in Problem 20, so the rod being heated is initially at temperature zero, deduce from the result of part (b) that

$$u(x, t) = \frac{Cx}{2k}(L - x)$$

$$- \frac{4CL^2}{k\pi^3} \sum_{n\ odd} \frac{1}{n^3} \exp\left(-n^2\pi^2 kt/L^2\right) \sin\frac{n\pi x}{L}.$$

22. Consider the temperature $u(x, t)$ in a bare slender wire with $u(0, t) = u(L, t) = 0$ and $u(x, 0) = f(x)$. Instead of being laterally insulated, the wire loses heat to a surrounding medium (at fixed temperature zero) at a rate proportional to $u(x, t)$. **(a)** Conclude from Problem 19 that

$$\frac{\partial u}{\partial t} = k\frac{\partial^2 u}{\partial x^2} - hu,$$

where h is a positive constant. **(b)** Then substitute

$$u(x, t) = e^{-ht} v(x, t)$$

to show that $v(x, t)$ satisfies the boundary value problem having the solution given in (30) and (31). Hence conclude that

$$u(x, t) = e^{-ht} \sum_{n=1}^{\infty} c_n \exp\left(-n^2\pi^2 kt/L^2\right) \sin\frac{n\pi x}{L},$$

where

$$c_n = \frac{2}{L} \int_0^L f(x) \sin\frac{n\pi x}{L} dx.$$

23. Consider a slab with thermal conductivity K occupying the region $0 \le x \le L$. Suppose that, in accord with Newton's law of cooling, each face of the slab loses heat to the surrounding medium (at temperature zero) at the rate of Hu calories per second per square centimeter. Deduce from Eq. (2) that the temperature $u(x, t)$ in the slab satisfies the boundary conditions

$$hu(0, t) - u_x(0, t) = 0 = hu(L, t) + u_x(L, t)$$

where $h = H/K$.

24. Suppose that a laterally insulated rod with length L, thermal diffusivity k, and initial temperature $u(x, 0) = f(x)$ is insulated at the end $x = L$ and held at temperature zero at $x = 0$. **(a)** Separate the variables to show that the eigenfunctions are

$$X_n(x) = \sin\frac{n\pi x}{2L}$$

for n odd. **(b)** Use the odd half-multiple sine series of Problem 21 in Section 9.3 to derive the solution

$$u(x, t) = \sum_{n\ odd} c_n \exp\left(-n^2\pi^2 kt/4L^2\right) \sin\frac{n\pi x}{2L},$$

where

$$c_n = \frac{2}{L} \int_0^L f(x) \sin\frac{n\pi x}{2L} dx.$$

9.5 Application Heated-Rod Investigations

First let's investigate numerically the temperature function

$$u(x, t) = \frac{4u_0}{\pi} \sum_{n\ odd} \frac{1}{n} \exp\left(-\frac{n^2\pi^2 kt}{L^2}\right) \sin\frac{n\pi x}{L}$$

of the heated rod of Example 2, having length $L = 50$ cm, uniform initial temperature $u_0 = 100°$C, and thermal diffusivity $k = 0.15$ (for iron). The following MATLAB function sums the first N nonzero terms of this series.

```
function u = u(x,t)
k = 0.15;          % diffusivity of iron
L = 50;            % length of rod
u0 = 100;          % initial temperature
S = 0;             % initial sum
```

```
N = 50;                        % number of terms
for n = 1:2:2*N+1;
    S = S +(1/n)*exp(-n^2*pi^2*k*t/L^2).*sin(n*pi*x/L);
end
u = 4*u0*S/pi;
```

This function was used to plot Figs. 9.5.7 through 9.5.10. The corresponding *Maple* and *Mathematica* functions are provided in the applications manual that accompanies this text. As a practical matter, $N = 50$ terms suffice to give the value $u(x, t)$ after 10 seconds (or longer) with two decimal places of accuracy throughout the interval $0 \leqq x \leqq 50$. (How might you check this assertion?)

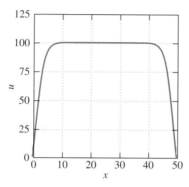

FIGURE 9.5.7. The graph of $u(x, 30)$ giving rod temperatures after 30 seconds.

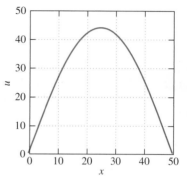

FIGURE 9.5.8. The graph of $u(x, 1800)$ giving rod temperature after 30 minutes.

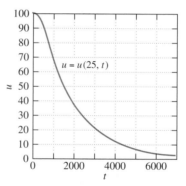

FIGURE 9.5.9. The graph of $u(25, t)$ giving the midpoint temperatures of the rod.

FIGURE 9.5.10. Magnification of the graph of $u(25, t)$ giving the midpoint temperatures of the rod.

The graph of $u(x, 30)$ in Fig. 9.5.7 shows that after 30 seconds the rod has cooled appreciably only near its two ends and still has temperature near $100°$C for $10 \leqq x \leqq 40$. Figure 9.5.8 shows the graph of $u(x, 1800)$ after 30 minutes and illustrates the fact (?) that the rod's maximum temperature is always at its midpoint, where $x = 25$.

The graph of $u(25, t)$ for a two-hour period shown in Fig. 9.5.9 indicates that the midpoint temperature takes something more than 1500 seconds (25 minutes) to fall to $50°$. Figure 9.5.10 shows a magnification of the graph near its intersection point with the horizontal line $u = 50$ and indicates that this actually takes about 1578 seconds (26 min 18 s).

For your very own rod with constant initial temperature $f(x) = T_0 = 100$ to investigate in this manner, let

$$L = 100 + 10p \quad \text{and} \quad k = 1 + (0.1)q,$$

where p is the largest and q is the smallest nonzero digit of your student ID number.

1. If the two ends of the rod are both held at temperature zero, then determine how long (to the nearest second) it will take for the rod's midpoint temperature to fall to $50°$.
2. If the end $x = L$ of the rod is insulated, but the end $x = 0$ is held at temperature zero, then the temperature function $u(x, t)$ is given by the series in Problem 24 of this section. Determine how long it will be until the maximum temperature anywhere in the rod is $50°$.

9.6 Vibrating Strings and the One-Dimensional Wave Equation

FIGURE 9.6.1. Forces on a short segment of the vibrating string.

Although Fourier systematized the method of separation of variables, trigonometric series solutions of partial differential equations had appeared earlier in eighteenth-century investigations of vibrating strings by Euler, d'Alembert, and Daniel Bernoulli. To derive the partial differential equation that models the vibrations of a string, we begin with a flexible uniform string with linear density ρ (in grams per centimeter or slugs per foot) stretched under a tension of T (dynes or pounds) between the fixed points $x = 0$ and $x = L$. Suppose that, as the string vibrates in the xy-plane around its equilibrium position, each point moves parallel to the y-axis, so we can denote by $y(x, t)$ the displacement at time t of the point x of the string. Then, for any fixed value of t, the shape of the string at time t is the curve $y = y(x, t)$. We assume also that the deflection of the string remains so slight that the approximation $\sin\theta \approx \tan\theta = y_x(x, t)$ is quite accurate (Fig. 9.6.1). Finally, we assume that in addition to the internal forces of tension acting tangentially to the string, it is acted on by an external vertical force with linear density $F(x)$ in such units as dynes per centimeter or pounds per foot.

We want to apply Newton's second law $F = ma$ to the short segment of string of mass $\rho\Delta x$ corresponding to the interval $[x, x + \Delta x]$, with a being the vertical acceleration $y_{tt}(\overline{x}, t)$ of its midpoint. Reading the vertical components of the force shown in Fig. 9.6.1, we get

$$(\rho\,\Delta x) \cdot y_{tt}(\overline{x}, t) \approx T\sin(\theta + \Delta\theta) - T\sin\theta + F(\overline{x})\,\Delta x$$
$$\approx Ty_x(x + \Delta x, t) - Ty_x(x, t) + F(\overline{x})\,\Delta x,$$

so division by Δx yields

$$\rho y_{tt}(\overline{x}, t) \approx T\frac{y_x(x + \Delta x, t) - y_x(x, t)}{\Delta x} + F(\overline{x}).$$

We now take limits in this equation as $\Delta x \to 0$, so $\overline{x} \to x$ (because $\overline{x}$ lies in the interval $[x, x + \Delta x]$ with fixed left endpoint x). Then the two sides of the equation approach the two sides of the partial differential equation

$$\rho\frac{\partial^2 y}{\partial t^2} = T\frac{\partial^2 y}{\partial x^2} + F(x) \tag{1}$$

that describes the vertical vibrations of a flexible string with constant linear density ρ and tension T under the influence of an external vertical force with linear density $F(x)$.

If we set

$$a^2 = \frac{T}{\rho} \tag{2}$$

and set $F(x) \equiv 0$ in Eq. (1), we get the **one-dimensional wave equation**

➤
$$\frac{\partial^2 y}{\partial t^2} = a^2 \frac{\partial^2 y}{\partial x^2} \tag{3}$$

that models the *free* vibrations of a uniform flexible string.

The fixed ends of the string at the points $x = 0$ and $x = L$ on the x-axis correspond to the *endpoint conditions*

$$y(0, t) = y(L, t) = 0. \tag{4}$$

Our intuition about the physics of the situation suggests that the motion of the string will be determined if we specify both its **initial position function**

$$y(x, 0) = f(x) \qquad (0 < x < L) \tag{5}$$

and its **initial velocity function**

$$y_t(x, 0) = g(x) \qquad (0 < x < L). \tag{6}$$

On combining Eqs. (3) through (6), we get the boundary value problem

$$\frac{\partial^2 y}{\partial t^2} = a^2 \frac{\partial^2 y}{\partial x^2} \qquad (0 < x < L, \ t > 0); \tag{7a}$$

➤
$$y(0, t) = y(L, t) = 0, \tag{7b}$$
$$y(x, 0) = f(x) \qquad (0 < x < L), \tag{7c}$$
$$y_t(x, 0) = g(x) \qquad (0 < x < L) \tag{7d}$$

for the displacement function $y(x, t)$ of a freely vibrating string with fixed ends, initial position $f(x)$, and initial velocity $g(x)$.

Solution by Separation of Variables

Like the heat equation, the wave equation in (7a) is linear: Any linear combination of two solutions is again a solution. Another similarity is that the endpoint conditions in (7b) are homogeneous. Unfortunately, the conditions in both (7c) and (7d) are nonhomogeneous; we must deal with *two* nonhomogeneous boundary conditions.

As we described in Section 9.5, the method of separation of variables involves superposition of solutions satisfying the homogeneous conditions to obtain a solution that also satisfies a single nonhomogeneous boundary condition. To adapt the technique to the situation at hand, we adopt the "divide and conquer" strategy of splitting the problem in (7) into the following two separate boundary value problems, each involving only a single nonhomogeneous boundary condition:

Problem A	Problem B
$y_{tt} = a^2 y_{xx};$	$y_{tt} = a^2 y_{xx};$
$y(0, t) = y(L, t) = 0,$	$y(0, t) = y(L, t) = 0,$
$y(x, 0) = f(x),$	$y(x, 0) = 0,$
$y_t(x, 0) = 0.$	$y_t(x, 0) = g(x).$

If we can separately find a solution $y_A(x, t)$ of Problem A and a solution $y_B(x, t)$ of Problem B, then their sum $y(x, t) = y_A(x, t) + y_B(x, t)$ will be a solution of the original problem in (7), because

$$y(x, 0) = y_A(x, 0) + y_B(x, 0) = f(x) + 0 = f(x)$$

and

$$y_t(x, 0) = \{y_A\}_t(x, 0) + \{y_B\}_t(x, 0) = 0 + g(x) = g(x).$$

So let us attack Problem A with the method of separation of variables. Substitution of

$$y(x, t) = X(x)T(t) \tag{8}$$

in $y_{tt} = a^2 y_{xx}$ yields $XT'' = a^2 X''T$ where (as before) we write X'' for $X''(x)$ and T'' for $T''(t)$. Therefore,

$$\frac{X''}{X} = \frac{T''}{a^2 T}. \tag{9}$$

The functions X''/X of x and $T''/a^2 T$ of t can agree for all x and t only if each is equal to the same constant. Consequently, we may conclude that

$$\frac{X''}{X} = \frac{T''}{a^2 T} = -\lambda \tag{10}$$

for some constant λ; the minus sign is inserted here merely to facilitate recognition of the eigenvalue problem in (13). Thus our partial differential equation separates into the two ordinary differential equations

$$X'' + \lambda X = 0, \tag{11}$$

$$T'' + \lambda a^2 T = 0. \tag{12}$$

The endpoint conditions

$$y(0, t) = X(0)T(t) = 0, \quad y(L, t) = X(L)T(t) = 0$$

require that $X(0) = X(L) = 0$ if $T(t)$ is nontrivial. Hence $X(x)$ must satisfy the now familiar eigenvalue problem

$$X'' + \lambda X = 0, \quad X(0) = X(L) = 0. \tag{13}$$

As in Eqs. (23) and (24) of Section 9.5, the eigenvalues of this problem are the numbers

$$\lambda_n = \frac{n^2 \pi^2}{L^2}, \quad n = 1, 2, 3, \ldots, \tag{14}$$

and the eigenfunction associated with λ_n is

$$X_n(x) = \sin \frac{n\pi x}{L}, \quad n = 1, 2, 3, \ldots. \tag{15}$$

Now we turn to Eq. (12). The homogeneous initial condition

$$y_t(x, 0) = X(x)T'(0) = 0$$

implies that $T'(0) = 0$. Therefore, the solution $T_n(t)$ associated with the eigenvalue $\lambda_n = n^2\pi^2/L^2$ must satisfy the conditions

$$T_n'' + \frac{n^2\pi^2 a^2}{L^2} T_n = 0, \quad T_n'(0) = 0. \tag{16}$$

The general solution of the differential equation in (16) is

$$T_n(t) = A_n \cos \frac{n\pi at}{L} + B_n \sin \frac{n\pi at}{L}. \tag{17}$$

Its derivative

$$T_n'(t) = \frac{n\pi a}{L}\left(-A_n \sin \frac{n\pi at}{L} + B_n \cos \frac{n\pi at}{L}\right)$$

satisfies the condition $T_n'(0) = 0$ if $B_n = 0$. Thus a nontrivial solution of (16) is

$$T_n(t) = \cos \frac{n\pi at}{L}. \tag{18}$$

We combine the results in Eqs. (15) and (18) to obtain the infinite sequence of product functions

$$y_n(x, t) = X_n(x)T_n(t) = \cos \frac{n\pi at}{L} \sin \frac{n\pi x}{L}, \tag{19}$$

$n = 1, 2, 3, \ldots.$ Each of these *building block* functions satisfies both the wave equation $y_{tt} = a^2 y_{xx}$ and the homogeneous boundary conditions in Problem A. By superposition we get the infinite series

$$y_n(x, t) = \sum_{n=1}^{\infty} A_n X_n(x) T_n(t) = \sum_{n=1}^{\infty} A_n \cos \frac{n\pi at}{L} \sin \frac{n\pi x}{L}. \tag{20}$$

It remains only to choose the coefficients $\{A_n\}$ to satisfy the nonhomogeneous boundary condition

$$y(x, 0) = \sum_{n=1}^{\infty} A_n \sin \frac{n\pi x}{L} = f(x) \tag{21}$$

for $0 < x < L$. But this will be the Fourier sine series of $f(x)$ on $[0, L]$ provided that we choose

$$A_n = \frac{2}{L} \int_0^L f(x) \sin \frac{n\pi x}{L} \, dx. \tag{22}$$

Thus we see finally that a formal series solution of Problem A is

$$
\blacktriangleright \qquad y_A(x,t) = \sum_{n=1}^{\infty} A_n \cos \frac{n\pi a t}{L} \sin \frac{n\pi x}{L}, \tag{23}
$$

with the coefficients $\{A_n\}_1^{\infty}$ computed using Eq. (22). Note that the series in (23) is obtained from the Fourier sine series of $f(x)$ simply by inserting the factor $\cos(n\pi a t/L)$ in the nth term. Note also that this term has (circular) frequency $\omega_n = n\pi a/L$.

Example 1 It follows immediately that the solution of the boundary value problem

$$
\frac{\partial^2 y}{\partial t^2} = 4\frac{\partial^2 y}{\partial x^2} \qquad (0 < x < \pi, \ t > 0);
$$

$$
y(0,t) = y(\pi,t) = 0,
$$

$$
y(x,0) = \tfrac{1}{10}\sin^3 x = \tfrac{3}{40}\sin x - \tfrac{1}{40}\sin 3x,
$$

$$
y_t(x,0) = 0,
$$

for which $L = \pi$ and $a = 2$, is

$$
y(x,t) = \tfrac{3}{40}\cos 2t \ \sin x - \tfrac{1}{40}\cos 6t \ \sin 3x.
$$

The reason is that we are given explicitly the Fourier sine series of $f(x)$ with $A_1 = \tfrac{3}{40}$, $A_3 = -\tfrac{1}{40}$, and $A_n = 0$ otherwise. ∎

Example 2 **A plucked string** Figure 9.6.2 shows the initial position function $f(x)$ for a stretched string (of length L) that is set in motion by moving its midpoint $x = L/2$ aside the distance $\tfrac{1}{2}bL$ and then releasing it from rest at time $t = 0$. The corresponding boundary value problem is

$$
y_{tt} = a^2 y_{xx} \qquad (0 < x < L, \ t > 0);
$$
$$
y(0,t) = y(L,t) = 0,
$$
$$
y(x,0) = f(x),
$$
$$
y_t(x,0) = 0,
$$

where $f(x) = bx$ for $0 \leqq x \leqq L/2$ and $f(x) = b(L-x)$ for $L/2 \leqq x \leqq L$. Find $y(x,t)$.

FIGURE 9.6.2. The initial position of the plucked string of Example 2.

Solution The nth Fourier sine coefficient of $f(x)$ is

$$
A_n = \frac{2}{L}\int_0^L f(x)\sin \frac{n\pi x}{L}\, dx
$$

$$
= \frac{2}{L}\int_0^{L/2} bx \sin \frac{n\pi x}{L}\, dx + \frac{2}{L}\int_{L/2}^L b(L-x)\sin \frac{n\pi x}{L}\, dx;
$$

it follows that

$$
A_n = \frac{4bL}{n^2\pi^2}\sin \frac{n\pi}{2}.
$$

Hence Eq. (23) yields the formal series solution

$$y(x, t) = \frac{4bL}{\pi^2} \sum_{n=1}^{\infty} \frac{1}{n^2} \sin \frac{n\pi}{2} \cos \frac{n\pi at}{L} \sin \frac{n\pi x}{L}$$

$$= \frac{4bL}{\pi^2} \left(\cos \frac{\pi at}{L} \sin \frac{\pi x}{L} - \frac{1}{3^2} \cos \frac{3\pi at}{L} \sin \frac{3\pi x}{L} + \cdots \right). \qquad (24)$$

■

Music

Numerous familiar musical instruments employ vibrating strings to generate the sounds they produce. When a string vibrates with a given frequency, vibrations at this frequency are transmitted through the air—in the form of periodic variations in air density called **sound waves**—to the ear of the listener. For example, middle C is a *tone* with a frequency of approximately 256 Hz. When several tones are heard simultaneously, the combination is perceived as harmonious if the ratios of their frequencies are nearly ratios of small whole numbers; otherwise many perceive the combinations as dissonant.

The series in Eq. (23) represents the motion of a string as a superposition of infinitely many vibrations with different frequencies. The *n*th term

$$A_n \cos \frac{n\pi at}{L} \sin \frac{n\pi x}{L}$$

represents a vibration with frequency

$$\nu_n = \frac{\omega_n}{2\pi} = \frac{n\pi a/L}{2\pi} = \frac{n}{2L} \sqrt{\frac{T}{\rho}} \qquad (\text{Hz}). \qquad (25)$$

The lowest of these frequencies,

$$\nu_1 = \frac{1}{2L} \sqrt{\frac{T}{\rho}} \qquad (\text{Hz}), \qquad (26)$$

is called the **fundamental frequency,** and it is ordinarily predominant in the sound we hear. The frequency $\nu_n = n\nu_1$ of the *n*th **overtone** or **harmonic** is an integral multiple of ν_1, and this is why the sound of a single vibrating string is harmonious rather than dissonant.

Note in Eq. (26) that the fundamental frequency ν_1 is proportional to $\sqrt{T}$ and inversely proportional to L and to $\sqrt{\rho}$. Thus we can double this frequency—and hence get a fundamental tone one **octave** higher—either by halving the length L or by quadrupling the tension T. The initial conditions do *not* affect ν_1; instead, they determine the coefficients in (23) and hence the extent to which the higher harmonics contribute to the sound produced. Therefore the initial conditions affect the **timbre,** or overall frequency mixture, rather than the fundamental frequency. (Technically this is true only for relatively small displacements of the string; if you strike a piano key rather forcefully you can detect a slight and brief initial deviation from the usual frequency of the note.)

According to one (rather simplistic) theory of hearing, the loudness of the sound produced by a vibrating string is proportional to its total (kinetic plus potential) energy, which is given by

$$E = \frac{1}{2} \int_0^L \left[\rho \left(\frac{\partial y}{\partial t} \right)^2 + T \left(\frac{\partial y}{\partial x} \right)^2 \right] dx. \qquad (27)$$

In Problem 17 we ask you to show that substitution of the series in (23) in the formula in (27) yields

$$E = \frac{\pi^2 T}{4L} \sum_{n=1}^{\infty} n^2 A_n^2. \tag{28}$$

The ratio of the nth term $n^2 A_n^2$ to the sum $\sum n^2 A_n^2$ is then the portion of the whole sound attributable to the nth harmonic.

We illustrate this theory with the series in (24), which describes the motion of the plucked string of Example 2. Note that the even harmonics are missing, and that $A_n = 4bL/(\pi^2 n^2)$ for n odd. Hence Eq. (28) gives

$$E = \frac{\pi^2 T}{4L} \sum_{n \text{ odd}} n^2 \frac{16b^2 L^2}{\pi^4 n^4} = \frac{4b^2 LT}{\pi^2} \sum_{n \text{ odd}} \frac{1}{n^2},$$

so the proportion of the sound associated with the nth harmonic (for n odd) is

$$\frac{1/n^2}{\displaystyle\sum_{n \text{ odd}} 1/n^2} = \frac{1/n^2}{\pi^2/8} = \frac{8}{\pi^2 n^2}.$$

Substituting $n = 1$ and $n = 3$, we find that 81.06% of the sound of the string of Example 2 is associated with the fundamental tone and 9.01% with the harmonic corresponding to $n = 3$.

The d'Alembert Solution

In contrast with series solutions of the heat equation, formal series solutions of the wave equation ordinarily do *not* possess sufficient termwise differentiability to permit verification of the solution by application of a superposition theorem analogous to the one stated in Section 9.5. For instance, termwise differentiation of the series in (24) would yield the series

$$\frac{\partial^2 y}{\partial x^2} = -\frac{4b}{L} \sum_{n=1}^{\infty} \sin \frac{n\pi}{2} \cos \frac{n\pi at}{L} \sin \frac{n\pi x}{L},$$

which generally fails to converge, because the "convergence factor" $1/n^2$ has disappeared after the second differentiation.

There is, however, an alternative approach that both verifies the solution in (23) and yields valuable additional information about it. If we apply the trigonometric identity

$$2 \sin A \cos B = \sin(A + B) + \sin(A - B)$$

with $A = n\pi x/L$ and $B = n\pi at/L$, then (23) gives

$$y(x, t) = \sum_{n=1}^{\infty} A_n \sin \frac{n\pi x}{L} \cos \frac{n\pi at}{L}$$

$$= \frac{1}{2} \sum_{n=1}^{\infty} A_n \sin \frac{n\pi}{L}(x + at) + \frac{1}{2} \sum_{n=1}^{\infty} A_n \sin \frac{n\pi}{L}(x - at). \tag{29}$$

But by definition of the coefficients,

$$\sum_{n=1}^{\infty} A_n \sin \frac{n\pi x}{L} = F(x)$$

for all x, where $F(x)$ is the *odd* extension of period $2L$ of the initial position function $f(x)$. Hence Eq. (29) means that

$$y(x,t) = \tfrac{1}{2}\left[F(x+at) + F(x-at)\right]. \tag{30}$$

Therefore, the series in (23) converges to the expression on the right-hand side in (30), which is known as the **d'Alembert form** of the solution of Problem A for the vibrating string. Moreover, using the chain rule, it is easy to verify (Problems 13 and 14) that the function $y(x,t)$ defined in (30) does, indeed, satisfy the equation $y_{tt} = a^2 y_{xx}$ (under the assumption that F is twice differentiable), as well as the boundary conditions $y(0,t) = y(L,t) = 0$ and $y(x,0) = f(x)$.

For any function $F(x)$, the functions $F(x+at)$ and $F(x-at)$ represent "waves" moving to the left and right, respectively, along the x-axis with speed a. This fact is illustrated in Fig. 9.6.3, which shows the graphs of these two functions for successive values of t, in a typical case where the initial position function $F(x)$ is a pulse function centered at the midpoint $x = \pi/2$ of a string of length $L = \pi$ with $a = 1$ (so the fundamental period of vibration is 2π). Thus the d'Alembert solution in (30) expresses $y(x,t)$ as a superposition of two waves moving in opposite directions with speed a. This is why the equation $y_{tt} = a^2 y_{xx}$ is called the *wave equation*.

(a) At time $t = 0$

(b) At time $t = \pi/8$

(c) At time $t = \pi/4$

(d) At time $t = 3\pi/8$

FIGURE 9.6.3. The pulse $F(x)$ produces two waves—one moving to the left, one to the right.

Strings with Initial Velocity

The separation-of-variables solution of Problem B, with initial conditions $y(x,0) = 0$ and $y_t(x,0) = g(x)$, proceeds precisely as did that of Problem A until Eq. (16) is reached. But then $y(x, 0) = X(x)T(0) = 0$ implies that $T(0) = 0$, so instead of (16) we have

$$\frac{d^2 T_n}{dt^2} + \frac{n^2 \pi^2 a^2}{L^2} T_n = 0, \quad T_n(0) = 0. \tag{31}$$

From Eq. (17) we see that a nontrivial solution of (31) is

$$T_n(t) = \sin \frac{n \pi a t}{L}. \tag{32}$$

The resulting formal power series solution is therefore of the form

$$\blacktriangleright \qquad y_B(x, t) = \sum_{n=1}^{\infty} B_n \sin \frac{n \pi a t}{L} \sin \frac{n \pi x}{L}, \tag{33}$$

so we want to choose the coefficients $\{B_n\}$ so that

$$y_t(x, 0) = \sum_{n=1}^{\infty} B_n \frac{n \pi a}{L} \sin \frac{n \pi x}{L} = g(x). \tag{34}$$

Thus we want $B_n \cdot n \pi a / L$ to be the Fourier sine coefficient b_n of $g(x)$ on $[0, L]$:

$$B_n \frac{n \pi a}{L} = b_n = \frac{2}{L} \int_0^L g(x) \sin \frac{n \pi x}{L} \, dx.$$

Hence we choose

$$\blacktriangleright \qquad B_n = \frac{2}{n \pi a} \int_0^L g(x) \sin \frac{n \pi x}{L} \, dx \tag{35}$$

in order for $y_B(x, t)$ in (33) to be a formal series solution of Problem B—and thus for $y(x, t) = y_A(x, t) + y_B(x, t)$ to be a formal series solution of our original boundary value problem in Eqs. (7a)–(7d).

Example 3　Consider a string on a guitar lying crosswise in the back of a pickup truck that at time $t = 0$ slams into a brick wall with speed v_0. Then $g(x) \equiv v_0$, so

$$B_n = \frac{2}{n \pi a} \int_0^L v_0 \sin \frac{n \pi x}{L} \, dx = \frac{2 v_0 L}{n^2 \pi^2 a} \left[1 - (-1)^n \right].$$

Hence the series in (33) gives

$$y(x, t) = \frac{4 v_0 L}{\pi^2 a} \sum_{n \text{ odd}} \frac{1}{n^2} \sin \frac{n \pi a t}{L} \sin \frac{n \pi x}{L}. \qquad \blacksquare$$

If we differentiate the series in (33) termwise with respect to t, we get

$$y_t(x, t) = \sum_{n=1}^{\infty} b_n \sin \frac{n \pi x}{L} \cos \frac{n \pi a t}{L} = \tfrac{1}{2} \left[G(x + at) + G(x - at) \right], \tag{36}$$

where G is the odd period $2L$ extension of the initial velocity function $g(x)$, using the same device as in the derivation of Eq. (30). In Problem 15 we ask you to deduce that

$$y(x, t) = \frac{1}{2a} [H(x + at) + H(x - at)], \qquad (37)$$

where the function $H(x)$ is defined to be

$$H(x) = \int_0^x G(s)\, ds. \qquad (38)$$

If, finally, a string has both a nonzero initial position function $y(x, 0) = f(x)$ and a nonzero initial velocity function $y_t(x, 0) = g(x)$, then we can obtain its displacement function by adding the d'Alembert solutions of Problems A and B given in Eqs. (30) and (37), respectively. Hence the vibrations of this string with general initial conditions are described by

$$y(x, t) = \frac{1}{2} [F(x + at) + F(x - at)] + \frac{1}{2a} [H(x + at) + H(x - at)], \qquad (39)$$

a superposition of four waves moving along the x-axis with speed a, two moving to the left and two to the right.

9.6 Problems

Solve the boundary value problems in Problems 1 through 10.

1. $y_{tt} = 4y_{xx}$, $0 < x < \pi$, $t > 0$; $y(0, t) = y(\pi, t) = 0$, $y(x, 0) = \frac{1}{10} \sin 2x$, $y_t(x, 0) = 0$

2. $y_{tt} = y_{xx}$, $0 < x < 1$, $t > 0$; $y(0, t) = y(1, t) = 0$, $y(x, 0) = \frac{1}{10} \sin \pi x - \frac{1}{20} \sin 3\pi x$, $y_t(x, 0) = 0$

3. $4y_{tt} = y_{xx}$, $0 < x < \pi$, $t > 0$; $y(0, t) = y(\pi, t) = 0$, $y(x, 0) = y_t(x, 0) = \frac{1}{10} \sin x$

4. $4y_{tt} = y_{xx}$, $0 < x < 2$, $t > 0$; $y(0, t) = y(2, t) = 0$, $y(x, 0) = \frac{1}{5} \sin \pi x \cos \pi x$, $y_t(x, 0) = 0$

5. $y_{tt} = 25y_{xx}$, $0 < x < 3$, $t > 0$; $y(0, t) = y(3, t) = 0$, $y(x, 0) = \frac{1}{4} \sin \pi x$, $y_t(x, 0) = 10 \sin 2\pi x$

6. $y_{tt} = 100y_{xx}$, $0 < x < \pi$, $t > 0$; $y(0, t) = y(\pi, t) = 0$, $y(x, 0) = x(\pi - x)$, $y_t(x, 0) = 0$

7. $y_{tt} = 100y_{xx}$, $0 < x < 1$, $t > 0$; $y(0, t) = y(1, t) = 0$, $y(x, 0) = 0$, $y_t(x, 0) = x$

8. $y_{tt} = 4y_{xx}$, $0 < x < \pi$, $t > 0$; $y(0, t) = y(\pi, t) = 0$, $y(x, 0) = \sin x$, $y_t(x, 0) = 1$

9. $y_{tt} = 4y_{xx}$, $0 < x < 1$, $t > 0$; $y(0, t) = y(1, t) = 0$, $y(x, 0) = 0$, $y_t(x, 0) = x(1 - x)$

10. $y_{tt} = 25y_{xx}$, $0 < x < \pi$, $t > 0$; $y(0, t) = y(\pi, t) = 0$, $y(x, 0) = y_t(x, 0) = \sin^2 x$

11. Suppose that a string 2 ft long weighs $\frac{1}{32}$ oz and is subjected to a tension of 32 lb. Find the fundamental frequency with which it vibrates and the velocity with which the vibration waves travel along it.

12. Show that the amplitude of the oscillations of the midpoint

of the string of Example 3 is

$$y\left(\frac{L}{2}, \frac{L}{2a}\right) = \frac{4v_0 L}{\pi^2 a} \sum_{n \text{ odd}} \frac{1}{n^2} = \frac{v_0 L}{2a}.$$

If the string is the string of Problem 11 and the impact speed of the pickup truck is 60 mi/h, show that this amplitude is approximately 1 in.

13. Suppose that the function $F(x)$ is twice differentiable for all x. Use the chain rule to verify that the functions

$$y(x, t) = F(x + at) \quad \text{and} \quad y(x, t) = F(x - at)$$

satisfy the equation $y_{tt} = a^2 y_{xx}$.

14. Given the differentiable odd period $2L$ function $F(x)$, show that the function

$$y(x, t) = \frac{1}{2} [F(x + at) + F(x - at)]$$

satisfies the conditions $y(0, t) = y(L, t) = 0$, $y(x, 0) = F(x)$, and $y_t(x, 0) = 0$.

15. If $y(x, 0) = 0$, then Eq. (36) implies (why?) that

$$y(x, t) = \frac{1}{2} \int_0^t G(x + a\tau)\, d\tau + \frac{1}{2} \int_0^t G(x - a\tau)\, d\tau.$$

Make appropriate substitutions in these integrals to derive Eqs. (37) and (38).

16. (a) Show that the substitutions $u = x + at$ and $v = x - at$ transform the equation $y_{tt} = a^2 y_{xx}$ into the equation $y_{uv} = 0$. **(b)** Conclude that every solution of $y_{tt} = a^2 y_{xx}$ is of the form

$$y(x, t) = F(x + at) + G(x - at),$$

which represents two waves traveling in opposite directions, each with speed a.

17. Suppose that

$$y(x, t) = \sum_{n=1}^{\infty} A_n \cos \frac{n\pi at}{L} \sin \frac{n\pi x}{L}.$$

Square the derivatives y_t and y_x and then integrate termwise—applying the orthogonality of the sine and cosine functions—to verify that

$$E = \frac{1}{2} \int_0^L (\rho y_t^2 + T y_x^2) \, dx = \frac{\pi^2 T}{4L} \sum_{n=1}^{\infty} n^2 A_n^2.$$

18. Consider a stretched string, initially at rest; its end at $x = 0$ is fixed, but its end at $x = L$ is partially free—it is allowed to slide without friction along the vertical line $x = L$. The corresponding boundary value problem is

$$y_{tt} = a^2 y_{xx} \qquad (0 < x < L, \quad t > 0);$$
$$y(0, t) = y_x(L, t) = 0,$$
$$y(x, 0) = f(x),$$
$$y_t(x, 0) = 0.$$

Separate the variables and use the odd half-multiple sine series of $f(x)$, as in Problem 24 of Section 9.5, to derive the solution

$$y(x, t) = \sum_{n \text{ odd}} A_n \cos \frac{n\pi at}{2L} \sin \frac{n\pi x}{2L},$$

where

$$A_n = \frac{2}{L} \int_0^L f(x) \sin \frac{n\pi x}{2L} \, dx.$$

Problems 19 and 20 deal with the vibrations of a string under the influence of the downward force $F(x) = -\rho g$ of gravity. According to Eq. (1), its displacement function satisfies the partial differential equation

$$\frac{\partial^2 y}{\partial t^2} = a^2 \frac{\partial^2 y}{\partial x^2} - g \tag{40}$$

with endpoint conditions $y(0, t) = y(L, t) = 0$.

19. Suppose first that the string hangs in a stationary position, so that $y = y(x)$ and $y_{tt} = 0$, and hence its differential equation of motion takes the simple form $a^2 y'' = g$. Derive the stationary solution

$$y(x) = \phi(x) = \frac{gx}{2a^2}(x - L).$$

20. Now suppose that the string is released from rest in equilibrium; consequently the initial conditions are $y(x, 0) = 0$ and $y_t(x, 0) = 0$. Define

$$v(x, t) = y(x, t) - \phi(x),$$

where $\phi(x)$ is the stationary solution of Problem 19. Deduce from Eq. (40) that $v(x, t)$ satisfies the boundary value problem

$$v_{tt} = a^2 v_{xx};$$
$$v(0, t) = v(L, t) = 0,$$
$$v(x, 0) = -\phi(x),$$
$$v_t(x, 0) = 0.$$

Conclude from Eqs. (22) and (23) that

$$y(x, t) - \phi(x) = \sum_{n=1}^{\infty} A_n \cos \frac{n\pi at}{L} \sin \frac{n\pi x}{L},$$

where the coefficients $\{A_n\}$ are the Fourier sine coefficients of $f(x) = -\phi(x)$. Finally, explain why it follows that the string oscillates between the positions $y = 0$ and $y = 2\phi(x)$.

21. For a string vibrating in air with resistance proportional to velocity, the boundary value problem is

$$y_{tt} = a^2 y_{xx} - 2h y_t;$$
$$y(0, t) = y(L, t) = 0,$$
$$y(x, 0) = f(x), \tag{41}$$
$$y_t(x, 0) = 0.$$

Assume that $0 < h < \pi a/L$. **(a)** Substitute

$$y(x, t) = X(x) T(t)$$

in (41) to obtain the equations

$$X'' + \lambda X = 0, \qquad X(0) = X(L) = 0 \tag{42}$$

and

$$T'' + 2h T' + a^2 \lambda T = 0, \qquad T'(0) = 0. \tag{43}$$

(b) The eigenvalues and eigenfunctions of (42) are

$$\lambda_n = \frac{n^2 \pi^2}{L^2} \quad \text{and} \quad X_n(x) = \sin \frac{n\pi x}{L}$$

(as usual). Show that the general solution with $\lambda = n^2\pi^2/L^2$ of the differential equation in (43) is

$$T_n(t) = e^{-ht}(A_n \cos \omega_n t + B_n \sin \omega_n t),$$

where $\omega_n = \sqrt{(n^2\pi^2 a^2/L^2) - h^2} < n\pi a/L$. **(c)** Show that $T_n'(0) = 0$ implies that $B_n = h A_n/\omega_n$, and hence that to within a constant multiplicative coefficient,

$$T_n(t) = e^{-ht} \cos(\omega_n t - \alpha_n)$$

where $\alpha_n = \tan^{-1}(h/\omega_n)$. **(d)** Finally, conclude that

$$y(x, t) = e^{-ht} \sum_{n=1}^{\infty} c_n \cos(\omega_n t - \alpha_n) \sin \frac{n\pi x}{L},$$

where

$$c_n = \frac{2}{L \cos \alpha_n} \int_0^L f(x) \sin \frac{n \pi x}{L} \, dx.$$

From this formula we see that the air resistance has three main effects: exponential damping of amplitudes, decreased frequencies $\omega_n < n \pi a / L$, and the introduction of the phase delay angles α_n.

22. Rework Problem 21 as follows: First substitute $y(x, t) = e^{-ht} v(x, t)$ in Eq. (41) and then show that the boundary value problem for $v(x, t)$ is

$$v_{tt} = a^2 v_{xx} + h^2 v;$$
$$v(0, t) = v(L, t) = 0,$$
$$v(x, 0) = f(x),$$
$$v_t(x, 0) = hf(x).$$

Next show that the substitution $v(x, t) = X(x)T(t)$ leads to the equations

$$X'' + \lambda X = 0, \quad X(0) = X(L) = 0,$$
$$T'' + (\lambda a^2 - h^2)T = 0.$$

Proceed in this manner to derive the solution $y(x, t)$ given in part (d) of Problem 21.

The snapshots in Fig. 9.6.4 show successive positions of a vibrating string with length $L = \pi$ and $a = 1$ (so its period of oscillation is 2π). The string is initially at rest with fixed endpoints, and at time $t = 0$ it is set in motion with initial position function

$$f(x) = 2 \sin^2 x = 1 - \cos 2x. \tag{44}$$

23. The most interesting snapshot is the one in Fig. 9.6.4(e), where it appears that the string exhibits a momentary "flat spot" at the instant $t = \pi/4$. Indeed, apply the d'Alembert formula in (30) to prove that the string's position function $y(x, t)$ satisfies the condition

$$y\left(x, \frac{\pi}{4}\right) = 1 \quad \text{for} \quad \frac{\pi}{4} \le x \le \frac{3\pi}{4}.$$

24. (a) Show that the position function $f(x)$ defined in Eq. (44) has inflection points $[f''(x) = 0]$ at $x = \pi/4$ and at $x = 3\pi/4$. **(b)** In snapshots (a)–(e) of Fig. 9.6.4 it appears that these two inflection points may remain fixed during some initial portion of the string's vibration. Indeed, apply the d'Alembert formula to show that if either $x = \pi/4$ or $x = 3\pi/4$, then $y(x, t) = 1$ for $0 \le t \le \pi/4$.

9.6 Application ▪ Vibrating-String Investigations

Here we describe a *Mathematica* implementation of the d'Alembert solution

$$y(x, t) = \tfrac{1}{2} [F(x + at) + F(x - at)] \tag{1}$$

of the vibrating-string problem, and apply it to investigate graphically the motions that result from a variety of different initial positions of the string. *Maple* and MATLAB versions of this implementation are included in the applications manual that accompanies this text.

To plot the snapshots shown in Fig. 9.6.4, we began with the initial position function

```
f[x_] := 2*Sin[x]^2
```

To define the odd period 2π extension $F(x)$ of $f(x)$, we need the function $s(x)$ that shifts the point x by an integral multiple of π into the interval $[0, \pi]$.

```
s[x_] := Block[{k}, k = Floor[N[x/Pi]];
            If[EvenQ[k], (* k is even *)
            (* then *) N[x - k*Pi],
            (* else *) N[x - k*Pi - Pi]]]
```

Then the desired odd extension is defined by

```
F[x_] := If[s[x] > 0, (* then *) f[s[x]],
            (* else *)-f[-s[x]]]
```

Finally, the d'Alembert solution in (1) is

```
G[x_, t_] := ( F[x + t] + F[x - t] )/2
```

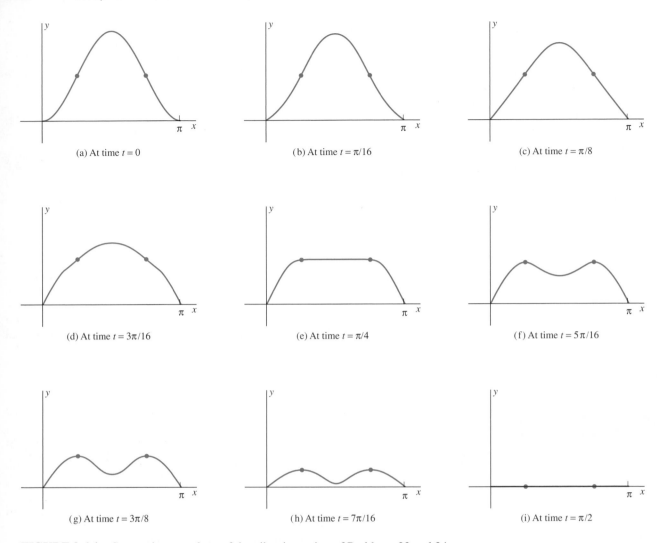

FIGURE 9.6.4. Successive snapshots of the vibrating string of Problems 23 and 24.

A snapshot of the position of the string at time t is defined by

```
stringAt[t_] := Plot[G[x,t], {x, 0, Pi},
                     PlotRange -> {-2, 2}];
```

For example, the command **stringAt[Pi/4]** plots the snapshot corresponding to $t = \pi/4$ shown in Fig. 9.6.4(e), which exhibits the apparent flat spot discussed in Problem 23. We can plot a whole sequence of shapshots at once:

```
snapshots = Table[ stringAt[t], {t, 0, Pi, Pi/12}]
```

These snapshots can be animated to show the vibrating string in motion, or we can exhibit simultaneously the successive positions of the string in a single composite figure (see Fig. 9.6.5) with the command **Show[snapshots]**.
The initial position function

```
f[x_] := If[x < Pi/2, (* then *) x,
              (* else *) Pi - x] // N
```

(corresponding to the triangular wave function of Fig. 9.2.4) generates in this way

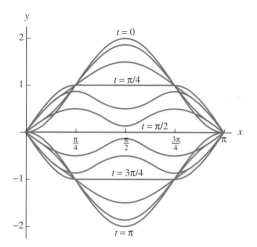

FIGURE 9.6.5. Successive positions of the vibrating string with initial position $f(x) = 2\sin^2 x$.

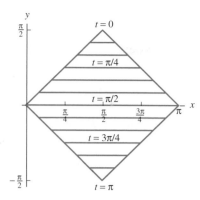

FIGURE 9.6.6. Successive positions of the vibrating string with triangular initial position.

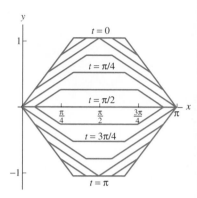

FIGURE 9.6.7. Successive positions of the vibrating string with trapezoidal initial position.

the composite picture shown in Fig. 9.6.6. Similarly, the initial position function

```
f[x_] := Which[ 0 <= x < Pi/3, x,
               Pi/3 <= x < 2*Pi/3, Pi/3,
               2*Pi/3 <= x <= Pi, Pi - x ] // N
```

(corresponding to the trapezoidal wave function of Fig. 9.2.5) produces the picture shown in Fig. 9.6.7.

You can test your implementation of d'Alembert's method by attempting to generate Figs. 9.6.6 and 9.6.7 for yourself. The initial position "bump function"

$$f(x) = \sin^{200} x, \quad 0 \leqq x \leqq \pi$$

generates traveling waves traveling (initially) in opposite directions, as indicated in Fig. 9.6.3 in the text. The initial position function

$$f(x) = \begin{cases} \sin^{200}\left(x + \frac{\pi}{2}\right) & \text{for } 0 < x < \pi/2, \\ 0 & \text{for } \pi/2 < x < \pi \end{cases}$$

generates a single wave that begins at $x = 0$ and (initially) travels to the right. (Think of a jump rope tied to a tree, whose free end is given a "snap" at time $t = 0$.)

After exploring some of the possibilities indicated previously, try some initial position functions of your own choice. Any continuous function f such that $f(0) = f(\pi) = 0$ is fair game. The more exotic the resulting vibration of the string, the better.

9.7 Steady-State Temperature and Laplace's Equation

We now consider the temperature in a two-dimensional plate, or lamina, that occupies a region R in the xy-plane bounded by a piecewise smooth curve C, as shown in Fig. 9.7.1. We assume that the faces of the plate are insulated, and that it is so thin that the temperature within it does not vary in the direction perpendicular to the xy-plane. We want to determine, under various conditions, the temperature $u(x, y, t)$ at the point (x, y) at time t.

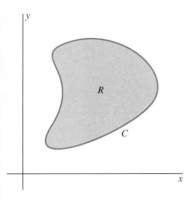

FIGURE 9.7.1. A plane region R and its bounding curve C.

Let the plate consist of material with density δ (mass per unit volume), specific heat c (per unit mass), and thermal conductivity K, all assumed constant throughout the plate. Under these assumptions, it can be shown (by a generalization of the derivation of the one-dimensional heat equation in Section 9.5) that the temperature function $u(x, y, t)$ satisfies the **two-dimensional heat equation**

$$\frac{\partial u}{\partial t} = k\left(\frac{\partial^2 u}{\partial x^2} + \frac{\partial^2 u}{\partial y^2}\right). \tag{1}$$

As in Section 9.5, k denotes the thermal diffusivity,

$$k = \frac{K}{c\delta}, \tag{2}$$

of the material of the plate. The sum of second derivatives on the right-hand side in (1) is the **Laplacian** of the function u, commonly denoted by

$$\nabla^2 u = \frac{\partial^2 u}{\partial x^2} + \frac{\partial^2 u}{\partial y^2}, \tag{3}$$

so the two-dimensional heat equation may be written as

$$\frac{\partial u}{\partial t} = k\nabla^2 u. \tag{1'}$$

In comparing Eq. (1′) with the one-dimensional heat equation $u_t = ku_{xx}$, we see that in passing from one to two dimensions, the second-order space derivative u_{xx} is replaced with the Laplacian $\nabla^2 u$. This is an instance of a general phenomenon. For instance, if a flexible stretched membrane occupies in equilibrium a region in the xy-plane and vibrates in the (perpendicular) z-direction, then its displacement function $z = z(x, y, t)$ satisfies the **two-dimensional wave equation**

$$\frac{\partial^2 z}{\partial t^2} = a^2\left(\frac{\partial^2 z}{\partial x^2} + \frac{\partial^2 z}{\partial y^2}\right) = a^2\nabla^2 z. \tag{4}$$

This equation has the same relation to the one-dimensional wave equation $z_{tt} = a^2 z_{xx}$ (here writing $z(x, t)$ for the displacement of a string) as Eq. (1′) has to the one-dimensional heat equation.

In this section we confine our attention to the steady-state situation in which the temperature u does not vary with time, and so is a function only of x and y. Thus we are interested in the *steady-state temperature* of a plate. In this case $u_t = 0$, so Eq. (1) becomes the **two-dimensional Laplace equation**

$$\nabla^2 u = \frac{\partial^2 u}{\partial x^2} + \frac{\partial^2 u}{\partial y^2} = 0. \tag{5}$$

This important partial differential equation is also known as the **potential equation.** The three-dimensional Laplace equation $u_{xx} + u_{yy} + u_{zz} = 0$ is satisfied (in empty space) by electric and gravitational potential functions. It is also satisfied by the velocity potential function for the steady irrotational flow of an incompressible and inviscid fluid (that is, one having zero viscosity).

Dirichlet Problems

A particular solution of Laplace's equation in a bounded plane region R is determined by appropriate boundary conditions. For example, it is plausible on physical grounds that the steady-state temperature $u(x, y)$ in a plate is determined if we know that $u(x, y)$ agrees with a given function $f(x, y)$ at each point of the boundary curve C of the plate. To find the steady-state temperature in a plate with assigned boundary values, we need to solve the boundary value problem

$$\frac{\partial^2 u}{\partial x^2} + \frac{\partial^2 u}{\partial y^2} = 0 \qquad \text{(within } R\text{);}$$
$$u(x, y) = f(x, y) \qquad \text{(if } (x, y) \text{ is on } C\text{).}$$

(6)

Such a problem, finding a solution of Laplace's equation in a region R with given boundary values, is called a **Dirichlet problem.** It is known that if the boundary curve C and the boundary value function f are reasonably well behaved, then there exists a unique solution of the Dirichlet problem in (6).

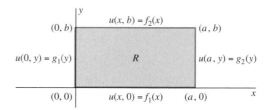

FIGURE 9.7.2. A rectangular plate with given boundary values.

Figure 9.7.2 shows a rectangular plate with indicated boundary values along its four edges. The corresponding Dirichlet problem is

$$u_{xx} + u_{yy} = 0 \qquad\qquad\qquad \text{(within } R\text{);}$$
$$u(x, 0) = f_1(x), \quad u(x, b) = f_2(x) \qquad (0 < x < a),$$
$$u(0, y) = g_1(y), \quad u(a, y) = g_2(y) \qquad (0 < y < b).$$

(7)

Because there are four nonhomogeneous conditions (rather than one), this boundary value problem is not directly susceptible to the method of separation of variables. In Section 9.6, when confronted with this difficulty, we split the problem of the vibrating string with both nonzero initial position and nonzero initial velocity into problems with a single nonhomogeneous condition each. In a similar way, the boundary value problem in (7) can be split into *four* problems, each with a single nonhomogeneous boundary condition. For each of these problems, $u(x, y)$ will be zero along three edges of the rectangle and will have assigned values on the fourth. Each of these four boundary values can be solved by the method of separation of variables, and the sum of the four solutions is the solution of the original problem in (7). In the following example we solve one of these four problems—the one illustrated in Fig. 9.7.3.

Example 1 Solve the boundary value problem

$$u_{xx} + u_{yy} = 0;$$
$$u(0, y) = u(a, y) = u(x, b) = 0, \tag{8}$$
$$u(x, 0) = f(x)$$

for the rectangle in Fig. 9.7.3.

Solution Substitution of $u(x, y) = X(x)Y(y)$ gives $X''Y + XY'' = 0$, so

$$\frac{X''}{X} = -\frac{Y''}{Y} = -\lambda \tag{9}$$

for some constant λ. Thus $X(x)$ must satisfy the familiar eigenvalue problem

$$X'' + \lambda X = 0,$$
$$X(0) = X(a) = 0.$$

The eigenvalues and associated eigenfunctions are

$$\lambda_n = \frac{n^2 \pi^2}{a^2}, \quad X_n(x) = \sin \frac{n\pi x}{a} \tag{10}$$

for $n = 1, 2, 3, \ldots$. From Eq. (9) with $\lambda = n^2\pi^2/a^2$ and the remaining homogeneous boundary conditions in (8), we get

$$Y_n'' - \frac{n^2 \pi^2}{a^2} Y_n = 0, \quad Y_n(b) = 0. \tag{11}$$

The general solution of the differential equation in (11) is

$$Y_n(y) = A_n \cosh \frac{n\pi y}{a} + B_n \sinh \frac{n\pi y}{a},$$

and the condition

$$Y_n(b) = A_n \cosh \frac{n\pi b}{a} + B_n \sinh \frac{n\pi b}{a} = 0$$

implies that $B_n = -[A_n \cosh(n\pi b/a)]/[\sinh(n\pi b/a)]$, so

$$Y_n(y) = A_n \cosh \frac{n\pi y}{a} - \frac{A_n \cosh(n\pi b/a)}{\sinh(n\pi b/a)} \sinh \frac{n\pi y}{a}$$

$$= \frac{A_n}{\sinh(n\pi b/a)} \left(\sinh \frac{n\pi b}{a} \cosh \frac{n\pi y}{a} - \cosh \frac{n\pi b}{a} \sinh \frac{n\pi y}{a} \right).$$

Therefore,

$$Y_n(y) = c_n \sinh \frac{n\pi (b - y)}{a} \tag{12}$$

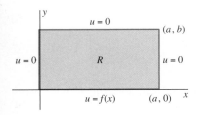

FIGURE 9.7.3. The boundary value problem of Example 1.

where $c_n = A_n/\sinh(n\pi b/a)$. From (10) and (12) we obtain the formal series solution

$$\blacktriangleright \qquad u(x, y) = \sum_{n=1}^{\infty} X_n(x) Y_n(y) = \sum_{n=1}^{\infty} c_n \sin \frac{n\pi x}{a} \sinh \frac{n\pi (b - y)}{a}. \qquad (13)$$

It remains only to choose the coefficients $\{c_n\}$ to satisfy the nonhomogeneous condition

$$u(x, 0) = \sum_{n=1}^{\infty} \left(c_n \sinh \frac{n\pi b}{a} \right) \sin \frac{n\pi x}{a} = f(x).$$

For this purpose we want

$$c_n \sinh \frac{n\pi b}{a} = b_n = \frac{2}{a} \int_0^a f(x) \sin \frac{n\pi x}{a} \, dx,$$

so

$$\blacktriangleright \qquad c_n = \frac{2}{a \sinh(n\pi b/a)} \int_0^a f(x) \sin \frac{n\pi x}{a} \, dx. \qquad (14)$$

With this choice of coefficients, the series in (13) is a formal series solution of the Dirichlet problem in (8). ∎

For instance, suppose that

$$f(x) \equiv T_0 = \frac{4T_0}{\pi} \sum_{n \text{ odd}} \frac{1}{n} \sin \frac{n\pi x}{a}$$

if $0 < x < a$, so that $b_n = 4T_0/(\pi n)$ for n odd and $b_n = 0$ for n even. Then the formulas in (13) and (14) yield

$$u(x, y) = \frac{4T_0}{\pi} \sum_{n \text{ odd}} \frac{\sin(n\pi x/a) \, \sinh[n\pi (b - y)/a]}{n \sinh(n\pi b/a)} \qquad (15)$$

for the steady-state temperature in a rectangular plate with its base held at temperature T_0 and its other three edges at temperature zero. In particular, suppose that $T_0 = 100$ and that $a = b = 10$. Then from Eq. (15) we find that the temperature at the center of the plate is

$$u(5, 5) = \frac{400}{\pi} \sum_{n \text{ odd}} \frac{\sin(n\pi/2) \, \sinh(n\pi/2)}{n \sinh n\pi}$$

$$\approx 25.3716 - 0.3812 + 0.0099 - 0.0003;$$

that is, $u(5, 5)$ is approximately 25.00.

Remark 1: Can you supply an argument—perhaps using symmetry—that proves (without using the series solution) that $u(5, 5)$ is exactly 25?

Remark 2: In practice, engineers use solutions like the one in Eq. (15) to plot the variation of temperature within a plate or piece of machinery; they are particularly interested in any "hot spots" that may appear. Such information is often presented by constructing *level curves* on which the temperature function $u(x, y)$ is constant. Figure 9.7.4 shows typical level curves for the function $u(x, y)$ in (15) with $a = b = 10$ and $T_0 = 100$. ∎

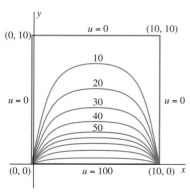

FIGURE 9.7.4. Typical level curves of the function $u(x, y)$ in Eq. (15).

Example 2   Let R be the "semi-infinite" strip shown in Fig. 9.7.5. Solve the boundary value problem

$$u_{xx} + u_{yy} = 0 \qquad \text{(in } R\text{);}$$
$$u(x, 0) = u(x, b) = 0 \qquad (0 < x < \infty),$$
$$u(x, y) \text{ is bounded as } x \to +\infty,$$
$$u(0, y) = g(y). \tag{16}$$

Solution   The condition that $u(x, y)$ is bounded as $x \to +\infty$ plays the role of a homogeneous boundary condition associated with the "missing" right edge of the "rectangle"; this is typical of Dirichlet problems for unbounded regions. With $u(x, y) = X(x)Y(y)$, the actual homogeneous conditions give $Y(0) = Y(b) = 0$. Hence it is $Y(y)$ that will satisfy an eigenvalue problem. We therefore write the separation in (9) as

$$\frac{Y''}{Y} = -\frac{X''}{X} = -\lambda, \tag{17}$$

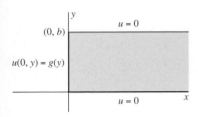

FIGURE 9.7.5. The "semi-infinite" strip of Example 2.

changing the sign of λ to get the familiar eigenvalue problem

$$Y'' + \lambda Y = 0, \qquad Y(0) = Y(b) = 0$$

with eigenvalues and associated eigenfunctions

$$\lambda_n = \frac{n^2 \pi^2}{b^2}, \qquad Y_n(y) = \sin \frac{n\pi y}{b}. \tag{18}$$

The general solution of

$$X_n'' - \frac{n^2 \pi^2}{b^2} X_n = 0$$

is $X_n(x) = A_n \exp(n\pi x/b) + B_n \exp(-n\pi x/b)$. We write the solution in exponential form—instead of using the hyperbolic sine and cosine—because then the condition that $u(x, y)$, and hence $X(x)$, is bounded as $x \to +\infty$ immediately implies that $A_n = 0$ for all n. Upon suppressing the constant B_n we are left with

$$X_n(x) = \exp\left(-\frac{n\pi x}{b}\right). \tag{19}$$

From Eqs. (18) and (19) we get the formal series solution

$$\blacktriangleright \qquad u(x, y) = \sum_{n=1}^{\infty} b_n X_n(x) Y_n(y) = \sum_{n=1}^{\infty} b_n \exp\left(-\frac{n\pi x}{b}\right) \sin \frac{n\pi y}{b} \tag{20}$$

that satisfies the homogeneous boundary conditions and the boundedness condition. In order also to satisfy the nonhomogeneous condition

$$u(0, y) = \sum_{n=1}^{\infty} b_n \sin \frac{n\pi y}{b} = g(y),$$

we choose b_n to be the Fourier sine coefficient

$$\blacktriangleright \qquad b_n = \frac{2}{b} \int_0^b g(y) \sin \frac{n\pi y}{b} \, dy \tag{21}$$

of the function $g(y)$ on $[0, b]$.

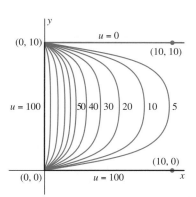

FIGURE 9.7.6. Typical level curves of the function $u(x, y)$ of Example 2.

For instance, if

$$g(y) = T_0 = \frac{4T_0}{\pi} \sum_{n \text{ odd}} \frac{1}{n} \sin \frac{n\pi y}{b}$$

for $0 < y < b$, then Eqs. (20) and (21) yield

$$u(x, y) = \frac{4T_0}{\pi} \sum_{n \text{ odd}} \frac{1}{n} \exp\left(-\frac{n\pi x}{b}\right) \sin \frac{n\pi y}{b}.$$

Figure 9.7.6 shows some typical level curves of the temperature function defined by this formula with $b = 10$ and $T_0 = 100$. Because of the negative exponential factors in the terms of the final series, we see that the temperature $u(x, y) \to 0$ as $x \to +\infty$ (whereas in (16) we assumed only that $u(x, y)$ remains bounded as $x \to +\infty$). ∎

The Dirichlet Problem for a Circular Disk

We now investigate the steady-state temperature in a circular disk of radius a with insulated faces and with given boundary temperatures. Obviously we should accommodate the geometry of the circle by expressing $u = u(r, \theta)$ in terms of polar coordinates r and θ, with $x = r \cos\theta$ and $y = r \sin\theta$. When these equations are used to transform the Laplacian—see, for instance, Problem 45 in Section 12.7 of Edwards and Penney, *Calculus: Early Transcendentals*, 7th edition, (Upper Saddle River, NJ: Prentice Hall, 2008)—the result is **Laplace's equation in polar coordinates**:

➤
$$\nabla^2 u = \frac{\partial^2 u}{\partial r^2} + \frac{1}{r}\frac{\partial u}{\partial r} + \frac{1}{r^2}\frac{\partial^2 u}{\partial \theta^2} = 0. \tag{22}$$

We prescribe assigned boundary temperatures (as indicated in Fig. 9.7.7) by requiring that

➤
$$u(a, \theta) = f(\theta), \tag{23}$$

where the function $f(\theta)$ of period 2π is given. In addition, because (r, θ) and $(r, \theta + 2\pi)$ are the polar coordinates of the same point, we impose on u the periodicity condition

➤
$$u(r, \theta) = u(r, \theta + 2\pi) \tag{24}$$

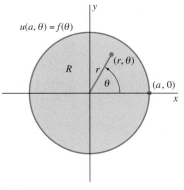

FIGURE 9.7.7. The Dirichlet problem for a circular disk.

for $r < a$ and all θ; this will play the role of a homogeneous boundary condition.

To solve the boundary value problem in Eqs. (22) through (24), we substitute $u(r, \theta) = R(r)\Theta(\theta)$ in Eq. (22); the result is

$$R''\Theta + \frac{1}{r}R'\Theta + \frac{1}{r^2}R\Theta'' = 0.$$

Division by $R\Theta/r^2$ gives

$$\frac{r^2 R'' + r R'}{R} + \frac{\Theta''}{\Theta} = 0,$$

so it follows that

$$\frac{r^2 R'' + r R'}{R} = -\frac{\Theta''}{\Theta} = \lambda$$

for some constant λ. This yields the two ordinary differential equations

$$r^2 R'' + r R' - \lambda R = 0 \tag{25}$$

and

$$\Theta'' + \lambda \Theta = 0. \tag{26}$$

The general solution of Eq. (26) is

$$\Theta(\theta) = A \cos \alpha\theta + B \sin \alpha\theta \quad \text{if } \lambda = \alpha^2 > 0, \tag{27a}$$
$$\Theta(\theta) = A + B\Theta \quad \text{if } \lambda = 0, \tag{27b}$$
$$\Theta(\theta) = A e^{\alpha\theta} + B e^{-\alpha\theta} \quad \text{if } \lambda = -\alpha^2 < 0. \tag{27c}$$

Now we apply the condition in (24), which implies that $\Theta(\theta) = \Theta(\theta + 2\pi)$; that is, that $\Theta(\theta)$ has period 2π. In Problems 22 and 23 we ask you to show that this is so only if $\lambda = n^2$ (n an integer) in (27a) or if $\lambda = 0$ and $B = 0$ in (27b). Thus we have the eigenvalues and associated eigenfunctions

$$\lambda_0 = 0, \quad \Theta_0(\theta) = 1; \tag{28a}$$
$$\lambda_n = n^2, \quad \Theta_n(\theta) = A_n \cos n\theta + B_n \sin n\theta \tag{28b}$$

for $n = 1, 2, 3, \ldots$.

Next we turn our attention to Eq. (25). With $\lambda_0 = 0$ it reduces to the equation $r^2 R_0'' + r R_0' = 0$ with general solution

$$R_0(r) = C_0 + D_0 \ln r. \tag{29}$$

Of course we want $u(r, \theta)$, and hence $R(r)$, to be continuous at $r = 0$; this requires that $D_0 = 0$ in Eq. (29), so $R_0(r) = C_0$. Then, with $\lambda = \lambda_n = n^2$, Eq. (25) is

$$r^2 R_n'' + r R_n' - n^2 R_n = 0.$$

On substituting the trial solution $R(r) = r^k$, we find that $k = \pm n$, so the general solution of the previous equation is

$$R_n(r) = C_n r^n + \frac{D_n}{r^n}. \tag{30}$$

Continuity at $r = 0$ then requires that $D_n = 0$, so $R_n(r) = C_n r^n$.

Finally we combine the results in Eqs. (28) through (30) with $D_n \equiv 0$ to obtain a formal series solution of the form

$$u(r, \theta) = \sum_{n=0}^{\infty} R_n(r) \Theta_n(\theta);$$

that is,

$$u(r, \theta) = \frac{a_0}{2} + \sum_{n=1}^{\infty} (a_n \cos n\theta + b_n \sin n\theta) r^n. \tag{31}$$

In order that the boundary condition $u(a, \theta) = f(\theta)$ be satisfied, we want

$$u(a, \theta) = \frac{a_0}{2} + \sum_{n=1}^{\infty}(a_n a^n \cos n\theta + b_n a^n \sin n\theta)$$

to be the Fourier series of $f(\theta)$ on $[0, 2\pi]$. Hence we choose

$$a_n = \frac{1}{\pi a^n}\int_0^{2\pi} f(\theta) \cos n\theta \, d\theta \qquad (n = 0, 1, 2, \dots) \qquad \text{(32a)}$$

and

$$b_n = \frac{1}{\pi a^n}\int_0^{2\pi} f(\theta) \sin n\theta \, d\theta \qquad (n = 1, 2, 3, \dots). \qquad \text{(32b)}$$

Example 3   For instance, if $f(\theta) = T_0$ for $0 < \theta < \pi$ and $f(\theta) = -T_0$ for $\pi < \theta < 2\pi$, so that

$$f(\theta) = \frac{4T_0}{\pi}\sum_{n \text{ odd}}\frac{1}{n}\sin n\theta,$$

then $a_n = 0$ for all $n \geq 0$, $b_n = 0$ for n even, and $b_n = 4T_0/(\pi n a^n)$ for n odd. So Eqs. (31) and (32) yield

$$u(r, \theta) = \frac{4T_0}{\pi}\sum_{n \text{ odd}}\frac{r^n}{na^n}\sin n\theta. \qquad \blacksquare$$

Note: In the Dirichlet problems of this section, we have concentrated on temperature functions with preassigned boundary values. In the case of a plate with an *insulated* edge—across which no heat can flow—the boundary condition is that the derivative of $u(x, y)$ in the direction normal to this edge vanishes. For instance, consider the rectangular plate in Fig. 9.7.2. If the edge $x = 0$ is insulated, then $u_x(0, y) \equiv 0$, whereas if the edge $y = b$ is insulated, then $u_y(x, b) \equiv 0$.

9.7 Problems

In Problems 1 through 3, solve the Dirichlet problem for the rectangle $0 < x < a$, $0 < y < b$ consisting of Laplace's equation $u_{xx} + u_{yy} = 0$ and the given boundary value conditions.

1. $u(x, 0) = u(x, b) = u(0, y) = 0$, $u(a, y) = g(y)$
2. $u(x, 0) = u(x, b) = u(a, y) = 0$, $u(0, y) = g(y)$
3. $u(x, 0) = u(0, y) = u(a, y) = 0$, $u(x, b) = f(x)$
4. Consider the boundary value problem

$$u_{xx} + u_{yy} = 0;$$
$$u_x(0, y) = u_x(a, y) = u(x, 0) = 0,$$
$$u(x, b) = f(x)$$

corresponding to a rectangular plate $0 < x < a$, $0 < y < b$ with the edges $x = 0$ and $x = a$ insulated. Derive the solution

$$u(x, y) = \frac{a_0 y}{2b} + \sum_{n=1}^{\infty} a_n \left(\cos\frac{n\pi x}{a}\right)\left(\frac{\sinh(n\pi y/a)}{\sinh(n\pi b/a)}\right),$$

where

$$a_n = \frac{2}{a}\int_0^a f(x) \cos\frac{n\pi x}{a}\, dx \qquad (n = 0, 1, 2, \dots).$$

(*Suggestion:*   Show first that λ_0 is an eigenvalue with $X_0(x) \equiv 1$ and $Y_0(y) = y$.)

In Problems 5 and 6, find a solution of Laplace's equation $u_{xx} + u_{yy} = 0$ in the rectangle $0 < x < a$, $0 < y < b$ that satisfies the given boundary conditions (see Problem 4).

5. $u_y(x, 0) = u_y(x, b) = u(a, y) = 0$, $u(0, y) = g(y)$

6. $u_x(0, y) = u_x(a, y) = u_y(x, 0) = 0$, $u(x, b) = f(x)$

In Problems 7 and 8, find a solution of Laplace's equation in the semi-infinite strip $0 < x < a$, $y > 0$ that satisfies the given boundary conditions and the additional condition that $u(x, y)$ is bounded as $y \to +\infty$.

7. $u(0, y) = u(a, y) = 0$, $u(x, 0) = f(x)$

8. $u_x(0, y) = u_x(a, y) = 0$, $u(x, 0) = f(x)$

9. Suppose that $a = 10$ and $f(x) = 10x$ in Problem 8. Show that

$$u(x, y) = 50 - \frac{400}{\pi^2} \sum_{n \text{ odd}} \frac{1}{n^2} e^{-n\pi y/10} \cos \frac{n\pi x}{10}.$$

Then compute (with two-decimal-place accuracy) the values $u(0, 5)$, $u(5, 5)$, and $u(10, 5)$.

10. The edge $x = a$ of the rectangular plate $0 < x < a$, $0 < y < b$ is insulated, the edges $x = 0$ and $y = 0$ are held at temperature zero, and $u(x, b) = f(x)$. Use the odd half-multiple sine series of Problem 21 of Section 9.3 to derive a solution of the form

$$u(x, y) = \sum_{n \text{ odd}} c_n \sin \frac{n\pi x}{2a} \sinh \frac{n\pi y}{2a}.$$

Then give a formula for c_n.

11. The edge $y = 0$ of the rectangular plate $0 < x < a$, $0 < y < b$ is insulated, the edges $x = a$ and $y = b$ are held at temperature zero, and $u(0, y) = g(y)$. Use the odd half-multiple cosine series of Problem 22 of Section 9.3 to find $u(x, y)$.

12. A vertical cross section of a long high wall 30 cm thick has the shape of the semi-infinite strip $0 < x < 30$, $y > 0$. The face $x = 0$ is held at temperature zero, but the face $x = 30$ is insulated. Given $u(x, 0) = 25$, derive the formula

$$u(x, y) = \frac{100}{\pi} \sum_{n \text{ odd}} \frac{1}{n} e^{-n\pi y/60} \sin \frac{n\pi x}{60}$$

for the steady-state temperature within the wall.

Problems 13 through 15 deal with the semicircular plate of radius a shown in Fig. 9.7.8. The circular edge has a given temperature $u(a, \theta) = f(\theta)$. In each problem, derive the given series for the steady-state temperature $u(r, \theta)$ satisfying the given boundary conditions along $\theta = 0$ and $\theta = \pi$, and give the formula for the coefficients c_n.

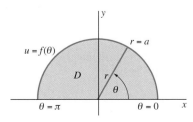

FIGURE 9.7.8.   The semicircular plate of Problems 13 through 15.

13. $u(r, 0) = u(r, \pi) = 0$;

$$u(r, \theta) = \sum_{n=1}^{\infty} c_n r^n \sin n\theta$$

14. $u_\theta(r, 0) = u_\theta(r, \pi) = 0$;

$$u(r, \theta) = \frac{c_0}{2} + \sum_{n=1}^{\infty} c_n r^n \cos n\theta$$

15. $u(r, 0) = u_\theta(r, \pi) = 0$;

$$u(r, \theta) = \sum_{n \text{ odd}} c_n r^{n/2} \sin \frac{n\theta}{2}$$

16. Consider Dirichlet's problem for the region *exterior* to the circle $r = a$. You want to find a solution of

$$r^2 u_{rr} + r u_r + u_{\theta\theta} = 0$$

such that $u(a, \theta) = f(\theta)$ and $u(r, \theta)$ is bounded as $r \to +\infty$. Derive the series

$$u(r, \theta) = \frac{a_0}{2} + \sum_{n=1}^{\infty} \frac{1}{r^n}(a_n \cos n\theta + b_n \sin n\theta),$$

and give formulas for the coefficients $\{a_n\}$ and $\{b_n\}$.

17. The velocity potential function $u(r, \theta)$ for steady flow of an ideal fluid around a cylinder of radius $r = a$ satisfies the boundary value problem

$$r^2 u_{rr} + r u_r + u_{\theta\theta} = 0 \qquad (r > a);$$
$$u_r(a, \theta) = 0, \qquad u(r, \theta) = u(r, -\theta),$$
$$\lim_{r \to \infty}[u(r, \theta) - U_0 r \cos \theta] = 0.$$

(a) By separation of variables, derive the solution

$$u(r, \theta) = \frac{U_0}{r}(r^2 + a^2) \cos \theta.$$

(b) Hence show that the velocity components of the flow are

$$u_x = \frac{\partial u}{\partial x} = \frac{U_0}{r^2}(r^2 - a^2 \cos 2\theta)$$

and

$$u_y = \frac{\partial u}{\partial y} = -\frac{U_0}{r^2} a^2 \sin 2\theta.$$

The streamlines for this fluid flow around the cylinder are shown in Fig. 9.7.9.

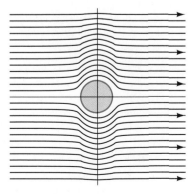

FIGURE 9.7.9.   Streamlines for ideal fluid flow around a cylinder.

Comment: *The streamlines in Fig. 9.7.9 are the level curves of the function $\psi(x, y)$ given in part (b) of Problem 18. It is troublesome to write a computer program to plot such level curves. It is far easier to plot some solutions of the differential equation $dy/dx = u_y/u_x$. We did so with initial conditions $x_0 = -5$, $y_0 = -2.7, -2.5, -2.3, \ldots, 2.5, 2.7$. The solutions were obtained numerically using the improved Euler method (Section 2.5) with step size 0.02.*

18. (a) Show that the velocity potential in part (a) of Problem 17 can be written in rectangular coordinates as

$$u(x, y) = U_0 x \left(1 + \frac{a^2}{x^2 + y^2} \right).$$

(b) The stream function for the flow is

$$\psi(x, y) = U_0 y \left(\frac{a^2}{x^2 + y^2} - 1 \right).$$

Show that $\nabla u \cdot \nabla \psi \equiv 0$. Because $\mathbf{v} = \nabla u$ is the velocity vector, this shows that the streamlines of the flow are the level curves of $\psi(x, y)$.

Problems 19 through 21 deal with a solid spherical ball of radius $r = a$ with initial temperature T_0 throughout. At time $t = 0$ it is packed in ice, so its temperature at the surface $r = a$ is zero thereafter. Its temperature then depends only on time t and the distance r from the center of the ball, so we write $u = u(r, t)$.

19. (a) The heat content of the spherical shell with inner radius r and outer radius $r + \Delta r$ is

$$Q(t) = \int_r^{r+\Delta r} c\delta u(x, t) \cdot 4\pi s^2 \, ds.$$

Show that $Q'(t) = 4\pi c\delta r^2 u_t(\bar{r}, t)$ for some $\bar{r}$ in the interval $(r, r + \Delta r)$. **(b)** The radial heat flux is $\phi = -Ku_r$ across the bounding spherical surfaces of the shell in part (a). Conclude that

$$Q'(t) = 4\pi K \left[(r + \Delta r)^2 u_r(r + \Delta r, t) - r^2 u_r(r, t) \right].$$

(c) Equate the values of $Q'(t)$ in parts (a) and (b); then take the limit as $\Delta r \to 0$ to get the equation

$$\frac{\partial u}{\partial t} = \frac{k}{r^2} \frac{\partial}{\partial r} \left(r^2 \frac{\partial u}{\partial r} \right).$$

(d) Finally, show that this last equation is equivalent to

$$\frac{\partial}{\partial t}(ru) = k \frac{\partial^2}{\partial r^2}(ru).$$

20. It follows from part (d) of Problem 19 that $u(r, t)$ satisfies the boundary value problem

$$\frac{\partial}{\partial t}(ru) = k \frac{\partial^2}{\partial r^2}(ru) \qquad (r < a);$$

$$u(a, t) = 0, \quad u(r, 0) = T_0.$$

Show that the new function $v(r, t) = ru(r, t)$ satisfies a familiar boundary value problem (in Section 9.5), and thus derive the solution

$$u(r, t) = \frac{2aT_0}{\pi} \sum_{n=1}^{\infty} \frac{(-1)^{n+1}}{nr} \exp\left(-\frac{n^2\pi^2 kt}{a^2} \right) \sin \frac{n\pi r}{a}.$$

21. (a) Deduce from the solution to Problem 20 that the temperature at the center of the ball at time t is

$$u(0, t) = 2T_0 \sum_{n=1}^{\infty} (-1)^{n+1} \exp\left(-\frac{n^2\pi^2 kt}{a^2} \right).$$

(b) Let $a = 30$ cm and $T_0 = 100°$C. Compute $u(0, t)$ after 15 min if the ball is made of iron with $k = 0.15$ cgs. (*Answer:* Approximately $45°$C.) **(c)** If you have access to a programmable calculator, repeat part (b) for a ball made of concrete with $k = 0.005$ in cgs units. About 15 terms are required to show that $u = 100.00°$C accurate to two decimal places.

22. In the discussion of the Dirichlet problem for a circular disk in this section, we obtained the ordinary differential equation $\Theta'' + \lambda\Theta = 0$ with the periodicity condition $\Theta(\theta) = \Theta(\theta + 2\pi)$. **(a)** Suppose that $\lambda = \alpha^2 > 0$. Show that the general solution

$$\Theta(\theta) = A \cos \alpha\theta + B \sin \alpha\theta$$

has period 2π only if $\lambda = n^2$ with n an integer. **(b)** In the case $\lambda = 0$, show that the general solution

$$\Theta(\theta) = A\theta + B$$

is periodic only if $A = 0$.

23. If $\lambda = -\alpha^2 < 0$ in Problem 22, then the general solution of the differential equation is

$$\Theta(\theta) = Ae^{\alpha\theta} + Be^{-\alpha\theta}.$$

Show that this function is not periodic unless $A = B = 0$.

Eigenvalues and Boundary Value Problems

Sturm–Liouville Problems and Eigenfunction Expansions

$\mathbf{I}$n the last three sections of Chapter 9, we saw that numerous different boundary value problems all lead—by separation of variables—to the same ordinary differential equation

$$X''(x) + \lambda X(x) = 0 \qquad (0 < x < L), \tag{1}$$

containing an eigenvalue λ, but with different endpoint conditions, such as

$$X(0) = X(L) = 0 \tag{2}$$

or

$$X'(0) = X'(L) = 0 \tag{3}$$

or

$$X(0) = X'(L) = 0, \tag{4}$$

depending on the original boundary conditions.

For example, recall the problem (in Section 9.5) of finding the temperature $u(x, t)$ in a rod $0 \leq x \leq L$ with given initial temperature $u(x, 0) = f(x)$. As a boundary value problem, this problem of the rod is the same as the problem of finding the temperature within a large slab that occupies the region $0 \leq x \leq L$ in xyz-space. If its initial temperature depends only on x and is independent of y and z—that is, if $u(x, 0) = f(x)$—then the same will be true of its temperature $u = u(x, t)$ at time t. When we substitute

$$u(x, t) = X(x)T(t)$$

in the heat equation

$$\frac{\partial u}{\partial t} = k\frac{\partial^2 u}{\partial x^2},$$

we find that $X(x)$ satisfies the endpoint conditions in (2) if the faces $x = 0$ and $x = L$ of the slab are held at temperature zero, those in (3) if both faces are insulated, and those in (4) if one face is insulated and the other is held at temperature zero. But if each face loses heat to a surrounding medium (at temperature zero) in accord with Newton's law of cooling, then (according to Problem 23 of Section 9.5) the endpoint conditions take the form

$$hX(0) - X'(0) = 0 = hX(L) + X'(L), \tag{5}$$

where h is a nonnegative heat transfer coefficient.

The point is that when we impose different endpoint conditions on the solution of Eq. (1), we get different eigenvalue problems, and hence different eigenvalues $\{\lambda_n\}$ and different eigenfunctions $\{X_n(x)\}$ to use in constructing a formal power series solution

$$u(x, t) = \sum c_n X_n(x) T_n(t) \tag{6}$$

of the boundary value problem. The final step in this construction is to choose the coefficient $\{c_n\}$ in Eq. (6) so that

$$u(x, 0) = \sum c_n T_n(0) X_n(x) = f(x). \tag{7}$$

Thus we need finally an *eigenfunction expansion* of the given function $f(x)$ in terms of the eigenfunctions of the pertinent endpoint value problem.

Sturm–Liouville Problems

In order to unify and generalize the method of separation of variables, it is useful to formulate a general type of eigenvalue problem that includes as special cases each of those mentioned previously. Equation (1), with y instead of X as the dependent variable, can be written in the form

$$\frac{d}{dx}\left[p(x)\frac{dy}{dx}\right] - q(x)y + \lambda r(x)y = 0, \tag{8}$$

where $p(x) = r(x) \equiv 1$ and $q(x) \equiv 0$. Indeed, we indicate in Problem 16 that essentially any linear second-order differential equation of the form

$$A(x)y'' + B(x)y' + C(x)y + \lambda D(x)y = 0$$

takes the form in (8) after multiplication by a suitable factor.

Example 1

If we multiply the parametric Bessel equation

$$x^2 y'' + xy' + (\lambda x^2 - n^2)y = 0 \qquad (x > 0)$$

of order n by $1/x$, the result may be written as

$$\frac{d}{dx}\left[x\frac{dy}{dx}\right] - \frac{n^2}{x}y + \lambda xy = 0,$$

which is of the form in (8) with $p(x) = r(x) = x$ and $q(x) = n^2/x$. ∎

Now, on solutions of Eq. (8) in a bounded open interval (a, b), let us impose homogeneous (linear) endpoint conditions of the form

$$\alpha_1 y(a) - \alpha_2 y'(a) = 0, \quad \beta_1 y(b) + \beta_2 y'(b) = 0, \tag{9}$$

where the coefficients α_1, α_2, β_1, and β_2 are constants. In addition to being homogeneous, these two conditions are *separated*, in that one of them involves the values of $y(x)$ and $y'(x)$ at one endpoint $x = a$, whereas the other involves values at the other endpoint $x = b$. For instance, note that the conditions $y(a) = y'(b) = 0$ are of the form in (9) with $\alpha_1 = \beta_2 = 1$ and $\alpha_2 = \beta_1 = 0$.

DEFINITION Sturm–Liouville Problem

A **Sturm–Liouville problem** is an endpoint value problem of the form

$$\frac{d}{dx}\left[p(x) \frac{dy}{dx} \right] - q(x)y + \lambda r(x)y = 0 \qquad (a < x < b); \tag{8}$$

$$\alpha_1 y(a) - \alpha_2 y'(a) = 0, \qquad \beta_1 y(b) + \beta_2 y'(b) = 0, \tag{9}$$

with neither α_1 and α_2 both zero nor β_1 and β_2 both zero. The parameter λ in (8) is the "eigenvalue" whose possible (constant) values are sought.

Sturm–Liouville problems generalize the endpoint value problems of Section 3.8 with sine and cosine solutions. They are named for the French mathematicians Charles Sturm (1803–1855) and Joseph Liouville (1809–1882), who investigated such problems in the 1830s.

Example 2 We get different Sturm–Liouville problems by pairing the same differential equation

$$y'' + \lambda y = 0 \qquad (\text{for } 0 < x < L)$$

with the different homogeneous endpoint conditions

- $y(0) = y(L) = 0$ (where $\alpha_1 = \beta_1 = 1$ and $\alpha_2 = \beta_2 = 0$),
- $y'(0) = y'(L) = 0$ (where $\alpha_1 = \beta_1 = 0$ and $\alpha_2 = \beta_2 = 1$), and
- $y(0) = y'(L) = 0$ (where $\alpha_1 = \beta_2 = 1$ and $\alpha_2 = \beta_1 = 0$). ∎

Note that the Sturm–Liouville problem in (8)–(9) always has the trivial solution $y(x) \equiv 0$. We seek the values of λ—the **eigenvalues**—for which this problem has a *nontrivial* real-valued solution (an **eigenfunction**), and for each eigenvalue its associated eigenfunction (or eigenfunctions). Note that any constant (nonzero) multiple of an eigenfunction will also be an eigenfunction. The following theorem provides sufficient conditions under which the problem in (8)–(9) has an infinite sequence $\{\lambda_n\}_1^\infty$ of nonnegative eigenvalues, with each eigenvalue λ_n having (to within a constant multiple) exactly one associated eigenfunction $y_n(x)$. A proof of this theorem is outlined in Chapter 9 of G. P. Tolstov, *Fourier Series* (New York: Dover, 1976).

> ### THEOREM 1   Sturm–Liouville Eigenvalues
>
> Suppose that the functions $p(x)$, $p'(x)$, $q(x)$, and $r(x)$ in Eq. (8) are continuous on the interval $[a, b]$ and that $p(x) > 0$ and $r(x) > 0$ at each point of $[a, b]$. Then the eigenvalues of the Sturm–Liouville problem in (8)–(9) constitute an increasing sequence
>
> $$\lambda_1 < \lambda_2 < \lambda_3 < \cdots < \lambda_{n-1} < \lambda_n < \cdots \qquad (10)$$
>
> of real numbers with
>
> $$\lim_{n \to \infty} \lambda_n = +\infty. \qquad (11)$$
>
> To within a constant factor, only a single eigenfunction $y_n(x)$ is associated with each eigenvalue λ_n. Moreover, if $q(x) \geq 0$ on $[a, b]$ and the coefficients $\alpha_1, \alpha_2, \beta_1,$ and β_2 in (9) are all nonnegative, then the eigenvalues are all nonnegative.

Note: It is important to observe the signs in (8) and (9) when verifying the hypotheses of Theorem 1. Sometimes the Sturm–Liouville problem in (8)–(9) is called **regular** if it satisfies the hypotheses of Theorem 1; otherwise it is **singular**. In this section we will confine our attention to regular Sturm–Liouville problems. Singular Sturm–Liouville problems associated with Bessel's equation will appear in Section 10.4.

Example 3   In Example 3 of Section 3.8, we saw that the Sturm–Liouville problem

$$y'' + \lambda y = 0 \qquad (0 < x < L);$$
$$y(0) = 0, \qquad y(L) = 0 \qquad (12)$$

has eigenvalues $\lambda_n = n^2\pi^2/L^2$ and associated eigenfunctions $y_n(x) = \sin(n\pi x/L)$ ($n = 1, 2, 3, \ldots$). There we had to consider the cases $\lambda = -\alpha^2 < 0$, $\lambda = 0$, and $\lambda = \alpha^2 > 0$ separately. Here $p(x) = r(x) \equiv 1$, $q(x) \equiv 0$, $\alpha_1 = \beta_1 = 1$, and $\alpha_2 = \beta_2 = 0$, so we know from Theorem 1 that the problem in (12) has only nonnegative eigenvalues. Therefore, only the two cases $\lambda = 0$ and $\lambda = \alpha^2 > 0$ would need to be considered if we were starting afresh. ∎

We are also familiar (from the problems in Section 9.5) with the Sturm–Liouville problem

$$y'' + \lambda y = 0 \qquad (0 < x < L);$$
$$y'(0) = 0, \qquad y'(L) = 0, \qquad (13)$$

which has eigenvalues $\lambda_0 = 0$, $\lambda_n = n^2\pi^2/L^2$ ($n = 1, 2, 3, \ldots$) and associated eigenfunctions $y_0(x) \equiv 1$, $y_n(x) = \cos(n\pi x/L)$. We will customarily write $\lambda_0 = 0$ if 0 is an eigenvalue and otherwise write λ_1 for the smallest eigenvalue; thus λ_1 always denotes the smallest positive eigenvalue.

Example 4   Find the eigenvalues and associated eigenfunctions of the Sturm–Liouville problem

$$y'' + \lambda y = 0 \qquad (0 < x < L);$$
$$y'(0) = 0, \qquad y(L) = 0. \qquad (14)$$

Solution   This is a Sturm–Liouville problem satisfying the hypotheses of Theorem 1 with $\alpha_1 = \beta_2 = 0$ and $\alpha_2 = \beta_1 = 1$, so there are no negative eigenvalues. If $\lambda = 0$, then $y(x) = Ax + B$, and thus $y'(0) = A = 0$ and $y(L) = B = 0$. Therefore 0 is not an eigenvalue. If $\lambda = \alpha^2$, then

$$y(x) = A\cos\alpha x + B\sin\alpha x \quad \text{and} \quad y'(x) = -A\alpha\sin\alpha x + B\alpha\cos\alpha x.$$

Hence $y'(0) = 0$ implies that $B = 0$, and then $y(L) = A\cos\alpha L = 0$, so it follows that αL is an *odd* integral multiple of $\pi/2$: $\alpha L = (2n-1)\pi/2$. Thus we have the eigenvalues and associated eigenfunctions

$$\lambda_n = \alpha_n^2 = \frac{(2n-1)^2\pi^2}{4L^2} \quad \text{and} \quad y_n(x) = \cos\frac{(2n-1)\pi x}{2L}$$

for $n = 1, 2, 3, \ldots$. ∎

Example 5   Find the eigenvalues and associated eigenfunctions of the Sturm–Liouville problem

$$\begin{aligned} y'' + \lambda y &= 0 \qquad (0 < x < L); \\ y(0) &= 0, \qquad hy(L) + y'(L) = 0 \quad (h > 0). \end{aligned} \tag{15}$$

Solution   This problem satisfies the hypotheses of Theorem 1 with $\alpha_1 = \beta_2 = 1$, $\alpha_2 = 0$, and $\beta_1 = h > 0$, so there are no negative eigenvalues. If $\lambda = 0$, then $y(x) = Ax + B$, thus $y(0) = B = 0$. Then

$$hy(L) + y'(L) = h \cdot AL + A = A \cdot (hL + 1) = 0,$$

and it follows that $A = 0$ as well. Thus 0 is not an eigenvalue.
If $\lambda = \alpha^2$, then

$$y(x) = A\cos\alpha x + B\sin\alpha x.$$

Hence $y(0) = A = 0$, so

$$y(x) = B\sin\alpha x \quad \text{and} \quad y'(x) = B\alpha\cos\alpha x.$$

Therefore,

$$hy(L) + y'(L) = hB\sin\alpha L + B\alpha\cos\alpha L = 0.$$

If $B \neq 0$, it follows that

$$\tan\alpha L = -\frac{\alpha}{h} = -\frac{\alpha L}{hL}. \tag{16}$$

Thus $\beta = \alpha L$ is a (positive) solution of the equation

$$\tan x = -\frac{x}{hL}. \tag{17}$$

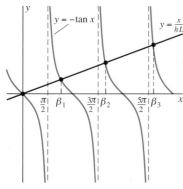

FIGURE 10.1.1.   The solution of Eq. (17) by geometric methods.

The solutions of Eq. (17) are the points of intersection of the graphs of $y(x) = -\tan x$ and $y(x) = x/hL$, as indicated in Fig. 10.1.1. It is apparent from the figure that there is an infinite sequence of positive roots $\beta_1, \beta_2, \beta_3, \ldots$, and that when n is large, β_n is only slightly larger than $(2n-1)\pi/2$. See the table in Fig. 10.1.2, in which the first eight solutions of Eq. (17) are listed for the case $hL = 1$. At any

n	x_n	$(2n-1)\pi/2$
1	2.0288	1.5708
2	4.9132	4.7124
3	7.9787	7.8540
4	11.0855	10.9956
5	14.2074	14.1372
6	17.3364	17.2788
7	20.4692	20.4204
8	23.6043	23.5619

FIGURE 10.1.2. Approximate values of the first eight positive solutions of $\tan x = -x$.

rate, the eigenvalues and associated eigenfunctions of the problem in (15) are given by

$$\lambda_n = \alpha_n^2 = \frac{\beta_n^2}{L^2}, \quad y_n(x) = \sin\alpha_n x = \sin\frac{\beta_n x}{L} \tag{18}$$

for $n = 1, 2, 3, \ldots$. Equation (17) appears frequently in certain applications (mechanical vibrations and heat conduction are only two of many examples), and its solutions for various values of hL are tabulated in Table 4.19 of Abramowitz and Stegun, *Handbook of Mathematical Functions* (New York: Dover, 1965). ∎

Orthogonal Eigenfunctions

Recall from Section 9.1 that the familiar formulas for the coefficients in a Fourier series follow from the orthogonality of the sine and cosine functions. Similarly, the expansion of a given function in terms of the eigenfunctions of a Sturm–Liouville problem depends on a crucial orthogonality property of these eigenfunctions. The functions $\phi(x)$ and $\psi(x)$ are said to be **orthogonal** on the interval $[a, b]$ with respect to the **weight function** $r(x)$ provided that

$$\int_a^b \phi(x)\psi(x)r(x)\,dx = 0. \tag{19}$$

The following theorem implies that any two eigenfunctions of a regular Sturm–Liouville problem that are associated with distinct eigenvalues are orthogonal with respect to the weight function $r(x)$ in Eq. (8).

THEOREM 2   Orthogonality of Eigenfunctions

Suppose that the functions p, q, and r in the Sturm–Liouville problem in Eqs. (8)–(9) satisfy the hypotheses of Theorem 1, and let $y_i(x)$ and $y_j(x)$ be eigenfunctions associated with the distinct eigenvalues λ_i and λ_j. Then

$$\int_a^b y_i(x)y_j(x)r(x)\,dx = 0. \tag{20}$$

Proof: We begin with the equations

$$\frac{d}{dx}\left[p(x)\frac{dy_i}{dx}\right] - q(x)y_i + \lambda_i r(x)y_i = 0,$$

$$\frac{d}{dx}\left[p(x)\frac{dy_j}{dx}\right] - q(x)y_j + \lambda_j r(x)y_j = 0. \tag{21}$$

These equations imply that λ_i, y_i and λ_j, y_j are eigenvalue–eigenfunction pairs. If we multiply the first equation by y_j and the second by y_i, then subtract the results, we get

$$y_j\frac{d}{dx}\left[p(x)\frac{dy_i}{dx}\right] - y_i\frac{d}{dx}\left[p(x)\frac{dy_j}{dx}\right] + (\lambda_i - \lambda_j)r(x)y_i y_j = 0.$$

Hence

$$(\lambda_i - \lambda_j)y_i y_j r(x) = y_i \frac{d}{dx}\left[p(x)\frac{dy_j}{dx}\right] - y_j \frac{d}{dx}\left[p(x)\frac{dy_i}{dx}\right]$$

$$= \frac{d}{dx}\left[p(x)\left(y_i\frac{dy_j}{dx} - y_j\frac{dy_i}{dx}\right)\right],$$

the latter of the two equalities being verifiable by direct differentiation. Therefore, integration from $x = a$ to $x = b$ yields

$$(\lambda_i - \lambda_j)\int_a^b y_i(x)y_j(x)r(x)\,dx = \left[p(x)\left(y_i(x)y_j'(x) - y_j(x)y_i'(x)\right)\right]_a^b. \qquad (22)$$

From the endpoint condition in (9), we have

$$\alpha_1 y_i(a) - \alpha_2 y_i'(a) = 0 \quad \text{and} \quad \alpha_1 y_j(a) - \alpha_2 y_j'(a) = 0.$$

Because α_1 and α_2 are not both zero, it follows that the determinant of coefficients must be zero:

$$y_i(a)y_j'(a) - y_j(a)y_i'(a) = 0.$$

Similarly, the second endpoint condition in (9) implies that

$$y_i(b)y_j'(b) - y_j(b)y_i'(b) = 0.$$

Thus the right-hand side in Eq. (22) vanishes. Inasmuch as $\lambda_i \neq \lambda_j$, the result in (20) follows, and the proof is complete. ▲

Eigenfunction Expansions

Now suppose that the function $f(x)$ can be represented in the interval $[a, b]$ by an **eigenfunction series**

$$\blacktriangleright \qquad f(x) = \sum_{m=1}^{\infty} c_m y_m(x), \qquad (23)$$

where the functions y_1, y_2, y_3, ... are the eigenfunctions of the regular Sturm–Liouville problem in Eqs. (8)–(9). To determine the coefficients $c_1, c_2, c_3, \ldots$, we generalize the technique by which we determined the ordinary Fourier coefficients in Section 9.1. First we multiply each side of Eq. (23) by $y_n(x)r(x)$, and then we integrate from $x = a$ to $x = b$. Under the assumption that termwise integration is valid, we obtain

$$\int_a^b f(x)y_n(x)r(x)\,dx = \sum_{m=1}^{\infty} c_m \int_a^b y_m(x)y_n(x)r(x)\,dx. \qquad (24)$$

But because of the orthogonality in (20), the only nonzero term on the right-hand side in Eq. (24) is the one for which $m = n$. Thus Eq. (24) takes the form

$$\int_a^b f(x)y_n(x)r(x)\,dx = c_n \int_a^b [y_n(x)]^2 r(x)\,dx,$$

and therefore

$$\blacktriangleright \qquad c_n = \frac{\displaystyle\int_a^b f(x) y_n(x) r(x)\, dx}{\displaystyle\int_a^b [y_n(x)]^2 r(x)\, dx}. \tag{25}$$

We therefore *define* the eigenfunction series in (23)—representing $f(x)$ in terms of the eigenfunctions of the given Sturm–Liouville problem—by means of the choice of the coefficients specified by Eq. (25).

For instance, suppose that the Sturm–Liouville problem is the familiar

$$\begin{aligned} y'' + \lambda y &= 0 \qquad (0 < x < \pi); \\ y(0) &= y(\pi) = 0, \end{aligned} \tag{26}$$

for which $r(x) \equiv 1$ and the eigenfunctions are $y_n(x) = \sin nx$ for $n = 1, 2, 3, \ldots$. Then Eq. (25) yields

$$c_n = \frac{\displaystyle\int_0^\pi f(x) \sin nx\, dx}{\displaystyle\int_0^\pi \sin^2 nx\, dx} = \frac{2}{\pi} \int_0^\pi f(x) \sin nx\, dx,$$

because

$$\int_0^\pi \sin^2 x\, dx = \frac{\pi}{2}.$$

This is the familiar formula for the Fourier sine coefficients, and so the eigenfunction series in (23) is simply the familiar Fourier sine series

$$f(x) = \sum_{n=1}^\infty c_n \sin nx$$

of $f(x)$ on $[0, \pi]$.

The following theorem, stated without proof, generalizes the Fourier convergence theorem of Section 9.2.

THEOREM 3   Convergence of Eigenfunction Series

Let $y_1, y_2, y_3, \ldots$ be the eigenfunctions of a regular Sturm–Liouville problem on $[a, b]$. If the function $f(x)$ is piecewise smooth on $[a, b]$, then the eigenfunction series in Eq. (23) converges for $a < x < b$ to the value $f(x)$ wherever f is continuous, and to the average $\frac{1}{2}[f(x+) + f(x-)]$ of right-hand and left-hand limits at each point of discontinuity.

Example 6   For the Sturm–Liouville problem $y'' + \lambda y = 0$ $(0 < x < L)$, $y'(0) = y(L) = 0$ of Example 4, we found the eigenfunctions $y_n(x) = \cos(2n - 1)\pi x/(2L)$, $n = 1, 2, 3, \ldots$. The corresponding eigenfunction series for a function $f(x)$ is

$$f(x) = \sum_{n=1}^\infty c_n \cos \frac{(2n - 1)\pi x}{2L} \tag{27}$$

with

$$c_n = \frac{\displaystyle\int_0^L f(x) \cos\left[(2n-1)\pi x/2L\right] dx}{\displaystyle\int_0^L \cos^2\left[(2n-1)\pi x/2L\right] dx}$$

$$= \frac{2}{L} \int_0^L f(x) \cos\frac{(2n-1)\pi x}{2L} \, dx, \tag{28}$$

because

$$\int_0^L \cos^2\frac{(2n-1)\pi x}{2L} \, dx = \frac{L}{2}.$$

Thus the series in Eq. (27) is the odd half-multiple cosine series of Problem 22 of Section 9.3. Similarly, the Sturm–Liouville problem $y'' + \lambda y = 0$, $y(0) = y'(L) = 0$ leads to the odd half-multiple sine series

$$f(x) = \sum_{n=1}^{\infty} c_n \sin\frac{(2n-1)\pi x}{2L}, \qquad c_n = \frac{2}{L} \int_0^L f(x) \sin\frac{(2n-1)\pi x}{2L} \, dx \tag{29}$$

of Problem 21 of Section 9.3. ∎

Example 7 Represent the function $f(x) = A$ (a constant) for $0 < x < 1$ as a series of eigenfunctions of the Sturm–Liouville problem

$$\begin{aligned} y'' + \lambda y &= 0 \qquad (0 < x < 1); \\ y(0) &= 0, \qquad y(1) + 2y'(1) = 0. \end{aligned} \tag{30}$$

Solution Comparing (30) with (15), we see that this is the Sturm–Liouville problem of Example 5 with $L = 1$ and $h = \frac{1}{2}$. From (17) and (18) we see that the eigenfunctions of the problem are therefore $y_n(x) = \sin\beta_n x$ where $\beta_1, \beta_2, \beta_3, \ldots$ are the positive roots of the equation $\tan x = -2x$. Hence the coefficients in the desired series are given by

$$c_n = \frac{\displaystyle\int_0^1 A \sin\beta_n x \, dx}{\displaystyle\int_0^1 \sin^2 \beta_n x \, dx}. \tag{31}$$

Now $\displaystyle\int_0^1 A \sin\beta_n x \, dx = A(1 - \cos\beta_n)/\beta_n$ and

$$\int_0^1 \sin^2 \beta_n x \, dx = \int_0^1 \frac{1}{2}(1 - \cos 2\beta_n x) \, dx = \frac{1}{2}\left[x - \frac{1}{2\beta_n}\sin 2\beta_n x\right]_0^1$$

$$= \frac{1}{2}\left(1 - \frac{\sin\beta_n \cos\beta_n}{\beta_n}\right).$$

Consequently,

$$\int_0^1 \sin^2 \beta_n x \, dx = \frac{1}{2}\left(1 + 2\cos^2 \beta_n\right).$$

In the last step we used the fact from Eq. (17) that $(\sin \beta_n)/\beta_n = -2 \cos \beta_n$. Substituting these values for the integrals in (31), we get the eigenfunction series

$$f(x) = \sum_{n=1}^{\infty} \frac{2A(1 - \cos \beta_n)}{\beta_n(1 + 2\cos^2 \beta_n)} \sin \beta_n x. \tag{32}$$

∎

Remark: A numerical investigation of the eigenfunction series in Eq. (32) is outlined in the computing project for this section. ∎

Summary

According to the theorems in this section, every regular Sturm–Liouville problem has the following three properties:

- It has an infinite sequence of eigenvalues diverging to infinity (Theorem 1).
- The eigenfunctions are orthogonal with appropriate weight function (Theorem 2).
- Any piecewise smooth function can be represented by an eigenfunction series (Theorem 3).

There are other types of eigenvalue problems in applied mathematics that also enjoy these three important properties. Some isolated examples will appear in subsequent sections, though we will confine our attention largely to applications of Sturm–Liouville problems.

10.1 Problems

The problems for Section 3.8 deal with eigenvalues and eigenfunctions and may be used here as well. In Problems 1 through 5, verify that the eigenvalues and eigenfunctions for the indicated Sturm–Liouville problem are those listed.

1. $y'' + \lambda y = 0$, $y'(0) = y'(L) = 0$; $\lambda_0 = 0$, $y_0(x) \equiv 1$ and $\lambda_n = n^2\pi^2/L^2$, $y_n(x) = \cos n\pi x/L$

2. $y'' + \lambda y = 0$, $y(0) = y'(L) = 0$; $\lambda_n = (2n-1)^2\pi^2/4L^2$, $y_n(x) = \sin(2n-1)\pi x/2L$, $n \geq 1$

3. $y'' + \lambda y = 0$, $y'(0) = hy(L) + y'(L) = 0$ ($h > 0$); $\lambda_n = \beta_n^2/L^2$, $y_n(x) = \cos \beta_n x/L$ ($n \geq 1$), where β_n is the nth positive root of $\tan x = hL/x$. Sketch $y = \tan x$ and $y = hL/x$ to estimate the value of β_n for n large.

4. $y'' + \lambda y = 0$, $hy(0) - y'(0) = y(L) = 0$ ($h > 0$); $\lambda_n = \beta_n^2/L^2$, $y_n(x) = \beta_n \cos \beta_n x/L + hL \sin \beta_n x/L$ ($n \geq 1$), where β_n is the nth positive root of $\tan x = -x/hL$.

5. $y'' + \lambda y = 0$, $hy(0) - y'(0) = hy(L) + y'(L) = 0$ ($h > 0$); $\lambda_n = \beta_n^2/L^2$, $y_n(x) = \beta_n \cos \beta_n x/L + hL \sin \beta_n x/L$ ($n \geq 1$), where β_n is the nth positive root of $\tan x = 2hLx/(x^2 - h^2L^2)$. Estimate β_n for n large by sketching the graphs of $y = 2hL \cot x$ and the hyperbola $y = (x^2 - h^2L^2)/x$.

6. Show that the Sturm–Liouville problem $y'' + \lambda y = 0$, $y(0) = y'(L) = 0$ leads to the odd half-multiple sine series in Eq. (29) (see Problem 2).

In Problems 7 through 10, represent the given function $f(x)$ as a series of eigenfunctions of the indicated Sturm–Liouville problem.

7. $f(x) \equiv 1$; the Sturm–Liouville problem of Example 5
8. $f(x) \equiv 1$; the Sturm–Liouville problem of Problem 3
9. $f(x) = x$; the Sturm–Liouville problem of Example 5 with $L = 1$
10. $f(x) = x$; the Sturm–Liouville problem of Problem 3 with $L = 1$

Problems 11 through 14 deal with the regular Sturm–Liouville problem

$$\begin{aligned} y'' + \lambda y &= 0 && (0 < x < L); \\ y(0) &= 0, && hy(L) - y'(L) = 0, \end{aligned} \tag{33}$$

where $h > 0$. Note that Theorem 1 does not exclude the possibility of negative eigenvalues.

11. Show that $\lambda_0 = 0$ is an eigenvalue if and only if $hL = 1$, in which case the associated eigenfunction is $y_0(x) = x$.
12. Show that the problem in (33) has a single negative eigenvalue λ_0 if and only if $hL > 1$, in which case $\lambda_0 = -\beta_0^2/L^2$ and $y_0(x) = \sinh \beta_0 x/L$, where β_0 is the positive root of the equation $\tanh x = x/hL$. (*Suggestion:* Sketch the graphs of $y = \tanh x$ and $y = x/hL$.)

13. Show that the positive eigenvalues and associated eigenfunctions of the problem in (33) are $\lambda_n = \beta_n^2/L^2$ and $y_n(x) = \sin \beta_n x/L$ ($n \geq 1$), where β_n is the nth positive root of $\tan x = x/hL$.

14. Suppose that $hL = 1$ in (33) and that $f(x)$ is piecewise smooth. Show that

$$f(x) = c_0 x + \sum_{n=1}^{\infty} c_n \sin \frac{\beta_n x}{L},$$

where $\{\beta_n\}_1^{\infty}$ are the positive roots of $\tan x = x$, and

$$c_0 = \frac{3}{L^3} \int_0^L x f(x)\, dx,$$

$$c_n = \frac{2}{L \sin^2 \beta_n} \int_0^L f(x) \sin \frac{\beta_n x}{L}\, dx.$$

15. Show that the eigenvalues and eigenfunctions of the Sturm–Liouville problem

$$y'' + \lambda y = 0 \qquad (0 < x < 1);$$
$$y(0) + y'(0) = 0, \qquad y(1) = 0$$

are given by $\lambda_0 = 0$, $y_0(x) = x - 1$ and

$$\lambda_n = \beta_n^2, \qquad y_n(x) = \beta_n \cos \beta_n x - \sin \beta_n x$$

for $n \geq 1$, where $\{\beta_n\}_1^{\infty}$ are the positive roots of $\tan x = x$.

16. Beginning with the equation

$$A(x)y'' + B(x)y' + C(x)y + \lambda D(x)y = 0,$$

first divide by $A(x)$ and then multiply by

$$p(x) = \exp\left(\int \frac{B(x)}{A(x)}\, dx\right).$$

Show that the resulting equation can be written in the Sturm–Liouville form

$$\frac{d}{dx}\left[p(x)\frac{dy}{dx}\right] - q(x)y + \lambda r(x)y = 0$$

with $q(x) = -p(x)C(x)/A(x)$ and

$$r(x) = p(x)D(x)/A(x).$$

Loaded Uniform Beam

Consider a uniform beam with (downward) load $w(x)$, whose deflection function $y(x)$ satisfies the fourth-order equation

$$EIy^{(4)} = w(x)$$

for $0 < x < L$ and the endpoint conditions

- $y = y'' = 0$ *at a hinged (or simply supported) end;*
- $y = y' = 0$ *at a fixed (built-in) end;*
- $y'' = y^{(3)} = 0$ *at a free end.*

In the case in which each end is hinged, $y(x)$ can be found by the Fourier series method discussed in Section 9.4—that is, by substituting the Fourier series

$$y(x) = \sum b_n \sin \frac{n\pi x}{L}$$

in the differential equation

$$EIy^{(4)} = w(x) = \sum_{n=1}^{\infty} c_n \sin \frac{n\pi x}{L} \qquad (34)$$

(where c_n is the nth Fourier sine coefficient of $w(x)$) to determine the coefficients $\{b_n\}$.

17. Suppose that w is constant in Eq. (34). Apply the method described here to obtain the deflection function

$$y(x) = \frac{4wL^4}{EI\pi^5} \sum_{n \text{ odd}} \frac{1}{n^5} \sin \frac{n\pi x}{L}.$$

18. Suppose that $w = bx$ in (34). Derive the deflection function

$$y(x) = \frac{2bL^5}{EI\pi^5} \sum_{n=1}^{\infty} \frac{(-1)^{n+1}}{n^5} \sin \frac{n\pi x}{L}.$$

The method used in Problems 17 and 18 succeeds because the functions $\sin(n\pi x/L)$ satisfy the hinged/hinged conditions $y(0) = y''(0) = y(L) = y''(L) = 0$, so that $y(x)$ does also.

If, instead, both ends of the beam are fixed, in place of the sine functions we can use the eigenfunctions of the problem

$$y^{(4)} - \lambda y = 0 \qquad (0 < x < L);$$
$$y(0) = y'(0) = 0, \qquad y(L) = y'(L) = 0, \qquad (35)$$

because these eigenfunctions satisfy the fixed/fixed endpoint conditions. The eigenvalues of this problem are all positive, and by Problem 22 the associated eigenfunctions are orthogonal with weight function $r(x) \equiv 1$. Hence we can write

$$w(x) = \sum_{n=1}^{\infty} c_n y_n(x), \qquad c_n = \frac{\int_0^L w(x)y_n(x)\, dx}{\int_0^L [y_n(x)]^2\, dx}, \qquad (36)$$

according to the analog of Theorem 3 that holds for the problem in (35). If we write $\lambda = \alpha^4$, then $y_n(x)$ is of the form

$$y(x) = A \cosh \alpha x$$
$$+ B \sinh \alpha x + C \cos \alpha x + D \sin \alpha x, \qquad (37)$$

with $\alpha = \alpha_n$, so it follows that $y_n^{(4)}(x) = \alpha_n^4 y_n(x)$. When we substitute the series $y(x) = \sum b_n y_n(x)$—which evidently satisfies the fixed/fixed endpoint conditions—in (35), we obtain

$$EI \sum_{n=1}^{\infty} b_n \alpha_n^4 y_n(x) = \sum_{n=1}^{\infty} c_n y_n(x).$$

Hence $EI b_n \alpha_n^4 = c_n$, so the deflection function of the beam is

$$y(x) = \sum_{n=1}^{\infty} \frac{c_n}{EI\alpha_n^4} y_n(x). \qquad (38)$$

The following problems deal with the eigenvalues and eigenfunctions of the problem in (35) and similar problems.

19. Begin with the general solution in (37) of $y^{(4)} - \alpha^4 y = 0$. First note that $y(0) = y'(0) = 0$ implies that $C = -A$ and $D = -B$. Then impose the conditions $y(L) = y'(L) = 0$ to get two homogeneous linear equations in A and B. Hence the determinant of coefficients of A and B must vanish; deduce from this that $\cosh \alpha L \cos \alpha L = 1$. Conclude that the nth eigenvalue is $\lambda_n = \beta_n^4/L^4$ where $\{\beta_n\}_1^\infty$ are the positive roots of the equation $\cosh x \cos x = 1$ (see Fig. 10.1.3). Finally, show that an associated eigenfunction is

$$y_n(x) = (\sinh \beta_n - \sin \beta_n) \left(\cosh \frac{\beta_n x}{L} - \cos \frac{\beta_n x}{L} \right)$$

$$- (\cosh \beta_n - \cos \beta_n) \left(\sinh \frac{\beta_n x}{L} - \sin \frac{\beta_n x}{L} \right).$$

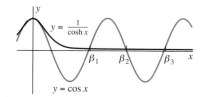

FIGURE 10.1.3. The solutions of $\cosh x \cos x = 1$ (the graph is not drawn to scale).

20. For the case of a cantilever (fixed/free) beam, we need to solve the eigenvalue problem

$$y^{(4)} - \lambda y = 0 \qquad (0 < x < L);$$

$$y(0) = y'(0) = 0, \qquad y''(L) = y^{(3)}(L) = 0.$$

Proceeding as in Problem 19, show that the nth eigenvalue is $\lambda_n = \beta_n^4/L^4$, where $\{\beta_n\}_1^\infty$ are the positive roots of the equation $\cosh x \cos x = -1$. Then find the associated eigenfunction.

21. For the eigenvalue problem

$$y^{(4)} - \lambda y = 0, \quad y(0) = y'(0) = 0 = y(L) = y''(L)$$

corresponding to a fixed/hinged beam, show that the nth eigenvalue is $\lambda_n = \beta_n^4/L^4$, where $\{\beta_n\}_1^\infty$ are the positive roots of the equation $\tanh x = \tan x$.

22. Suppose that $y_m^{(4)} = \lambda_m y_m$ and $y_n^{(4)} = \lambda_n y_n$. Apply the method of proof of Theorem 2 and integrate by parts twice to show that

$$(\lambda_m - \lambda_n) \int_0^L y_m(x) y_n(x) \, dx$$

$$= \left[y_n(x) \frac{d^3 y_m}{dx^3} - y_m(x) \frac{d^3 y_n}{dx^3} \right.$$

$$\left. - \frac{dy_n}{dx} \frac{d^2 y_m}{dx^2} + \frac{dy_m}{dx} \frac{d^2 y_n}{dx^2} \right]_0^L.$$

Conclude that if each endpoint condition is either $y = y' = 0$, $y = y'' = 0$, or $y'' = y^{(3)} = 0$, then y_m and y_n are orthogonal if $\lambda_m \neq \lambda_n$.

10.1 Application Numerical Eigenfunction Expansions

We outline a MATLAB-based numerical investigation of the eigenfunction series

$$f(x) = \sum_{n=1}^\infty \frac{2(1 - \cos \beta_n)}{\beta_n (1 + 2 \cos^2 \beta_n)} \sin \beta_n x \tag{1}$$

for $0 < x < 1$. (We have taken $A = 1$ in Eq. (32) of this section.) *Maple* and *Mathematica* versions of this investigation are included in the applications manual that accompanies this text.

We saw in the solution of Example 7 that the values $\{\beta_n\}_1^\infty$ in Eq. (1) are the positive solutions of the equation $\tan x = -2x$. Just as indicated in Fig. 10.1.1 (for the similar equation $\tan x = -x$), the value of β_n is (for n large) just slightly larger than $(2n - 1)\pi/2$. But because of the discontinuities in the tangent function near these solutions, it is best for automatic root-finding to rewrite our eigenvalue equation in the form

$$\sin x + 2x \cos x = 0. \tag{2}$$

Then the MATLAB command

```
b = fsolve('sin(x)+2*x.*cos(x)', pi/2+0.1+(0:pi:99*pi));
```

n	β_n
1	1.8366
2	4.8158
3	7.9171
4	11.0408
5	14.1724
6	17.3076
7	20.4448
8	23.5831
9	26.7222
10	29.8619

FIGURE 10.1.4. The first ten positive solutions of Eq. (2).

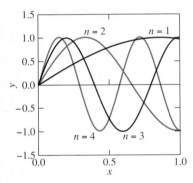

FIGURE 10.1.5. The eigenfunctions $y_n(x) = \sin \beta_n x$ for $n = 1, 2, 3, 4$.

quickly generates the first 100 values of β_n (see Fig. 10.1.4). (We have provided a vector

$$\mathbf{x}_0 = \frac{\pi}{2} + 0.1 + \begin{bmatrix} 0 & \pi & 2\pi & 3\pi & \cdots & 99\pi \end{bmatrix}$$

of 100 initial guesses.) The commands

```
x = 0 : 1/200 : 1;
for n = 1 : 4
    plot(x, sin(b(n)*x)
end
```

graph the first four eigenfunctions (Fig. 10.1.5).

You may find it interesting to apply the MATLAB command **diff(b)** to verify that $\beta_n - \beta_{n-1} \approx 3.1416$ for $n \geq 65$. Thus successive eigenvalues do, indeed, appear to be separated by π. The command

```
c = 2*(1 - cos(b))./(b.*(1 + 2*cos(b).^2));
```

calculates the first 100 coefficients in the eigenfunction series in (1). We find that

$$\begin{aligned} f(x) \approx \;&(1.2083)\sin\beta_1 x + (0.3646)\sin\beta_2 x + (0.2664)\sin\beta_3 x \\ &+ (0.1722)\sin\beta_4 x + \cdots + (0.0066)\sin\beta_{97}x + (0.0065)\sin\beta_{98}x \\ &+ (0.0065)\sin\beta_{99}x + (0.0064)\sin\beta_{100}x \end{aligned}$$

with the numerical coefficients evidently decreasing quite slowly. Finally, the commands

```
x = 0 : 1/500 : 1;
y = zeros(size(x));
for n = 1 : 100
    y = y + c(n)*sin(b(n)*x);
end
plot(x,y)
```

graph this partial sum (Fig. 10.1.6). Note the Gibbs phenomenon that appears at $x = 0$.

You can check your understanding of eigenfunction expansions by reworking Example 7, except on the interval $0 < x < L$ and with the right-endpoint condition

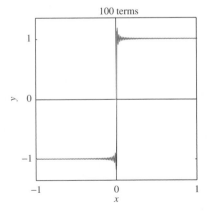

FIGURE 10.1.6. Graphs with $N = 25$, $N = 50$, $N = 100$ of the partial sum $\sum_{n=1}^{N} c_n \sin \beta_n x$ of the eigenfunction series in Eq. (1).

in (30) replaced with $y(L) + ky'(L) = 0$. Select your own values $L > 1$ and $k > 2$. Then calculate the resulting values of β_n and construct graphs like those in Figs. 10.1.5 and 10.1.6. In Fig. 10.1.6 we see convergence to $f(x) \equiv 1$ within the interval $0 < x < 1$, but a typical Gibbs phenomenon at $x = 0$.

10.2 Applications of Eigenfunction Series

This section is devoted to three examples that illustrate the application of the eigenfunction series of Section 10.1 to boundary value problems. In each, the method of separation of variables leads to a Sturm–Liouville problem in which the eigenfunctions are used as building blocks to construct a solution satisfying the nonhomogeneous boundary condition in the original problem.

Example 1 A uniform slab of material with thermal diffusivity k occupies the space region $0 \leq x \leq L$ and initially has temperature U_0 throughout. Beginning at time $t = 0$, the face $x = 0$ is held at temperature zero, while at the face $x = L$, heat exchange takes place with a surrounding medium at temperature zero, so $hu + u_x = 0$ there (by Problem 23 of Section 9.5; the constant h is an appropriate heat transfer coefficient). We want to find the temperature $u(x, t)$ of the slab at position x at time t; $u(x, t)$ satisfies the boundary value problem

$$u_t = ku_{xx} \qquad (0 < x < L, \ t > 0); \qquad (1)$$
$$u(0, t) = 0, \qquad (2)$$
$$hu(L, t) + u_x(L, t) = 0, \qquad (3)$$
$$u(x, 0) = U_0. \qquad (4)$$

Solution As in Section 9.5, we begin by substituting $u(x, t) = X(x)T(t)$ in Eq. (1) and thereby obtain

$$\frac{X''}{X} = \frac{T'}{kT} = -\lambda$$

as usual, so

$$X'' + \lambda X = T' + \lambda kT = 0. \qquad (5)$$

Now Eq. (2) gives $X(0) = 0$, and Eq. (3) yields $hX(L)T(t) + X'(L)T(t) = 0$. We naturally assume that $T(t)$ is not identically zero (because we are not looking for a trivial solution); it follows that $X(x)$ and λ satisfy the Sturm–Liouville problem

$$X'' + \lambda X = 0 \qquad (0 < x < L);$$
$$X(0) = 0, \qquad hX(L) + X'(L) = 0. \qquad (6)$$

In Example 3 of Section 10.1, we found that the eigenvalues and associated eigenfunctions of this problem are

$$\lambda_n = \frac{\beta_n^2}{L^2}, \qquad X_n(x) = \sin\frac{\beta_n x}{L} \qquad (7)$$

for $n = 1, 2, 3, \ldots$, where β_n denotes the nth positive root of the equation

$$\tan x = -\frac{x}{hL}. \qquad (8)$$

When we substitute $\lambda = \beta_n^2/L^2$ in the right-hand equation in (5), we get the first-order equation

$$T_n' = -\frac{\beta_n^2 k}{L^2} T_n$$

with solution (to within a multiplicative constant)

$$T_n(t) = \exp\left(-\frac{\beta_n^2 kt}{L^2}\right). \tag{9}$$

Consequently, each of the functions

$$u_n(x,t) = X_n(x)T_n(t) = \exp\left(-\frac{\beta_n^2 kt}{L^2}\right)\sin\frac{\beta_n x}{L}$$

satisfies the homogeneous conditions in (1)–(3) of the boundary value problem. It remains only for us to choose the coefficients so that the formal series

$$u(x,t) = \sum_{n=1}^{\infty} c_n \exp\left(-\frac{\beta_n^2 kt}{L^2}\right)\sin\frac{\beta_n x}{L} \tag{10}$$

also satisfies the nonhomogeneous condition

$$u(x,0) = \sum_{n=1}^{\infty} c_n \sin\frac{\beta_n x}{L} = U_0. \tag{11}$$

Now $r(x) \equiv 1$ in the Sturm–Liouville problem in (6), so by Theorem 3 and Eq. (25) of Section 10.1, we can satisfy Eq. (11) by choosing

$$c_n = \frac{\displaystyle\int_0^L U_0 \sin\frac{\beta_n x}{L}\,dx}{\displaystyle\int_0^L \sin^2\frac{\beta_n x}{L}\,dx}.$$

But

$$\int_0^L U_0 \sin\frac{\beta_n x}{L}\,dx = \frac{U_0 L}{\beta_n}(1 - \cos\beta_n),$$

and by essentially the same computations as in Example 5 of Section 10.1 we find that

$$\int_0^L \sin^2\frac{\beta_n x}{L}\,dx = \frac{1}{2h}\left(hL + \cos^2\beta_n\right).$$

Hence

$$c_n = \frac{2U_0 hL(1 - \cos^2\beta_n)}{\beta_n(hL + \cos^2\beta_n)},$$

and substitution of this value in (10) yields the formal series solution

$$u(x,t) = 2U_0 hL \sum_{n=1}^{\infty} \frac{1 - \cos\beta_n}{\beta_n(hL + \cos^2\beta_n)} \exp\left(-\frac{\beta_n^2 kt}{L^2}\right)\sin\frac{\beta_n x}{L}. \tag{12}$$

Remark: A numerical investigation of the eigenfunction series in (12) is outlined in the computing project for this section. ∎

Longitudinal Vibrations of Bars

Suppose that a uniform elastic bar has length L, cross-sectional area A, and density δ (mass per unit volume), and occupies the interval $0 \leq x \leq L$ when it is unstretched. We consider longitudinal vibrations of the bar in which each cross section (normal to the x-axis) moves only in the x-direction. We can then describe the motion of the bar in terms of the displacement $u(x, t)$ at time t of the cross section whose position is x when the bar is unstretched (and at rest); we may refer to this particular cross section as the cross section x of the bar. Then the position at time t of the cross section x is $x + u(x, t)$. It follows (see Problem 13) from Hooke's law and the definition of the Young's modulus E of the material of the bar that the force $F(x, t)$ exerted on the cross section x by the part of the bar to the *left* of this section is

$$F(x, t) = -AEu_x(x, t), \tag{13}$$

$F(x, t)$ $F(x + \Delta x, t)$

x $x + \Delta x$

FIGURE 10.2.1. A small segment of the bar.

the minus sign signifying that F acts to the *left* when $u_x(x, t) > 0$. To see why this is so, we consider the segment of the bar that lies between cross section x and cross section $x + \Delta x$ (Fig. 10.2.1). At time t the ends of this segment are at $x + u(x, t)$ and $x + \Delta x + u(x + \Delta x, t)$, respectively, so its length (originally $\Delta x > 0$) is now (using the mean value theorem)

$$\Delta x + u(x + \Delta x, t) - u(x, t) = \Delta x + u_x(\hat{x}, t)\,\Delta x$$

for some $\hat{x}$ between x and $x + \Delta x$. So if $u_x(x, t) > 0$ and Δx is sufficiently small, then (by continuity) $u_x(\hat{x}, t)\,\Delta x > 0$. Hence the segment is indeed stretched to a length greater than Δx. And therefore forces $F(x, t)$ and $F(x + \Delta x, t)$ acting to the *left* and right, respectively (as indicated in Fig. 10.2.1), would be required to sustain this stretching.

We take Eq. (13) as the starting point for our derivation of the partial differential equation that the displacement function $u(x, t)$ satisfies when the displacements are sufficiently small that Hooke's law may be applied. If we apply Newton's second law of motion to the segment of the bar between cross section x and cross section $x + \Delta x$, we get

$$\begin{aligned}(\delta A\,\Delta x)u_{tt}(\overline{x}, t) &\approx -F(x + \Delta x, t) + F(x, t) \\ &= AE\,[u_x(x + \Delta x, t) - u_x(x, t)], \end{aligned} \tag{14}$$

where $\overline{x}$ denotes the midpoint of $[x, x + \Delta x]$, because this segment has mass $\delta A\,\Delta x$ and approximate acceleration $u_{tt}(\overline{x}, t)$. When we divide the expression in (14) by $\delta A\,\Delta x$ and then take the limit as $\Delta x \to 0$, the result is the one-dimensional wave equation

$$\frac{\partial^2 u}{\partial t^2} = a^2 \frac{\partial^2 u}{\partial x^2}, \tag{15}$$

where

$$a^2 = \frac{E}{\delta}. \tag{16}$$

Because Eq. (15) is identical to the equation of the vibrating string, it follows from our discussion of the d'Alembert solution in Section 9.6 that the (free) longitudinal vibrations of a bar with fixed ends are represented by waves of the form $u(x, t) = g(x \pm at)$. The velocity $a = \sqrt{E/\delta}$ with which these waves travel is the velocity of sound in the material of the bar. Indeed, the wave equation in (15) also describes ordinary one-dimensional sound waves in a gas in a pipe. In this case, E in Eq. (16) denotes the bulk modulus (fractional increase in density per unit increase in pressure) of the gas and δ is its equilibrium density.

Example 2

FIGURE 10.2.2. The bar-and-mass system of Example 2.

A bar has length L, density δ, cross-sectional area A, Young's modulus E, and total mass $M = \delta A L$. Its end $x = 0$ is fixed and a mass m is attached to its free end (Fig. 10.2.2). The bar initially is stretched linearly by moving m a distance $d = bL$ to the right (so the cross section x of the bar is initially displaced by bx). Then at time $t = 0$ the system is released from rest. To determine the subsequent vibrations of the bar, we must solve the boundary value problem

$$u_{tt} = a^2 u_{xx} \qquad (0 < x < L, \ t > 0); \tag{17a}$$

$$u(0, t) = 0, \tag{17b}$$

$$mu_{tt}(L, t) = -AEu_x(L, t), \tag{17c}$$

$$u(x, 0) = bx, \qquad u_t(x, 0) = 0. \tag{17d}$$

Solution The endpoint condition at $x = L$ in (17c) comes from equating $ma = mu_{tt}$ for the mass with the force $F = -AEu_x$ given in (13)—the mass being acted on only by the bar. Substitution of $u(x, t) = X(x)T(t)$ in $u_{tt} = a^2 u_{xx}$ leads, as usual, to the equations

$$X'' + \lambda X = 0, \quad T'' + \lambda a^2 T = 0. \tag{18}$$

The boundary condition in (17b) yields $u(0, t) = X(0)T(t) = 0$, so one endpoint condition is $X(0) = 0$. Because $u_{tt} = XT''$ and $u_x = X'T$, Eq. (17c) yields

$$mX(L)T''(t) = -AEX'(L)T(t)$$

as the other endpoint condition. Substitution of

$$T''(t) = -\lambda a^2 T(t) = -\frac{\lambda E}{\delta} T(t),$$

followed by division by $-ET(t)/\delta$, gives $m\lambda X(L) = A\delta X'(L)$. Thus the eigenvalue problem for $X(x)$ is

$$X'' + \lambda X = 0; \\ X(0) = 0, \quad m\lambda X(L) = A\delta X'(L). \tag{19}$$

It is important to note that—because of the presence of λ in the right-endpoint condition—this is *not* a Sturm–Liouville problem, so Theorems 1 through 3 of Section 10.1 do not apply. Nevertheless, all eigenvalues of (19) are positive (Problem 9). We therefore write $\lambda = \alpha^2$, and note that $X(x) = \sin \alpha x$ satisfies $X(0) = 0$. The right-endpoint condition in (19) then yields

$$m\alpha^2 \sin \alpha L = A\delta \alpha \cos \alpha L,$$

and thus

$$\tan \alpha L = \frac{A\delta}{m\alpha} = \frac{M/m}{\alpha L} \tag{20}$$

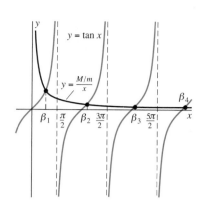

FIGURE 10.2.3. The positive roots $\{\beta_n\}_1^\infty$ of Eq. (22).

because $M = A\delta L$. We put $\beta = \alpha L$; it follows that the eigenvalues of (19) and associated eigenfunctions are

$$\lambda_n = \frac{\beta_n^2}{L^2}, \quad X_n(x) = \sin\frac{\beta_n x}{L} \tag{21}$$

for $n = 1, 2, 3, \ldots$, where $\{\beta_n\}_1^\infty$ are the positive roots of the equation

$$\tan x = \frac{M/m}{x}, \tag{22}$$

indicated in Fig. 10.2.3.

Next, we deduce in the usual way from

$$T_n'' + \frac{\beta_n^2 a^2}{L^2}T_n = 0, \quad T_n'(0) = 0 \tag{23}$$

that $T_n(t) = \cos(\beta_n at/L)$ to within a multiplicative constant. Thus it remains only to find coefficients $\{c_n\}_1^\infty$ so that the series

$$u(x, t) = \sum_{n=1}^\infty c_n \cos\frac{\beta_n at}{L} \sin\frac{\beta_n x}{L} \tag{24}$$

satisfies the nonhomogeneous condition

$$u(x, 0) = \sum_{n=1}^\infty c_n \sin\frac{\beta_n x}{L} = f(x) = bx. \tag{25}$$

Caution is required because (19) is not a Sturm–Liouville problem. Indeed, we ask you to show in Problems 14 and 15 that the eigenfunctions $\{\sin(\beta_n x/L)\}_1^\infty$ are *not* orthogonal on the interval $[0, L]$ with respect to the putative weight function $r(x) \equiv 1$, so the coefficient formula in Eq. (25), Section 10.1, is not applicable here.

But in the case of longitudinal vibrations one ordinarily is not so much concerned with the displacement function $u(x, t)$ itself. Of greater interest is the question of how the bar's natural frequencies of vibration are affected by the mass m on its free end. Whatever the coefficients in Eq. (25) may be, we see from Eq. (24) that the nth circular frequency is

$$\omega_n = \frac{\beta_n a}{L} = \frac{\beta_n}{L}\sqrt{\frac{E}{\delta}}, \tag{26}$$

where β_n is the nth positive solution of Eq. (22), which can be rewritten in the form

$$\cot x = \frac{mx}{M}. \tag{27}$$

Thus the natural frequencies are determined by the ratio of the mass m to the total mass M of the bar. ∎

Remark: The case of *no* mass on the free end of the bar corresponds to $m = 0$. Then Eq. (27) reduces to the equation $\cos x = 0$, whose nth positive solution is $\beta_n = (2n - 1)\pi/2$. Then the nth circular frequency is given by

$$\omega_n = \frac{(2n - 1)\pi}{2L}\sqrt{\frac{E}{\delta}}. \tag{28}$$

In Problem 8 we ask you to derive this result directly, beginning with the boundary value problem for a bar with one end fixed and the other end (completely) free. ∎

Transverse Vibrations of Bars

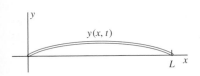

FIGURE 10.2.4. A bar undergoing transverse vibrations.

We now discuss vibrations of a uniform elastic bar in which the motion of each point is not longitudinal, but instead is perpendicular to the x-axis (the axis of the bar in its equilibrium position). Let $y(x, t)$ denote the transverse displacement of the cross section at x at time t, as indicated in Fig. 10.2.4. We merely want to outline a derivation of the partial differential equation that the deflection function $y(x, t)$ satisfies. Recall first that in Section 3.8 we introduced the equation $EIy^{(4)} = F$ for the static deflection of a bar or beam under the influence of a transverse external force F (per unit length). According to a general dynamical principle, we can transform the static equation $EIy^{(4)} = F$ into a dynamical equation (with no external force) by replacing F with the reversed inertial force $F = -\rho y_{tt}$, where ρ is the linear density (mass/length) of the bar, and also by replacing $y^{(4)}$ with y_{xxxx}. This gives

$$EI\frac{\partial^4 y}{\partial x^4} = -\rho\frac{\partial^2 y}{\partial t^2},$$

which may be written in the form

$$\frac{\partial^2 y}{\partial t^2} + a^4\frac{\partial^4 y}{\partial x^4} = 0, \tag{29}$$

where

$$a^4 = \frac{EI}{\rho}. \tag{30}$$

The following example illustrates the solution of this fourth-order partial differential equation by the method of separation of variables.

Example 3   A uniform bar with linear density ρ, Young's modulus E, and cross-sectional moment of inertia I is simply supported (or hinged) at its two ends $x = 0$ and $x = L$. If the bar is set in motion from rest with given initial position $f(x)$, then its displacement function $y(x, t)$ satisfies the boundary value problem

$$y_{tt} + a^4 y_{xxxx} = 0 \qquad (0 < x < L, \ t > 0); \tag{31a}$$
$$y(0, t) = y_{xx}(0, t) = y(L, t) = y_{xx}(L, t) = 0, \tag{31b}$$
$$y(x, 0) = f(x), \qquad y_t(x, 0) = 0. \tag{31c}$$

Find $y(x, t)$. The boundary conditions in (31b) are the hinged-end conditions that we accept without proof, and those in (31c) are the initial conditions.

Solution   Substitution of $y(x, t) = X(x)T(t)$ in the differential equation yields $XT'' + a^4 X^{(4)} T = 0$, so

$$\frac{X^{(4)}}{X} = -\frac{T''}{a^4 T} = \lambda. \tag{32}$$

To determine the sign of λ, we reason that the equation

$$T'' + \lambda a^4 T = 0 \tag{33}$$

must have trigonometric rather than exponential solutions. The reason is that on the basis of practical experience—with tuning forks or xylophone bars, for instance—one expects periodic vibrations to take place. This could not occur if λ were negative and Eq. (33) had exponential solutions. Hence λ must be positive, and it is convenient to write $\lambda = \alpha^4 > 0$. Then $X(t)$ must satisfy the equation

$$X^{(4)}(x) - \alpha^4 X(x) = 0, \tag{34}$$

which has the general solution

$$X(x) = A \cos \alpha x + B \sin \alpha x + C \cosh \alpha x + D \sinh \alpha x,$$

with

$$X''(t) = \alpha^2(-A \cos \alpha x - B \sin \alpha x + C \cosh \alpha x + D \sinh \alpha x).$$

The endpoint conditions in (31) yield

$$X(0) = X''(0) = X(L) = X''(L) = 0. \tag{35}$$

Hence

$$X(0) = A + C = 0 \quad \text{and} \quad X''(0) = -A + C = 0,$$

and these two equations imply that $A = C = 0$. Therefore,

$$X(L) = B \sin \alpha L + D \sinh \alpha L = 0$$

and

$$X''(L) = \alpha^2(-B \sin \alpha L + D \sinh \alpha L) = 0.$$

It follows that

$$B \sin \alpha L = 0 \quad \text{and} \quad D \sinh \alpha L = 0.$$

But $\sinh \alpha L \neq 0$ because $\alpha \neq 0$; consequently, $D = 0$. Hence $B \neq 0$ if we are to have a nontrivial solution, so $\sin \alpha L = 0$. Thus α must be an integral multiple of π/L. Therefore, the eigenvalues and associated eigenfunctions of the problem determined by Eqs. (34) and (35) are

$$\lambda_n = \alpha_n^4 = \frac{n^4 \pi^4}{L^4}, \quad X_n(x) = \sin \frac{n \pi x}{L} \tag{36}$$

for $n = 1, 2, 3, \ldots$.
  With $\lambda = n^4 \pi^4 / L^4$ in (33) we get the equation

$$T_n'' + \frac{n^4 \pi^4 a^4}{L^4} T_n = 0. \tag{37}$$

Because the initial condition $y_t(x, 0) = 0$ yields $T_n'(0) = 0$, we take

$$T_n(t) = \cos \frac{n^2 \pi^2 a^2 t}{L^2}. \tag{38}$$

Combining the results in (36) and (38), we construct the series

$$y(x, t) = \sum_{n=1}^{\infty} c_n \cos \frac{n^2 \pi^2 a^2 t}{L^2} \sin \frac{n \pi x}{L} \tag{39}$$

that formally satisfies the partial differential equation in (31) and the homogeneous boundary conditions. The nonhomogeneous condition is

$$y(x, 0) = \sum_{n=1}^{\infty} c_n \sin \frac{n\pi x}{L} = f(x),$$

so we choose the Fourier sine coefficients, given by

$$c_n = \frac{2}{L} \int_0^L f(x) \sin \frac{n\pi x}{L} \, dx, \tag{40}$$

in order for Eq. (39) to provide a formal series solution. ■

Note that the circular frequency of the nth term in (39) is

$$\omega_n = \frac{n^2 \pi^2 a^2}{L^2} = n^2 \omega_1, \tag{41}$$

where the fundamental frequency of the bar is

$$\omega_1 = \frac{\pi^2 a^2}{L^2} = \frac{\pi^2}{L^2} \sqrt{\frac{EI}{\rho}}. \tag{42}$$

Because the frequency of each of the higher harmonics is an integral multiple of ω_1, the sound of a vibrating bar with simply supported ends is musical. Because the higher frequencies $\{n^2\omega_1\}_2^{\infty}$ are sparser than the higher frequencies $\{n\omega_1\}_2^{\infty}$ of a vibrating string, the tone of a vibrating bar is purer than that of a vibrating string. This partly accounts for the silkiness of the sound of the vibraphone as played by Milt Jackson, former member of the Modern Jazz Quartet.

10.2 Problems

Find formal series solutions of the boundary value problems in Problems 1 through 6. Express each answer in the form given in Problem 1.

1. $u_t = k u_{xx}$ $(0 < x < L, \quad t > 0); \quad u_x(0, t) = hu(L, t) + u_x(L, t) = 0, u(x, 0) = f(x)$
Answer:

$$u(x, t) = \sum_{n=1}^{\infty} c_n \exp\left(-\frac{\beta_n^2 kt}{L^2}\right) \cos \frac{\beta_n x}{L},$$

where $\{\beta_n\}_1^{\infty}$ are the positive roots of the equation $\tan x = hL/x$ and

$$c_n = \frac{2h}{hL + \sin^2 \beta_n} \int_0^L f(x) \cos \frac{\beta_n x}{L} \, dx.$$

2. $u_{xx} + u_{yy} = 0$ $(0 < x < L, 0 < y < L); u(0, y) = hu(L, y) + u_x(L, y) = 0, \quad u(x, L) = 0, u(x, 0) = f(x)$

3. $u_{xx} + u_{yy} = 0$ $(0 < x < L, \quad 0 < y < L); u_y(x, 0) = hu(x, L) + u_y(x, L) = 0, \quad u(L, y) = 0, u(0, y) = g(y)$

4. $u_{xx} + u_{yy} = 0$ $(0 < x < L, \quad y > 0); u(0, y) = hu(L, y) + u_x(L, y) = 0, u(x, y)$ bounded as $y \to +\infty$, $u(x, 0) = f(x)$

5. $u_t = k u_{xx}$ $(0 < x < L, \quad t > 0); hu(0, t) - u_x(0, t) = u(L, t) = 0, u(x, 0) = f(x)$

6. $u_t = k u_{xx}$ $(0 < x < L, \quad t > 0); hu(0, t) - u_x(0, t) = hu(L, t) + u_x(L, t) = 0, u(x, 0) = f(x)$

7. Let $u(x, y)$ denote the bounded steady-state temperature in an infinitely high wall with base $y = 0$ and faces $x = 0$ and $x = 1$. The face $x = 0$ is insulated, the base $y = 0$ is kept at temperature $100°C$, and heat transfer with $h = 1$ takes place at the face $x = 1$. Derive the solution

$$u(x, y) = 200 \sum_{n=1}^{\infty} \frac{\exp(-\alpha_n y) \sin \alpha_n \cos \alpha_n x}{\alpha_n + \sin \alpha_n \cos \alpha_n},$$

where $\{\alpha_n\}_1^{\infty}$ are the positive roots of the equation $\cot x = x$. Given $\alpha_1 = 0.860, \alpha_2 = 3.426, \alpha_3 = 6.437$, and $\alpha_4 = 9.529$, calculate the temperature $u(1, 1)$ accurate to $0.1°C$.

8. If the bar in Example 2 has *no* mass attached to the end $x = L$, then Eq. (17c) is replaced with the free end condition $u_x(L, t) = 0$. Separate variables in the resulting boundary value problem to derive the series solution

$$u(x, t) = \sum_{n=1}^{\infty} c_n \cos \frac{(2n-1)\pi at}{2L} \sin \frac{(2n-1)\pi x}{2L},$$

where

$$c_n = \frac{2}{L} \int_0^L bx \sin \frac{(2n-1)\pi x}{2L} dx = \frac{8bL(-1)^{n+1}}{(2n-1)^2 \pi^2}.$$

In particular, the bar's natural frequencies of longitudinal vibration are given by Eq. (28).

9. (a) Show that $\lambda = 0$ is not an eigenvalue of the problem in (19). **(b)** Show that this problem has no negative eigenvalues. (*Suggestion:* Sketch the graphs $y = \tanh x$ and $y = -k/x$ with $k > 0$.)

10. Calculate the speed (in miles per hour) of longitudinal sound waves in each case. **(a)** Steel, with $\delta = 7.75$ g/cm^3 and $E = 2 \times 10^{12}$ in cgs units. **(b)** Water, with $\delta = 1$ g/cm^3 and bulk modulus $K = 2.25 \times 10^{10}$ in cgs units.

11. Consider a mass $m = nm_0$ of an ideal gas of molecular weight m_0 whose pressure p and volume V satisfy the law $pV = nRT_K$, where n is the number of moles of the gas, $R = 8314$ in mks units, and $T_K = T_C + 273$, where T_C is the Celsius temperature. The bulk modulus of the gas is $K = \gamma p$, where the value of the dimensionless constant γ is 1.4 for air having molecular weight $m_0 = 29$. **(a)** Show that the velocity of sound in this gas is

$$a = \sqrt{\frac{K}{\delta}} = \sqrt{\frac{\gamma R T_K}{m_0}}.$$

(b) Use this formula to show that the speed of sound in air at Celsius temperature T_C is approximately $740+(1.36)T_C$ miles per hour.

12. Suppose that the free end of the bar of Example 2 is attached to a spring (rather than to a mass), as shown in Fig. 10.2.5. The endpoint condition then becomes $ku(L, t) + AEu_x(L, t) = 0$. (Why?) Assume that $u(x, 0) = f(x)$ and that $u_t(x, 0) = 0$. Derive a solution of the form

$$u(x, t) = \sum_{n=1}^{\infty} c_n \cos \frac{\beta_n at}{L} \sin \frac{\beta_n x}{L},$$

where $\{\beta_n\}_1^{\infty}$ are the positive roots of the equation $\tan x = -AEx/kL$.

FIGURE 10.2.5. The bar of Problem 12.

13. If a bar has natural length L, cross-sectional area A, and Young's modulus E, then (as a consequence of Hooke's law) the axial force at each end required to stretch it the small amount ΔL is $F = (AE \, \Delta L)/L$. Apply this result to a segment of the bar of natural length $L = \Delta x$ between the cross sections at x and $x + \Delta x$ that is stretched by the amount $\Delta L = u(x + \Delta x, t) - u(x, t)$. Then let $\Delta x \to 0$ to derive Eq. (13).

14. Show that the eigenfunctions $\{X_n(x)\}_1^{\infty}$ of the problem in (19) are not orthogonal. (*Suggestion:* Apply Eq. (22) of Section 10.1 to show that if $m \neq n$, then

$$\int_0^L X_m(x) X_n(x) \, dx = -\frac{m}{A\delta} X_m(L) X_n(L).)$$

15. Show that the eigenfunctions $\{\sin \beta_n x/L\}_1^{\infty}$ of the problem in (19) are not orthogonal; do so by obtaining the explicit value of the integral

$$\int_0^L \sin \frac{\beta_m x}{L} \sin \frac{\beta_n x}{L} \, dx.$$

(*Suggestion:* Use the fact that $\{\beta_n\}_1^{\infty}$ are the roots of the equation $x \tan x = M/m$.)

16. According to Problem 19 of Section 9.7, the temperature $u(r, t)$ in a uniform solid spherical ball of radius a satisfies the partial differential equation $(ru)_t = k(ru)_{rr}$. Suppose that the ball has initial temperature $u(r, 0) = f(r)$ and that its surface $r = a$ is insulated, so that $u_r(a, t) = 0$. Substitute $v(r, t) = ru(r, t)$ to derive the solution

$$u(r, t) = c_0 + \sum_{n=1}^{\infty} \frac{c_n}{r} \exp\left(-\frac{\beta_n^2 kt}{a^2}\right) \sin \frac{\beta_n r}{a},$$

where $\{\beta_n\}_1^{\infty}$ are the positive roots of the equation $\tan x = x$ and

$$c_0 = \frac{3}{a^3} \int_0^a r^2 f(r) \, dr,$$

$$c_n = \frac{2}{a \sin^2 \beta_n} \int_0^a r f(r) \sin \frac{\beta_n r}{a} \, dr$$

(see Problem 14 of Section 10.1).

17. A problem concerning the diffusion of gas through a membrane leads to the boundary value problem

$$u_t = k u_{xx} \qquad (0 < x < L, \ t > 0);$$
$$u(0, t) = u_t(L, t) + hku_x(L, t) = 0,$$
$$u(x, 0) = 1.$$

Derive the solution

$$u(x, t) = 4 \sum_{n=1}^{\infty} \frac{1 - \cos \beta_n}{2\beta_n - \sin 2\beta_n} \exp\left(-\frac{\beta_n^2 kt}{L^2}\right) \sin \frac{\beta_n x}{L},$$

where $\{\beta_n\}_1^{\infty}$ are the positive roots of the equation $x \tan x = hL$.

18. Suppose that the simply supported uniform bar of Example 3 has, instead, initial position $y(x, 0) = 0$ and initial velocity $y_t(x, 0) = g(x)$. Then derive the solution

$$y(x, t) = \sum_{n=1}^{\infty} c_n \sin \frac{n^2 \pi^2 a^2 t}{L^2} \sin \frac{n \pi x}{L},$$

where

$$c_n = \frac{2L}{n^2 \pi^2 a^2} \int_0^L g(x) \sin \frac{n \pi x}{L} dx.$$

19. To approximate the effect of an initial momentum impulse P applied at the midpoint $x = L/2$ of a simply supported bar, substitute

$$g(x) = \begin{cases} \dfrac{P}{2\rho\epsilon} & \text{if } \dfrac{L}{2} - \epsilon < x < \dfrac{L}{2} + \epsilon, \\ 0 & \text{otherwise} \end{cases}$$

in the result of Problem 18. Then let $\epsilon \to 0$ to obtain the solution

$$y(x, t) = C \sum_{n=1}^{\infty} \frac{1}{n^2} \sin \frac{n \pi}{2} \sin \frac{n^2 \pi^2 a^2 t}{L^2} \sin \frac{n \pi x}{L},$$

where

$$C = \frac{2PL}{\pi^2 \sqrt{EI\rho}}.$$

20. **(a)** If $g(x) = v_0$ (a constant) in Problem 18, show that

$$y(x, t) = \frac{4v_0 L^2}{\pi^3 a^2} \sum_{n \text{ odd}} \frac{1}{n^3} \sin \frac{n^2 \pi^2 a^2 t}{L^2} \sin \frac{n \pi x}{L}.$$

This describes the vibrations of a hinged bar lying crosswise in the back of a pickup truck that hits a brick wall with speed v_0 at time $t = 0$. **(b)** Now suppose that the bar is made of steel ($E = 2 \times 10^{12}$ dyn/cm², $\delta = 7.75$ g/cm³), has a square cross section with edge $a = 1$ in. (so that $I = \frac{1}{12} a^4$), and length $L = 19$ in. What is its fundamental frequency (in hertz)?

10.2 Application   Numerical Heat Flow Investigations

We outline a *Mathematica*-based numerical investigation of the temperature function

$$u(x, t) = 2u_0 h L \sum_{n=1}^{\infty} \frac{1 - \cos \beta_n}{\beta_n (h L + \cos^2 \beta_n)} \exp\left(-\frac{\beta_n^2 kt}{L^2}\right) \sin \frac{\beta_n x}{L} \qquad (1)$$

n	β_n
1	2.6537
2	5.4544
3	8.3913
4	11.4086
5	14.4699
6	17.5562
7	20.6578
8	23.7693
9	26.8874
10	30.0102

FIGURE 10.2.6. The first 10 positive solutions of the eigenvalue equation

$$\tan x = -\frac{x}{hL}$$

with $L = 50$ and $h = 0.1$.

of the heated slab of Example 1 in this section. *Maple* and MATLAB versions of this investigation are included in the applications manual that accompanies this text.

We suppose that the slab has thickness $L = 50$ cm, uniform initial temperature $u_0 = 100°$, fixed temperature $0°$ at the slab's left-hand boundary $x = 0$, thermal diffusivity $k = 0.15$ (for iron), and heat transfer coefficient $h = 0.1$ at the right-hand boundary $x = L$. According to Eq. (8) of this section, the eigenvalues $\{\beta_n\}_1^\infty$ in (1) are the positive solutions of the equation $\tan x = -x/(hL)$. As in Fig. 10.1.1, we see that if n is large then β_n is slightly larger than $(2n - 1)\pi/2$. We can therefore approximate the first 20 of these eigenvalues using the commands

```
L = 50;   h = 0.1;
roots = Table[ FindRoot[ Tan[x] == -x/(h*L),
                {x, (2*n - 1)*Pi/2 + 0.1}], {n,1,20}];
beta = x /. roots
```

The first ten of these eigenvalues are listed in the table of Fig. 10.2.6.

The following *Mathematica* function now sums the first 20 nonzero terms of the series in Eq. (1).

```
b = beta;   u0 = 100;   k = 0.15;
c = (1 - Cos[b])/(b*(h*L + Cos[b]^2));   (* coeffs *)
u[x_, t_] := 2*u0*h*L*Apply[ Plus,
            c*Exp[-b*b*k*t/L^2]*Sin[b*x/L]] // N
```

As a practical matter, this suffices to calculate the value $u(x, t)$ for $t \geq 10$ (sec) with two-place accuracy throughout the interval $0 \leq x \leq 50$. (How might you verify this assertion?) The command

Plot[u[x,900], {x, 0, 50}];

then yields the graph $u = u(x, 900)$ for $0 \leq x \leq 50$ shown in Fig. 10.2.7. We see that after 15 minutes the right boundary $x = 50$ of the slab has cooled below 40°, whereas interior temperatures near $x = 30$ remain above 80°. The command

Plot[{u[50,t], 25}, {t, 0, 3600}];

yields the graph $u = u(50, t)$ for $0 \leq t \leq 3600$ shown in Fig. 10.2.8. Now we see that the right boundary temperature of the slab falls to 25° in a bit less than 2000 seconds. The calculation

t1 = t /. FindRoot[u[50,t] == 25, {t, 2000}]

shows that this actually occurs in about 1951 s; that is, about 32 min 31 s.

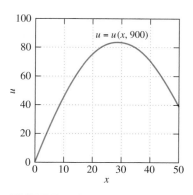

FIGURE 10.2.7. Temperatures in the slab after 15 minutes.

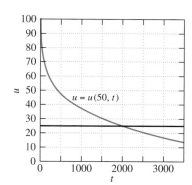

FIGURE 10.2.8. Right boundary temperatures of the slab.

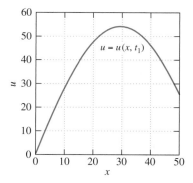

FIGURE 10.2.9. Interior temperatures when the right boundary temperature is 25°.

Figure 10.2.9 indicates that interior temperatures of the slab at time t_1 still remain above 50° at some points, with a maximum occurring near $x = 30$. We can find this maximum value of the temperature $u(x, t_1)$ by finding the minimum value of its negative $-u(x, t_1)$. The command

FindMinimum[-u[x,t1], {x, 30}]

yields the result that the maximum value is $u(29.36, t_1) \approx 53.80°$.

For your own slab with uniform initial temperature $u(x, 0) = 100°$ to investigate in this manner, let $h = 0.1$, $L = 50(10 + p)$, and $k = q/10$, where p is the largest and q is the smallest nonzero digit of your student ID number. Then carry out the investigations outlined here to find

- When the right boundary temperature of the slab is 25°, and
- The maximum temperature within the slab at that instant.

As an alternative to finding roots and maximum values numerically, you can "zoom in" graphically on appropriate points in figures like 10.2.8 and 10.2.9.

10.3 Steady Periodic Solutions and Natural Frequencies

In Section 9.6 we derived the solution

$$y(x, t) = \sum_{n=1}^{\infty} \left(A_n \cos \frac{n\pi at}{L} + B_n \sin \frac{n\pi at}{L} \right) \sin \frac{n\pi x}{L}$$

$$= \sum_{n=1}^{\infty} C_n \cos \left(\frac{n\pi at}{L} - \gamma_n \right) \sin \frac{n\pi x}{L} \tag{1}$$

of the vibrating-string problem

$$\frac{\partial^2 y}{\partial t^2} = a^2 \frac{\partial^2 y}{\partial x^2} \qquad \left(a = \sqrt{\frac{T}{\rho}} \right); \tag{2}$$

$$y(0, t) = y(L, t) = 0, \tag{3}$$

$$y(x, 0) = f(x), \quad y_t(x, 0) = g(x). \tag{4}$$

The solution in Eq. (1) describes the *free* vibrations of a string with length L and linear density ρ under tension T; the constant coefficients in Eq. (1) are determined by the initial conditions in (4).

In particular, we see from the terms in Eq. (1) that the natural (circular) frequencies of vibration (in radians per second) of the string are given by

$$\omega_n = \frac{n\pi a}{L}, \tag{5}$$

$n = 1, 2, 3, \ldots$. These are the only values of ω for which Eq. (2) has a steady periodic solution of the form

$$y(x, t) = X(x) \cos(\omega t - \gamma) \tag{6}$$

that satisfies the endpoint conditions in (3). For if we substitute Eq. (6) in (2) and cancel the factor $\cos(\omega t - \gamma)$, we find that $X(x)$ must satisfy the equation

$$a^2 X''(x) + \omega^2 X(x) = 0,$$

whose general solution

$$X(x) = A \cos \frac{\omega x}{a} + B \sin \frac{\omega x}{a}$$

satisfies the conditions in (3) only if $A = 0$ and $\omega = n\pi a/L$ for some positive integer n.

Forced Vibrations and Resonance

Now suppose that the string is influenced by a periodic external force $F(t) = F_0 \cos \omega t$ (force per unit mass) that acts uniformly on the string along its length. Then, according to Eq. (1) of Section 9.6, the displacement $y(x, t)$ of the string will satisfy the nonhomogeneous partial differential equation

$$\frac{\partial^2 y}{\partial t^2} = a^2 \frac{\partial^2 y}{\partial x^2} + F_0 \cos \omega t \tag{7}$$

together with boundary conditions such as those in (3) and (4). For instance, if the string is initially at rest in equilibrium when the external force begins to act, we want to find a solution of Eq. (7) that satisfies the conditions

$$y(0, t) = y(L, t) = y(x, 0) = y_t(x, 0) = 0 \tag{8}$$

for $0 < x < L$. To do this, it suffices first to find a particular solution $y_p(x, t)$ of Eq. (7) that satisfies the fixed endpoint conditions in (3), and second to find a solution $y_c(x, t)$ like Eq. (1) of the familiar problem in (2)–(4) with

$$f(x) = -y_p(x, 0) \quad \text{and} \quad g(x) = -D_t y_p(x, 0).$$

Evidently,
$$y(x, t) = y_c(x, t) + y_p(x, t)$$

will then satisfy Eqs. (7) and (8).

So our new task is to find $y_p(x, t)$. Examination of the individual terms in Eq. (7) suggests that we try

$$y_p(x, t) = X(x) \cos \omega t. \tag{9}$$

Substitution of this in Eq. (7) and cancellation of the common factor $\cos \omega t$ yields the ordinary differential equation

$$a^2 X'' + \omega^2 X = -F_0$$

with general solution

$$X(x) = A \cos \frac{\omega x}{a} + B \sin \frac{\omega x}{a} - \frac{F_0}{\omega^2}. \tag{10}$$

The condition $x(0) = 0$ requires that $A = F_0/\omega^2$, and then $X(L) = 0$ requires that

$$X(L) = \frac{F_0}{\omega^2} \left(\cos \frac{\omega L}{a} - 1 \right) + B \sin \frac{\omega L}{a} = 0. \tag{11}$$

Now suppose that the frequency ω of the periodic external force is *not* equal to any one of the natural frequencies $\omega_n = n\pi a/L$ of the string. Then $\sin(\omega L/a) \neq 0$, so we can solve Eq. (11) for B and then substitute the result in Eq. (10) to obtain

$$X(x) = \frac{F_0}{\omega^2} \left(\cos \frac{\omega x}{a} - 1 \right) - \frac{F_0[\cos(\omega L/a) - 1]}{\omega^2 \sin(\omega L/a)} \sin \frac{\omega x}{a}. \tag{12}$$

Then Eq. (9), with this choice of $X(x)$, gives the desired particular solution $y_p(x, t)$.

Note, however, that as the value of ω approaches $\omega_n = n\pi a/L$ with n odd, the coefficient of $\sin(\omega x/a)$ in Eq. (12) approaches $\pm\infty$; thus *resonance* occurs. This explains the fact that when (only) one of two nearby identical strings is plucked, the other will begin to vibrate as well, due to its being acted on (through the medium of the air) by an external periodic force at its fundamental frequency. Observe also that if $\omega = \omega_n = n\pi a/L$ with n even, then we can choose $B = 0$ in Eq. (11), so resonance does not occur in this case. Problem 20 explains why some of the resonance possibilities are absent.

The vibrating string is typical of continuous systems that have an infinite sequence of natural frequencies of vibration. When a periodic external force acts on such a system, potentially destructive resonance vibrations may occur if the imposed frequency is close to one of the natural frequencies of the system. Hence an important aspect of proper structural design is the avoidance of such resonance vibrations.

Natural Frequencies of Beams

$y(x, t)$

$x = 0$ $x = L$

FIGURE 10.3.1. A bar clamped at each end.

Figure 10.3.1 shows a uniform beam of length L, linear density ρ, and Young's modulus E, clamped at each end. For $0 < x < L$ and $t > 0$, its deflection function $y(x, t)$ satisfies the fourth-order equation

$$\frac{\partial^2 y}{\partial t^2} + a^4 \frac{\partial^4 y}{\partial x^4} = 0 \qquad \left(a^4 = \frac{EI}{\rho} \right) \tag{13}$$

that we discussed in Section 10.2; I denotes the moment of inertia of the cross section of the beam around its horizontal axis of symmetry. Because both the displacement and the slope are zero at each fixed end, the endpoint conditions are

$$y(0, t) = y_x(0, t) = 0 \tag{14}$$

and

$$y(L, t) = y_x(L, t) = 0. \tag{15}$$

Here we want only to find the natural frequencies of vibration of the beam, so we will not be concerned with initial conditions. The natural frequencies are the values of ω for which Eq. (13) has a nontrivial solution of the form

$$y(x, t) = X(x) \cos(\omega t - \gamma) \tag{16}$$

that satisfies the conditions in Eqs. (14) and (15). When we substitute $y(x, t)$ from (16) into (13) and then cancel the common factor $\cos(\omega t - \gamma)$, we obtain the fourth-order ordinary differential equation $-\omega^2 X + a^4 X^{(4)} = 0$; that is,

$$X^{(4)} - \frac{\omega^2}{a^4} X = 0. \tag{17}$$

If we write $\alpha^4 = \omega^2/a^4$, we can express the general solution of Eq. (17) as

$$X(x) = A \cosh \alpha x + B \sinh \alpha x + C \cos \alpha x + D \sin \alpha x,$$

with

$$X'(x) = \alpha(A \sinh \alpha x + B \cosh \alpha x - C \sin \alpha x + D \cos \alpha x).$$

The conditions in (14) give

$$X(0) = A + C = 0 \quad \text{and} \quad X'(0) = \alpha(B + D) = 0,$$

so $C = -A$ and $D = -B$. Hence the conditions in (15) give

$$X(L) = A(\cosh \alpha L - \cos \alpha L) + B(\sinh \alpha L - \sin \alpha L) = 0$$

and

$$\frac{1}{\alpha} X'(L) = A(\sinh \alpha L + \sin \alpha L) + B(\cosh \alpha L - \cos \alpha L) = 0.$$

In order for these two linear homogeneous equations in A and B to have a nontrivial solution, the determinant of coefficients must be zero:

$$(\cosh \alpha L - \cos \alpha L)^2 - (\sinh^2 \alpha L - \sin^2 \alpha L) = 0;$$

$$(\cosh^2 \alpha L - \sinh^2 \alpha L) + (\cos^2 \alpha L + \sin^2 \alpha L) - 2 \cosh \alpha L \cos \alpha L = 0;$$

$$2 - 2 \cosh \alpha L \cos \alpha L = 0.$$

Then $\beta = \alpha L$ must be a nonzero root of the equation

$$\cosh x \cos x = 1. \tag{18}$$

From Fig. 10.3.2 we see that this equation has an increasing sequence of positive roots $\{\beta_n\}_1^\infty$. Now $\omega = \alpha^2 a = \beta^2 a^2/L^2$ and $a^2 = \sqrt{EI/\rho}$, so it follows that the natural (circular) frequencies of vibration of the beam with clamped ends are given by

$y = \dfrac{1}{\cosh x}$

$y = \cos x$

FIGURE 10.3.2. Solutions of $\cosh x \cos x = 1$.

$$\omega_n = \frac{\beta_n^2}{L^2}\sqrt{\frac{EI}{\rho}} \quad \text{(rad/s)} \tag{19}$$

for $n = 1, 2, 3, \ldots$. The roots of Eq. (18) are $\beta_1 \approx 4.73004$, $\beta_2 \approx 7.85320$, $\beta_3 \approx 10.99561$, and $\beta_n \approx (2n + 1)\pi/2$ for $n \geq 4$ (as indicated in Fig. 10.3.2).

Example 1

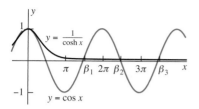

FIGURE 10.3.3. An idealized I beam.

For example, suppose that the basic structural element of a bridge is a 120-ft-long steel I beam with the cross section indicated in Fig. 10.3.3, having moment of inertia $I = 9000 \text{ cm}^4$. If we substitute the values

$$L = (120 \text{ ft})\left(30.48\,\frac{\text{cm}}{\text{ft}}\right), \quad \rho = \left(7.75\,\frac{\text{g}}{\text{cm}^3}\right)(40 \text{ cm}^2), \quad E = 2 \times 10^{12}\,\frac{\text{dyn}}{\text{cm}^2},$$

and the values of β_1 and β_2 in Eq. (19), we find that the lowest two natural frequencies of the beam are

$$\omega_1 \approx 12.74\,\frac{\text{rad}}{\text{s}}\;\left(122\,\frac{\text{cycles}}{\text{min}}\right) \quad \text{and} \quad \omega_2 \approx 35.13\,\frac{\text{rad}}{\text{s}}\;\left(335\,\frac{\text{cycles}}{\text{min}}\right).$$

If a company of soldiers marching at about 120 steps per minute approaches this bridge, they therefore would be well advised to break cadence before crossing. From time to time bridges collapse because of resonance vibrations. Recall the Kansas City hotel disaster of July 17, 1981, in which a skywalk filled with dancers collapsed. Newspapers quoted investigators who speculated that the rhythmic movement of the dancers had set up destructive resonance vibrations in the steel I beams that supported the skywalk. ∎

Underground Temperature Oscillations

Let us assume that the underground temperature at a particular location is a function $u(x, t)$ of time t and the depth x beneath the surface. Then u satisfies the heat equation $u_t = ku_{xx}$, with k being the thermal diffusivity of the soil. We may regard the temperature $u(0, t)$ at the surface $x = 0$ as being known from weather records. In fact, the periodic seasonal variation of monthly average surface temperatures, with a maximum in midsummer (July in the northern hemisphere) and a minimum in midwinter (January), is very close to a sine or cosine oscillation. We shall therefore assume that

$$u(0, t) = T_0 + A_0 \cos \omega t, \tag{20}$$

where we take $t = 0$ at midsummer. Here T_0 is the average annual temperature, A_0 the amplitude of seasonal temperature variation, and ω is chosen to make the period of $u(0, t)$ exactly one year. (In cgs units, for instance, ω would be 2π divided by the number of seconds—31,557,341—in a year; thus $\omega \approx 1.991 \times 10^{-7}$.)

It is reasonable to assume that the temperature at a fixed depth also varies periodically with t. If we introduce $U(x, t) = u(x, t) - T_0$ for convenience, then we are interested in periodic solutions of the heat equation of the form

$$U(x, t) = A(x) \cos(\omega t - \gamma) = V(x) \cos \omega t + W(x) \sin \omega t \qquad (21)$$

of the problem

$$\frac{\partial U}{\partial t} = k \frac{\partial^2 U}{\partial x^2} \qquad (x > 0, \ t > 0), \qquad (22)$$

$$U(0, t) = A_0 \cos \omega t. \qquad (23)$$

To solve this problem, let us regard $U(x, t)$ in Eq. (21) as the real part of the complex-valued function

$$\tilde{U}(x, t) = X(x)e^{i\omega t}. \qquad (24)$$

Then we want $\tilde{U}(x, t)$ to satisfy the conditions

$$\tilde{U}_t = k\tilde{U}_{xx}, \qquad (22')$$

$$\tilde{U}(0, t) = A_0 e^{i\omega t}. \qquad (23')$$

If we substitute Eq. (24) in Eq. (22'), we get $i\omega X = kX''$; that is,

$$X'' - \alpha^2 X = 0, \qquad (25)$$

where

$$\alpha = \pm\sqrt{\frac{i\omega}{k}} = \pm(1 + i)\sqrt{\frac{\omega}{2k}} \qquad (26)$$

because $\sqrt{i} = \pm(1 + i)/\sqrt{2}$. Hence the general solution of Eq. (25) is

$$X(x) = A \exp\left(-(1 + i)x\sqrt{\omega/2k}\right) + B \exp\left(+(1 + i)x\sqrt{\omega/2k}\right). \qquad (27)$$

In order that $\tilde{U}(x, t)$, and hence $X(x)$, be bounded as $x \to +\infty$, it is necessary that $B = 0$. Also, we see from Eqs. (23') and (24) that $A = X(0) = A_0$. So

$$X(x) = A_0 \exp\left(-(1 + i)x\sqrt{\omega/2k}\right). \qquad (28)$$

Finally, the solution of our original problem in (22)–(23) is

$$U(x, t) = \operatorname{Re} \tilde{U}(x, t) = \operatorname{Re} X(x)e^{i\omega t}$$

$$= \operatorname{Re}\left[(A_0 \exp(i\omega t)) \exp\left(-(1 + i)x\sqrt{\omega/2k}\right) \right]$$

$$= \operatorname{Re}\left[A_0 \exp\left(-x\sqrt{\omega/2k}\right) \exp\left(i(\omega t - x\sqrt{\omega/2k})\right) \right];$$

hence

$$U(x, t) = A_0 \exp\left(-x\sqrt{\omega/2k}\right) \cos\left(\omega t - x\sqrt{\omega/2k}\right). \tag{29}$$

Thus the amplitude $A(x)$ of the annual temperature is exponentially damped as a function of the depth x:

$$A(x) = A_0 \exp\left(-x\sqrt{\omega/2k}\right). \tag{30}$$

In addition, there is a phase delay $\gamma(x) = x\sqrt{\omega/2k}$ at the depth x.

Example 2   With $k = 0.005$ (a typical value for soil in cgs units) and the value of ω previously mentioned, we find that $\sqrt{\omega/2k} \approx 0.004462$ cm^{-1}. For instance, we then see from Eq. (30) that the amplitude is one-half the surface amplitude, $A(x) = \frac{1}{2}A_0$, when $(0.004462)x = \ln 2$; that is, when $x \approx 155.34$ cm ≈ 5.10 ft. If $A_0 = 16°$C, it follows that at a depth of about 20 ft, the amplitude of annual temperature variation is only $1°$.   ■

Example 3   Another interesting consequence of Eq. (29) is the "reversal of seasons" that occurs when $\gamma(x) = (0.004462)x = \pi$; that is, at a depth of $x \approx 704.06$ cm, about 23.11 ft. Figure 10.3.4 shows the graph $U = U(x, t)$ for $0 \leq x \leq X, 0 \leq t \leq T$, where X corresponds to 23 feet in centimeters and T to 2.5 years in seconds. Can you see by inspection of the right edge of the graph that the temperature at depth 23 feet appears to be at a maximum when the surface temperature is at a minimum?   ■

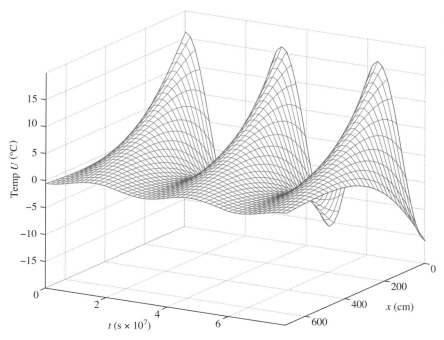

FIGURE 10.3.4.   The graph of the temperature function $U(x, t)$ in Eq. (29).

10.3 Problems

A uniform bar of length L is made of material with density δ and Young's modulus E. In Problems 1 through 6, substitute $u(x, t) = X(x) \cos \omega t$ in $\delta u_{tt} = E u_{xx}$ to find the natural frequencies of longitudinal vibration of the bar with the two given conditions at its ends $x = 0$ and $x = L$.

1. Both ends are fixed.
2. Both ends are free.
3. The end at $x = 0$ is fixed; the end at $x = L$ is free.
4. The end at $x = 0$ is fixed; the free end at $x = L$ is attached to a mass m as in Example 2 of Section 10.2.
5. Each end is free, but the end at $x = L$ is attached to a spring with Hooke's constant k as in Problem 12 of Section 10.2.
6. The free ends are attached to masses m_0 and m_1.
7. Suppose that the mass on the free end at $x = L$ in Problem 4 is attached also to the spring of Problem 5. Show that the natural frequencies are given by $\omega_n = (\beta_n/L)\sqrt{E/\delta}$, where $\{\beta_n\}_1^\infty$ are the positive roots of the equation

$$(mEx^2 - k\delta L^2) \sin x = MEx \cos x.$$

(*Note:* The condition at $x = L$ is $mu_{tt} = -AEu_x - ku$.)

Problems 8 through 14 deal with transverse vibrations of the uniform beam of this section, but with various end conditions. In each case show that the natural frequencies are given by the formula in Eq. (19), with $\{\beta_n\}_1^\infty$ being the positive roots of the given frequency equation. Recall that $y = y' = 0$ at a fixed end, $y = y'' = 0$ at a hinged end, and $y'' = y^{(3)} = 0$ at a free end (primes denote derivatives with respect to x).

8. The ends at $x = 0$ and $x = L$ are both hinged; the frequency equation is $\sin x = 0$, so that $\beta_n = n\pi$.
9. The end at $x = 0$ is fixed and the end at $x = L$ is hinged; the frequency equation is $\tanh x = \tan x$.
10. The beam is a cantilever with the end at $x = 0$ fixed and the end at $x = L$ free; the frequency equation is $\cosh x \cos x = -1$.
11. The end at $x = 0$ is fixed and the end at $x = L$ is attached to a vertically sliding clamp, so $y' = y^{(3)} = 0$ there; the frequency equation is $\tanh x + \tan x = 0$.
12. The cantilever of Problem 10 has total mass $M = \rho L$ and has a mass m attached to its free end; the frequency equation is

$$M(1 + \cosh x \cos x) = mx(\cosh x \sin x - \sinh x \cos x).$$

The conditions at $x = L$ are $y_{xx} = 0$ and $my_{tt} = EIy_{xxx}$.
13. The free end at $x = L$ of the cantilever of Problem 10 is attached (as in Fig. 10.3.5) to a spring with Hooke's constant k; the frequency equation is

$$EIx^3(1 + \cosh x \cos x)$$
$$= kL^3(\sinh x \cos x - \cosh x \sin x).$$

The conditions at $x = L$ are $y_{xx} = 0$ and $ky = EIy_{xxx}$.

FIGURE 10.3.5. The cantilever of Problem 13.

14. Suppose that the mass m on the free end of the cantilever of Problem 12 is attached to the spring of Problem 13. The conditions at $x = L$ are $y_{xx} = 0$ and $my_{tt} = EIy_{xxx} - ky$. Derive the frequency equation

$$MEIx^3(1 + \cosh x \cos x)$$
$$= (kML^3 - mEIx^4)(\sinh x \cos x - \cosh x \sin x).$$

Note that the frequency equations in Problems 12 and 13 are the special cases $k = 0$ and $m = 0$, respectively.

15. Suppose that the cantilever of Problem 10 is a diving board made of steel with density $\delta = 7.75$ g/cm³. The diving board is 4 m long and its cross section is a rectangle of width $a = 30$ cm and thickness $b = 2$ cm. The moment of inertia of this rectangle around its horizontal axis of symmetry is $I = \frac{1}{12}ab^3$. Given that the least positive root of the equation $\cosh x \cos x = -1$ is $\beta_1 \approx 1.8751$, determine the frequency (in hertz) at which a person should bounce up and down at the tip of the diving board for maximal (resonant) effect.

16. If a uniform bar hinged at each end is subjected to an axial force of compression P, then its transverse vibrations satisfy the equation

$$\rho \frac{\partial^2 y}{\partial t^2} + P \frac{\partial^2 y}{\partial x^2} + EI \frac{\partial^4 y}{\partial x^4} = 0.$$

Show that its natural frequencies are given by

$$\omega_n = \frac{n^2 \pi^2}{L^2} \left(1 - \frac{PL^2}{n^2\pi^2 EI}\right)^{1/2} \sqrt{\frac{EI}{\rho}}$$

for $n = 1, 2, 3, \ldots$. Note that with $P = 0$, this reduces to the result in Example 3 of Section 10.2 and that the effect of $P > 0$ is to decrease each of the bar's natural frequencies of vibration. (Does this seem intuitively correct? That is, would you expect an axially compressed bar to vibrate more slowly than an uncompressed bar?)

17. A beam hinged at each end is sufficiently thick that its kinetic energy of rotation must be taken into account. Then the differential equation for its transverse vibrations is

$$\rho \frac{\partial^2 y}{\partial t^2} - \frac{I}{A}\frac{\partial^4 y}{\partial x^2 \partial t^2} + EI \frac{\partial^4 y}{\partial x^4} = 0.$$

Show that its natural frequencies are given by

$$\omega_n = \frac{n^2 \pi^2}{L^2} \left(1 + \frac{n^2 \pi^2 I}{\rho A L^2} \right)^{-1/2} \sqrt{\frac{EI}{\rho}}$$

for $n = 1, 2, 3, \ldots$.

18. Suppose that the end $x = 0$ of a uniform bar with cross-sectional area A and Young's modulus E is fixed, while the longitudinal force $F(t) = F_0 \sin \omega t$ acts on its end $x = L$, so that $AEu_x(L, t) = F_0 \sin \omega t$. Derive the steady periodic solution

$$u(x, t) = \frac{F_0 a \sin(\omega x/a) \sin \omega t}{AE\omega \cos(\omega L/a)}.$$

19. Repeat Problem 18, except here a transverse force $F(t) = F_0 \sin \omega t$ acts at the free end $x = L$, so that

$$y_{xx}(L, t) = EIy_{xxx}(L, t) + F_0 \sin \omega t = 0.$$

Determine the steady periodic transverse oscillations of the cantilever in the form $y(x, t) = X(x) \sin \omega t$.

20. A string with fixed ends is acted on by a periodic force $F(x, t) = F(x) \sin \omega t$ per unit mass, so

$$y_{tt} = a^2 y_{xx} + F(x) \sin \omega t.$$

Substitute

$$y(x, t) = \sum_{n=1}^{\infty} c_n \sin \frac{n \pi x}{L} \sin \omega t$$

and

$$F(x) = \sum_{n=1}^{\infty} F_n \sin \frac{n \pi x}{L}$$

to derive the steady periodic solution

$$y(x, t) = \sum_{n=1}^{\infty} \frac{F_n \sin(n \pi x/a) \sin \omega t}{\omega_n^2 - \omega^2},$$

where $\omega_n = n \pi a/L$. Hence resonance does not result if $\omega = \omega_n$ but $F_n = 0$.

21. Suppose that the string of Problem 20 is also subject to air resistance proportional to its velocity, so that

$$y_{tt} = a^2 y_{xx} - cy_t + F(x) \sin \omega t.$$

Generalize the method of Problem 20 to derive the steady periodic solution

$$y(x, t) = \sum_{n=1}^{\infty} \rho_n F_n \sin \frac{n \pi x}{L} \sin(\omega t - \alpha_n),$$

where

$$\rho_n = \left[(\omega_n^2 - \omega^2)^2 + \omega^2 c^2 \right]^{-1/2}$$

and

$$\alpha_n = \tan^{-1} \frac{\omega c}{\omega_n^2 - \omega^2}.$$

Note the similarity to damped forced motion of a mass on a spring.

22. The **telephone equation** for the voltage $e(x, t)$ in a long transmission line at the point $x \geq 0$ at time t is

$$\frac{\partial^2 e}{\partial x^2} = LC \frac{\partial^2 e}{\partial t^2} + (RC + LG) \frac{\partial e}{\partial t} + RGe,$$

where $R, L, G,$ and C denote resistance, inductance, conductance, and capacitance (all per unit length of line), respectively. The condition $e(0, t) = E_0 \cos \omega t$ represents a periodic signal voltage at the origin of transmission at $x = 0$. Assume that $e(x, t)$ is bounded as $x \to +\infty$. Substitute $\tilde{e}(x, t) = E(x)e^{i\omega t}$ to derive the steady periodic solution

$$e(x, t) = E_0 e^{-\alpha x} \cos(\omega t - \beta x),$$

where α and β are the real and imaginary parts, respectively, of the complex number

$$\left[(RG - LC\omega^2) + i\omega(RC + LG) \right]^{1/2}.$$

23. The temperature $u(x, t)$ at the point $x \geq 0$ at time t of water moving with velocity $\gamma \geq 0$ in a long pipe satisfies the equation

$$\frac{\partial u}{\partial t} = k \frac{\partial^2 u}{\partial x^2} - \gamma \frac{\partial u}{\partial x}.$$

Suppose that $u(0, t) = A_0 \cos \omega t$ and that $u(x, t)$ is bounded as $x \to +\infty$. Substitute $\tilde{u}(x, t) = X(x)e^{i\omega t}$ to derive the steady periodic solution

$$u(x, t) = A_0 e^{-\alpha x} \cos(\omega t - \beta x),$$

where

$$\alpha = \frac{1}{2k} \left(\gamma^4 + 16k^2 \omega^2 \right)^{1/4} \cos \frac{\phi}{2} - \frac{\gamma}{2k},$$

$$\beta = \frac{1}{2k} \left(\gamma^4 + 16k^2 \omega^2 \right)^{1/4} \sin \frac{\phi}{2}, \quad \text{and}$$

$$\phi = \tan^{-1} \frac{4k}{\gamma^2}.$$

Show also that when $\gamma = 0$, this solution reduces to that in Eq. (29).

10.3 Application   Vibrating Beams and Diving Boards

In this project you are to investigate further the transverse vibrations of an elastic bar or beam of length L whose position function $y(x, t)$ satisfies the partial differential equation

$$\rho \frac{\partial^2 y}{\partial t^2} + EI \frac{\partial^4 y}{\partial x^4} = 0 \qquad (0 < x < L)$$

and the initial conditions $y(x, 0) = f(x)$, $y_t(x, 0) = 0$.

First separate the variables (as in Example 3 of Section 10.3) to derive the formal series solution

$$y(x, t) = \sum_{n=1}^{\infty} c_n \left(\cos \frac{\beta_n^2 a^2 t}{L^2} \right) X_n(x),$$

n	β_n
1	4.7300
2	7.8532
3	10.9956
4	14.1372
5	17.2788
6	20.4204
7	23.5619
8	26.7035
9	29.8451
10	32.9867

FIGURE 10.3.6. The first 10 positive solutions of the eigenvalue equation $\cosh x \, \cos x = 1$ for the vibrating beam with fixed ends.

where $a^4 = EI/\rho$, the $\{c_n\}$ are the appropriate eigenfunction expansion coefficients of the initial position function $f(x)$, and $\{\beta_n\}_1^{\infty}$ and $X_n(x)$ are determined by the end conditions imposed on the bar. In a particular case, we want to find both the **frequency equation** whose positive roots are the $\{\beta_n\}_1^{\infty}$ and the eigenfunctions $\{X_n(x)\}$. In this section we saw that the frequency equation for the fixed/fixed case (with $y(0) = y'(0) = y(L) = y'(L) = 0$) is $\cosh x \, \cos x = 1$. This equation can be solved using computer system methods like those illustrated in the applications for Sections 10.1 and 10.2; the table in Fig. 10.3.6 lists the first ten positive solutions $\{\beta_n\}_1^{10}$. The calculations preceding Eq. (18) in this section imply that the nth eigenfunction is then given by

$$X_n(x) = A_n \left(\cosh \frac{\beta_n x}{L} - \cos \frac{\beta_n x}{L} \right) + B_n \left(\sinh \frac{\beta_n x}{L} - \sin \frac{\beta_n x}{L} \right)$$

where the ratio A_n/B_n is determined by the endpoint condition $X_n(L) = 0$. The first three of these eigenfunctions are graphed in Fig. 10.3.7, which was plotted with each $A_n = 1$ and with $L = 3657.6$ cm for the 120-ft steel I beam of this section. The fact that each (correctly) appears to have slope zero at both endpoints serves to corroborate the calculations that generated the figure.

The following cases describe other vibrating-beam situations that you can investigate similarly.

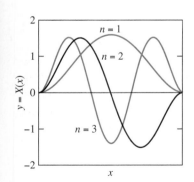

FIGURE 10.3.7. The first three eigenfunction graphs $y = X_n(x)$ for the fixed-fixed I beam.

Case 1: Hinged at each end

The boundary conditions are

$$y(0) = y''(0) = y(L) = y''(L) = 0.$$

According to Problem 8, the frequency equation is $\sin x = 0$, so $\beta_n = n\pi$ and $X_n(x) = \sin n\pi x$. Suppose that the bar is made of steel (with density $\delta = 7.75$ g/cm^3 and Young's modulus $E = 2 \times 10^{12}$ dyn/cm^2) and is 19 in. long with square cross section of edge $w = 1$ in. (so its moment of inertia is $I = \frac{1}{12} w^4$). Determine its first few natural frequencies of vibration (in Hz). How does this bar sound when it vibrates?

Case 2: Free at each end

The boundary conditions are

$$y''(0) = y^{(3)}(0) = y''(L) = y^{(3)}(L) = 0.$$

This case models, for example, a weightless bar suspended in space in an orbiting spacecraft. Now show that the frequency equation is $\cosh x \cos x = 1$ (although the eigenfunctions differ from those in the fixed/fixed case). Solve this equation (either graphically or numerically, as in the Section 10.2 application) to approximate the first several natural frequencies of vibration of the same bar considered in Case 1. How does it sound now?

Case 3: Fixed at $x = 0$, free at $x = L$

Now the boundary conditions are

$$y(0) = y'(0) = y''(L) = y^{(3)}(L) = 0.$$

This is a **cantilever** like the diving board illustrated in Fig. 10.3.8. According to Problem 15, the frequency equation is $\cosh x \cos x = -1$. Approximate the first several positive solutions of this equation and show graphically that $\beta_n \approx (2n - 1)\pi/2$ for n large. Thereby determine the first several natural frequencies (in Hz) of vibration of the particular diving board described in Problem 15. These are the frequencies at which a diver on this board should bounce up and down at the free end for maximal resonant effect.

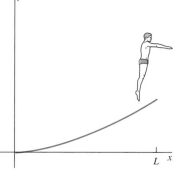

FIGURE 10.3.8. The most spectacular dives are determined by the frequency equation of Case 3.

10.4 Cylindrical Coordinate Problems

When the Laplacian $\nabla^2 u = u_{xx} + u_{yy} + u_{zz}$ of a function $u = u(x, y, z)$ is transformed by means of the substitution $x = r \cos\theta$, $y = r \sin\theta$, the result is the **Laplacian in cylindrical coordinates,**

$$\nabla^2 u = \frac{\partial^2 u}{\partial r^2} + \frac{1}{r}\frac{\partial u}{\partial r} + \frac{1}{r^2}\frac{\partial^2 u}{\partial \theta^2} + \frac{\partial^2 u}{\partial z^2}. \tag{1}$$

[See, for instance, Problem 45 in Section 12.7 of Edwards and Penney, *Calculus: Early Transcendentals*, 7th edition (Upper Saddle River, NJ: Prentice Hall, 2008)]. For a typical application, consider a very long uniform solid cylinder of radius c that is centered along the z-axis (Fig. 10.4.1). Suppose that it is heated to a "radially symmetric" initial ($t = 0$) temperature that depends only on the distance r from the z-axis (but not on the angular coordinate θ or the height z of a point). Suppose also that beginning at time $t = 0$ the boundary condition

$$\left(\beta_1 u + \beta_2 \frac{\partial u}{\partial r}\right)\bigg|_{r=c} = 0 \tag{2}$$

is imposed at the lateral surface $r = c$ of the cylinder. Note the following special cases for Eq. (2):

FIGURE 10.4.1. Long uniform solid cylinder of radius $r = c$.

- It reduces to the condition $u = 0$ if $\beta_1 = 1$ and $\beta_2 = 0$.
- It reduces to the insulation condition $u_r = 0$ if $\beta_1 = 0$ and $\beta_2 = 1$.
- It reduces to the heat transfer condition $hu + u_r = 0$ if $\beta_1 = h$ and $\beta_2 = 1$.

It is reasonable to expect the temperature u within the cylinder at time t to depend only on r, so we write $u = u(r, t)$. Then $u_{\theta\theta} = u_{zz} = 0$, so substitution of (1) in the heat equation $u_t = k\nabla^2 u$ yields the boundary value problem

$$\frac{\partial u}{\partial t} = k\left(\frac{\partial^2 u}{\partial r^2} + \frac{1}{r}\frac{\partial u}{\partial r}\right) \qquad (r < c, \ t > 0);$$
(3)

$$\beta_1 u(c, t) + \beta_2 u_r(c, t) = 0,$$
(4)

$$u(r, 0) = f(r) \qquad \text{(initial temperature)}.$$
(5)

To solve this problem by separation of variables, we substitute

$$u(r, t) = R(r)T(t)$$

in Eq. (3); thus we obtain

$$RT' = k\left(R''T + \frac{1}{r}R'T\right).$$
(6)

Division by kRT yields

$$\frac{R'' + R'/r}{R} = \frac{T'}{kT} = -\lambda.$$
(7)

Hence $R(r)$ must satisfy the equation

$$R'' + \frac{1}{r}R' + \lambda R = 0,$$
(8)

as well as the equation $\beta_1 R(c) + \beta_2 R'(c) = 0$ that follows from Eq. (4). Moreover, the equation

$$T' = -\lambda kT$$

implies that $T(t) = e^{-\lambda k t}$ to within a constant multiple. Because the diffusivity k is positive, it follows that λ must be nonnegative if $T(t)$ is to remain bounded as $t \to +\infty$, as is required by the physical problem that Eqs. (3)–(5) model. We therefore write $\lambda = \alpha^2$, so Eq. (8) takes the form

$$r^2 R'' + r R' + \alpha^2 r^2 R = 0.$$
(8')

A Singular Sturm–Liouville Problem

Equation (8') is—with $x = r$ and $y(x) = R(r)$—the parametric Bessel equation

$$x^2 y'' + x y' + \alpha^2 x^2 y = 0$$
(9)

of order zero that we discussed in Section 8.5. More generally, recall that the parametric Bessel equation

$$x^2 y'' + x y' + (\alpha^2 x^2 - n^2)y = 0$$
(10)

has general solution

$$y(x) = A J_n(\alpha x) + B Y_n(\alpha x)$$
(11)

if $\alpha > 0$. Upon division by x, the Bessel equation in (10) takes the Sturm–Liouville form

$$\frac{d}{dx}\left(x\frac{dy}{dx}\right) - \frac{n^2}{x}y + \lambda xy = 0 \tag{12}$$

with $p(x) = x$, $q(x) = n^2/x$, $r(x) = x$, and $\lambda = \alpha^2$. We want to determine the nonnegative values of λ for which there is a solution of Eq. (12) in $(0, c)$ that is *continuous* (along with its derivative dy/dx) on the closed interval $[0, c]$ and satisfies the endpoint condition

$$\beta_1 y(c) + \beta_2 y'(c) = 0, \tag{13}$$

where β_1 and β_2 are not both zero.

The Sturm–Liouville problem associated with Eqs. (12) and (13) is *singular* because $p(0) = r(0) = 0$ and $q(x) \to +\infty$ as $x \to 0^+$, whereas we assumed in Theorem 1 of Section 10.1 that $p(x)$ and $r(x)$ were positive and that $q(x)$ was continuous on the entire interval. This problem also fails to fit the pattern of Section 10.1 in that no condition like (13) is imposed at the left endpoint $x = 0$. Nevertheless, the requirement that $y(x)$ be continuous on $[0, c]$ plays the role of such a condition. Because $Y_n(x) \to -\infty$ as $x \to 0$, the solution in Eq. (11) for $\alpha > 0$ can be continuous at $x = 0$ only if $B = 0$, so

$$y(x) = J_n(\alpha x)$$

to within a constant multiple. It remains only to impose the condition in Eq. (13) at $x = c$.

It is convenient to distinguish the cases $\beta_2 = 0$ and $\beta_2 \neq 0$. If $\beta_2 = 0$, then Eq. (13) takes the simple form

$$y(c) = 0. \tag{13a}$$

If $\beta_2 \neq 0$, we multiply each term in Eq. (13) by c/β_2 and then write $h = c\beta_1/\beta_2$ to obtain the equivalent condition

$$hy(c) + cy'(c) = 0. \tag{13b}$$

We assume hereafter that $h \geq 0$.

CASE 1: $\lambda = 0$. We first consider the possibility of a zero eigenvalue $\lambda = 0$. If both $\lambda = 0$ and $n = 0$, then Eq. (12) reduces to the equation $(xy')' = 0$ with general solution

$$y(x) = A \ln x + B,$$

and continuity on $[0, c]$ requires that $A = 0$. But then Eq. (13a) implies that $B = 0$ as well, as does Eq. (13b) unless $h = 0$, in which case $\lambda = 0$ is an eigenvalue with associated eigenfunction $y(x) \equiv 1$.

If $\lambda = 0$ but $n > 0$, then Eq. (12) is simply the equation

$$x^2 y'' + xy' - n^2 y = 0$$

with general solution (substituting the trial solution $y = x^k$ as in Section 9.7)

$$y(x) = Ax^n + Bx^{-n},$$

and continuity on $[0, c]$ requires that $B = 0$. But it is easy to check that $y(x) = Ax^n$ satisfies neither Eq. (13a) nor Eq. (13b) unless $A = 0$. Thus $\lambda = 0$ is not an eigenvalue if $n > 0$. We have therefore shown that $\lambda = 0$ *is an eigenvalue of the problem in* (12)–(13) *if and only if* $n = h = 0$ *and the endpoint condition at* $x = c$ *is* $y'(c) = 0$, *in which case an associated eigenfunction is* $y(x) \equiv 1$. In this case we write

$$\lambda_0 = 0 \quad \text{and} \quad y_0(x) \equiv 1.$$

CASE 2: $\lambda > 0$. If $\lambda > 0$, then $\lambda = \alpha^2 > 0$, and in this case the only solution of Eq. (12) that is continuous on $[0, c]$ is, to within a constant multiple,

$$y(x) = J_n(\alpha x).$$

Then Eq. (13a) implies that $J_n(\alpha c) = 0$; in other words, αc must be a positive root of the equation

$$J_n(x) = 0. \tag{14a}$$

Recall from Section 8.5 that the graphs of $J_0(x)$ and $J_1(x)$ look as indicated in Fig. 10.4.2. The graph of $J_n(x)$ for $n > 1$ resembles that of $J_1(x)$, even in the detail that $J_n(0) = 0$. In particular, for each $n = 1, 2, 3, \ldots$, Eq. (14a) has an increasing infinite sequence $\{\gamma_{nk}\}_{k=1}^{\infty}$ of positive roots such that $\gamma_{nk} \to +\infty$ as $k \to +\infty$. These roots for $n \leq 8$ and $k \leq 20$ are given in Table 9.5 of Abramowitz and Stegun's *Handbook of Mathematical Functions*.

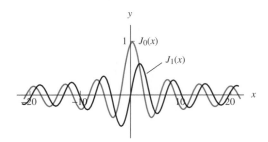

FIGURE 10.4.2. The graphs of the Bessel functions $J_0(x)$ and $J_1(x)$.

If $y(x) = J_n(\alpha x)$, so that $dy/dx = \alpha J_n'(\alpha x)$, then Eq. (13b) implies that

$$h J_n(\alpha c) + \alpha c J_n'(\alpha c) = 0$$

—that is, that αc is a positive root of the equation

$$h J_n(x) + x J_n'(x) = 0. \tag{14b}$$

It is known that this equation also has an increasing infinite sequence $\{\gamma_{nk}\}_{k=1}^{\infty}$ of positive roots diverging to $+\infty$. If $h = 0$, then Eq. (14b) reduces to the equation $J_n'(x) = 0$; the roots of this equation appear in Table 9.5 of Abramowitz and Stegun. In the important case $n = 0$, the first five roots of Eq. (14b) for various values of h can be found in Table 9.7 of the same reference.

If either of the boundary conditions in Eqs. (13a) and (13b) holds, then the kth positive eigenvalue is

$$\lambda_k = \frac{\gamma_k^2}{c^2},$$

where we write γ_k for the kth positive root of the appropriate one of Eqs. (14a) and (14b); the associated eigenfunction is

➤ $$y_k(x) = J_n\left(\frac{\gamma_k x}{c}\right).$$

The table in Fig. 10.4.3 summarizes this situation for ready reference. The exceptional case $n = h = 0$ corresponding to the endpoint condition $y'(c) = 0$ is listed separately. We have discussed only nonnegative eigenvalues, but it can be proved that the problem in (12)–(13) has no negative eigenvalues. [See Section 78 of R. V. Churchill and J. W. Brown, *Fourier Series and Boundary Value Problems*, third edition (New York: McGraw-Hill, 1978).]

Endpoint Condition	Eigenvalues	Associated Eigenfunctions
Case 1: $y(c) = 0$	$\lambda_k = \gamma_k^2/c^2$; $\{\gamma_k\}_1^\infty$ the positive roots of $J_n(x) = 0$	$y_k(x) = J_n\left(\frac{\gamma_k x}{c}\right)$
Case 2: $hy(c) + cy'(c) = 0$; h and n not both zero	$\lambda_k = \gamma_k^2/c^2$; $\{\gamma_k\}_1^\infty$ the positive roots of $hJ_n(x) + xJ_n'(x) = 0$	$y_k(x) = J_n\left(\frac{\gamma_k x}{c}\right)$
Case 3: $y'(c) = 0$, $n = 0$	$\lambda_0 = 0, \lambda_k = \gamma_k^2/c^2$; $\{\gamma_k\}_1^\infty$ the positive roots of $J_0'(x) = 0$	$y_0(x) = 1$, $y_k(x) = J_0\left(\frac{\gamma_k x}{c}\right)$

FIGURE 10.4.3. Eigenvalues and eigenfunctions of the singular Sturm–Liouville problem

$$\frac{d}{dx}\left[x\frac{dy}{dx}\right] - \frac{n^2}{x}y + \lambda xy = 0, \quad \beta_1 y(c) + \beta_2 y'(c) = 0 \quad \text{on } [0, c].$$

Fourier-Bessel Series

Now that we know that the singular Sturm–Liouville problem in (12)–(13) has an infinite sequence of eigenvalues and associated eigenfunctions similar to those of a regular Sturm–Liouville problem, we can discuss eigenfunction expansions. In either case 1 or case 2 of Fig. 10.4.3, we expect a piecewise smooth function $f(x)$ on $[0, c]$ to have an eigenfunction series of the form

➤ $$f(x) = \sum_{k=1}^{\infty} c_k y_k(x) = \sum_{k=1}^{\infty} c_k J_n\left(\frac{\gamma_k x}{c}\right), \tag{15}$$

while in the exceptional case 3, the series will also contain a constant term c_0 corresponding to $\lambda_0 = 0$, $y_0(x) \equiv 1$. If the conclusion of Theorem 2 of Section 10.1 is to hold (despite the fact that its hypotheses are not satisfied), then the eigenfunctions

$$J_n\left(\frac{\gamma_k x}{c}\right), \quad k = 1, 2, 3, \ldots$$

must be orthogonal on $[0, c]$ with weight function $r(x) = x$. Indeed, if we substitute $p(x) = r(x) = x$ and

$$y_k(x) = J_n\left(\frac{\gamma_k x}{c}\right), \quad y_k'(x) = \frac{\gamma_k}{c} J_n'\left(\frac{\gamma_k x}{c}\right)$$

in Eq. (22) of Section 10.1, the result is

$$(\lambda_i - \lambda_j) \int_0^c x J_n\left(\frac{\gamma_i x}{c}\right) J_n\left(\frac{\gamma_j x}{c}\right) dx$$

$$= \left[x\left\{\frac{\gamma_j}{c} J_n\left(\frac{\gamma_i x}{c}\right) J_n'\left(\frac{\gamma_j x}{c}\right) - \frac{\gamma_i}{c} J_n\left(\frac{\gamma_j x}{c}\right) J_n'\left(\frac{\gamma_i x}{c}\right)\right\}\right]_0^c$$

$$= \gamma_j J_n(\gamma_i) J_n'(\gamma_j) - \gamma_i J_n(\gamma_j) J_n'(\gamma_i). \tag{16}$$

It is clear that the quantity in Eq. (16) is zero if γ_i and γ_j are both roots of Eq. (14a), $J_n(x) = 0$, whereas if both are roots of Eq. (14b) it reduces to

$$J_n(\gamma_i)\left[-h J_n(\gamma_j)\right] - J_n(\gamma_j)\left[-h J_n(\gamma_i)\right] = 0.$$

In either event we thus see that if $i \neq j$, then

$$\int_0^c x J_n\left(\frac{\gamma_i x}{c}\right) J_n\left(\frac{\gamma_j x}{c}\right) dx = 0. \tag{17}$$

This orthogonality with weight function $r(x) = x$ is what we need to determine the coefficients in the eigenfunction series in Eq. (15). If we multiply each term in Eq. (15) by $x J_n(\gamma_k x/c)$ and then integrate termwise, we get

$$\int_0^c x f(x) J_n\left(\frac{\gamma_k x}{c}\right) dx = \sum_{j=1}^{\infty} c_j \int_0^c x J_n\left(\frac{\gamma_j x}{c}\right) J_n\left(\frac{\gamma_k x}{c}\right) dx$$

$$= c_k \int_0^c x \left[J_n\left(\frac{\gamma_k x}{c}\right)\right]^2 dx$$

by Eq. (17). Hence

$$c_k = \frac{\displaystyle\int_0^c x f(x) J_n(\gamma_k x/c) \, dx}{\displaystyle\int_0^c x \left[J_n(\gamma_k x/c)\right]^2 dx}. \tag{18}$$

With these coefficients, series of the form in Eq. (15) are often called **Fourier–Bessel series**. It is known that a Fourier–Bessel series for a piecewise smooth function $f(x)$ satisfies the convergence conclusion of Theorem 3 of Section 10.1. That is, it converges to the average value $\frac{1}{2}[f(x+) + f(x-)]$ at each point of $(0, c)$, and hence to the value $f(x)$ at each interior point of continuity.

The Fourier–Bessel Coefficients

In spite of their appearance, the denominator integrals in Eq. (18) are not difficult to evaluate. Suppose that $y(x) = J_n(\alpha x)$, so that $y(x)$ satisfies the parametric Bessel equation of order n,

$$\frac{d}{dx}\left[x\frac{dy}{dx}\right] + \left(\alpha^2 x - \frac{n^2}{x}\right)y = 0. \tag{19}$$

By multiplying this equation by $2xy'(x)$ and integrating by parts (Problem 8), we can readily derive the formula

$$2\alpha^2 \int_0^c x\,[J_n(\alpha x)]^2\,dx = \alpha^2 c^2\left[J_n'(\alpha c)\right]^2 + (\alpha^2 c^2 - n^2)\,[J_n(\alpha c)]^2. \tag{20}$$

Now suppose that $\alpha = \gamma_k/c$, where γ_k is a root of the equation $J_n(x) = 0$. We apply Eq. (20) as well as the recurrence formula

$$x J_n'(x) = n J_n(x) - x J_{n+1}(x)$$

of Section 8.5, which implies that $J_n'(\gamma_k) = -J_{n+1}(\gamma_k)$. The result is

$$\int_0^c x\left[J_n\left(\frac{\gamma_k x}{c}\right)\right]^2 dx = \frac{c^2}{2}\left[J_n'(\gamma_k)\right]^2 = \frac{c^2}{2}\left[J_{n+1}(\gamma_k)\right]^2. \tag{21}$$

The other entries in the table in Fig. 10.4.4 follow similarly from Eq. (20). Fourier–Bessel series with $n = 0$ are the most common (Problem 9). The forms they take in our three cases are listed next.

$\{\gamma_k\}_1^\infty$ the Positive Roots of the Equation	Value of $\displaystyle\int_0^c x\left[J_n\left(\frac{\gamma_k x}{c}\right)\right]^2 dx$
Case 1: $J_n(x) = 0$	$\dfrac{c^2}{2}\,[J_{n+1}(\gamma_k)]^2$
Case 2: $h J_n(x) + x J_n'(x) = 0$ (n and h not both zero)	$\dfrac{c^2(\gamma_k^2 - n^2 + h^2)}{2\gamma_k^2}\,[J_n(\gamma_k)]^2$
Case 3: $J_0'(x) = 0$	$\dfrac{c^2}{2}\,[J_0(\gamma_k)]^2$

FIGURE 10.4.4.

CASE 1 WITH $n = 0$:   If $\{\gamma_k\}_{k=1}^\infty$ are the positive roots of the equation $J_0(x) = 0$, then

$$f(x) = \sum_{k=1}^\infty c_k J_0\left(\frac{\gamma_k x}{c}\right);$$

$$c_k = \frac{2}{c^2\,[J_1(\gamma_k)]^2}\int_0^c x f(x) J_0\left(\frac{\gamma_k x}{c}\right) dx. \tag{22}$$

CASE 2 WITH $n = 0$: If $\{\gamma_k\}_{k=1}^{\infty}$ are the positive roots of the equation $hJ_0(x) + xJ_0'(x) = 0$ with $h > 0$, then

$$f(x) = \sum_{k=1}^{\infty} c_k J_0 \left(\frac{\gamma_k x}{c} \right);$$

$$c_k = \frac{2\gamma_k^2}{c^2(\gamma_k^2 + h^2)\,[J_0(\gamma_k)]^2} \int_0^c xf(x)J_0 \left(\frac{\gamma_k x}{c} \right) dx. \tag{23}$$

CASE 3: If $\{\gamma_k\}_{k=1}^{\infty}$ are the positive roots of the equation $J_0'(x) = 0$, then (Problem 10)

$$f(x) = c_0 + \sum_{k=1}^{\infty} c_k J_0 \left(\frac{\gamma_k x}{c} \right); \tag{24a}$$

$$c_0 = \frac{2}{c^2} \int_0^c xf(x)\,dx, \tag{24b}$$

$$c_k = \frac{2}{c^2\,[J_0(\gamma_k)]^2} \int_0^c xf(x)J_0 \left(\frac{\gamma_k x}{c} \right) dx. \tag{24c}$$

Applications

Example 1 Suppose that a long circular cylinder of radius c has initial temperature $u(r, 0) = u_0$, a constant. Find $u(r, t)$ in each of the following three cases:

(a) $u(c, t) = 0$ (zero boundary temperature);

(b) The boundary of the cylinder is insulated, so that $u_r(c, t) = 0$;

(c) Heat transfer takes place across the boundary of the cylinder, so that

$$Hu(c, t) + Ku_r(c, t) = 0, \quad \text{where } H > 0, K > 0.$$

Solution With $u(r, t) = R(r)T(t)$, we saw previously that $\lambda = \alpha^2 > 0$ in Eq. (7), so

$$r^2 R'' + rR' + \alpha^2 r^2 R = 0 \tag{25}$$

and

$$T' = -\alpha^2 kT. \tag{26}$$

Equation (25) is Bessel's parametric equation of order zero, and its only continuous nontrivial solutions on $[0, c]$ are of the form

$$R(r) = A J_0(\alpha r). \tag{27}$$

But the possible values of α depend on the boundary conditions that are imposed.

CASE (a): *Zero Boundary Temperature.* The condition $u(c, t) = 0$ yields $R(c) = A J_0(\alpha c) = 0$, so αc must be one of the roots $\{\gamma_k\}_{k=1}^{\infty}$ of the equation $J_0(x) = 0$. Thus the eigenvalues and eigenfunctions are

$$\lambda_n = \frac{\gamma_n^2}{c^2}, \quad R_n(r) = J_0\left(\frac{\gamma_n r}{c}\right) \tag{28}$$

for $n = 1, 2, 3, \ldots$. Then the equation

$$T_n' = -\left(\frac{\gamma_n^2}{c^2}\right) k T_n$$

yields

$$T_n(t) = \exp\left(-\frac{\gamma_n^2 k t}{c^2}\right)$$

to within a constant factor. Hence the series

$$u(r, t) = \sum_{n=1}^{\infty} c_n \exp\left(-\frac{\gamma_n^2 k t}{c^2}\right) J_0\left(\frac{\gamma_n r}{c}\right) \tag{29}$$

satisfies formally the heat equation and the boundary condition $u(c, t) = 0$. It remains to choose the coefficients so that

$$u(r, 0) = \sum_{n=1}^{\infty} c_n J_0\left(\frac{\gamma_n r}{c}\right) = u_0.$$

Because $J_0(\gamma_n) = 0$, Eq. (22) yields

$$c_n = \frac{2u_0}{c^2 [J_1(\gamma_n)]^2} \int_0^c r J_0\left(\frac{\gamma_n r}{c}\right) dr$$

$$= \frac{2u_0}{\gamma_n^2 [J_1(\gamma_n)]^2} \int_0^{\gamma_n} x J_0(x) dx \quad \left(x = \frac{\gamma_n r}{c}\right)$$

$$= \frac{2u_0}{\gamma_n^2 [J_1(\gamma_n)]^2} \left[x J_1(x)\right]_0^{\gamma_n} = \frac{2u_0}{\gamma_n J_1(\gamma_n)}.$$

Here we have used the integral

$$\int x J_0(x) dx = x J_1(x) + C.$$

n	γ_n	$J_1(\gamma_n)$
1	2.40483	+0.51915
2	5.52008	−0.34026
3	8.65373	+0.27145
4	11.79153	−0.23246
5	14.93092	+0.20655

FIGURE 10.4.5. Roots of $J_0(\gamma) = 0$.

On substitution of the coefficients $\{c_n\}$ in Eq. (29), we finally obtain

$$u(r, t) = 2u_0 \sum_{n=1}^{\infty} \frac{1}{\gamma_n J_1(\gamma_n)} \exp\left(\frac{-\gamma_n^2 k t}{c^2}\right) J_0\left(\frac{\gamma_n r}{c}\right). \tag{30}$$

Because of the presence of exponential factors, only a few terms are ordinarily needed for numerical computations. The data required for the first five terms are listed in Fig. 10.4.5. For instance, suppose that the cylinder has radius $c = 10$ cm, is made of iron with thermal diffusivity $k = 0.15$, and has initial temperature

$u_0 = 100°C$ throughout. Then, because $J_0(0) = 1$, we find from Eq. (30) that the temperature at its axis ($r = 0$) after two minutes ($t = 120$) will be

$$u(0, 120) = 200 \sum_{n=1}^{\infty} \frac{1}{\gamma_n J_1(\gamma_n)} \exp\left(-0.18\gamma_n^2\right)$$

$$\approx 200 \cdot (0.28283 - 0.00221 + 0.00000 - \cdots);$$

thus $u(0, 120)$ will be approximately $56.12°C$.

CASE (b):   *Insulated Boundary.* In this case no heat ever escapes from the heated cylinder, so we certainly should find that its temperature remains constant: $u(r, t) \equiv u_0$. Inasmuch as $u_r(c, t) = 0$ implies that $R'(c) = 0$, we have $n = h = 0$ in Eq. (14b), and hence case 3 in Fig. 10.4.3. Therefore, $\lambda_0 = 0$ is an eigenvalue with associated eigenfunction $R_0(r) \equiv 1$. A corresponding solution of Eq. (26) is $T_0(t) = 1$. The positive eigenvalues are again given by (28), except that now the numbers $\{\gamma_n\}_1^{\infty}$ are the positive roots of $J_0'(x) = 0$. The solution is therefore of the form

$$u(r, t) = c_0 + \sum_{n=1}^{\infty} c_n \exp\left(-\frac{\gamma_n^2 kt}{c^2}\right) J_0\left(\frac{\gamma_n r}{c}\right),$$

and we want

$$u(r, 0) = c_0 + \sum_{n=1}^{\infty} c_n J_0\left(\frac{\gamma_n r}{c}\right) = u_0.$$

But now the case 3 coefficient formulas in (24) yield

$$c_0 = \frac{2}{c^2} \int_0^c r u_0 \, dr = \frac{2u_0}{c^2} \left[\frac{1}{2}r^2\right]_0^c = u_0;$$

$$c_n = \frac{2u_0}{c^2 [J_0(\gamma_n)]^2} \int_0^c r J_0\left(\frac{\gamma_n r}{c}\right) dr = \frac{2u_0}{\gamma_n^2 [J_0(\gamma_n)]^2} \int_0^{\gamma_n} x J_0(x) \, dx$$

$$= \frac{2u_0}{\gamma_n^2 [J_0(\gamma_n)]^2} \left[x J_1(x)\right]_0^{\gamma_n} = \frac{2u_0 J_1(\gamma_n)}{\gamma_n [J_0(\gamma_n)]^2} = 0$$

because $J_1(\gamma_n) = -J_0'(\gamma_n) = 0$. Thus we find that $u(r, t) \equiv u_0$, as expected.

CASE (c):   *Heat Transfer at the Boundary.* Substitution of $R(r) = J_0(\alpha r)$ in the boundary condition $H R(c) + K R'(c) = 0$ gives the equation

$$H J_0(\alpha c) + K \alpha J_0'(\alpha c) = 0$$

that takes the form

$$h J_0(\alpha c) + \alpha c J_0'(\alpha c) = 0 \tag{31}$$

with $h = cH/K > 0$. Comparing Eq. (31) with Eq. (14b), we see that we have case 2 in Fig. 10.4.3 with $n = 0$. Hence the eigenvalues and associated eigenfunctions are given by

$$\lambda_n = \frac{\gamma_n^2}{c^2}, \quad R_n(r) = J_0\left(\frac{\gamma_n r}{c}\right), \tag{32}$$

where $\{\gamma_n\}_1^\infty$ are the positive roots of the equation $h J_0(x) + x J_0'(x) = 0$. Now $T' = -\lambda k T$ as before; consequently, the solution is of the form

$$u(r, t) = \sum_{n=1}^{\infty} c_n \exp\left(-\frac{\gamma_n^2 kt}{c^2}\right) J_0\left(\frac{\gamma_n r}{c}\right), \tag{33}$$

and Eq. (23) yields

$$c_n = \frac{2u_0\gamma_n^2}{c^2(\gamma_n^2 + h^2)\,[J_0(\gamma_n)]^2} \int_0^c r J_0\left(\frac{\gamma_n r}{c}\right) dr$$

$$= \frac{2u_0}{(\gamma_n^2 + h^2)\,[J_0(\gamma_n)]^2} \int_0^{\gamma_n} x J_0(x)\,dx = \frac{2u_0\gamma_n J_1(\gamma_n)}{(\gamma_n^2 + h^2)\,[J_0(\gamma_n)]^2}.$$

Hence

$$u(x, t) = 2u_0 \sum_{n=1}^{\infty} \frac{\gamma_n J_1(\gamma_n)}{(\gamma_n^2 + h^2)\,[J_0(\gamma_n)]^2} \exp\left(-\frac{\gamma_n^2 kt}{c^2}\right) J_0\left(\frac{\gamma_n r}{c}\right). \tag{34}$$

∎

Example 2 Suppose that a flexible circular membrane of radius c vibrates under tension T in such a way that its (normal) displacement u depends only on time t and the distance r from its center. (This is the case of *radial vibrations*.) Then $u = u(r, t)$ satisfies the partial differential equation

$$\frac{\partial^2 u}{\partial t^2} = a^2 \nabla^2 u = a^2 \left(\frac{\partial^2 u}{\partial r^2} + \frac{1}{r}\frac{\partial u}{\partial r}\right) \tag{35}$$

where $a^2 = T/\rho$, and $u(c, t) = 0$ if the boundary of the membrane is fixed. Find the natural frequencies and normal modes of radial vibration of the membrane.

Solution We apply the method of Section 10.3: Substitution of the function $u(r, t) = R(r) \sin \omega t$ in Eq. (35) yields

$$-\omega^2 R \sin \omega t = a^2 \left(R'' \sin \omega t + \frac{1}{r} R' \sin \omega t\right).$$

Thus ω and $R(r)$ must satisfy the equation

$$r^2 R'' + r R' + \frac{\omega^2}{a^2} r^2 R = 0, \tag{36}$$

as well as the condition $R(c) = 0$ that follows from $u(c, t) = 0$. Equation (36) is the parametric Bessel equation of order zero with parameter $\alpha = \omega/a$, and its only nontrivial solution is (to within a constant multiple)

$$R(r) = J_0\left(\frac{\omega r}{a}\right); \quad \text{hence} \quad R(c) = J_0\left(\frac{\omega c}{a}\right) = 0,$$

so $\omega c/a$ must be one of the positive roots $\{\gamma_n\}_1^\infty$ of the equation $J_0(x) = 0$. Thus the nth natural (circular) frequency and a corresponding natural mode of vibration are

$$\omega_n = \frac{\gamma_n a}{c}, \quad u_n(r, t) = J_0\left(\frac{\gamma_n r}{c}\right) \sin \frac{\gamma_n a t}{c}. \tag{37}$$

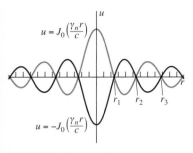

$u = J_0\left(\frac{\gamma_n r}{c}\right)$

$u = -J_0\left(\frac{\gamma_n r}{c}\right)$

FIGURE 10.4.6. Cross section of the vibrating circular membrane.

On inspection of the table of values of $\{\gamma_n\}$ in Fig. 10.4.5, we see that the higher natural frequencies ω_n are *not* integral multiples of $\omega_1 = \gamma_1 a/c$; this is why the sound of a vibrating circular drumhead is not perceived as being harmonious. The vibration of the membrane in the nth normal mode in (37) is illustrated in Fig. 10.4.6, which shows a vertical cross section through the center of the drumhead. In addition to the boundary $r = c$, there are $n - 1$ fixed circles, called *nodal circles*, with radii $r_i = \gamma_i c/\gamma_n$, $i = 1, 2, \ldots, n - 1$. The annular regions of the membrane between consecutive pairs of nodal circles move alternately up and down between the surfaces $u = \pm J_0(\gamma_n r/c)$. Figure 10.4.7 shows how the surface $u = J_0(\gamma_n r/c)$ looks for $n = 1, 2, 3$, and 4. ■

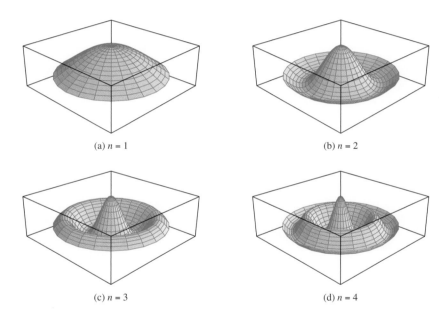

(a) $n = 1$　　　　　(b) $n = 2$

(c) $n = 3$　　　　　(d) $n = 4$

FIGURE 10.4.7. The surface $u = J_0(\gamma_n r/c)$ for $n = 1, 2, 3, 4$.

10.4 Problems

1. Suppose that the circular membrane of Example 2 has initial position $u(r, 0) = f(r)$ and initial velocity $u_t(r, 0) = 0$. Derive by separation of variables the solution

$$u(r, t) = \sum_{n=1}^\infty c_n J_0\left(\frac{\gamma_n r}{c}\right) \cos \frac{\gamma_n a t}{c},$$

where $\{\gamma_n\}_1^\infty$ are the positive roots of $J_0(x) = 0$ and

$$c_n = \frac{2}{c^2 [J_1(\gamma_n)]^2} \int_0^c r f(r) J_0\left(\frac{\gamma_n r}{c}\right) dr.$$

2. Assume that the circular membrane of Example 2 has initial position $u(r, 0) = 0$ and initial velocity $u_t(r, 0) = v_0$ (constant). Derive the solution

$$u(r, t) = \frac{2cv_0}{a} \sum_{n=1}^\infty \frac{J_0(\gamma_n r/c) \sin(\gamma_n a t/c)}{\gamma_n^2 J_1(\gamma_n)},$$

where $\{\gamma_n\}_1^\infty$ are the positive roots of $J_0(x) = 0$.

3. (a) Find $u(r, t)$ in the case in which the circular membrane of Example 2 has initial position $u(r, 0) \equiv 0$ and initial velocity

$$u_r(r, 0) = \begin{cases} \dfrac{P_0}{\rho \pi \epsilon^2} & \text{if } 0 \leq r \leq \epsilon, \\ 0 & \text{if } \epsilon < r \leq c. \end{cases}$$

(b) Use the fact that $[J_1(x)]/x \to \frac{1}{2}$ as $x \to 0$ to find the limiting value of the result in part (a) as $\epsilon \to 0$. You should obtain

$$u(r, t) = \frac{a P_0}{\pi c T} \sum_{n=1}^{\infty} \frac{J_0(\gamma_n r/c) \sin(\gamma_n at/c)}{\gamma_n [J_1(\gamma_n)]^2},$$

where $\{\gamma_n\}_1^\infty$ are the positive roots of $J_0(x) = 0$. This function describes the motion of a drumhead resulting from an initial momentum impulse P_0 at its center.

4. (a) A circular plate of radius c has insulated faces and heat capacity s calories per degree per square centimeter. Find $u(r, t)$ given $u(c, t) = 0$ and

$$u(r, 0) = \begin{cases} \dfrac{q_0}{s \pi \epsilon^2} & \text{if } 0 \leq r \leq \epsilon, \\ 0 & \text{if } \epsilon < r \leq c. \end{cases}$$

(b) Take the limit as $\epsilon \to 0$ of the result in part (a) to obtain

$$u(r, t) = \frac{q_0}{s \pi c^2} \sum_{n=1}^{\infty} \frac{1}{[J_1(\gamma_n)]^2} \exp\left(-\frac{\gamma_n^2 kt}{c^2}\right) J_0\left(\frac{\gamma_n r}{c}\right),$$

(where $\{\gamma_n\}_1^\infty$ are the positive roots of $J_0(x) = 0$) for the temperature resulting from an injection of q_0 calories of heat at the center of the plate.

Problems 5 through 7 deal with the steady-state temperature $u = u(r, z)$ in a solid cylinder of radius $r = c$ with bottom $z = 0$ and top $z = L$, given that u satisfies Laplace's equation

$$\frac{\partial^2 u}{\partial r^2} + \frac{1}{r} \frac{\partial u}{\partial r} + \frac{\partial^2 u}{\partial z^2} = 0.$$

5. If $u(r, L) = u_0$ and the rest of the surface of the cylinder is held at temperature zero, use separation of variables to derive the solution

$$u(r, z) = 2u_0 \sum_{n=1}^{\infty} \frac{J_0(\gamma_n r/c)}{\gamma_n J_1(\gamma_n)} \cdot \frac{\sinh(\gamma_n z/c)}{\sinh(\gamma_n L/c)},$$

where $\{\gamma_n\}_1^\infty$ are the positive roots of $J_0(x) = 0$.

6. (a) If $u(r, L) = f(r)$, $u(r, 0) = 0$, and the cylindrical surface $r = c$ is insulated, derive a solution of the form

$$u(r, z) = c_0 z + \sum_{n=1}^{\infty} c_n J_0\left(\frac{\gamma_n r}{c}\right) \sinh \frac{\gamma_n z}{c},$$

where $\{\gamma_n\}_1^\infty$ are the positive roots of $J_0'(x) = 0$. **(b)** Suppose that $f(r) = u_0$ (constant). Deduce from the result in part (a) that $u(r, z) = u_0 z/L$.

7. Let $c = 1$ and $L = +\infty$, so that the cylinder is semi-infinite. If $u(r, 0) = u_0$, $hu(1, z) + u_r(1, z) = 0$ (heat transfer on the cylindrical surface), and $u(r, z)$ is bounded as $z \to +\infty$, derive the solution

$$u(r, z) = 2hu_0 \sum_{n=1}^{\infty} \frac{\exp(-\gamma_n z) J_0(\gamma_n r)}{(\gamma_n^2 + h^2) J_0(\gamma_n)},$$

where $\{\gamma_n\}_1^\infty$ are the positive roots of the equation $h J_0(x) = x J_1(x)$.

8. Begin with the parametric Bessel equation of order n,

$$\frac{d}{dx}\left[x \frac{dy}{dx}\right] + \left(\alpha^2 x - \frac{n^2}{x}\right) y = 0. \tag{38}$$

Multiply each term by $2x \, dy/dx$; then write the result as

$$\frac{d}{dx}\left[x \frac{dy}{dx}\right]^2 + (\alpha^2 x^2 - n^2) \frac{d}{dx}(y^2) = 0.$$

Integrate each term, using integration by parts for the second term, to obtain

$$\left[\left(x \frac{dy}{dx}\right)^2 + (\alpha^2 x^2 - n^2) y^2\right]_0^c - 2\alpha^2 \int_0^c x y^2 \, dx = 0.$$

Finally, substitute $y(x) = J_0(\alpha x)$, a solution of Eq. (38), to get the formula in Eq. (20) in the text.

9. This problem provides the coefficient integrals for Fourier-Bessel series with $n = 0$. **(a)** Substitute $n = 0$ in the result of Problem 8 to obtain the integral formula

$$\int_0^c x [J_0(\alpha x)]^2 \, dx = \frac{c^2}{2} \left([J_0(\alpha c)]^2 + [J_1(\alpha c)]^2\right). \tag{39}$$

(b) Suppose that $\alpha = \gamma_k/c$ where γ_k is a root of the equation $J_0(x) = 0$. Deduce that

$$\int_0^c x \left[J_0\left(\frac{\gamma_k x}{c}\right)\right]^2 dx = \frac{c^2}{2} [J_1(\gamma_k)]^2.$$

(c) Suppose that $\alpha = \gamma_k/c$ where γ_k is a root of the equation $J_0'(x) = 0$. Deduce that

$$\int_0^c x \left[J_0\left(\frac{\gamma_k x}{c}\right)\right]^2 dx = \frac{c^2}{2} [J_0(\gamma_k)]^2.$$

(d) Suppose that $\alpha = \gamma_k/c$ where γ_k is a root of the equation $h J_0(x) + x J_0'(x) = 0$. Deduce that

$$\int_0^c x \left[J_0\left(\frac{\gamma_k x}{c}\right)\right]^2 dx = \frac{c^2(\gamma_k^2 + h^2)}{2\gamma_k^2} [J_0(\gamma_k)]^2.$$

10. Suppose that $\{\gamma_m\}_1^\infty$ are the positive roots of the equation $J_0'(x) = 0$ and that

$$f(x) = c_0 + \sum_{m=1}^{\infty} c_m J_0\left(\frac{\gamma_m x}{c}\right). \tag{40}$$

(a) Multiply each side of Eq. (40) by x and then integrate termwise from $x = 0$ to $x = c$ to show that

$$c_0 = \frac{2}{c^2} \int_0^c x f(x)\, dx.$$

(b) Multiply each side of Eq. (40) by $x J_0(\gamma_n x/c)$ and then integrate termwise to show that

$$c_m = \frac{2}{c^2 [J_0(\gamma_m)]^2} \int_0^c x f(x) J_0\left(\frac{\gamma_m x}{c}\right) dx.$$

11. If a circular membrane with fixed boundary is subjected to a periodic force $F_0 \sin \omega t$ per unit mass uniformly distributed over the membrane, then its displacement function $u(r, t)$ satisfies the equation

$$\frac{\partial^2 u}{\partial t^2} = a^2 \left(\frac{\partial^2 u}{\partial r^2} + \frac{1}{r}\frac{\partial u}{\partial r}\right) + F_0 \sin \omega t.$$

Substitute $u(r, t) = R(r) \sin \omega t$ to find a steady periodic solution.

12. Consider a vertically hanging cable of length L and weight w per unit length, with fixed upper end at $x = L$ and free lower end at $x = 0$, as shown in Fig. 10.4.8. When the cable vibrates transversely, its displacement function $y(x, t)$ satisfies the equation

$$\frac{w}{g}\frac{\partial^2 y}{\partial t^2} = \frac{\partial}{\partial x}\left(wx\frac{\partial y}{\partial x}\right)$$

because the tension is $T(x) = wx$. Substitute the function $y(x, t) = X(x) \sin \omega t$, then apply the theorem of Section 8.6 to solve the ordinary differential equation that results. Deduce from the solution that the natural frequencies of vibration of the hanging cable are given by

$$\omega_n = \frac{\gamma_n}{2}\sqrt{\frac{g}{L}} \quad \text{(rad/s)},$$

where $\{\gamma_n\}_1^\infty$ are the roots of $J_0(x) = 0$. Historically, this problem was the first in which Bessel functions appeared.

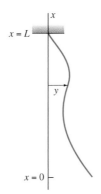

FIGURE 10.4.8. The vertical hanging cable of Problem 12.

Problems 13 through 15 deal with a canal of length L off the ocean (see Fig. 10.4.9 for a top view). Its vertical cross section

at x is rectangular with width $w(x)$ and depth $h(x)$; the latter is the equilibrium depth of the water at x. Consider a periodic canal tide such that the vertical displacement of the water surface is $y(x, t) = X(x)\cos \omega t$ at time t. Then $y(x, t)$ satisfies the equation

$$\frac{w(x)}{g}\frac{\partial^2 y}{\partial t^2} = \frac{\partial}{\partial x}\left[w(x)h(x)\frac{\partial y}{\partial x}\right].$$

Let $y_0 = X(L)$ be the amplitude of the tide at the mouth of the canal.

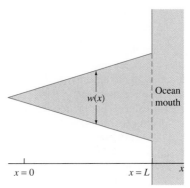

FIGURE 10.4.9. The canal of Problems 13 through 15.

13. Suppose that $w(x) = wx$ and $h(x) = h$ (a constant). Show that

$$y(x, t) = y_0 \frac{J_0\left(wx/\sqrt{gh}\right)}{J_0\left(wL\sqrt{gh}\right)} \cos \omega t.$$

(Suggestion: Apply the theorem of Section 8.6.)

14. Suppose that $w(x) = w$ (a constant) and that $h(x) = hx$. Show that

$$y(x, t) = y_0 \frac{J_0\left(2w\sqrt{x/gh}\right)}{J_0\left(2w\sqrt{L/gh}\right)} \cos \omega t.$$

15. Suppose that $w(x) = wx$ and $h(x) = hx$ with w and h both constant. Show that

$$y(x, t) = y_0 \sqrt{\frac{L}{x}} \frac{J_1\left(2w\sqrt{x/gh}\right)}{J_1\left(2w\sqrt{L/gh}\right)} \cos \omega t.$$

16. If $0 < a < b$, then the eigenvalue problem

$$\frac{d}{dx}\left[x\frac{dy}{dx}\right] + \lambda x y = 0, \quad y(a) = y(b) = 0$$

for the parametric Bessel equation of order zero is a regular Sturm–Liouville problem. By Problem 1 of Section 10.1, it therefore has an infinite sequence of nonnegative eigenvalues. **(a)** Prove that zero is not an eigenvalue. **(b)** Show that the nth eigenvalue is $\lambda_n = \gamma_n^2$, where $\{\gamma_n\}_1^\infty$ are the positive roots of the equation

$$J_0(ax)Y_0(bx) - J_0(bx)Y_0(ax) = 0. \tag{41}$$

The first five roots of Eq. (41) for various values of a/b are listed in Table 9.7 of Abramowitz and Stegun's *Handbook of Mathematical Functions*. **(c)** Show that an associated eigenfunction is

$$R_n(x) = Y_0(\gamma_n a) J_0(\gamma_n x) - J_0(\gamma_n a) Y_0(\gamma_n x). \quad (42)$$

17. Suppose that an annular membrane with constant density ρ (per unit area) is stretched under constant tension T between the circles $r = a$ and $r = b > a$. Show that its nth natural (circular) frequency is $\omega_n = \gamma_n \sqrt{T/\rho}$, where $\{\gamma_n\}_1^\infty$ are the positive roots of Eq. (41).

18. Suppose that the infinite cylindrical shell $a \leq r \leq b$ has initial temperature $u(r, 0) = f(r)$, and thereafter $u(a, t) = u(b, t) = 0$. By separation of variables, derive the solution

$$u(r, t) = \sum_{n=1}^\infty c_n \exp\left(-\gamma_n^2 kt\right) R_n(r),$$

where $R_n(r)$ is the function in Eq. (42) and

$$c_n \int_a^b r\, [R_n(r)]^2 \, dr = \int_a^b r f(r) R_n(r)\, dr.$$

19. Consider the semi-infinite cylindrical shell

$$0 < a \leq r \leq b, \quad z \geq 0.$$

If $u(a, z) = u(b, z) = 0$ and $u(r, 0) = f(r)$, derive by separation of variables the steady-state temperature

$$u(r, z) = \sum_{n=1}^\infty c_n \exp\left(-\gamma_n z\right) R_n(r),$$

where $\{c_n\}$ and $\{R_n\}$ are as given in Problems 18 and 16.

10.4 Application Bessel Functions and Heated Cylinders

Here we outline a *Maple*-based numerical investigation of the temperature function

$$u(r, t) = \sum_{n=1}^\infty a_n \exp\left(-\frac{\gamma_n^2 kt}{c^2}\right) J_0\left(\frac{\gamma_n r}{c}\right) \quad (1)$$

of the heated cylindrical rod of Example 1 in this section. *Mathematica* and MATLAB versions of this investigation are included in the applications manual that accompanies this text.

We assume that the cylindrical rod has radius $c = 10$ cm, constant initial temperature $u_0 = 100°$, and thermal diffusivity $k = 0.15$ (for iron). The coefficients $\{a_n\}_1^\infty$ in Eq. (1) depend on the condition imposed at the boundary $r = c$ of the cylinder. In the case of the zero boundary condition $u(c, t) = 0$, Eq. (30) in this section implies that $a_n = 2u_0/(\gamma_n J_1(\gamma_n))$, where the $\{\gamma_n\}_1^\infty$ are the positive solutions of the equation $J_0(x) = 0$.

Knowing that $\gamma_1 \approx 2.4$ and that successive roots differ approximately by π, we can we can approximate the first 20 values of γ_n by using the *Maple* commands

n	γ_n
1	2.4048
2	5.5201
3	8.6537
4	11.7915
5	14.9309
6	18.0711
7	21.2116
8	24.3525
9	27.4935
10	30.6346

FIGURE 10.4.10. The first 10 positive zeros of $J_0(x) = 0$.

```
g := array(1..20):          #   g for gamma
for n from 1 to 20 do
    g[n] := fsolve(BesselJ(0,x)=0, x = 2.4 + (n-1)*Pi):
od:
```

The table in Fig. 10.4.10 lists the first ten values of γ_n. Then the first 20 coefficients in (1) are calculated by the commands

```
a := array(1..20):
c := 10:     u0 := 100:     k := 0.15:
for n from 1 to 20 do
    a[n] := 2*u0/(g[n]*BesselJ(1, g[n])):
od:
```

Finally, the following *Maple* function sums the corresponding terms of the series:

```
u := (r, t) -> sum(a[n]*exp(-g[n]^2*k*t/c^2)*
               BesselJ(0, g[n]*r/c), n = 1..20);
```

The graph of $u(r, 120)$ in Fig. 10.4.11 shows how the temperature within the rod after two minutes varies with the distance r from its center, and we see that the centerline temperature has already fallen below $60°$. The graph of $u(0, t)$ for a five-minute period shown in Fig. 10.4.12 indicates that the centerline temperature takes a bit more than 200 seconds to fall to $25°$. Indeed, the computation

```
fsolve(u(0, t) = 25, t = 200..250);
```

reveals that this requires about 214 seconds.

For your own cylindrical rod with constant initial temperature $u_0 = 100°$ to investigate in the manner we illustrate, let $c = 2p$ and $k = q/10$, where p is the largest and q the smallest nonzero digit of your student ID number.

INVESTIGATION A: If the cylindrical boundary of the rod is held at zero temperature $u(c, t) = 0$, plot graphs like Figs. 10.4.11 and 10.4.12, then determine how long it will take for the rod's centerline temperature to fall to $25°$.

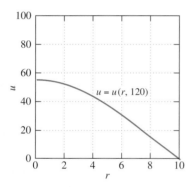

FIGURE 10.4.11.   Temperature as a function of distance r from the rod's centerline.

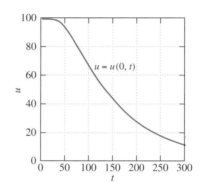

FIGURE 10.4.12.   Centerline temperature as a function of time t.

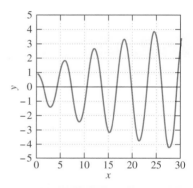

FIGURE 10.4.13.   The graph $y = J_0(x) - x J_0'(x)$.

INVESTIGATION B: Now suppose that heat transfer occurs at the rod's cylindrical boundary, so that the coefficients in the series in (1) are those appearing in Eq. (34) of the text. Assume that $h = 1$, so that the $\{\gamma_n\}_1^\infty$ are now the positive roots of the equation

$$J_0(x) + x J_0'(x) = J_0(x) - x J_1(x) = 0 \qquad (2)$$

(because $J_0'(x) = -J_1(x)$). Figure 10.4.13 shows the graph of the left-hand side in Eq. (2) and indicates that $\gamma_1 \approx 1.25$, with successive roots differing (as usual) by approximately π. Determine in this case *both* how long it takes the centerline temperature to fall to $25°$ *and* how long it takes the boundary temperature at $r = c$ to fall to $25°$.

10.5 Higher-Dimensional Phenomena

In this section we discuss the application of the method of separation of variables to heat flow and vibration problems in which two or more space variables are involved. The section consists largely of illustrative examples, problems, and projects grouped according to whether rectangular, cylindrical, or spherical coordinates are most appropriate for their solutions.

Rectangular Coordinate Applications and Two-Dimensional Fourier Series

As indicated in Section 9.7, the Laplacian in two dimensions takes the form

$$\nabla^2 u = \frac{\partial^2 u}{\partial x^2} + \frac{\partial^2 u}{\partial y^2}.$$

For instance, consider a thin plate lying in the xy-plane with its two parallel faces insulated, so that heat flows within the plate only in the x- and y-directions. If $u(x, y, t)$ denotes the temperature at time t at the point (x, y) within the plate, then under standard assumptions it follows that u satisfies the **two-dimensional heat equation**

$$\frac{\partial u}{\partial t} = k\nabla^2 u = k\left(\frac{\partial^2 u}{\partial x^2} + \frac{\partial^2 u}{\partial y^2}\right). \tag{1}$$

Here k denotes the thermal diffusivity of the material comprising the plate. The heat equation in (1) governs the change with time of temperatures within the plate. Note that if $\partial r/\partial t \equiv 0$, then the heat equation reduces to Laplace's equation $\nabla^2 u = 0$, which (as in Section 9.7) determines the steady-state distribution of temperature in the plate.

If the plate is rectangular and homogeneous boundary conditions are imposed along its four edges, then the method of separation of variables can be applied in a straightforward manner.

Example 1 Suppose that a thin rectangular plate occupies the plane region $0 \leqq x \leqq a, 0 \leqq y \leqq b$, that its top and bottom faces are insulated, and that its four edges are held at temperature zero. If the plate has the initial temperature function $u(x, y, 0) = f(x, y)$, then its temperature function $u(x, y, t)$ satisfies the boundary value problem consisting of the heat equation in (1) and the boundary conditions

$$u(0, y, t) = u(a, y, t) = u(x, 0, t) = u(x, b, t) = 0, \tag{2}$$
$$u(x, y, 0) = f(x, y). \tag{3}$$

Find $u(x, y, t)$.

Solution We substitute $u(x, y, t) = X(x)Y(y)T(t)$ in Eq. (1). After division by $kXYT$, we obtain

$$\frac{T'}{kT} = \frac{X''}{X} + \frac{Y''}{Y}.$$

This relation can hold for all x, y, and t only if each term is a constant, so we write

$$\frac{X''}{X} = -\lambda, \quad \frac{Y''}{Y} = -\mu, \quad \frac{T'}{kT} = -(\lambda + \mu). \tag{4}$$

Taking into account the boundary conditions in (2), we see that $X(x)$ and $Y(y)$ satisfy the separate Sturm–Liouville problems

$$X'' + \lambda X = 0, \quad X(0) = X(a) = 0 \tag{5}$$

and

$$Y'' + \mu Y = 0, \quad Y(0) = Y(b) = 0. \tag{6}$$

The eigenvalues and eigenfunctions of the familiar problem in (5) are

$$\lambda_m = \frac{m^2 \pi^2}{a^2}, \quad X_m(x) = \sin \frac{m\pi x}{a} \tag{7}$$

for $m = 1, 2, 3, \ldots$. Similarly, the eigenvalues and eigenfunctions of the problem in (6) are

$$\mu_n = \frac{n^2 \pi^2}{b^2}, \quad Y_n(y) = \sin \frac{n\pi y}{b} \tag{8}$$

for $n = 1, 2, 3, \ldots$. We use distinct indices m and n in (7) and (8) because the two problems in Eqs. (5) and (6) are independent of each other.

For each pair m, n of positive integers, we must solve the third equation in (4),

$$T'_{mn} = -(\lambda_m + \mu_n)k T_{mn} = -\left(\frac{m^2}{a^2} + \frac{n^2}{b^2}\right)\pi^2 k T_{mn}. \tag{9}$$

To within a multiplicative constant, the solution of Eq. (9) is

$$T_{mn}(t) = \exp\left(-\gamma_{mn}^2 k t\right), \tag{10}$$

where

$$\gamma_{mn} = \pi \sqrt{\frac{m^2}{a^2} + \frac{n^2}{b^2}}. \tag{11}$$

Thus we have found a "doubly infinite" collection of building blocks, and it follows that the "doubly infinite" series

$$u(x, y, t) = \sum_{m=1}^{\infty}\sum_{n=1}^{\infty} c_{mn} \exp\left(-\gamma_{mn}^2 k t\right) \sin \frac{m\pi x}{a} \sin \frac{n\pi y}{b} \tag{12}$$

formally satisfies the heat equation in (1) and the homogeneous boundary conditions in (2).

It remains only to determine the coefficients $\{c_{mn}\}$ so that the series satisfies also the nonhomogeneous condition

$$u(x, y, 0) = \sum_{m=1}^{\infty}\sum_{n=1}^{\infty} c_{mn} \sin \frac{m\pi x}{a} \sin \frac{n\pi y}{b} = f(x, y). \tag{13}$$

To do so, we first group the terms in this *two-dimensional Fourier series* to display the total coefficient of $\sin(n\pi y/b)$ and write

$$f(x, y) = \sum_{n=1}^{\infty}\left(\sum_{m=1}^{\infty} c_{mn} \sin \frac{m\pi x}{a}\right) \sin \frac{n\pi y}{b}. \tag{14}$$

For each fixed x, we want the series in (14) to be the Fourier sine series of $f(x, y)$ on $0 \leq y \leq b$. This will be true provided that

$$\sum_{m=1}^{\infty} c_{mn} \sin \frac{m\pi x}{a} = \frac{2}{b} \int_0^b f(x, y) \sin \frac{n\pi y}{b} \, dy. \tag{15}$$

The right-hand side in (15) is, for each n, a function $F_n(x)$; viz.,

$$F_n(x) = \sum_{m=1}^{\infty} c_{mn} \sin \frac{m\pi x}{a}. \tag{16}$$

This requires that c_{mn} be the mth Fourier sine coefficient of $F_n(x)$ on $0 \leq x \leq a$; that is, that

$$c_{mn} = \frac{2}{a} \int_0^a F_n(x) \sin \frac{m\pi x}{a} \, dx. \tag{17}$$

Substituting the right-hand side in Eq. (15) for $F_n(x)$ in Eq. (17), we finally get

$$c_{mn} = \frac{4}{ab} \int_0^a \int_0^b f(x, y) \sin \frac{m\pi x}{a} \sin \frac{n\pi y}{b} \, dy \, dx \tag{18}$$

for $m, n = 1, 2, 3, \ldots$. With these coefficients, the series in (13) is the **double Fourier sine series** of $f(x, y)$ on the rectangle $0 \leq x \leq a$, $0 \leq y \leq b$, and the series in (12) formally satisfies the boundary value problem in (1)–(3). ∎

PROBLEM 1 Suppose that $f(x, y) = u_0$, a constant. Compute the coefficients in (18) to obtain the solution

$$u(x, y, t) = \frac{16u_0}{\pi^2} \sum_{m \text{ odd}} \sum_{n \text{ odd}} \frac{\exp\left(-\gamma_{mn}^2 kt\right)}{mn} \sin \frac{m\pi x}{a} \sin \frac{n\pi y}{b}.$$

PROBLEM 2 Replace the boundary conditions (2) in Example 1 with

$$u(0, y, t) = u(x, 0, t) = 0,$$
$$hu(a, y, t) + u_x(a, y, t) = hu(x, b, t) + u_y(x, b, t) = 0.$$

Thus the edges $x = 0$ and $y = 0$ are still held at temperature zero, but now heat transfer takes place along the edges $x = a$ and $y = b$. Then derive the solution

$$u(x, y, t) = \sum_{m=1}^{\infty} \sum_{n=1}^{\infty} c_{mn} \exp\left(-\gamma_{mn}^2 kt\right) \sin \frac{\alpha_m x}{a} \sin \frac{\beta_n y}{b}$$

where $\gamma_{mn}^2 = (\alpha_m/a)^2 + (\beta_n/b)^2$, $\{\alpha_m\}$ are the positive roots of $ha \tan x = -x$, $\{\beta_n\}$ are the positive roots of $hb \tan x = -x$, and

$$c_{mn} = \frac{4}{A_m B_n} \int_0^a \int_0^b f(x, y) \sin \frac{\alpha_m x}{a} \sin \frac{\beta_n y}{b} \, dy \, dx,$$

where $A_m = (ha + \cos^2 \alpha_m)/h$ and $B_n = (hb + \cos^2 \beta_n)/h$.

PROJECT A Suppose that the three edges $x = 0$, $y = 0$, and $y = b$ of the plate of Example 1 are held at temperature zero, but the fourth edge $x = a$ is insulated, with corresponding boundary conditions

$$u(0, y, t) = u(x, 0, t) = u(x, b, t) = u_x(a, y, t) = 0.$$

If the plate's initial temperature is $u(x, y, 0) = f(x, y)$, show that its temperature function is given by

$$u(x, y, t) = \sum_{m=1}^{\infty} \sum_{n=1}^{\infty} c_{mn} \exp\left(-\gamma_{mn}^2 kt\right) \sin \frac{(2m-1)\pi x}{2a} \sin \frac{n\pi y}{b}, \qquad (19)$$

where

$$\left(\frac{\gamma_{mn}}{\pi}\right)^2 = \left(\frac{2m-1}{a}\right)^2 + \left(\frac{n}{b}\right)^2$$

and

$$c_{mn} = \frac{4}{ab} \int_0^a \int_0^b f(x, y) \sin \frac{(2m-1)\pi x}{2a} \sin \frac{n\pi y}{b} \, dy \, dx.$$

The result of Problem 21 in Section 9.3 may be useful. If $f(x, y) \equiv u_0$ (a constant), show that Eq. (19) yields

$$u(x, y, t) = \frac{16u_0}{\pi^2} \sum_{m=1}^{\infty} \sum_{n \text{ odd}} \frac{\exp\left(-\gamma_{mn}^2 kt\right)}{(2m-1)n} \sin \frac{(2m-1)\pi x}{2a} \sin \frac{n\pi y}{b}. \qquad (20)$$

For your personal plate to investigate numerically, take $u_0 = 100$, $a = 10p$, $b = 10q$, and $k = r/10$, where p and q are the two largest digits and r is the smallest nonzero digit in your student ID number. Plot $z = u(x, y, t)$ for typical values of t to verify that each such graph is symmetric with respect to the midline $y = b/2$, so it follows (why?) that the maximum temperature in the plate occurs at a point of this midline. Then determine (perhaps using the method of the Section 10.2 project)

- How long it takes for the maximum temperature on the edge $x = a$ to fall to $25°$;
- What is then the maximum interior temperature in the plate.

Vibrations of Rectangular Membranes

Now let's consider a two-dimensional flexible membrane whose equilibrium position occupies a region in the horizontal xy-plane. Suppose that this membrane vibrates up and down, with $u(x, y, t)$ denoting the vertical (normal) displacement of the point (x, y) of the membrane at time t. If T and ρ denote the membrane's tension and density (per unit area), respectively, then under standard assumptions it follows that its displacement function $u(x, y, t)$ satisfies the **two-dimensional wave equation**

$$\frac{\partial^2 u}{\partial t^2} = c^2 \nabla^2 u = c^2 \left(\frac{\partial^2 u}{\partial x^2} + \frac{\partial^2 u}{\partial y^2}\right), \qquad (21)$$

where $c^2 = T/\rho$.

PROBLEM 3 Suppose that the rectangular membrane $0 \le x \le a, 0 \le y \le b$ is released from rest with given initial displacement $u(x, y, 0) = f(x, y)$. If the four edges of the membrane are held fixed thereafter with zero displacement, then the displacement function $u(x, y, t)$ satisfies the boundary value problem consisting of the wave equation in (21) and the boundary conditions

$$u(0, y, t) = u(a, y, t) = u(x, 0, t) = u(x, b, t) = 0,$$
$$u(x, y, 0) = f(x, y) \quad \text{(initial position)}, \tag{22}$$
$$u_t(x, y, 0) = 0 \qquad \text{(initial velocity)}.$$

Derive the solution

$$u(x, y, t) = \sum_{m=1}^{\infty} \sum_{n=1}^{\infty} c_{mn} \cos \gamma_{mn} ct \sin \frac{m\pi x}{a} \sin \frac{n\pi y}{b}, \tag{23}$$

where the numbers $\{\gamma_{mn}\}$ and the coefficients $\{c_{mn}\}$ are given by the formulas in (11) and (18), respectively.

The *mn*th term in Eq. (23) defines the rectangular membrane's *mn*th *natural mode of oscillation*, with displacement function

$$u_{mn}(x, y, t) = \sin \frac{m\pi x}{a} \sin \frac{n\pi y}{b} \cos \gamma_{mn} ct. \tag{24}$$

In this mode the membrane travels up and down between the (imaginary) surfaces

$$u = \pm \sin \frac{m\pi x}{a} \sin \frac{n\pi y}{b}$$

with circular frequency $\omega_{mn} = \gamma_{mn} c$ of oscillation. Figure 10.5.1 illustrates how these surfaces look for typical small values of m and n. If $c = 1$ and $a = b = \pi$ (for instance), then the successive frequencies

$$\omega_{12} = \omega_{21} = \sqrt{5} \approx 2.24, \qquad \omega_{22} = \sqrt{8} \approx 2.83,$$
$$\omega_{13} = \omega_{31} = \sqrt{10} \approx 3.16, \qquad \omega_{23} = \omega_{32} = \sqrt{13} \approx 3.61,$$
$$\omega_{33} = \sqrt{18} \approx 4.24, \qquad \cdots$$

are not integral multiples of the fundamental frequency $\omega_{11} = \sqrt{2} \approx 1.41$. This correctly suggests that the sound of a vibrating rectangular membrane is not harmonious, and therefore is usually perceived as noise rather than music.

PROBLEM 4 Suppose that the membrane in Problem 3 is a square tambourine lying upright and crosswise in a pickup truck that hits a brick wall at time $t = 0$. Then the membrane is set in motion with zero initial displacement and constant initial velocity, so the initial conditions are

$$u(x, y, 0) = 0, \quad u_t(x, y, 0) = v_0 \quad \text{(a constant)}.$$

Then derive the solution

$$u(x, y, t) = \frac{16 v_0}{\pi^2 c} \sum_{m \text{ odd}} \sum_{n \text{ odd}} \frac{\sin \gamma_{mn} ct}{mn \gamma_{mn}} \sin \frac{m\pi x}{a} \sin \frac{n\pi y}{b}.$$

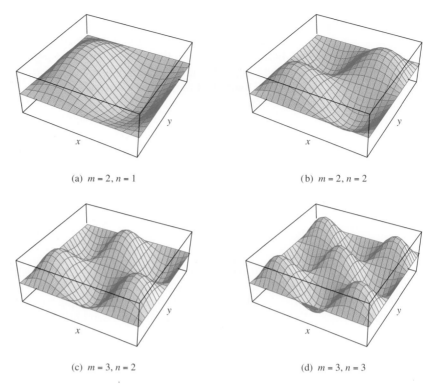

(a) $m = 2, n = 1$ (b) $m = 2, n = 2$

(c) $m = 3, n = 2$ (d) $m = 3, n = 3$

FIGURE 10.5.1.   Surfaces of the form $u = \sin \dfrac{m\pi x}{a} \sin \dfrac{n\pi y}{b}$.

PROJECT B Suppose that the square membrane $0 \leq x \leq \pi, 0 \leq y \leq \pi$ is plucked at its center point and set in motion from rest with the initial position function

$$u(x, y, 0) = f(x, y) = \min\{x, y, \pi - x, \pi - y\}, \tag{25}$$

whose graph over the square $0 \leq x \leq \pi, 0 \leq y \leq \pi$ resembles a square-based tent or pyramid with height $\pi/2$ at its center. Thus the "tent function" $f(x, y)$ is the two-dimensional analog of the familiar one-dimensional triangle function. It can be defined piecewise as indicated in Fig. 10.5.2.

Use a computer algebra system such as *Maple* or *Mathematica* to show that the double integral formula in (18) yields $c_{mn} = 0$ if $m \neq n$ and

$$c_{nn} = \frac{2[1 - (-1)^n]}{\pi n^2} = \begin{cases} \dfrac{4}{\pi n^2} & \text{for } n \text{ odd,} \\[2mm] 0 & \text{for } n \text{ even.} \end{cases}$$

It therefore follows from (23) that the membrane's resulting displacement function is given by

$$u(x, y, t) = \frac{4}{\pi} \sum_{n \text{ odd}} \frac{\sin nx \, \sin ny \, \cos nt \sqrt{2}}{n^2}. \tag{26}$$

Is it clear that—because the summand in (26) contains no terms with $m \neq n$—the function $u(x, y, t)$ is periodic (in t) with period $\pi \sqrt{2}$? The fact that the tent function in (25) thus yields a "musical" vibration of a square membrane was first pointed out to us by John Polking. Figure 10.5.3 shows some typical snapshots of this vibration.

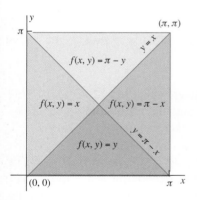

FIGURE 10.5.2.   Piecewise definition of the tent function.

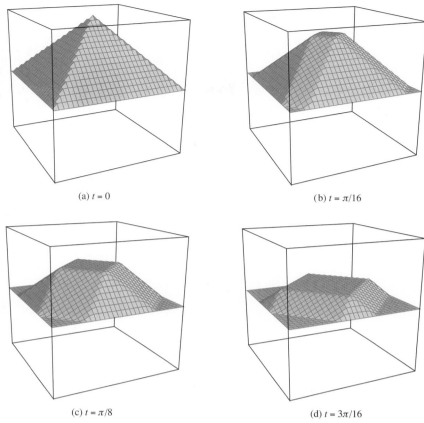

(a) $t = 0$ (b) $t = \pi/16$

(c) $t = \pi/8$ (d) $t = 3\pi/16$

FIGURE 10.5.3. Vibrations of the square membrane with period $P = \pi\sqrt{2}$.

Polar Coordinate Applications

In problems involving regions that enjoy circular symmetry around the origin in the plane (or the vertical z-axis in space), the use of polar (or cylindrical) coordinates is advantageous. In Section 9.7 we discussed the expression of the two-dimensional Laplacian in terms of the familiar plane polar coordinates (r, θ) for which $x = r\cos\theta$ and $y = r\sin\theta$. Recall from Eq. (1) in Section 10.4 that the three-dimensional Laplacian for a function $u(r, \theta, t)$ expressed in cylindrical coordinates is given by

$$\nabla^2 u = \frac{\partial^2 u}{\partial r^2} + \frac{1}{r}\frac{\partial u}{\partial r} + \frac{1}{r^2}\frac{\partial^2 u}{\partial\theta^2} + \frac{\partial^2 u}{\partial z^2}. \tag{27}$$

FIGURE 10.5.4. The solid cylinder of Example 2.

If u is independent of either θ or z, then the corresponding second derivative is absent from the right-hand side in Eq. (27).

| Example 2 | Suppose that the solid cylinder $0 \leqq r \leqq c$, $0 \leqq z \leqq h$ of Fig. 10.5.4 is made of a uniform material with thermal diffusivity k and has an axially symmetric initial temperature $u(r, z, 0) = f(r, z)$ that is independent of θ. If the cylinder's boundary—consisting of the vertical cylindrical surface $r = c$ and its circular top and bottom—is thereafter held at temperature zero (perhaps because the cylinder is embedded in ice at time $t = 0$), then the resulting axially symmetric temperature function |

$u(r, z, t)$ satisfies the boundary value problem

$$\frac{\partial u}{\partial t} = k\nabla^2 u = k\left(\frac{\partial^2 u}{\partial r^2} + \frac{1}{r}\frac{\partial u}{\partial r} + \frac{\partial^2 u}{\partial z^2}\right), \tag{28}$$

$$u(c, z, t) = u(r, 0, t) = u(r, h, t) = 0, \tag{29}$$
$$\text{(boundary temperature zero)}$$

$$u(r, z, 0) = f(r, z). \tag{30}$$
$$\text{(given initial temperature)} \qquad \blacksquare$$

The following two problems outline a solution of this heat problem for the case of constant initial temperature.

PROBLEM 5 Show that the substitution

$$u(r, z, t) = R(r)Z(z)T(t)$$

in Eq. (28) yields the separation of variables

$$r^2 R'' + r R' + \alpha^2 r^2 R = 0, \qquad R(c) = 0; \tag{31}$$
$$Z'' + \beta^2 Z = 0, \qquad Z(0) = Z(h) = 0; \tag{32}$$
$$T' = -(\alpha^2 + \beta^2)kT. \tag{33}$$

Note that the differential equation in (31) is the parametric Bessel equation of order zero for $R(r)$, and so (31) has the eigenvalues and eigenfunctions given in case 1 of the table in Fig. 10.4.2. Of course, the differential equations in (32) and (33) have familiar trigonometric and exponential solutions. Hence derive the formal series solution

$$u(r, z, t) = \sum_{m=1}^{\infty}\sum_{n=1}^{\infty} c_{mn} \exp(-\lambda_{mn}kt) J_0\left(\frac{\gamma_m r}{c}\right) \sin\frac{n\pi z}{h}, \tag{34}$$

where the $\{\gamma_m\}_1^{\infty}$ are the positive solutions of the equation $J_0(x) = 0$ (as listed in the Section 10.4 project),

$$\lambda_{mn} = \frac{\gamma_m^2}{c^2} + \frac{n^2\pi^2}{h^2}, \tag{35}$$

and the coefficients in Eq. (34) are given by the formula

$$c_{mn} = \frac{4}{hc^2 [J_1(\gamma_m)]^2}\int_0^c\int_0^h r f(r, z) J_0\left(\frac{\gamma_m r}{c}\right)\sin\frac{n\pi z}{h} dz\, dr. \tag{36}$$

The derivation of Eq. (36) is similar to that of the double Fourier series coefficient formula in (18).

PROBLEM 6 If the initial temperature function is constant, $f(r, z) \equiv u_0$, deduce from Eqs. (34) and (36) that

$$u(r, z, t) = \frac{8u_0}{\pi}\sum_{m=1}^{\infty}\sum_{n\text{ odd}} \frac{\exp(-\lambda_{mn}kt) J_0\left(\frac{\gamma_m r}{c}\right)\sin\frac{n\pi z}{h}}{n\gamma_m J_1(\gamma_m)}, \tag{37}$$

where λ_{mn} is defined in Eq. (35).

PROJECT C   For your personal heated cylinder to investigate numerically, take $u_0 = 100$, $h = 10p$, $c = 5q$, and $k = r/10$, where p and q are the two largest digits and r is the smallest nonzero digit in your student ID number. Assume zero boundary temperatures as in Problems 5 and 6. Plot the surface $z = u(r, z, t)$ for typical values of t to substantiate the physically plausible conjecture that, at any time t, the maximum temperature within the cylinder occurs at its center point, where $r = 0$ and $z = h/2$. It may help to plot also graphs of

1. u as a function of r with $z = h/2$ and t constant; and
2. u as a function of z with $r = 0$ and t constant.

Then determine how long it takes for the maximum temperature within the cylinder to fall to $25°$.

Repeat this investigation with the temperature held at zero on the cylinder's bottom and curved surface, but with its top now insulated, so that the boundary conditions in (29) are replaced with

$$u(c, z, t) = u(r, 0, t) = u_z(r, h, t) = 0.$$

Using (as in Project A) the result of Problem 21 in Section 9.3, you should find that (37) is replaced with

$$u(r, z, t) = \frac{8u_0}{\pi} \sum_{m=1}^{\infty} \sum_{n=1}^{\infty} \frac{\exp(-\lambda_{mn} kt) J_0\left(\frac{\gamma_m r}{c}\right) \sin\frac{(2n-1)\pi z}{2h}}{(2n-1)\gamma_m J_1(\gamma_m)}, \qquad (38)$$

where

$$\lambda_{mn} = \frac{\gamma_m^2}{c^2} + \frac{(2n-1)^2\pi^2}{4h^2}.$$

Is it plausible that the cylinder's maximum temperature now always occurs at the center of its top? Substantiate this conjecture with appropriate graphical investigations. Also determine how long it takes for this maximum temperature to fall to $25°$.

PROJECT D   This project deals with a vibrating uniform circular membrane of radius a. If the membrane's initial displacement and velocity functions depend on both polar coordinates r and θ, then the wave equation in (19) takes the polar coordinate form

$$\frac{\partial^2 u}{\partial t^2} = c^2 \nabla^2 u = c^2 \left(\frac{\partial^2 u}{\partial r^2} + \frac{1}{r}\frac{\partial u}{\partial r} + \frac{1}{r^2}\frac{\partial^2 u}{\partial \theta^2}\right). \qquad (39)$$

If the membrane is released from rest at time $t = 0$ and thereafter its boundary is held fixed (so on the circle $r = a$ we have the displacement u always zero), then the membrane's displacement function $u(r, \theta, t)$ satisfies both Eq. (39) and the boundary conditions

$$u(a, \theta, t) = 0 \qquad \text{(fixed boundary)}, \qquad (40)$$
$$u(r, \theta, 0) = f(r, \theta) \qquad \text{(given initial displacement)}, \qquad (41)$$
$$u_t(r, \theta, 0) = 0 \qquad \text{(zero initial velocity)}. \qquad (42)$$

Fill in the details in the following outline of a solution. Show first that the substitution

$$u(r, \theta, t) = R(t)\Theta(\theta)T(t)$$

in Eq. (39) yields the separation of variables

$$\frac{T''}{c^2 T} = \frac{R'' + \frac{1}{r} R'}{R} + \frac{\Theta''}{r^2 \Theta} = -\alpha^2 \quad \text{(constant)}. \tag{43}$$

Then

$$T'' + \alpha^2 c^2 T = 0, \quad T'(0) = 0 \tag{44}$$

implies that, to within a constant multiple,

$$T(t) = \cos \alpha c t. \tag{45}$$

Next, the right-hand equality in (43) yields the equation

$$\frac{r^2 R'' + r R'}{R} + \alpha^2 r^2 + \frac{\Theta''}{\Theta} = 0, \tag{46}$$

from which it follows that

$$\frac{\Theta''}{\Theta} = -\beta^2 \quad \text{(constant)}. \tag{47}$$

In order that a solution $\Theta(\theta)$ of $\Theta'' + \beta^2 \Theta = 0$ have the necessary periodicity of period 2π, the parameter β must be an integer, so we have the θ-solutions

$$\Theta_n(\theta) = \begin{cases} \cos n\theta, \\ \sin n\theta \end{cases} \tag{48}$$

for $n = 0, 1, 2, 3, \ldots$.

Substitution of $\Theta''/\Theta = -n^2$ in (46) now yields the parametric Bessel equation

$$r^2 R'' + r R' + (\alpha^2 r^2 - n^2) R = 0 \tag{49}$$

of order n, with bounded solution $J_n(\alpha r)$. Because the zero boundary condition in (40) yields $J_n(\alpha a) = 0$, case 1 in the table in Fig. 10.4.2 yields the r-eigenfunctions

$$R_{mn}(r) = J_n\left(\frac{\gamma_{mn} r}{a}\right) \quad (m = 1, 2, 3, \ldots; n = 0, 1, 2, \ldots), \tag{50}$$

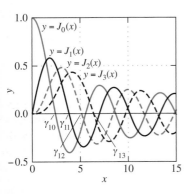

FIGURE 10.5.5. The graphs and initial zeros of the first several Bessel functions.

where γ_{mn} denotes the mth positive solution of the equation $J_n(x) = 0$. The numerical value of γ_{mn} can be approximated by first estimating the value $r_1 \approx \gamma_{1n}$ of the first root by inspecting a graph of $J_n(x)$ as in Fig. 10.5.5 and then using a command such as *Mathematica*'s

```
FindRoot[ BesselJ[n,x] == 0, {r, r1 + (m - 1)*Pi}]
```

Finally, substitution of $\alpha_{mn} = (\gamma_{mn})/a$ in (45) yields the t-function

$$T_{mn}(t) = \cos \frac{\gamma_{mn}ct}{a}. \tag{51}$$

Combining (48), (50), and (51), we see that our boundary value problem for the circular membrane released from rest has the formal series solution

$$u(r, \theta, t) = \sum_{m=1}^{\infty} \sum_{n=0}^{\infty} J_n\left(\frac{\gamma_{mn}r}{a}\right) (a_{mn}\cos n\theta + b_{mn}\sin n\theta)\cos\frac{\gamma_{mn}ct}{a}. \tag{52}$$

Thus the vibrating circular membrane's typical natural mode of oscillation with zero initial velocity is of the form

$$u_{mn}(r, \theta, t) = J_n\left(\frac{\gamma_{mn}r}{a}\right)\cos n\theta \cos\frac{\gamma_{mn}ct}{a} \tag{53}$$

(a) $m = 2, n = 1$ (b) $m = 1, n = 2$

or the analogous form with $\sin n\theta$ in place of $\cos n\theta$. In this mode the membrane vibrates with $m - 1$ fixed *nodal circles* (in addition to its boundary $r = a$) with radii

$$r_{jn} = \frac{\gamma_{jn}a}{\gamma_{mn}} \qquad \text{for } j = 1, 2, \ldots, m-1.$$

(c) $m = 2, n = 3$ (d) $m = 3, n = 2$

FIGURE 10.5.6. Typical nodal circles and radii for a vibrating circular membrane.

It also has $2n$ fixed *nodal radii* spaced at angles of π/n starting with $\theta = \pi/(2n)$. Figure 10.5.6 shows some typical configurations of these nodal circles and radii, which divide the circle into annular sectors that move alternately up and down as the membrane vibrates.

Formulas for the coefficients in (52) often are not required for practical applications involving vibrating circular membranes. We suggest that you explore vibrating membrane possibilities by graphing convenient linear combinations of eigenfunctions defined as in (53). For instance, Fig. 10.5.7 shows snapshots of the oscillation defined by

$$u(r, \theta, t) = J_1(\gamma_{21}r)\cos\theta\cos\gamma_{21}t + J_2(\gamma_{32}r)\cos 2\theta\cos\gamma_{32}t \tag{54}$$

for a circular membrane with $c = 1$ and radius $a = 1$. If multimedia hardware and software are available, you might enjoy constructing a movie showing such an oscillation.

Spherical Coordinate Applications

In problems involving regions that enjoy spherical symmetry around the origin in space, it is appropriate to use the spherical coordinates indicated in Fig. 10.5.8. The three-dimensional Laplacian for a function $u(\rho, \phi, \theta)$ expressed in spherical coordinates is given by

$$\nabla^2 u = \frac{1}{\rho^2}\left[\frac{\partial}{\partial\rho}\left(\rho^2\frac{\partial u}{\partial\rho}\right) + \frac{1}{\sin\phi}\frac{\partial}{\partial\phi}\left(\frac{\partial u}{\partial\phi}\sin\phi\right) + \frac{1}{\sin^2\phi}\frac{\partial^2 u}{\partial\theta^2}\right]. \tag{55}$$

Note that $\rho = \sqrt{x^2 + y^2 + z^2}$ denotes the distance of the point P from the origin O, ϕ is the angle down from the positive z-axis to OP, and θ is the ordinary polar coordinate angle in the xy-plane (although some texts reverse the roles of ϕ and θ). Observe also that if u is independent of either ρ, ϕ, or θ, then the corresponding second derivative term is missing on the right-hand side in Eq. (55).

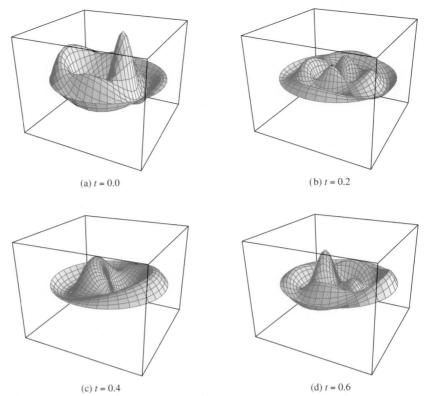

(a) $t = 0.0$

(b) $t = 0.2$

(c) $t = 0.4$

(d) $t = 0.6$

FIGURE 10.5.7. Snapshots of the circular membrane vibration defined by Eq. (54).

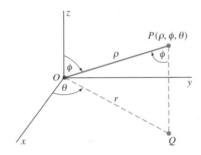

FIGURE 10.5.8. Finding the spherical coordinates of the point P.

Example 3

Suppose that a given axially symmetric temperature function $g(\phi)$ is imposed on the boundary sphere $\rho = a$ of the solid ball $0 \le \rho \le a$, and we seek the resulting axially symmetric steady-state temperature function $u(\rho, \phi)$ within the sphere. Because u is independent of θ, Laplace's equation $\nabla^2 u = 0$ takes (after multiplication by ρ^2 in Eq. (55)) the form

$$\frac{\partial}{\partial \rho}\left(\rho^2 \frac{\partial u}{\partial \rho}\right) + \frac{1}{\sin \phi} \frac{\partial}{\partial \phi}\left(\frac{\partial u}{\partial \phi} \sin \phi\right) = 0, \tag{56}$$

and we have the single boundary condition

$$u(a, \phi) = g(\phi) \qquad \text{(given boundary temperature)}. \tag{57}$$

∎

The following problems outline a solution of this boundary value problem to find the temperature function $u(\rho, \phi)$.

PROBLEM 7 Show that the substitution $u(\rho, \phi) = R(\rho)\Phi(\phi)$ in Eq. (56) yields the separation of variables

$$\rho^2 R'' + 2\rho R' - \lambda R = 0, \tag{58}$$
$$[(\sin\phi)\Phi']' + \lambda(\sin\phi)\Phi = 0, \tag{59}$$

where λ is the usual separation constant. We have no homogeneous boundary conditions to impose, but we do seek *continuous* functions $R(\rho)$ for $0 \le \rho \le a$ and $\Phi(\phi)$ for $0 \le \phi \le \pi$. Equation (58) is one for which the trial solution $R(\rho) = \rho^k$ suggests itself, but Eq. (59) appears to be completely unfamiliar.

PROBLEM 8 Show that the substitution

$$x = \cos\phi, \quad y(x) = \Phi(\cos^{-1}x) = \Phi(\phi) \quad (-1 \le x \le 1)$$

in Eq. (59) yields the *Legendre equation*

$$(1 - x^2)y'' - 2xy + \lambda y = 0$$

that we discussed in Section 8.2. This equation has a solution $y(x)$ that is continuous for $-1 \le x \le 1$ only if $\lambda = n(n+1)$, where n is a nonnegative integer. In this case $y(x)$ is a constant multiple of the nth *Legendre polynomial* $P_n(x)$. Thus we have eigenvalues and eigenfunctions of Eq. (59) given by

$$\lambda_n = n(n+1), \quad \Phi_n(\phi) = P_n(\cos\phi) \tag{60}$$

for $n = 1, 2, 3, \ldots$. Recall from Section 8.2 that the first several Legendre polynomials are

$$P_0(x) \equiv 1, \qquad\qquad P_1(x) = x,$$
$$P_2(x) = \tfrac{1}{2}(3x^2 - 1), \qquad P_3(x) = \tfrac{1}{2}(5x^3 - 3x),$$
$$P_4(x) = \tfrac{1}{8}(35x^4 - 30x^2 + 3), \qquad \ldots.$$

PROBLEM 9 With $\lambda = n(n+1)$, Eq. (58) takes the form

$$\rho^2 R'' + 2\rho R' - n(n+1)R = 0.$$

Show that the trial solution $R(\rho) = \rho^k$ yields the general solution

$$R(\rho) = A\rho^n + \frac{B}{\rho^{n+1}}.$$

But continuity at $\rho = 0$ implies that $B = 0$ here, so it follows that the eigenfunction of Eq. (58) corresponding to $\lambda_n = n(n+1)$ is (a constant multiple of) $R_n(\rho) = \rho^n$. Thus we have found the building-block solutions

$$u_n(\rho, \phi) = \rho^n P_n(\cos\phi) \quad (n = 0, 1, 2, \ldots)$$

of Laplace's equation in (56). In the usual fashion our next step is to write the formal series solution

$$u(\rho, \phi) = \sum_{n=0}^{\infty} b_n \rho^n P_n(\cos\phi). \tag{61}$$

PROBLEM 10   It remains only to discuss the choice of coefficients in Eq. (61) to satisfy the nonhomogeneous condition

$$u(a, \phi) = g(\phi) = \sum_{n=0}^{\infty} b_n a^n P_n(\cos \phi).$$

With $x = \cos \phi$, $f(x) = g(\phi) = g(\cos^{-1} x)$, and $c_n = b_n a^n$, this equation takes the form of the *Fourier–Legendre series*

$$f(x) = \sum_{n=0}^{\infty} c_n P_n(x), \tag{62}$$

expressing the function $f(x)$ on $[-1, 1]$ in terms of Legendre polynomials. Given that the Legendre polynomials $\{P_n(x)\}_0^{\infty}$ are mutually orthogonal on $[-1, 1]$ with weight function $r(x) \equiv 1$, apply the formal eigenfunction series method of Section 10.1—multiplying each side in Eq. (62) by $P_k(x)$ and integrating termwise—to derive the *Fourier–Legendre coefficient formula*

$$c_n = \frac{\displaystyle\int_{-1}^{1} f(x) P_n(x) \, dx}{\displaystyle\int_{-1}^{1} [P_n(x)]^2 \, dx}.$$

But then the known integral

$$\int_{-1}^{1} [P_n(x)]^2 \, dx = \frac{2}{2n + 1}$$

gives

$$c_n = \frac{2n + 1}{2} \int_{-1}^{1} f(x) P_n(x) \, dx. \tag{63}$$

Show, finally, that this choice of coefficients yields the formal series solution

$$u(\rho, \phi) = \sum_{n=0}^{\infty} c_n \left(\frac{\rho}{a}\right)^n P_n(\cos \phi) \tag{64}$$

of the boundary value problem in Eqs. (56) and (57).

PROBLEM 11   Recall the notation

$$k!! = k(k - 2)(k - 4) \cdots 4 \cdot 2$$

for k even and

$$k!! = k(k - 2)(k - 4) \cdots 3 \cdot 1$$

for k odd. Use the integral

$$\int_0^1 P_n(x) \, dx = \begin{cases} 1 & \text{if } n = 0, \\[2mm] \frac{1}{2} & \text{if } n = 1, \\[2mm] 0 & \text{if } n = 2, 4, 6, \ldots, \\[2mm] (-1)^{(n-1)/2} \dfrac{(n - 2)!!}{(n + 1)!!} & \text{if } n = 3, 5, 7, \ldots \end{cases} \tag{65}$$

to derive the Fourier–Legendre series

$$s(x) = \tfrac{3}{2} P_1(x) - \tfrac{7}{8} P_3(x) + \tfrac{11}{16} P_5(x) - \tfrac{75}{128} P_7(x) + \cdots$$

$$= \tfrac{3}{2} P_1(x) + \sum_{\substack{n \text{ odd} \\ n \geq 3}} (-1)^{(n-1)/2}(2n+1)\frac{(n-2)!!}{(n+1)!!} P_n(x) \qquad (66)$$

of the square-wave function

$$s(x) = \begin{cases} -1 & \text{if } -1 < x < 0, \\ +1 & \text{if } 0 < x < 1. \end{cases}$$

Figure 10.5.9 shows the graph of the partial sum with 25 terms of the series in Eq. (66), exhibiting a characteristic Gibbs phenomenon near $x = 0$.

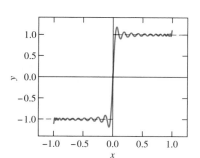

FIGURE 10.5.9. The graph of the 25-term partial sum of the rectangular wave series in Eq. (66).

PROJECT E Figure 10.5.10 shows a solid spherical buoy of radius $a = 1$ meter floating in water. If the buoy has uniform specific gravity $\delta = 0.5$ (density half that of water), then it sinks to a depth $h = 1$ meter as shown. Suppose that the temperature of the water is $10°$ and that of the air is $20°$. Then we want to find the temperature function $u(\rho, \phi)$ within the buoy subject to the boundary condition

$$u(1, \phi) = g(\phi) = \begin{cases} 20 & \text{if } 0 < \phi < \pi/2, \\ 10 & \text{if } \pi/2 < \phi < \pi. \end{cases}$$

Then

$$f(x) = g(\cos^{-1} x) = \begin{cases} 10 & \text{if } -1 < x < 0 \\ 20 & \text{if } 0 < x < 1 \end{cases} = 15 + 5s(x)$$

in terms of the step function $s(x)$ of Problem 11. Hence use Eqs. (64) and (66) to show that

$$u(\rho, \phi) = 15 + \tfrac{15}{2}\rho P_1(\cos \phi)$$

$$+ \sum_{\substack{n \text{ odd} \\ n \geq 3}} 5 \cdot (-1)^{(n-1)/2}(2n+1)\frac{(n-2)!!}{(n+1)!!}\rho^n P_n(\cos \phi). \qquad (67)$$

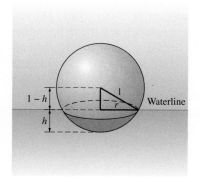

FIGURE 10.5.10. A floating spherical buoy with specific gravity $\delta = 0.5$.

Because the odd-degree Legendre polynomials have only terms of odd degree, it follows from Eq. (67) that the buoy has a constant average temperature of $15°$ on its water-level cross section (where $\phi = \pi/2$). As a first step in using the series in (67) to investigate the temperature distribution within the buoy, sum enough terms to plot u as a function $u(z)$ of height x ($-1 \leq z \leq 1$) on the vertical axis of symmetry of the buoy. Knowing that $u(0) = 15$, find the numerical values of z for which $u = 12.5°$ and $u = 17.5°$.

The buoy problem is more interesting if the specific gravity of the buoy is less than half that of water, $0 < \delta < 0.5$, so the buoy lies higher in the water as in Fig. 10.5.11. Archimedes' law of buoyancy implies that the buoy floats with the fraction δ of its total volume $4\pi/3$ submerged. Hence the part of the buoy lying beneath the waterline has volume $V = 4\pi\delta/3$. But this volume also is given by the sphere–segment volume formula

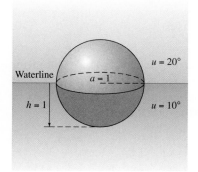

FIGURE 10.5.11. The floating buoy with $\delta < 0.5$.

$$V = \frac{\pi h}{6}(3r^2 + h^2).$$

Equate the two expressions for V to show that the depth h to which the buoy sinks in the water is a solution of the cubic equation

$$h^3 - 3h^2 + 4\delta = 0. \tag{68}$$

With your own choice of δ—perhaps one-tenth the smallest nonzero digit in your student ID number—graph this equation to see that it has a single root in the interval $0 < h < 1$. Approximate this root h accurate to at least two decimal places. Then the boundary condition (water temperature $10°$, air temperature $20°$) corresponds to

$$f(x) = \begin{cases} 10 & \text{if } -1 < x < h - 1, \\ 20 & \text{if } h - 1 < x < +1, \end{cases}$$

so (63) gives the formula

$$c_n = \int_{-1}^{h-1} 10 P_n(x)\, dx + \int_{h-1}^{1} 20 P_n(x)\, dx \tag{69}$$

for the coefficients $\{c_n\}_0^\infty$ in the series

$$u(\rho, \phi) = \sum_{n=0}^{\infty} c_n \rho^n P_n(\cos \phi). \tag{70}$$

Now the questions—as to the temperature at the waterline level within the buoy, and as to where within the buoy the temperature is exactly $12.5°$, $15°$, and $17.5°$—are more interesting. If $h \neq 0$ then numerical integration is necessary to evaluate the integrals in (69). For instance, the *Mathematica* command

```
c[n_] = ((2*n + 1)/2)*
            (10*NIntegrate[LegendreP[n,x], {x, -1, h - 1}] +
            20*NIntegrate[LegendreP[n,x], {x, h - 1, 1}])
```

can be used. Explain why Eq. (70) implies that the temperature $u(z)$ at the point $(0, 0, z)$ (on the buoy's vertical axis of symmetry with $-1 \leq z \leq 1$) is then given by

$$u(z) = \sum_{n=0}^{\infty} c_n z^n. \tag{71}$$

With δ chosen so that $h = 0.5$, the partial sum consisting of 50 terms in (71) was used to plot the graph of $u(z)$ shown in Fig. 10.5.12, where we see the temperature increasing nonlinearly from $u(-1) = 10$ to $u(1) = 20$. Using the *Mathematica* **FindRoot** function we find that $u(-0.6335) \approx 12.5$, $u(-0.3473) \approx 15$, and $u(0) = 17.5$.

Now the temperature at the center point of the buoy's cross section at the waterline is $u(-0.5) \approx 13.6603$ (rather than the average temperature of $15°$ that one might naively expect). In Fig. 10.5.13 we see that

$$\rho = \sqrt{x^2 + 0.25} \quad \text{and} \quad \phi = \pi - \arctan |2x|$$

at a point of the waterline cross section at distance x from the buoy's vertical axis. The graph of u (now as a function of x) shown in Fig. 10.5.14 was plotted by substituting these expressions for ρ and ϕ in a 50-term partial sum of the series in (67). Can you see intuitively why, as x increases starting at zero, the temperature $u(x)$ first decreases and then rises rapidly to $u = 15°$ at the boundary circle of the waterline cross section?

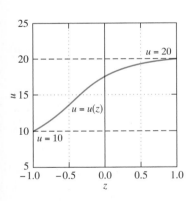

FIGURE 10.5.12. The temperature $u(z)$ at the point z on the vertical axis of the buoy with $h = 0.5$.

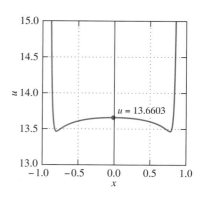

FIGURE 10.5.13.   The waterline cross section with $z = -0.5$, $-\frac{\sqrt{3}}{2} \leq x \leq \frac{\sqrt{3}}{2}$.

FIGURE 10.5.14.   The temperature $u(x)$ in the waterline cross section of the buoy with $h = 0.5$.

Spherical Harmonics and Ocean Waves

Equation (55) gives the three-dimensional Laplacian in spherical coordinates. For instance, consider radial vibrations of the surface of an elastic spherical planet of radius c. If $u(\phi, \theta, t)$ denotes the radial displacement at time t of the point (ϕ, θ) of the surface $\rho = c$ of the planet, then the wave equation $u_{tt} = a^2 \nabla^2 u$ (with $\rho = c$ and $u_\rho \equiv 0$) takes the form

$$\frac{\partial^2 u}{\partial t^2} = b^2 \nabla^2_{\phi\theta} u \tag{72}$$

where $b = a/c$ and

$$\nabla^2_{\phi\theta} u = \frac{1}{\sin\phi} \frac{\partial}{\partial\phi} \left((\sin\phi) \frac{\partial u}{\partial\phi} \right) + \frac{1}{\sin^2\phi} \frac{\partial^2 u}{\partial\theta^2}. \tag{73}$$

Alternatively, Eq. (72) models the oscillations of tidal waves on the surface of a spherical planet of radius c. In this case, $u(\phi, \theta, t)$ denotes the radial displacement (from equilibrium) of the water surface at the point (ϕ, θ) at time t and $b^2 = gh/c^2$, where h is the average depth of the water and g denotes gravitational acceleration at the surface of the planet.

In the applications manual that accompanies this text, we show that the separation of variables

$$u(\phi, \theta, t) = Y(\phi, \theta)T(t)$$

in Eq. (72) leads to eigenfunctions of the typical form

$$u_{mn}(\phi, \theta, t) = Y_{mn}(\phi, \theta) \cos \omega_n t \tag{74}$$

for $0 \leqq m \leqq n = 1, 2, 3, \ldots$. The frequency of this oscillation is $\omega_n = b\sqrt{n(n+1)}$ and Y_{mn} denotes the **spherical harmonic** defined by

$$Y_{mn}(\phi, \theta) = P_n^m(\cos\phi) \cos m\theta \tag{75}$$

in terms of the so-called **associated Legendre function**

$$P_n^m(x) = (1 - x^2)^{m/2} P_n^{(m)}(x), \tag{76}$$

where the mth derivative of the ordinary Legendre polynomial $P_n(x)$ appears on the right.

For instance, let us consider water waves with a (quite unrealistic) average depth of $h = 1.25$ sloshing about on the surface of a small spherical planet of radius $c = 5$. In Figs. 10.5.15 and 10.5.16 we show a couple of typical water surface shapes of the form $\rho = c + hY_{mn}(\phi, \theta)$.

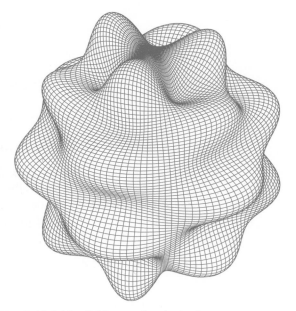

FIGURE 10.5.15.   With $m = 3$ and $n = 9$.

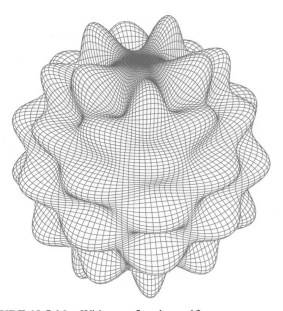

FIGURE 10.5.16.   With $m = 5$ and $n = 13$.

REFERENCES FOR FURTHER STUDY

The literature of the theory and applications of differential equations is vast. The following list includes a selection of books that might be useful to readers who wish to pursue further the topics introduced in this book.

1. ABRAMOWITZ, M. and I. A. STEGUN, *Handbook of Mathematical Functions*. New York: Dover, 1965. A comprehensive collection of tables to which frequent reference is made in the text.

2. BIRKHOFF, G. and G.-C. ROTA, *Ordinary Differential Equations* (2nd ed.). New York: John Wiley, 1969. An intermediate-level text that includes more complete treatment of existence and uniqueness theorems, Sturm–Liouville problems, and eigenfunction expansions.

3. BRAUN, M., *Differential Equations and Their Applications* (3rd ed.). New York: Springer-Verlag, 1983. An introductory text at a slightly higher level than this book; it includes several interesting "case study" applications.

4. CHURCHILL, R. V., *Operational Mathematics*, 3rd edition. New York: McGraw-Hill, 1972. The standard reference for theory and applications of Laplace transforms, starting at about the same level as Chapter 7 of this book.

5. CHURCHILL, R. V. and J. W. BROWN, *Fourier Series and Boundary Value Problems*, 3rd edition. New York: McGraw-Hill, 1978. A text at about the same level as Chapters 9 and 10 of this book.

6. CODDINGTON, E. A., *An Introduction to Ordinary Differential Equations*. Englewood Cliffs, N.J.: Prentice Hall, 1961. An intermediate-level introduction; Chapters 3 and 4 include proofs of the theorems on power series and Frobenius series solutions stated in Chapter 8 of this book.

7. CODDINGTON, E. A. and N. LEVINSON, *Theory of Ordinary Differential Equations*. New York: McGraw-Hill, 1955. An advanced theoretical text; Chapter 5 discusses solutions near an irregular singular point.

8. DORMAND, J. R., *Numerical Methods for Differential Equations*. Boca Raton: CRC Press, 1996. More complete coverage of modern computational methods for approximate solution of differential equations.

9. HABERMAN, R., *Elementary Applied Partial Differential Equations*, 3rd edition. Upper Saddle River, N.J.: Prentice Hall, 1998. A next step beyond Chapters 9 and 10 of this book, but still quite accessible.

10. HUBBARD, J. H. and B. H. WEST, *Differential Equations: A Dynamical Systems Approach*. New York: Springer-Verlag, 1992 (part I) and 1995 (Higher-Dimensional Systems). Detailed treatment of qualitative phenomena, with a balanced combination of computational and theoretical viewpoints.

11. INCE, E. L., *Ordinary Differential Equations*. New York: Dover, 1956. First published in 1926, this is the classic older reference work on the subject.

12. LEBEDEV, N. N., *Special Functions and Their Applications*. New York: Dover, 1972. A comprehensive account of Bessel functions and the other special functions of mathematical physics.

13. LEBEDEV, N. N., I. P. SKALSKAYA, and Y. S. UFLYAND, *Worked Problems in Applied Mathematics*. New York: Dover, 1979. A large collection of applied examples and problems similar to those discussed in Chapter 10 of this book.

14. MCLACHLAN, N. W., *Bessel Functions for Engineers*, 2nd edition. London: Oxford University Press, 1955. Includes numerous physical applications of Bessel functions.

15. MCLACHLAN, N. W., *Ordinary Non-Linear Differential Equations in Engineering and Physical Sciences*. London: Oxford University Press, 1956. A concrete introduction to the effects of nonlinearity in physical systems.

16. POLKING, J. C. and D. ARNOLD, *Ordinary Differential Equations Using MATLAB* (2nd ed.). Upper Saddle River, N.J.: Prentice Hall, 1999. A manual for using MATLAB in an elementary differential equations course; based on the MATLAB programs `dfield` and `pplane` that are used and referenced in this text.

17. PRESS, W. H., B. P. FLANNERY, S. A. TEUKOLSKY, and W. T. VETTERLING, *Numerical Recipes: The Art of Scientific Computing*. Cambridge: Cambridge University Press, 1986. Chapter 15 discusses modern techniques for the numerical solution of differential equations. This edition includes FORTRAN programs; Pascal and C editions have also been published.

18. RAINVILLE, E., *Intermediate Differential Equations*, 2nd edition. New York: Macmillan, 1964. Chapters 3 and 4 include proofs of the theorems on power series and Frobenius series solutions stated in Chapter 8 of this book.

19. SAGAN, H., *Boundary and Eigenvalue Problems in Mathematical Physics*. New York: John Wiley, 1961. Discusses the classical boundary value problems and the variational approach to Sturm–Liouville problems, eigenvalues, and eigenfunctions.

20. SIMMONS, G. F., *Differential Equations*. New York: McGraw-Hill, 1972. An introductory text with interesting historical notes and fascinating applications and with the most eloquent preface in any mathematics book currently in print.

21. TOLSTOV, G. P., *Fourier Series*. New York: Dover, 1976. An introductory text including detailed discussion of both convergence and applications of Fourier series.

22. THOMPSON, J. M. T. and H. B. STEWART, *Nonlinear Dynamics and Chaos*. New York: John Wiley, 1986. Includes more detailed discussions of the forced Duffing, Lorenz, and Rossler systems (among others that exhibit nonlinear chaos phenomena).

23. WEINBERGER, H. F., *A First Course in Partial Differential Equations*. New York: Blaisdell, 1965. Includes separation of variables, Sturm–Liouville methods, and applications of Laplace transform methods to partial differential equations.

24. WEINSTOCK, R., *Calculus of Variations*. New York: Dover, 1974. Includes variational derivations of the partial differential equations of vibrating strings, membranes, rods, and bars.

APPENDIX

Existence and Uniqueness of Solutions

In Chapter 1 we saw that an initial value problem of the form

$$\frac{dy}{dx} = f(x, y), \quad y(a) = b \tag{1}$$

can fail (on a given interval containing the point $x = a$) to have a unique solution. For instance, the answer to Problem 33 in Section 1.3 says that the initial value problem

$$x^2 \frac{dy}{dx} + y^2 = 0, \quad y(0) = b \tag{2}$$

has no solutions at all unless $b = 0$, in which case there are infinitely many solutions. According to Problem 31 of Section 1.3, the initial value problem

$$\frac{dy}{dx} = -\sqrt{1 - y^2}, \quad y(0) = 1 \tag{3}$$

has the two distinct solutions $y_1(x) \equiv 1$ and $y_2(x) = \cos x$ on the interval $0 \leqq x \leqq \pi$. In this appendix we investigate conditions on the function $f(x, y)$ that suffice to guarantee that the initial value problem in (1) has one and only one solution, and then proceed to establish appropriate versions of the existence-uniqueness theorems that were stated without proof in Sections 1.3, 3.1, 3.2, and 4.1.

A.1 Existence of Solutions

The approach we employ is the **method of successive approximations**, which was developed by the French mathematician Emile Picard (1856–1941). This method is based on the fact that the function $y(x)$ satisfies the initial value problem in (1) on the open interval I containing $x = a$ if and only if it satisfies the integral equation

$$y(x) = b + \int_a^x f(t, y(t)) \, dt \tag{4}$$

for all x in I. In particular, if $y(x)$ satisfies Eq. (4), then clearly $y(a) = b$, and differentiation of both sides in (4)—using the fundamental theorem of calculus—yields the differential equation $y'(x) = f(x, y(x))$.

To attempt to solve Eq. (4), we begin with the initial function

$$y_0(x) \equiv b, \tag{5}$$

and then define iteratively a sequence $y_1, y_2, y_3, \ldots$ of functions that we hope will converge to the solution. Specifically, we let

$$y_1(x) = b + \int_a^x f(t, y_0(t))\, dt \quad \text{and} \quad y_2(x) = b + \int_a^x f(t, y_1(t))\, dt. \tag{6}$$

In general, y_{n+1} is obtained by substitution of y_n for y in the right-hand side in Eq. (4):

$$y_{n+1}(x) = b + \int_a^x f(t, y_n(t))\, dt. \tag{7}$$

Suppose we know that each of these functions $\{y_n(x)\}_0^\infty$ is defined on some open interval (the same for each n) containing $x = a$, and that the limit

$$y(x) = \lim_{n \to \infty} y_n(x) \tag{8}$$

exists at each point of this interval. Then it will follow that

$$y(x) = \lim_{n \to \infty} y_{n+1}(x) = \lim_{n \to \infty} \left[b + \int_a^x f(t, y_n(t))\, dt \right]$$

$$= b + \lim_{n \to \infty} \int_a^x f(t, y_n(t))\, dt \tag{9}$$

$$= b + \int_a^x f\left(t, \lim_{n \to \infty} y_n(t)\right) dt \tag{10}$$

and hence that

$$y(x) = b + \int_a^x f(t, y(t))\, dt,$$

provided that we can validate the interchange of limit operations involved in passing from (9) to (10). It is therefore reasonable to expect that, under favorable conditions, the sequence $\{y_n(x)\}$ defined iteratively in Eqs. (5) and (7) will converge to a solution $y(x)$ of the integral equation in (4), and hence to a solution of the original initial value problem in (1).

Example 1 To apply the method of successive approximations to the initial value problem

$$\frac{dy}{dx} = y, \quad y(0) = 1, \tag{11}$$

we write Eqs. (5) and (7), thereby obtaining

$$y_0(x) \equiv 1, \quad y_{n+1}(x) = 1 + \int_0^x y_n(t)\, dt. \tag{12}$$

The iteration formula in (12) yields

$$y_1(x) = 1 + \int_0^x 1\, dt = 1 + x,$$

$$y_2(x) = 1 + \int_0^x (1 + t)\, dt = 1 + x + \tfrac{1}{2}x^2,$$

$$y_3(x) = 1 + \int_0^x \left(1 + t + \tfrac{1}{2}t^2\right) dt = 1 + x + \tfrac{1}{2}x^2 + \tfrac{1}{6}x^3,$$

and

$$y_4(x) = 1 + \int_0^x \left(1 + t + \tfrac{1}{2}t^2 + \tfrac{1}{6}t^3\right) dt$$

$$= 1 + x + \tfrac{1}{2}x^2 + \tfrac{1}{6}x^3 + \tfrac{1}{24}x^4.$$

It is clear that we are generating the sequence of partial sums of a power series solution; indeed, we immediately recognize the series as that of $y(x) = e^x$. There is no difficulty in demonstrating that the exponential function is indeed the solution of the initial value problem in (11); moreover, a diligent student can verify (using a proof by induction on n) that $y_n(x)$, obtained in the aforementioned manner, is indeed the nth partial sum for the Taylor series with center zero for $y(x) = e^x$. ∎

Example 2 To apply the method of successive approximations to the initial value problem

$$\frac{dy}{dx} = 4xy, \qquad y(0) = 3, \tag{13}$$

we write Eqs. (5) and (7) as in Example 1. Now we obtain

$$y_0(x) \equiv 3, \quad y_{n+1}(x) = 3 + \int_0^x 4t\, y_n(t)\, dt. \tag{14}$$

The iteration formula in (14) yields

$$y_1(x) = 3 + \int_0^x (4t)(3)\, dt = 3 + 6x^2,$$

$$y_2(x) = 3 + \int_0^x (4t)(3 + 6t^2)\, dt = 3 + 6x^2 + 6x^4,$$

$$y_3(x) = 3 + \int_0^x (4t)(3 + 6t^2 + 6t^4)\, dt = 3 + 6x^2 + 6x^4 + 4x^6,$$

and

$$y_4(x) = 3 + \int_0^x (4t)(3 + 6t^2 + 6t^4 + 4t^6)\, dt$$

$$= 3 + 6x^2 + 6x^4 + 4x^6 + 2x^8.$$

It is again clear that we are generating partial sums of a power series solution. It is not quite so obvious what function has such a power series representation, but the initial value problem in (13) is readily solved by separation of variables:

$$y(x) = 3 \exp\left(2x^2\right) = 3 \sum_{n=0}^{\infty} \frac{(2x^2)^n}{n!}$$

$$= 3 + 6x^2 + 6x^4 + 4x^6 + 2x^8 + \tfrac{4}{5}x^{10} + \cdots. \quad ∎$$

In some cases it may be necessary to compute a much large number of terms, either in order to identify the solution or to use a partial sum of its series with large subscript to approximate the solution accurately for x near its initial value. Fortunately, computer algebra systems such as *Maple* and *Mathematica* can perform the symbolic integrations (as opposed to numerical integrations) of the sort in Examples 1 and 2. If necessary, you could generate the first hundred terms in Example 2 in a matter of minutes.

In general, of course, we apply Picard's method because we cannot find a solution by elementary methods. Suppose that we have produced a large number of terms of what we believe to be the correct power series expansion of the solution. We *must* have conditions under which the sequence $\{y_n(x)\}$ provided by the method of successive approximations is guaranteed in advance to converge to a solution. It is just as convenient to discuss the initial value problem

$$\frac{d\mathbf{x}}{dt} = \mathbf{f}(\mathbf{x}, t), \quad \mathbf{x}(a) = \mathbf{b} \tag{15}$$

for a system of m first-order equations, where

$$\mathbf{x} = \begin{bmatrix} x_1 \\ x_2 \\ x_3 \\ \vdots \\ x_m \end{bmatrix}, \quad \mathbf{f} = \begin{bmatrix} f_1 \\ f_2 \\ f_3 \\ \vdots \\ f_m \end{bmatrix}, \quad \text{and} \quad \mathbf{b} = \begin{bmatrix} b_1 \\ b_2 \\ b_3 \\ \vdots \\ b_m \end{bmatrix}.$$

It turns out that with the aid of this vector notation (which we introduced in Section 5.1), most results concerning a single [scalar] equation $x' = f(x, t)$ can be generalized readily to analogous results for a system of m first-order equations, as abbreviated in (15). Consequently, the effort of using vector notation is amply justified by the generality it provides.

The method of successive approximations for the system in (15) calls for us to compute the sequence $\{\mathbf{x}_n(t)\}_0^\infty$ of vector-valued functions of t,

$$\mathbf{x}_n(t) = \begin{bmatrix} x_{1n}(t) \\ x_{2n}(t) \\ x_{3n}(t) \\ \vdots \\ x_{mn}(t) \end{bmatrix},$$

defined iteratively by

$$\mathbf{x}_0(a) \equiv \mathbf{b}, \quad \mathbf{x}_{n+1}(t) = \mathbf{b} + \int_a^t \mathbf{f}(\mathbf{x}_n(s), s)\, ds. \tag{16}$$

Recall that vector-valued functions are integrated componentwise.

Example 3 Consider the m-dimensional initial value problem

$$\frac{d\mathbf{x}}{dt} = \mathbf{A}\mathbf{x}, \quad \mathbf{x}(0) = \mathbf{b} \tag{17}$$

for a homogeneous linear system with $m \times m$ constant coefficient matrix $\mathbf{A}$. The equations in (16) take the form

$$\mathbf{x}_0(t) = \mathbf{b}, \quad \mathbf{x}_{n+1} = \mathbf{b} + \int_0^x \mathbf{A}\mathbf{x}_n(s)\, ds. \tag{18}$$

Thus

$$\mathbf{x}_1(t) = \mathbf{b} + \int_0^t \mathbf{A}\mathbf{b}\, ds = \mathbf{b} + \mathbf{A}\mathbf{b}t = (\mathbf{I} + \mathbf{A}t)\mathbf{b};$$

$$\mathbf{x}_2(t) = \mathbf{b} + \int_0^t \mathbf{A}(\mathbf{b} + \mathbf{A}\mathbf{b}s)\, ds = \mathbf{b} + \mathbf{A}\mathbf{b}t + \tfrac{1}{2}\mathbf{A}^2\mathbf{b}t^2 = (\mathbf{I} + \mathbf{A}t + \tfrac{1}{2}\mathbf{A}^2t^2)\mathbf{b}$$

and

$$\mathbf{x}_3(t) = \mathbf{b} + \int_0^t \mathbf{A}(\mathbf{b} + \mathbf{A}\mathbf{b}s + \tfrac{1}{2}\mathbf{A}^2\mathbf{b}s^2)\, ds = (\mathbf{I} + \mathbf{A}t + \tfrac{1}{2}\mathbf{A}^2t^2 + \tfrac{1}{6}\mathbf{A}^3t^3)\mathbf{b}.$$

We have therefore obtained the first several partial sums of the exponential series solution

$$\mathbf{x}(t) = e^{\mathbf{A}t}\mathbf{b} = \left(\sum_{n=0}^{\infty} \frac{(\mathbf{A}t)^n}{n!}\right)\mathbf{b} \tag{19}$$

of (17), which was derived earlier in Section 5.5.   ∎

The key to establishing convergence in the method of successive approximations is an appropriate condition on the rate at which $\mathbf{f}(\mathbf{x}, t)$ changes when $\mathbf{x}$ varies but t is held fixed. If R is a region in $(m + 1)$-dimensional $(\mathbf{x}, t)$-space, then the function $\mathbf{f}(\mathbf{x}, t)$ is said to be **Lipschitz continuous** on R if there exists a constant $k > 0$ such that

$$|\mathbf{f}(\mathbf{x}_1, t) - \mathbf{f}(\mathbf{x}_2, t)| \leqq k|\mathbf{x}_1 - \mathbf{x}_2| \tag{20}$$

if $(\mathbf{x}_1, t)$ and $(\mathbf{x}_2, t)$ are points of R. Recall that the **norm** of an m-dimensional point or vector $\mathbf{x}$ is defined to be

$$|\mathbf{x}| = \sqrt{x_1^2 + x_2^2 + x_3^2 + \cdots + x_m^2}. \tag{21}$$

Then $|\mathbf{x}_1 - \mathbf{x}_2|$ is simply the Euclidean distance between the points $\mathbf{x}_1$ and $\mathbf{x}_2$.

Example 4   Let $f(x, t) = x^2 \exp\left(-t^2\right) \sin t$ and let R be the strip $0 \leqq x \leqq 2$ in the xy-plane. If (x_1, t) and (x_2, t) are both points of R, then

$$|f(x_1, t) - f(x_2, t)| = |\exp\left(-t^2\right)\sin t| \cdot |x_1 + x_2| \cdot |x_1 - x_2| \leqq 4|x_1 - x_2|,$$

because $\left|\exp\left(-t^2\right)\sin t\right| \leqq 1$ for all t and $|x_1 + x_2| \leqq 4$ if x_1 and x_2 are both in the interval $[0, 2]$. Thus f satisfies the Lipschitz condition in (20) with $k = 4$ and is therefore Lipschitz continuous in the strip R.   ∎

Example 5   Let $f(x, t) = t\sqrt{x}$ on the rectangle R consisting of the points (x, t) in the xt-plane for which $0 \leqq x \leqq 1$ and $0 \leqq t \leqq 1$. Then, taking $x_1 = x$, $x_2 = 0$, and $t = 1$, we find that

$$|f(x, 1) - f(0, 1)| = \sqrt{x} = \frac{1}{\sqrt{x}}|x - 0|.$$

Because $x^{-1/2} \to +\infty$ as $x \to 0^+$, we see that the Lipschitz condition in (20) cannot be satisfied by any (finite) constant $k > 0$. Thus the function f, though obviously continuous on R, is *not* Lipschitz continuous on R.   ∎

Suppose, however, that the function $f(x, t)$ has a continuous partial derivative $f_x(x, t)$ on the closed rectangle R in the xt-plane, and denote by k the maximum value of $|f_x(x, t)|$ on R. Then the mean value theorem of differential calculus yields

$$|f(x_1, t) - f(x_2, t)| = |f_x(\overline{x}, t) \cdot (x_1 - x_2)|$$

for some $\overline{x}$ in (x_1, x_2), so it follows that

$$|f(x_1, t) - f(x_2, t)| \leq k|x_1 - x_2|$$

because $|f_x(\overline{x}, t)| \leq k$. Thus a continuously differentiable function $f(x, t)$ defined on a closed rectangle *is* Lipschitz continuous there. More generally, the multivariable mean value theorem of advanced calculus can be used similarly to prove that a *vector-valued function* $\mathbf{f}(\mathbf{x}, t)$ *with continuously differentiable component functions on a closed rectangular region* R *in* $(\mathbf{x}, t)$-*space is Lipschitz continuous on* R.

Example 6	The function $f(x, t) = x^2$ is Lipschitz continuous on any closed [bounded] region in the xt-plane. But consider this function on the infinite strip R consisting of the points (x, t) for which $0 \leq t \leq 1$ and x is arbitrary. Then

$$|f(x_1, t) - f(x_2, t)| = |x_1^2 - x_2^2| = |x_1 + x_2| \cdot |x_1 - x_2|.$$

Because $|x_1 + x_2|$ can be made arbitrarily large, it follows that f is *not* Lipschitz continuous on the infinite strip R. ∎

If I is an interval on the t-axis, then the set of all points $(\mathbf{x}, t)$ with t in I is an infinite strip or slab in $(m + 1)$-space (as indicated in Fig. A.1). Example 6 shows that Lipschitz continuity of $\mathbf{f}(\mathbf{x}, t)$ on such an infinite slab is a very strong condition. Nevertheless, the existence of a solution of the initial value problem

$$\frac{d\mathbf{x}}{dt} = \mathbf{f}(\mathbf{x}, t), \quad \mathbf{x}(a) = \mathbf{b} \tag{15}$$

under the hypothesis of Lipschitz continuity of $\mathbf{f}$ in such a slab is of considerable importance.

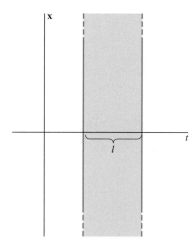

FIGURE A.1. An infinite slab in $(m + 1)$-space.

THEOREM 1   Global Existence of Solutions

Let $\mathbf{f}$ be a vector-valued function (with m components) of $m + 1$ real variables, and let I be a [bounded or unbounded] open interval containing $t = a$. If $\mathbf{f}(\mathbf{x}, t)$ is continuous and satisfies the Lipschitz condition in (20) for all t in I and for all $\mathbf{x}_1$ and $\mathbf{x}_2$, then the initial value problem in (15) has a solution on the [entire] interval I.

Proof: We want to show that the sequence $\{\mathbf{x}_n(t)\}_0^\infty$ of successive approximations determined iteratively by

$$\mathbf{x}_0(a) = \mathbf{b}, \quad \mathbf{x}_{n+1}(t) = \mathbf{b} + \int_0^t \mathbf{f}(\mathbf{x}_n(s), s)\, ds \tag{16}$$

converges to a solution $\mathbf{x}(t)$ of (15). We see that each of these functions in turn is continuous on I, as each is an [indefinite] integral of a continuous function.

We may assume that $a = 0$, because the transformation $t \to t + a$ converts (15) into an equivalent problem with initial point $t = 0$. Also, we will consider only the portion $t \geq 0$ of the interval I; the details for the case $t \leq 0$ are very similar.

The main part of the proof consists in showing that if $[0, T]$ is a closed (and bounded) interval contained in I, then the sequence $\{\mathbf{x}_n(t)\}$ converges *uniformly* on $[0, T]$ to a limit function $\mathbf{x}(t)$. This means that, given $\epsilon > 0$, there exists an integer N such that

$$|\mathbf{x}_n(t) - \mathbf{x}(t)| < \epsilon \tag{22}$$

for all $n \geq N$ and all t in $[0, T]$. For ordinary (perhaps nonuniform) convergence the integer N, for which (22) holds for all $n \geq N$, may depend on t, with no single value of N working for all t in I. Once this uniform convergence of the sequence $\{\mathbf{x}_n(t)\}$ has been established, the following conclusions will follow from standard theorems of advanced calculus (see pages 620–622 of A. E. Taylor and W. R. Mann, *Advanced Calculus*, 3rd ed. (New York: John Wiley, 1983)):

1. The limit function $\mathbf{x}(t)$ is continuous on $[0, T]$.
2. If N is so chosen that the inequality in (22) holds for $n \geq N$, then the Lipschitz continuity of $\mathbf{f}$ implies that

$$|\mathbf{f}(\mathbf{x}_n(t), t) - \mathbf{f}(\mathbf{x}(t), t)| \leq k|\mathbf{x}_n(t) - \mathbf{x}(t)| < k\epsilon$$

for all t in $[0, T]$ and $n \geq N$, so it follows that the sequence $\{\mathbf{f}(\mathbf{x}_n(t), t)\}_0^\infty$ converges uniformly to $\mathbf{f}(\mathbf{x}(t), t)$ on $[0, T]$.
3. But a uniformly convergent sequence or series can be integrated termwise, so it follows that, on taking limits in the iterative formula in (16),

$$\mathbf{x}(t) = \lim_{n \to \infty} \mathbf{x}_{n+1}(t) = \mathbf{b} + \lim_{n \to \infty} \int_0^t \mathbf{f}(\mathbf{x}_n(s), s)\, ds$$

$$= \mathbf{b} + \int_0^t \lim_{n \to \infty} \mathbf{f}(\mathbf{x}_n(s), s)\, ds;$$

thus

$$\mathbf{x}(t) = \mathbf{b} + \int_0^t \mathbf{f}(\mathbf{x}(s), s)\, ds. \tag{23}$$

4. Because the function $\mathbf{x}(t)$ is continuous on $[0, T]$, the integral equation in (23) (analogous to the one-dimensional case in (4)) implies that $\mathbf{x}'(t) = \mathbf{f}(\mathbf{x}(t), t)$ on $[0, T]$. But if this is true on every closed subinterval of the open interval I, then it is true on the entire interval I as well.

It therefore remains only to prove that the sequence $\{\mathbf{x}_n(t)\}_0^\infty$ converges uniformly on the closed interval $[0, T]$. Let M be the maximum value of $|\mathbf{f}(\mathbf{b}, t)|$ for t in $[0, T]$. Then

$$|\mathbf{x}_1(t) - \mathbf{x}_0(t)| = \left|\int_0^t \mathbf{f}(\mathbf{x}_0(s), s)\, ds\right| \leq \int_0^t |\mathbf{f}(\mathbf{b}, s)|\, ds \leq Mt. \tag{24}$$

Next,

$$|\mathbf{x}_2(t) - \mathbf{x}_1(t)| = \left|\int_0^t [\mathbf{f}(\mathbf{x}_1(s), s) - \mathbf{f}(\mathbf{x}_0(s), s)]\, ds\right| \leq k\int_0^t |\mathbf{x}_1(s) - \mathbf{x}_0(s)|\, ds,$$

and hence

$$|\mathbf{x}_2(t) - \mathbf{x}_1(t)| \leq k\int_0^t Ms\, ds = \tfrac{1}{2}kMt^2. \tag{25}$$

We now proceed by induction. Assume that

$$|\mathbf{x}_n(t) - \mathbf{x}_{n-1}(t)| \leq \frac{M}{k} \cdot \frac{(kt)^n}{n!}. \tag{26}$$

It then follows that

$$|\mathbf{x}_{n+1}(t) - \mathbf{x}_n(t)| = \left| \int_0^t \mathbf{f}(\mathbf{x}_n(s), s) - \mathbf{f}(\mathbf{x}_{n-1}(s), s)] \, ds \right|$$

$$\leq k \int_0^t |\mathbf{x}_n(s) - \mathbf{x}_{n-1}(s)| \, ds;$$

consequently,

$$|\mathbf{x}_{n+1}(t) - \mathbf{x}_n(t)| \leq k \int_0^t \frac{M}{k} \cdot \frac{(ks)^n}{n!} \, ds.$$

It follows upon evaluating this integral that

$$|\mathbf{x}_{n+1}(t) - \mathbf{x}_n(t)| \leq \frac{M}{k} \cdot \frac{(kt)^{n+1}}{(n+1)!}.$$

Thus (26) holds on $[0, T]$ for all $n \geq 1$.

Hence the terms of the infinite series

$$\mathbf{x}_0(t) + \sum_{n=1}^{\infty} \left[\mathbf{x}_n(t) - \mathbf{x}_{n-1}(t) \right] \tag{27}$$

are dominated (in magnitude on the interval $[0, T]$) by the terms of the convergent series

$$\sum_{n=1}^{\infty} \frac{M}{k} \cdot \frac{(kT)^{n+1}}{(n+1)!} = \frac{M}{k}(e^{kT} - 1), \tag{28}$$

which is a series of positive constants. It therefore follows (from the Weierstrass M-test on pages 618–619 of Taylor and Mann) that the series in (27) converges uniformly on $[0, T]$. But the sequence of partial sums of this series is simply our original sequence $\{\mathbf{x}_n(t)\}_0^{\infty}$ of successive approximations, so the proof of Theorem 1 is finally complete. ▲

A.2 Linear Systems

An important application of the global existence theorem just given is to the initial value problem

$$\frac{d\mathbf{x}}{dt} = \mathbf{A}(t)\mathbf{x} + \mathbf{g}(t), \quad \mathbf{x}(a) = \mathbf{b} \tag{29}$$

for a linear system, where the $m \times m$ matrix-valued function $\mathbf{A}(t)$ and the vector-valued function $\mathbf{g}(t)$ are continuous on a [bounded or unbounded] open interval I containing the point $t = a$. In order to apply Theorem 1 to the linear system in (29), we note first that the proof of Theorem 1 requires only that, for each closed and bounded subinterval J of I, there exists a Lipschitz constant k such that

$$|\mathbf{f}(\mathbf{x}_1, t) - \mathbf{f}(\mathbf{x}_2, t)| \leq k |\mathbf{x}_1 - \mathbf{x}_2| \tag{20}$$

for all t in J (and all $\mathbf{x}_1$ and $\mathbf{x}_2$). Thus we do not need a single Lipschitz constant for the entire open interval I.

In (29) we have $\mathbf{f}(\mathbf{x}, t) = \mathbf{A}(t)\mathbf{x} + \mathbf{g}$, so

$$\mathbf{f}(\mathbf{x}_1, t) - \mathbf{f}(\mathbf{x}_2, t) = \mathbf{A}(t)(\mathbf{x}_1 - \mathbf{x}_2). \tag{30}$$

It therefore suffices to show that, if $\mathbf{A}(t)$ is continuous on the closed and bounded interval J, then there is a constant k such that

$$|\mathbf{A}(t)\mathbf{x}| \leqq k|\mathbf{x}| \tag{31}$$

for all t in J. But this follows from the fact (Problem 17) that

$$|\mathbf{A}\mathbf{x}| \leqq \|\mathbf{A}\| \cdot |\mathbf{x}|, \tag{32}$$

where the **norm** $\|\mathbf{A}\|$ of the matrix $\mathbf{A}$ is defined to be

$$\|\mathbf{A}\| = \left(\sum_{i,j=1}^{m} (a_{ij})^2 \right)^{1/2}. \tag{33}$$

Because $\mathbf{A}(t)$ is continuous on the closed and bounded interval J, the norm $\|\mathbf{A}\|$ is bounded on J, so Eq. (31) follows, as desired. Thus we have the following global existence theorem for the linear initial value problem in (29).

THEOREM 2   Existence for Linear Systems

Let the $m \times m$ matrix-valued function $\mathbf{A}(t)$ and the vector-valued function $\mathbf{g}(t)$ be continuous on the [bounded or unbounded] open interval I containing the point $t = a$. Then the initial value problem

$$\frac{d\mathbf{x}}{dt} = \mathbf{A}(t)\mathbf{x} + \mathbf{g}(t), \quad \mathbf{x}(a) = \mathbf{b} \tag{29}$$

has a solution on the [entire] interval I.

As we saw in Section 4.1, the mth-order initial value problem

$$x^{(m)} + a_1(t)x^{(m-1)} + \cdots + a_{m-1}(t)x' + a_m(t)x = p(t),$$
$$x(a) = b_0, \quad x'(a) = b_1, \quad \ldots, \quad x^{(m-1)}(a) = b_{m-1} \tag{34}$$

is readily transformed into an equivalent $m \times m$ system of the form in (29). It therefore follows from Theorem 2 that if the functions $a_1(t), a_2(t), \ldots, a_m(t)$ and $p(t)$ in (34) are all continuous on the [bounded or unbounded] open interval I containing $t = a$, then the initial value problem in (34) has a solution on the [entire] interval I.

A.3 Local Existence

In the case of a *nonlinear* initial value problem

$$\frac{d\mathbf{x}}{dt} = \mathbf{f}(\mathbf{x}, t), \quad \mathbf{x}(a) = \mathbf{b}, \tag{35}$$

the hypothesis in Theorem 1 that $\mathbf{f}$ satisfies a Lipschitz condition on a slab $(\mathbf{x}, t)$ (t in I, all $\mathbf{x}$) is unrealistic and rarely satisfied. This is illustrated by the following simple example.

| Example 1 | Consider the initial value problem |

$$\frac{dy}{dx} = x^2, \quad x(0) = b > 0. \tag{36}$$

As we saw in Example 6, the equation $x' = x^2$ does not satisfy a "strip Lipschitz condition." When we solve (36) by separation of variables, we get

$$x(t) = \frac{b}{1 - bt}. \tag{37}$$

Because the denominator vanishes for $t = 1/b$, Eq. (37) provides a solution of the initial value problem in (36) only for $t < 1/b$, despite the fact that the differential equation $x' = x^2$ "looks nice" on the entire real line—certainly the function appearing on the right-hand side of the equation is continuous everywhere. In particular, if b is large, then we have a solution only on a very small interval to the right of $t = 0$.

■

Although Theorem 2 assures us that *linear* equations have global solutions, Example 7 shows that, in general, even a "nice" nonlinear differential equation can be expected to have a solution only on a small interval around the initial point $t = a$, and that the length of this interval of existence can depend on the initial value $\mathbf{x}(a) = \mathbf{b}$, as well as on the differential equation itself. The reason is this: If $\mathbf{f}(\mathbf{x}, t)$ is continuously differentiable in a neighborhood of the point $(\mathbf{b}, a)$ in $(m + 1)$-dimensional space, then—as indicated in the discussion preceding Example 6—we can conclude that $\mathbf{f}(\mathbf{x}, t)$ satisfies a Lipschitz condition on some rectangular region R centered at $(\mathbf{b}, a)$, of the form

$$|t - a| < A, \quad |x_i - b_i| < B_i \tag{38}$$

$(i = 1, 2, \ldots, m)$. In the proof of Theorem 1, we need to apply the Lipschitz condition on the function $\mathbf{f}$ in analyzing the iterative formula

$$\mathbf{x}_{n+1}(t) = \mathbf{b} + \int_a^t \mathbf{f}(\mathbf{x}_n(s), s)\, ds. \tag{39}$$

The potential difficulty is that unless the values of t are suitably restricted, then the point $(\mathbf{x}_n(t), t)$ appearing in the integrand in (39) may not lie in the region R where $\mathbf{f}$ is known to satisfy a Lipschitz condition. On the other hand, it can be shown that—on a sufficiently small open interval J containing the point $t = a$—the graphs of the functions $\{\mathbf{x}_n(t)\}$ given iteratively by the formula in (39) remain within the region R, so the proof of convergence can then be carried out as in the proof of Theorem 1. A proof of the following *local* existence theorem can be found in Chapter 6 of G. Birkhoff and G.-C. Rota, *Ordinary Differential Equations*, 2nd ed. (New York: John Wiley, 1969).

THEOREM 3   Local Existence of Solutions

Let $\mathbf{f}$ be a vector-valued function (with m components) of the $m + 1$ real variables $x_1, x_2, \ldots, x_m$, and t. If the first-order partial derivatives of $\mathbf{f}$ all exist and are continuous in some neighborhood of the point $\mathbf{x} = \mathbf{b}$, $t = a$, then the initial value problem

$$\frac{d\mathbf{x}}{dt} = \mathbf{f}(\mathbf{x}, t), \quad \mathbf{x}(a) = \mathbf{b}, \tag{35}$$

has a solution on some open interval containing the point $t = a$.

A.4 Uniqueness of Solutions

It is possible to establish the existence of solutions of the initial value problem in (35) under the much weaker hypothesis that $\mathbf{f}(\mathbf{x}, t)$ is merely continuous; techniques other than those used in this section are required. By contrast, the Lipschitz condition that we used in proving Theorem 1 is the key to *uniqueness* of solutions. In particular, the solution provided by Theorem 3 is unique near the point $t = a$.

THEOREM 4   Uniqueness of Solutions

Suppose that on some region R in $(m + 1)$-space, the function $\mathbf{f}$ in (35) is continuous and satisfies the Lipschitz condition

$$|\mathbf{f}(\mathbf{x}_1, t) - \mathbf{f}(\mathbf{x}_2, t)| \leqq k \cdot |\mathbf{x}_1 - \mathbf{x}_2|. \tag{20}$$

If $\mathbf{x}_1(t)$ and $\mathbf{x}_2(t)$ are two solutions of the initial problem in (35) on some open interval I containing $x = a$, such that the solution curves $(\mathbf{x}_1(t), t)$ and $(\mathbf{x}_2(t), t)$ both lie in R for all t in I, then $\mathbf{x}_1(t) = \mathbf{x}_2(t)$ for all t in I.

We will outline the proof of Theorem 4 for the one-dimensional case in which x is a real variable. A generalization of this proof to the multivariable case can be found in Chapter 6 of Birkhoff and Rota.

Let us consider the function

$$\phi(t) = [x_1(t) - x_2(t)]^2 \tag{40}$$

for which $\phi(a) = 0$, because $x_1(a) = x_2(a) = b$. We want to show that $\phi(t) \equiv 0$, so that $x_1(t) \equiv x_2(t)$. We will consider only the case $t \geqq a$; the details are similar for the case $t \leqq a$.

If we differentiate each side in Eq. (40), we find that

$$\begin{aligned} |\phi'(t)| &= |2[x_1(t) - x_2(t)] \cdot [x_1'(t) - x_2'(t)]| \\ &= \left|2[x_1(t) - x_2(t)] \cdot [f(x_1(t), t) - f(x_2(t), t)]\right| \\ &\leqq 2k|x_1(t) - x_2(t)|^2 = 2k\phi(t), \end{aligned}$$

using the Lipschitz condition on f. Hence

$$\phi'(t) \leqq 2k\phi(t). \tag{41}$$

Now let us temporarily ignore the fact that $\phi(a) = 0$ and compare $\phi(t)$ with the solution of the differential equation

$$\Phi'(t) = 2k\Phi(t) \tag{42}$$

such that $\Phi(a) = \phi(a)$; clearly

$$\Phi(t) = \Phi(a)e^{2k(t-a)}. \tag{43}$$

In comparing (41) with (42), it seems inevitable that

$$\phi(t) \leqq \Phi(t) \qquad \text{for } t \geqq a, \tag{44}$$

and this is easily proved (Problem 18). Hence

$$0 \leqq [x_1(t) - x_2(t)]^2 \leqq [x_1(a) - x_2(a)]^2 e^{2k(t-a)}.$$

On taking square roots, we get

$$0 \leqq |x_1(t) - x_2(t)| \leqq |x_1(a) - x_2(a)|e^{k(t-a)}. \tag{45}$$

But $x_1(a) - x_2(a) = 0$, so (45) implies that $x_1(t) \equiv x_2(t)$.

| **Example 1** | The initial value problem |

$$\frac{dx}{dt} = 3x^{2/3}, \quad x(0) = 0 \tag{46}$$

has both the obvious solution $x_1(t) \equiv 0$ and the solution $x_2(t) = t^3$ that is readily found by separation of variables. Hence the function $f(x, t)$ must *fail* to satisfy a Lipschitz condition near $(0, 0)$. Indeed, the mean value theorem yields

$$|f(x, 0) - f(0, 0)| = |f_x(\overline{x}, 0)| \cdot |x - 0|$$

for some $\overline{x}$ between 0 and x. But $f_x(x, 0) = 2x^{-1/3}$ is unbounded as $x \rightarrow 0$, so no Lipschitz condition can be satisfied. ■

A.5 Well-Posed Problems and Mathematical Models

In addition to uniqueness, another consequence of the inequality in (45) is the fact that solutions of the differential equation

$$\frac{dx}{dt} = f(x, t) \tag{47}$$

depend *continuously* on the initial value $x(a)$; that is, if $x_1(t)$ and $x_2(t)$ are two solutions of (47) on the interval $a \leqq t \leqq T$ such that the initial values $x_1(a)$ and $x_2(a)$ are sufficiently close to one another, then the values of $x_1(t)$ and $x_2(t)$ remain close to one another. In particular, if $|x_1(a) - x_2(a)| \leqq \delta$, then (45) implies that

$$|x_1(t) - x_2(t)| \leqq \delta e^{k(T-a)} = \epsilon \tag{48}$$

for all t with $a \leqq t \leqq T$. Obviously, we can make ϵ as small as we wish by choosing δ sufficiently close to zero.

This continuity of solutions of (47) with respect to initial values is important in practical applications where we are unlikely to know the initial value $x_0 = x(a)$ with absolute precision. For example, suppose that the initial value problem

$$\frac{dx}{dt} = f(x, t), \quad x(a) = x_0 \tag{49}$$

models a population for which we know only that the initial population is within $\delta > 0$ of the assumed value x_0. Then even if the function $f(x, t)$ is accurate, the solution $x(t)$ of (49) will be only an approximation to the actual population. But (45) implies that the actual population at time t will be within $\delta e^{k(T-a)}$ of the approximate population $x(t)$. Thus, on a given closed interval $[a, T]$, $x(t)$ will be a close approximation to the actual population provided that $\delta > 0$ is sufficiently small.

An initial value problem is usually considered *well posed* as a mathematical model for a real-world situation only if the differential equation has unique solutions that are continuous with respect to initial values. Otherwise it is unlikely that the initial value problem adequately mirrors the real-world situation.

An even stronger "continuous dependence" of solutions is often desirable. In addition to possible inaccuracy in the initial value, the function $f(x, t)$ may not model precisely the physical situation. For instance, it may involve physical parameters (such as resistance coefficients) whose values cannot be measured with absolute precision. Birkhoff and Rota generalize the proof of Theorem 4 to establish the following result.

THEOREM 5   Continuous Dependence of Solutions

Let $\mathbf{x}(t)$ and $\mathbf{y}(t)$ be solutions of the equations

$$\frac{d\mathbf{x}}{dt} = \mathbf{f}(\mathbf{x}, t) \quad \text{and} \quad \frac{d\mathbf{y}}{dt} = \mathbf{g}(\mathbf{y}, t) \tag{50}$$

on the closed interval $[a, T]$. Let $\mathbf{f}$ and $\mathbf{g}$ be continuous for $a \leqq t \leqq T$ and for $\mathbf{x}$ and $\mathbf{y}$ in a common region D of n-space and assume that $\mathbf{f}$ satisfies the Lipschitz condition in (20) on the region D. If

$$|\mathbf{f}(\mathbf{z}, t) - \mathbf{g}(\mathbf{z}, t)| \leqq \mu \tag{51}$$

for all t in the interval $[a, T]$ and all $\mathbf{z}$ in D, it then follows that

$$|\mathbf{x}(t) - \mathbf{y}(t)| \leqq |\mathbf{x}(a) - \mathbf{y}(a)| \cdot e^{k(t-a)} + \frac{\mu}{k} \left[e^{k(t-a)} - 1 \right] \tag{52}$$

on the interval $[a, T]$.

If $\mu > 0$ is small, then (51) implies that the functions $\mathbf{f}$ and $\mathbf{g}$ appearing in the two differential equations, though different, are "close" to each other. If $\epsilon > 0$ is given, then it is apparent from (52) that

$$|\mathbf{x}(t) - \mathbf{y}(t)| \leqq \epsilon \tag{53}$$

for all t in $[a, T]$ if both $|\mathbf{x}(a) - \mathbf{y}(a)|$ and μ are sufficiently small. Thus Theorem 5 says (roughly) that if both the two initial values and the two differential equations in (50) are close to each other, then the two solutions remain close to each other for $a \leqq t \leqq T$.

For example, suppose that a falling body is subject both to constant gravitational acceleration g and to resistance proportional to some power of its velocity, so (with the positive axis directed downward) its velocity v satisfies the differential equation

$$\frac{dv}{dt} = g - cv^\rho. \tag{54}$$

Assume, however, that only an approximation $\bar{c}$ to the actual resistance c and an approximation $\bar{\rho}$ to the actual exponent ρ are known. Then our mathematical model is based on the differential equation

$$\frac{du}{dt} = g - \bar{c}u^{\bar{\rho}} \tag{55}$$

instead of the actual equation in (54). Thus if we solve Eq. (55), we obtain only an approximation $u(t)$ to the actual velocity $v(t)$. But if the parameters $\bar{c}$ and $\bar{\rho}$ are sufficiently close to the actual values c and ρ, then the right-hand sides in (54) and (55) will be close to each other. If so, then Theorem 5 implies that the actual and approximate velocity functions $v(t)$ and $u(t)$ are close to each other. In this case the approximation in (55) will be a good model of the actual physical situation.

Problems

In Problems 1 through 8, apply the successive approximation formula to compute $y_n(x)$ for $n \leqq 4$. Then write the exponential series for which these approximations are partial sums (perhaps with the first term or two missing; for example,

$$e^x - 1 = x + \tfrac{1}{2}x^2 + \tfrac{1}{6}x^3 + \tfrac{1}{24}x^4 + \cdots).$$

1. $\dfrac{dy}{dx} = y,\ y(0) = 3$ **2.** $\dfrac{dy}{dx} = -2y,\ y(0) = 4$

3. $\dfrac{dy}{dx} = -2xy,\ y(0) = 1$ **4.** $\dfrac{dy}{dx} = 3x^2 y,\ y(0) = 2$

5. $\dfrac{dy}{dx} = 2y + 2,\ y(0) = 0$ **6.** $\dfrac{dy}{dx} = x + y,\ y(0) = 0$

7. $\dfrac{dy}{dx} = 2x(1 + y),\ y(0) = 0$

8. $\dfrac{dy}{dx} = 4x(y + 2x^2),\ y(0) = 0$

In Problems 9 through 12, compute the successive approximations $y_n(x)$ for $n \leqq 3$; then compare them with the appropriate partial sums of the Taylor series of the exact solution.

9. $\dfrac{dy}{dx} = x + y,\ y(0) = 1$ **10.** $\dfrac{dy}{dx} = y + e^x,\ y(0) = 0$

11. $\dfrac{dy}{dx} = y^2,\ y(0) = 1$ **12.** $\dfrac{dy}{dx} = \tfrac{1}{2}y^3,\ y(0) = 1$

13. Apply the iterative formula in (16) to compute the first three successive approximations to the solution of the initial value problem

$$\frac{dx}{dt} = 2x - y, \qquad x(0) = 1;$$

$$\frac{dy}{dt} = 3x - 2y, \qquad y(0) = -1.$$

14. Apply the matrix exponential series in (19) to solve (in closed form) the initial value problem

$$\mathbf{x}'(t) = \begin{bmatrix} 1 & 1 \\ 0 & 1 \end{bmatrix} \mathbf{x}, \qquad \mathbf{x}(0) = \begin{bmatrix} 1 \\ 1 \end{bmatrix}.$$

(*Suggestion:* Show first that

$$\begin{bmatrix} 1 & 1 \\ 0 & 1 \end{bmatrix}^n = \begin{bmatrix} 1 & n \\ 0 & 1 \end{bmatrix}$$

for each positive integer n.)

15. For the initial value problem $dy/dx = 1 + y^3,\ y(1) = 1$, show that the second Picard approximation is

$$y_2(x) = 1 + 2(x - 1) + 3(x - 1)^2 + 4(x - 1)^3 + 2(x - 1)^4.$$

Then compute $y_2(1.1)$ and $y_2(1.2)$. The fourth-order Runge-Kutta method with step size $h = 0.005$ yields $y(1.1) \approx 1.2391$ and $y(1.2) \approx 1.6269$.

16. For the initial value problem $dy/dx = x^2 + y^2,\ y(0) = 0$, show that the third Picard approximation is

$$y_3(x) = \frac{1}{3}x^3 + \frac{1}{63}x^7 + \frac{2}{2079}x^{11} + \frac{1}{59535}x^{15}.$$

Compute $y_3(1)$. The fourth-order Runge–Kutta method yields $y(1) \approx 0.350232$, both with step size $h = 0.05$ and with step size $h = 0.025$.

17. Prove as follows the inequality $|\mathbf{Ax}| \leqq \|\mathbf{A}\| \cdot |\mathbf{x}|$, where $\mathbf{A}$ is an $m \times m$ matrix with row vectors $\mathbf{a}_1, \mathbf{a}_2, \ldots, \mathbf{a}_m$, and $\mathbf{x}$ is an m-dimensional vector. First note that the components of the vector $\mathbf{Ax}$ are $\mathbf{a}_1 \cdot \mathbf{x}, \mathbf{a}_2 \cdot \mathbf{x}, \ldots, \mathbf{a}_m \cdot \mathbf{x}$, so

$$|\mathbf{Ax}| = \left[\sum_{n=1}^{m} (\mathbf{a}_i \cdot \mathbf{x})^2 \right]^{1/2}.$$

Then use the Cauchy–Schwarz inequality $(\mathbf{a} \cdot \mathbf{x})^2 \leqq |\mathbf{a}|^2 |\mathbf{x}|^2$ for the dot product.

18. Suppose that $\phi(t)$ is a differentiable function with

$$\phi'(t) \leqq k\phi(t) \qquad (k > 0)$$

for $t \geqq a$. Multiply both sides by e^{-kt}, then transpose to show that

$$\frac{d}{dt} \left[\phi(t)e^{-kt} \right] \leqq 0$$

for $t \geqq a$. Then apply the mean value theorem to conclude that

$$\phi(t) \leqq \phi(a)e^{k(t-a)}$$

for $t \geqq a$.

ANSWERS TO SELECTED PROBLEMS

Chapter 1

Section 1.1

11. If $y = y_1 = x^{-2}$, then $y'(x) = -2x^{-3}$ and $y''(x) = 6x^{-4}$, so
$x^2 y'' + 5xy' + 4y = x^2(6x^{-4}) + 5x(-2x^{-3}) + 4(x^{-2}) =$
$6x^{-2} - 10x^{-2} + 4x^{-2} = 0$. If $y = y_2 = x^{-2} \ln x$, then
$y'(x) = x^{-3} - 2x^{-3} \ln x$ and $y''(x) = -5x^{-4} + 6x^{-4} \ln x$, so
$x^2 y'' + 5xy' + 4y =$
$x^2(-5x^{-4} + 6x^{-4} \ln x) + 5x(x^{-3} - 2x^{-3} \ln x) + 4(x^{-2} \ln x) = 0$.

13. $r = \frac{2}{3}$ **14.** $r = \pm\frac{1}{2}$ **15.** $r = -2, 1$

16. $r = \frac{1}{6}(-3 \pm \sqrt{57})$

17. $C = 2$

18. $C = 3$

19. $C = 6$

20. $C = 11$

21. $C = 7$

22. $C = 1$

23. $C = -56$

24. $C = 17$

25. $C = \pi/4$

26. $C = -\pi$

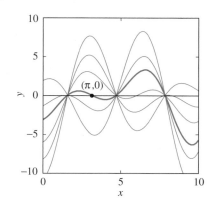

27. $y' = x + y$

28. $y' = 2y/x$

29. $y' = x/(1 - y)$

31. $y' = (y - x)/(y + x)$

32. $dP/dt = k\sqrt{P}$

33. $dv/dt = kv^2$

35. $dN/dt = k(P - N)$

37. $y \equiv 1$ or $y = x$

39. $y = x^2$

41. $y = \frac{1}{2}e^x$

42. $y = \cos x$ or $y = \sin x$

43. (b) The identically zero function $x(0) \equiv 0$

44. (a) The graphs (figure below) of typical solutions with $k = \frac{1}{2}$ suggest that (for each) the value $x(t)$ increases without bound as t increases.

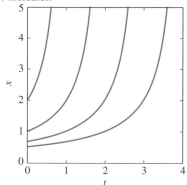

(b) The graphs (figure below) of typical solutions with $k = -\frac{1}{2}$ suggest that now the value $x(t)$ approaches 0 as t increases without bound.

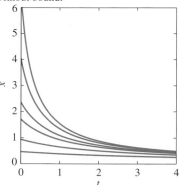

45. $P(t) = 100/(50 - t)$; $P = 100$ when $t = 49$, and $P = 1000$ when $t = 49.9$. Thus it appears that $P(t)$ grows without bound as t approaches 50.

46. $v(t) = 50/(5 + 2t)$; $v = 1$ when $t = 22.5$, and $v = \frac{1}{10}$ when $t = 247.5$. Thus it appears that $v(t)$ approaches 0 as t increases without bound.

47. (a) $C = 10.1$; (b) No such C, but the constant function $y(x) \equiv 0$ satisfies the conditions $y' = y^2$ and $y(0) = 0$.

Section 1.2

1. $y(x) = x^2 + x + 3$

2. $y(x) = \frac{1}{3}(x - 2)^2 + 1$

3. $y(x) = \frac{1}{3}(2x^{3/2} - 16)$

4. $y(x) = -1/x + 6$

5. $y(x) = 2\sqrt{x + 2} - 5$

6. $y(x) = \frac{1}{3}[(x^2 + 9)^{3/2} - 125]$

7. $y(x) = 10\tan^{-1} x$

8. $y(x) = \frac{1}{2}\sin 2x + 1$

9. $y(x) = \sin^{-1} x$

10. $y(x) = -(x + 1)e^{-x} + 2$

11. $x(t) = 25t^2 + 10t + 20$

12. $x(t) = -10t^2 - 15t + 5$

13. $x(t) = \frac{1}{2}t^3 + 5t$

14. $x(t) = \frac{1}{3}t^3 + \frac{1}{2}t^2 - 7t + 4$

15. $x(t) = \frac{1}{3}(t + 3)^4 - 37t - 26$

16. $x(t) = \frac{4}{3}(t + 4)^{3/2} - 5t - \frac{29}{3}$

17. $x(t) = \frac{1}{2}\left[(t + 1)^{-1} + t - 1\right]$

19. $x(t) = \begin{cases} 5t & \text{if } 0 \le t \le 5, \\ 10t - \frac{1}{2}t^2 - \frac{25}{2} & \text{if } 5 \le t \le 10. \end{cases}$

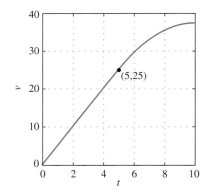

20. $x(t) = \begin{cases} \frac{1}{2}t^2 & \text{if } 0 \le t \le 5, \\ 5t - \frac{25}{2} & \text{if } 5 \le t \le 10. \end{cases}$

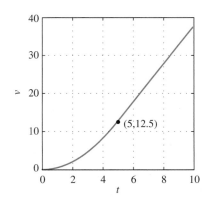

21. $x(t) = \begin{cases} \frac{1}{2}t^2 & \text{if } 0 \le t \le 5, \\ 10t - \frac{1}{2}t^2 - 25 & \text{if } 5 \le t \le 10. \end{cases}$

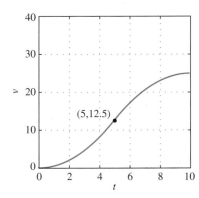

22. $x(t) = \begin{cases} \frac{5}{6}t^2 & \text{if } 0 \le t \le 3, \\ 5t - \frac{15}{2} & \text{if } 3 \le t \le 7, \\ \frac{1}{6}(-5t^2 + 100t - 290) & \text{if } 7 \le t \le 10. \end{cases}$

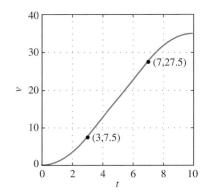

23. $v(t) = -(9.8)t + 49$, so the ball reaches its maximum height ($v = 0$) after $t = 5$ seconds. Its maximum height then is $y(5) = 122.5$ (m).

24. $v(5) = -160$ ft/s

25. The car stops when $t \approx 2.78$ (s), so the distance traveled before stopping is approximately $x(2.78) \approx 38.58$ (m).

26. (a) $y \approx 530$ m   (b) $t \approx 20.41$ s   (c) $t \approx 20.61$ s

27. $y_0 \approx 178.57$ (m)

28. $v(4.77) \approx -192.64$ ft/s

29. After 10 seconds the car has traveled 200 ft and is traveling at 70 ft/s.

30. $a = 22$ ft/s^2; it skids for 4 seconds.

31. $v_0 = 10\sqrt{30}$ (m/s), about 197.18 km/h

32. 60 m

33. $20\sqrt{10} \approx 63.25$ (ft/s)

34. 460.8 ft

36. About 13.6 ft

37. 25 (mi)

38. 1:10 pm

39. 6 mph

40. 2.4 mi

41. $\frac{544}{3} \approx 181.33$ ft/s

42. 25 mi

43. Time: 6.12245×10^9 s ≈ 194 years; Distance: 1.8367×10^{17} m ≈ 19.4 light-years

44. About 54 mi/h

Section 1.3

1.

2.

3.

4.

5.

6.

7.

8.

9.

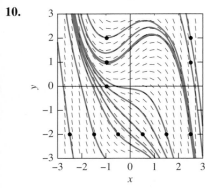

10.

11. A unique solution exists in some neighborhood of $x = 1$.

12. A unique solution exists in some neighborhood of $x = 1$.

13. A unique solution exists in some neighborhood of $x = 0$.

14. Existence but not uniqueness is guaranteed in some neighborhood of $x = 0$.

15. Neither existence nor uniqueness is guaranteed in any neighborhood of $x = 2$.

16. A unique solution exists in some neighborhood of $x = 2$.

17. A unique solution exists in some neighborhood of $x = 0$.

18. Neither existence nor uniqueness is guaranteed.

19. A unique solution exists in some neighborhood of $x = 0$.

20. A unique solution exists in some neighborhood of $x = 0$.

21. Your figure should suggest that $y(-4) \approx 3$; an exact solution of the differential equation gives $y(-4) = 3 + e^{-4} \approx 3.0183$.

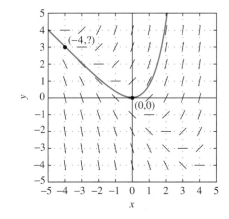

22. $y(-4) \approx -3$

23. Your figure should suggest that $y(2) \approx 1$; the actual value is closer to 1.004.

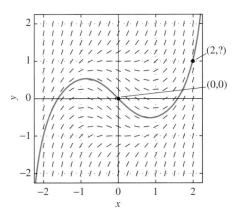

24. $y(2) \approx 1.5$

25. Your figure should suggest that the limiting velocity is about 20 ft/sec (quite survivable) and that the time required to reach 19 ft/sec is a little less than 2 seconds. An exact solution gives $v(t) = 19$ when $t = \frac{5}{8} \ln 20 \approx 1.8723$.

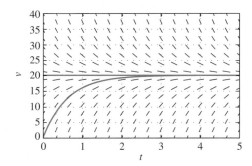

26. A figure suggests that there are 40 deer after about 60 months; a more accurate value is $t \approx 61.61$. The limiting population is 75 deer.

27. The initial value problem $y' = 2\sqrt{y}$, $y(0) = b$ has no solution if $b < 0$; a unique solution if $b > 0$; infinitely many solutions if $b = 0$.

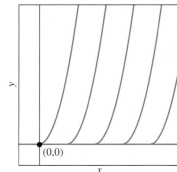

28. The initial value problem $xy' = y$, $y(a) = b$ has a unique solution if $a \neq 0$; infinitely many solutions if $a = b = 0$; no solution if $a = 0$ but $b \neq 0$.

29. The initial value problem $y' = 3y^{2/3}$, $y(a) = b$ always has infinitely many solutions defined for all x. However, if $b \neq 0$

then it has a unique solution near $x = a$.

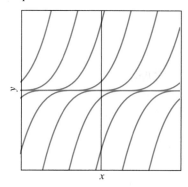

30. The initial value problem $y' = -\sqrt{1-y^2}$, $y(a) = b$ has a unique solution if $|b| < 1$; no solution if $|b| > 1$, and infinitely many solutions (defined for all x) if $b = \pm 1$.

31. The initial value problem $y' = \sqrt{1-y^2}$, $y(a) = b$ has a unique solution if $|b| < 1$; no solution if $|b| > 1$, and infinitely many solutions (defined for all x) if $b = \pm 1$.

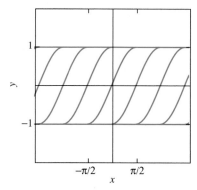

32. The initial value problem $y' = 4x\sqrt{y}$, $y(a) = b$ has infinitely many solutions (defined for all x) if $b \geq 0$; no solutions if $b < 0$. However, if $b > 0$ then it has a unique solution near $x = a$.

33. The initial value problem $x^2 y' + y^2 = 0$, $y(a) = b$ has a unique solution with initial point (a, b) if $a \neq 0$, no solution if $a = 0$ but $b \neq 0$, infinitely many solutions if $a = b = 0$.

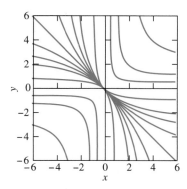

34. (a) If $y(-1) = -1.2$ then $y(1) \approx -0.48$. If $y(-1) = -0.8$ then $y(1) \approx 2.48$. (b) If $y(-3) = -3.01$ then $y(3) \approx -1.0343$. If $y(-3) = -2.99$ then $y(3) \approx 7.0343$.

35. (a) If $y(-3) = -0.2$ then $y(2) \approx 2.019$. If $y(-3) = +0.2$ then $y(2) \approx 2.022$. In either case, $y(2) \approx 2.02$.
(b) If $y(-3) \approx -0.5$ then $y(2) \approx 2.017$. If $y(-3) \approx +0.5$ then $y(2) \approx 2.024$. In either case, $y(2) \approx 2.02$.

Section 1.4

1. $y(x) = C \exp(-x^2)$

2. $y(x) = 1/(x^2 + C)$

3. $y(x) = C \exp(-\cos x)$

4. $y(x) = C(1 + x)^4$

5. $y(x) = \sin\left(C + \sqrt{x}\right)$

6. $y(x) = (x^{3/2} + C)^2$

7. $y(x) = (2x^{4/3} + C)^{3/2}$

8. $y(x) = \sin^{-1}(x^2 + C)$

9. $y(x) = C(1 + x)/(1 - x)$

10. $y(x) = (1 + x)/[1 + C(1 + x)] - 1$

11. $y(x) = (C - x^2)^{-1/2}$

12. $y^2 + 1 = Ce^{x^2}$

13. $\ln(y^4 + 1) = C + 4 \sin x$

14. $3y + 2y^{3/2} = 3x + 2x^{3/2} + C$

15. $1/(3y^3) - 2/y = 1/x + \ln|x| + C$

16. $y(x) = \sec^{-1}(C\sqrt{1 + x^2})$

17. $\ln|1 + y| = x + \frac{1}{2}x^2 + C$

18. $y(x) = \tan\left(C - \dfrac{1}{x} - x\right)$

19. $y(x) = 2 \exp(e^x)$

20. $y(x) = \tan(x^3 + \pi/4)$

21. $y^2 = 1 + \sqrt{x^2 - 16}$

22. $y(x) = -3 \exp(x^4 - x)$

23. $y(x) = \frac{1}{2}(1 + e^{2x-2})$

24. $y(x) = \frac{\pi}{2} \sin x$

25. $y(x) = x \exp(x^2 - 1)$

26. $y(x) = 1/(1 - x^2 - x^3)$

27. $y = \ln(3e^{2x} - 2)$

28. $y(x) = \tan^{-1}(\sqrt{x} - 1)$

29. (a) General solution $y(x) = -1/(x - C)$; (b) The singular solution $y(x) \equiv 0$. (c) In the following figure we see that there is a unique solution through every point of the xy- plane.

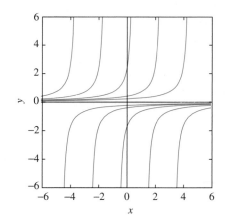

30. General solution $y(x) = (x - C)^2$; singular solution $y(x) \equiv 0$.
(a) No solution if $b < 0$; (b) Infinitely many solutions (for all x) if $b \geq 0$; (c) Two solutions near (a, b) if $b > 0$.

31. Separation of variables gives the same general solution $y = (x - C)^2$ as in Problem 30, but the restriction that $y' = 2\sqrt{y} \geq 0$ implies that only the *right halves* of the parabolas qualify as solution curves. In the figure below we see that through the point (a, b) there passes (a) No solution curve if $b < 0$, (b) a unique solution curve if $b > 0$, (c) Infinitely many solution curves if $b = 0$.

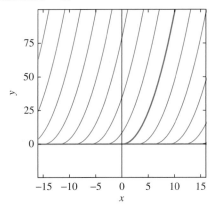

32. General solution $y(x) = \pm \sec(x - C)$; singular solutions
$y(x) \equiv \pm 1$.
(a) No solution if $|b| < 1$; (b) A unique solution if $|b| > 1$;
(c) Infinitely many solutions if $b = \pm 1$.

33. About 51840 persons   **34.** $t \approx 3.87$ hr
35. About 14735 years   **36.** Age about 686 years
37. \$21103.48   **38.** \$44.52
39. 2585 mg   **40.** About 35 years
41. About 4.86×10^9 years ago
42. About 1.25 billion years
43. After a total of about 63 min have elapsed
44. About 2.41 minutes
45. (a) 0.495 m; (b $(8.32 \times 10^{-7})I_0$; (c) 3.29 m
46. (a) About 9.60 inches; (b) About 18,200 ft
47. After about 46 days
48. About 6 billion years
49. After about 66 min 40 s
50. (a) $A(t) = 10 \cdot 3^{2t/15}$; (b) About 20.80 pu; (c) About 15.72
years
51. (a) $A(t) = 15 \cdot (\frac{2}{3})^{t/5}$; (b) approximately 7.84 su; (c) After about
33.4 months
52. About 120 thousand years ago
53. About 74 thousand years ago
54. 3 hours   **55.** 972 s
56. At time $t = 2048/1562 \approx 1.31$ (in hours)
58. 1:20 P.M.
59. (a) $y(t) = (8 - 7t)^{2/3}$; (b) at 1:08:34 P.M.;
(c) $r = \frac{1}{60}\sqrt{\frac{7}{12}} \approx 0.15$ (in.)
60. About 6 min 3 sec
61. Approximately 14 min 29 s
62. The tank is empty about 14 seconds after 2:00 P.M.
63. (a) 1:53:34 P.M.; (b) $r \approx 0.04442$ ft ≈ 0.53 in.
64. $r = \frac{1}{720}\sqrt{3}$ ft, about $\frac{1}{35}$ in.
65. At approximately 10:29 A.M.

Section 1.5

1. $y(x) = 2(1 - e^{-x})$ **2.** $y(x) = (3x + C)e^{2x}$
3. $y(x) = e^{-3x}(x^2 + C)$ **4.** $y(x) = (x + C)e^{x^2}$
5. $y(x) = x + 4x^{-2}$ **6.** $y(x) = x^2 + 32/x^5$
7. $y(x) = 5x^{1/2} + Cx^{-1/2}$ **8.** $y(x) = 3x + Cx^{-1/3}$
9. $y(x) = x(7 + \ln x)$ **10.** $y(x) = 3x^3 + Cx^{3/2}$
11. $y(x) \equiv 0$ **12.** $y(x) = \frac{1}{4}x^5 - 56x^{-3}$

13. $y(x) = (e^x + e^{-x})/2$ **14.** $y(x) = x^3 \ln x + 10x^3$
15. $y(x) = [1 - 5\exp(-x^2)]/2$
16. $y(x) = 1 + e^{-\sin x}$
17. $y(x) = (1 + \sin x)/(1 + x)$
18. $y(x) = x^2(\sin x + C)$
19. $y(x) = \frac{1}{2}\sin x + C \csc x$
20. $y(x) = -1 + \exp\left(x + \frac{1}{2}x^2\right)$
21. $y(x) = x^3 \sin x$
22. $y(x) = (x^3 + 5)e^{x^2}$
23. $y(x) = x^3(2 + Ce^{-2x})$
24. $y(x) = \frac{1}{3}[1 + 16(x^2 + 4)^{-3/2}]$
25. $y(x) = \left[\exp\left(-\frac{3}{2}x^2\right)\right]\left[3(x^2 + 1)^{3/2} - 2\right]$
26. $x(y) = 1/2y^2 + C/y^4$
27. $x(y) = e^y\left(C + \frac{1}{2}y^2\right)$
28. $x(y) = \frac{1}{2}[y + (1 + y^2)(\tan^{-1} y + C)]$
30. $y(x) = x^{1/2}\int_1^x t^{-1/2}\cos t\, dt$
29. $y(x) = \left[\exp(x^2)\right]\left[C + \frac{1}{2}\sqrt{\pi}\,\text{erf}(x)\right]$
32. (a) $y(x) = \sin x - \cos x$; (b) $y(x) = Ce^{-x} + \sin x - \cos x$;
(c) $y(x) = 2e^{-x} + \sin x - \cos x$
33. After about 7 min 41 s
34. About 22.2 days
35. About 5.5452 years
36. (a) $x(t) = (60 - t) - (60 - t)^3/3600$; (b) About 23.09 lb
37. 393.75 lb
38. (a) $x(t) = 50e^{-t/20}$; (b) $y(t) = 150e^{-t/40} - 100e^{-t/20}$;
(c) 56.25 lb
39. (b) $y_{\max} = 100e^{-1} \approx 36.79$ (gal)
41. (b) Approximately \$1,308,283
43. $-50.0529, -28.0265, -6.0000, 16.0265, 38.0529$
44. $3.99982, 4.00005, 4.00027, 4.00050, 4.00073$
45. $x(t) = 20(1 - e^{-t/10})$; $x = 10$ after $t = 10\ln 2 \approx 6.93$ months.
46. $x(t) = \frac{20}{101}(101 - 102e^{-t/10} + \cos t + 10\sin t)$; $x = 10$ after
$t = 6.47$ months.

Section 1.6

1. $x^2 - 2xy - y^2 = C$ **2.** $y^2 = x^2(\ln x + C)$
3. $y(x) = x(C + \ln |x|)^2$
4. $2\tan^{-1}(y/x) - \ln(y^2/x^2 + 1) = 2\ln x + C$
5. $\ln |xy| = C + xy^{-1}$ **6.** $2y\ln y = x + Cy$
7. $y^3 = 3x^3(C + \ln |x|)$ **8.** $y = -x\ln(C - \ln x)$
9. $y(x) = x/(C - \ln |x|)$ **10.** $x^2 + 2y^2 = Cx^6$
11. $y = C(x^2 + y^2)$
12. $4x^2 + y^2 = x^2(\ln x + C)^2$
13. $y + \sqrt{x^2 + y^2} = Cx^2$ **14.** $x - \sqrt{x^2 + y^2} = C$
15. $x^2(2xy + y^2) = C$
16. $x = 2\sqrt{x + y + 1} - 2\ln\left(1 + \sqrt{x + y + 1}\right) + C$
17. $y(x) = -4x + 2\tan(2x + C)$
18. $y = \ln(x + y + 1) + C$
19. $y^2 = x/(2 + Cx^5)$ **20.** $y^3 = 3 + Ce^{-3x^2}$
21. $y^2 = 1/(Ce^{-2x} - 1)$ **22.** $y^3 = 7x/(7Cx^7 + 15)$
23. $y(x) = (x + Cx^2)^{-3}$ **24.** $y^2 = e^{2x}/(C + \ln x)$
25. $2x^3y^3 = 3\sqrt{1 + x^4} + C$ **26.** $y^3 = e^{-x}(x + C)$
27. $y(x) = (x^4 + Cx)^{1/3}$ **28.** $y = \ln(Cx^2 + x^2e^{2x})$
29. $\sin^2 y = 4x^2 + Cx$ **30.** $x^2 - 2xe^y - e^{2y} = C$
31. $x^2 + 3xy + y^2 = C$ **32.** $2x^2 - xy + 3y^2 = C$
33. $x^3 + 2xy^2 + 2y^3 = C$ **34.** $x^3 + x^2y^2 + y^4 = C$
35. $3x^4 + 4y^3 + 12y\ln x = C$
36. $x + e^{xy} + y^2 = C$
37. $\sin x + x\ln y + e^y = C$

38. $x^2 + 2x \tan^{-1} y + \ln(1 + y^2) = C$
39. $5x^3 y^3 + 5xy^4 + y^5 = C$
40. $e^x \sin y + x \tan y = C$
41. $x^2 y^{-1} + y^2 x^{-3} + 2y^{1/2} = C$
42. $xy^{-2/3} + x^{-3/2} y = C$
43. $y(x) = Ax^2 + B$
44. $x(y) = Ay^2 + B$
45. $y(x) = A \cos 2x + B \sin 2x$
46. $y(x) = x^2 + A \ln x + B$
47. $y(x) = A - \ln |x + B|$
48. $y(x) = \ln x + Ax^{-2} + B$
49. $y(x) = \pm (A + Be^x)^{1/2}$
50. $y(x) = \ln | \sec(x + A)| - \frac{1}{2} x^2 + B$
51. $x(y) = -\frac{1}{3} (y^3 + Ay + B)$
52. $Ay^2 - (Ax + B)^2 = 1$
53. $y(x) = A \tan(Ax + B)$
54. $Ay^2 (B - x) = 1$
58. $y = \exp(x^2 + C/x^2)$
59. $x^2 - 2xy - y^2 - 2x - 6y = C$
60. $(x + 3y + 3)^5 = C(y - x - 5)$
61. $x = \tan(x - y) + \sec(x - y) + C$
64. $y(x) = x + e^{-x^2} \left[C + \frac{1}{2} \sqrt{\pi} \operatorname{erf}(x) \right]^{-1}$
65. $y(x) = x + (C - x)^{-1}$
69. Approximately 3.68 mi

Chapter 1 Review Problems

1. Linear: $y(x) = x^3 (C + \ln x)$
2. Separable: $y(x) = x/(3 - Cx - x \ln x)$
3. Homogeneous: $y(x) = x/(C - \ln x)$
4. Exact: $x^2 y^3 + e^x - \cos y = C$
5. Separable: $y(x) = C \exp(x^{-3} - x^{-2})$
6. Separable: $y(x) = x/(1 + Cx + 2x \ln x)$
7. Linear: $y(x) = x^{-2} (C + \ln x)$
8. Homogeneous: $y(x) = 3Cx/(C - x^3) = 3x/(1 + Kx^3)$
9. Bernoulli: $y(x) = (x^2 + Cx^{-1})^2$
10. Separable: $y(x) = \tan \left(C + x + \frac{1}{3} x^3 \right)$
11. Homogeneous: $y(x) = x/(C - 3 \ln x)$
12. Exact: $3x^2 y^3 + 2xy^4 = C$
13. Separable: $y(x) = 1/(C + 2x^2 - x^5)$
14. Homogeneous: $y^2 = x^2/(C + 2 \ln x)$
15. Linear: $y(x) = (x^3 + C)e^{-3x}$
16. Substitution: $v = y - x$; solution: $y - x - 1 = Ce^{2x}(y - x + 1)$
17. Exact: $e^x + e^y + e^{xy} = C$
18. Homogeneous: $y^2 = Cx^2(x^2 - y^2)$
19. Separable: $y(x) = x^2/(x^5 + Cx^2 + 1)$
20. Linear: $y(x) = 2x^{-3/2} + Cx^{-3}$
21. Linear: $y(x) = [C + \ln(x - 1)]/(x + 1)$
22. Bernoulli: $y(x) = (2x^4 + Cx^2)^3$
23. Exact: $xe^y + y \sin x = C$
24. Separable: $y(x) = x^{1/2}/(6x^2 + Cx^{1/2} + 2)$
25. Linear: $y(x) = (x + 1)^{-2}(x^3 + 3x^2 + 3x + C)$
$= x + 1 + K(x + 1)^{-2}$
26. Exact: $3x^{3/2} y^{4/3} - 5x^{6/5} y^{3/2} = C$
27. Bernoulli: $y(x) = x^{-1}(C + \ln x)^{-1/3}$
28. Linear: $y(x) = x^{-1}(C + e^{2x})$
29. Linear: $y(x) = (x^2 + x + C)(2x + 1)^{-1/2}$
30. Substitution: $v = x + y$; solution:
$x = 2(x + y)^{1/2} - 2 \ln[1 + (x + y)^{1/2}] + C$
31. Separable and linear

32. Separable and Bernoulli
33. Exact and homogeneous
34. Exact and homogeneous
35. Separable and linear
36. Separable and Bernoulli

Chapter 2

Section 2.1

1. $x(t) = \dfrac{2}{2 - e^{-t}}$

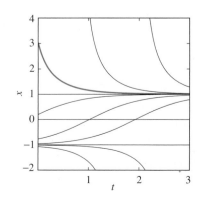

2. $x(t) = \dfrac{10}{1 + 9e^{-10t}}$

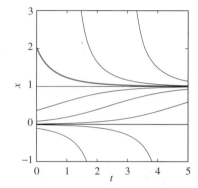

3. $x(t) = \dfrac{2 + e^{-2t}}{2 - e^{-2t}}$

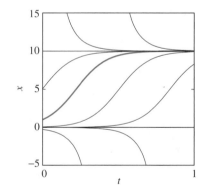

4. $x(t) = \dfrac{3(1 - e^{-12t})}{2(1 + e^{-12t})}$

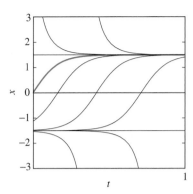

5. $x(t) = \dfrac{40}{8 - 3e^{-15t}}$

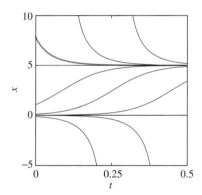

6. $x(t) = \dfrac{10}{2 + 3e^{15t}}$

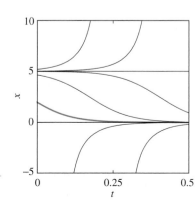

7. $x(t) = \dfrac{77}{11 - 4e^{-28t}}$

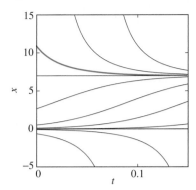

8. $x(t) = \dfrac{221}{17 - 4e^{91t}}$

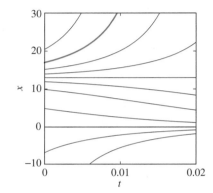

9. 484   **10.** 20 weeks

11. (b) $P(t) = \left(\frac{1}{2}t + 10\right)^2$

12. $P(t) = \dfrac{240}{20 - t}$

13. $P(t) = \dfrac{180}{30 - t}$

14. $P(t) = \dfrac{P_0}{1 + kP_0 t}$

16. About 27.69 months 17. About 44.22 months

19. About 24.41 months

20. About 42.12 months

21. $\dfrac{200}{1 + e^{-6/5}} \approx 153.7$ million

22. About 34.66 days

23. (a) $\lim\limits_{t \to \infty} x(t) = 200$ grams   (b) $\frac{5}{4} \ln 3 \approx 1.37$ seconds

24. About 9.24 days

25. (a) $M = 100$ and $k = 0.0002$; (b) In the year 2035

26. $50 \ln \frac{9}{8} \approx 5.89$ months

27. (a) $100 \ln \frac{9}{5} \approx 58.78$ months; (b) $100 \ln 2 \approx 69.31$ months

28. (a) The alligators eventually die out. (b) Doomsday occurs after about 9 years 2 months.

29. (a) $P(140) \approx 127.008$ million; (b) About 210.544 million; (c) In 2000 we get $P \approx 196.169$, whereas the actual 2000 population was about 281.422 million.

31. $\alpha \approx 0.3915$; 2.15×10^6 cells

37. $k \approx 0.0000668717$, $M \approx 338.027$

38. $k \approx 0.000146679$, $M \approx 208.250$

39. $P(t) = P_0 \exp\left(kt + \dfrac{b}{2\pi}\sin 2\pi t\right)$; the colored curve in the figure below shows the graph with $P_0 = 100$, $k = 0.03$, and $b = 0.06$. It oscillates about the black curve which represents natural growth with $P_0 = 100$ and $k = 0.03$. We see that the two agree at the end of each full year.

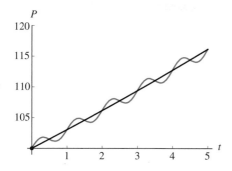

3. Stable critical point: $x = 0$; unstable critical point: $x = 4$;

$$x(t) = \frac{4x_0}{x_0 + (4 - x_0)e^{4t}}$$

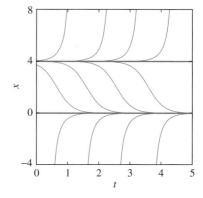

4. Stable critical point: $x = 3$; unstable critical point: $x = 0$;

$$x(t) = \frac{3x_0}{x_0 + (3 - x_0)e^{-3t}}$$

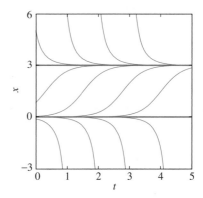

Section 2.2

1. Unstable critical point: $x = 4$;

$$x(t) = 4 + (x_0 - 4)e^t$$

5. Stable critical point: $x = -2$; unstable critical point: $x = 2$;

$$x(t) = \frac{2[x_0 + 2 + (x_0 - 2)e^{4t}]}{x_0 + 2 - (x_0 - 2)e^{4t}}$$

2. Stable critical point: $x = 3$;

$$x(t) = 3 + (x_0 - 3)e^{-t}$$

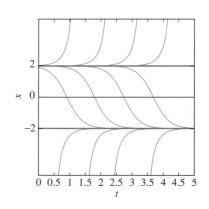

6. Stable critical point: $x = 3$; unstable critical point: $x = -3$;

$$x(t) = \frac{3[x_0 - 3 + (x_0 + 3)e^{6t}]}{3 - x_0 + (x_0 + 3)e^{6t}}$$

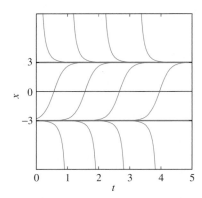

9. Stable critical point: $x = 1$; unstable critical point: $x = 4$;

$$x(t) = \frac{4(1 - x_0) + (x_0 - 4)e^{3t}}{1 - x_0 + (x_0 - 4)e^{3t}}$$

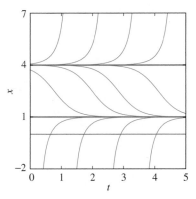

7. Semi-stable (see Problem 18) critical point: $x = 2$;

$$x(t) = \frac{(2t - 1)x_0 - 4t}{tx_0 - 2t - 1}$$

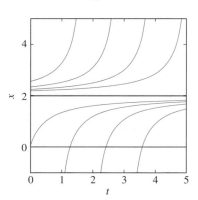

10. Stable critical point: $x = 5$; unstable critical point: $x = 2$;

$$x(t) = \frac{2(5 - x_0) + 5(x_0 - 2)e^{3t}}{5 - x_0 + (x_0 - 2)e^{3t}}$$

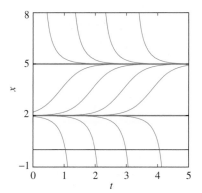

8. Semi-stable critical point: $x = 3$;

$$x(t) = \frac{(3t + 1)x_0 - 9t}{tx_0 - 3t + 1}$$

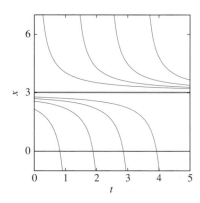

11. Unstable critical point: $x = 1$;

$$\frac{1}{(x(t) - 1)^2} = \frac{1}{(x_0 - 1)^2} - 2t$$

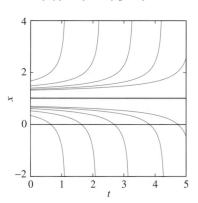

12. Stable critical point: $x = 2$;

$$\frac{1}{(2 - x(t))^2} = \frac{1}{(2 - x_0)^2} + 2t$$

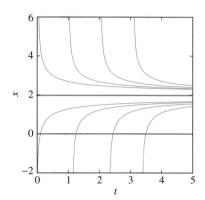

For each of Problems 13 through 18 we show a plot of slope field and typical solution curves. The equilibrium solutions of the given differential equation are labeled, and the stability or instability of each should be clear from the picture.

13.

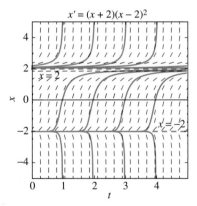

$x' = (x + 2)(x - 2)^2$

14.

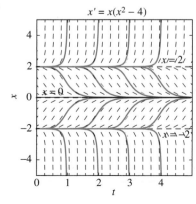

$x' = x(x^2 - 4)$

15.

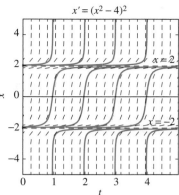

$x' = (x^2 - 4)^2$

16.

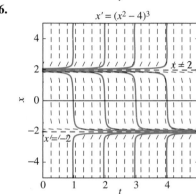

$x' = (x^2 - 4)^3$

17.

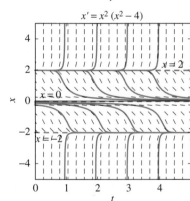

$x' = x^2 (x^2 - 4)$

18.

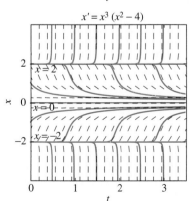

$x' = x^3 (x^2 - 4)$

19. There are two critical points if $h < 2\frac{1}{2}$, one critical point if $h = 2\frac{1}{2}$, and no critical points if $h > 2\frac{1}{2}$. The bifurcation diagram is the parabola $(c - 5)^2 = 25 - 10h$ in the hc-plane.

20. There are two critical points if $s < \frac{1}{16}$, one critical point if $s = \frac{1}{16}$, and no critical points if $s > \frac{1}{16}$. The bifurcation diagram is the parabola $(2c - 5)^2 = 25(1 - 16s)$ in the sc-plane.

Section 2.3

1. Approximately 31.5 s
3. $400/(\ln 2) \approx 577$ ft
5. $400 \ln 7 \approx 778$ ft
7. (a) 100 ft/sec; (b) about 23 sec and 1403 ft to reach 90 ft/sec
8. (a) 100 ft/sec; (b) about 14.7 sec and 830 ft to reach 90 ft/sec
9. 50 ft/s
10. About 5 min 47 s
11. Time of fall: about 12.5 s
12. Approximately 648 ft
19. Approximately 30.46 ft/s; exactly 40 ft/s
20. Approximately 277.26 ft
22. Approximately 20.67 ft/s; about 484.57 s
23. Approximately 259.304 s
24. (a) About 0.88 cm; (b) about 2.91 km
25. (b) About 1.389 km/sec; (c) $r_{max} = 100R/19 \approx 5.26R$
26. Yes
28. (b) After about $8\frac{1}{2}$ minutes it hits the surface at about 4.116 km/sec.
29. About 51.427 km
30. Approximately 11.11 km/sec (as compared with the earth's escape velocity of about 11.18 km/sec).

Section 2.4

In Problems 1 through 10 we round off the indicated values to 3 decimal places.

1. Approximate values 1.125 and 1.181; true value 1.213
2. Approximate values 1.125 and 1.244; true value 1.359
3. Approximate values 2.125 and 2.221; true value 2.297
4. Approximate values 0.625 and 0.681; true value 0.713
5. Approximate values 0.938 and 0.889; true value 0.851
6. Approximate values 1.750 and 1.627; true value 1.558
7. Approximate values 2.859 and 2.737; true value 2.647
8. Approximate values 0.445 and 0.420; true value 0.405
9. Approximate values 1.267 and 1.278; true value 1.287
10. Approximate values 1.125 and 1.231; true value 1.333

Problems 11 through 24 call for tables of values that would occupy too much space for inclusion here. In Problems 11 through 16 we give first the final x-value, next the corresponding approximate y-values obtained with step sizes $h = 0.01$ and $h = 0.005$, and then the final true y-value. (All y-values rounded off accurate to 4 decimal places.)

11. 1.0, −0.7048, −0.7115, −0.7183
12. 1.0, 2.9864, 2.9931, 3.0000
13. 2.0, 4.8890, 4.8940, 4.8990
14. 2.0, 3.2031, 3.2304, 3.2589
15. 3.0, 3.4422, 3.4433, 3.4444
16. 3.0, 8.8440, 8.8445, 8.8451

In Problems 17 through 24 we give first the final x-value and then the corresponding approximate y-values obtained with step sizes $h = 0.1, h = 0.02, h = 0.004$, and $h = 0.0008$ respectively. (All y-values rounded off accurate to 4 decimal places.)

17. 1.0, 0.2925, 0.3379, 0.3477, 0.3497
18. 2.0, 1.6680, 1.6771, 1.6790, 1.6794
19. 2.0, 6.1831, 6.3653, 6.4022, 6.4096

20. 2.0, −1.3792, −1.2843, −1.2649, −1.2610

21. 2.0, 2.8508, 2.8681, 2.8716, 2.8723

22. 2.0, 6.9879, 7.2601, 7.3154, 7.3264

23. 1.0, 1.2262, 1.2300, 1.2306, 1.2307

24. 1.0, 0.9585, 0.9918, 0.9984, 0.9997

25. With both step sizes $h = 0.01$ and $h = 0.005$, the approximate velocity after 1 second is 16.0 ft/sec (80% of the limiting velocity of 20 ft/sec); after 2 seconds it is 19.2 ft/sec (96% of the limiting velocity).

26. With both step sizes $h = 1$ and $h = 0.5$, the approximate population after 5 years is 49 deer (65% of the limiting population of 75 deer); after 10 years it is 66 deer (88% of the limiting population).

27. With successive step sizes $h = 0.1, 0.01, 0.001, \ldots$ the first four approximations to $y(2)$ we obtain are 0.7772, 0.9777, 1.0017, and 1.0042. It therefore seems likely that $y(2) \approx 1.00$.

28. With successive step sizes $h = 0.1, 0.01, 0.001, \ldots$ the first four approximations to $y(2)$ we obtain are 1.2900, 1.4435, 1.4613, and 1.4631. It therefore seems likely that $y(2) \approx 1.46$.

29.

x	$h = 0.15$ y	$h = 0.03$ y	$h = 0.006$ y
−1.0	1.0000	1.0000	1.0000
−0.7	1.0472	1.0512	1.0521
−0.4	1.1213	1.1358	1.1390
−0.1	1.2826	1.3612	1.3835
0.2	0.8900	1.4711	0.8210
0.5	0.7460	1.2808	0.7192

30.

x	$h = 0.1$ y	$h = 0.01$ y
1.8	2.8200	4.3308
1.9	3.9393	7.9425
2.0	5.8521	28.3926

31.

x	$h = 0.1$ y	$h = 0.01$ y
0.7	4.3460	6.4643
0.8	5.8670	11.8425
0.9	8.3349	39.5010

Section 2.5

1.

x	Improved Euler y	Actual y
0.1	1.8100	1.8097
0.2	1.6381	1.6375
0.3	1.4824	1.4816
0.4	1.3416	1.3406
0.5	1.2142	1.2131

Note: In Problems 2 through 10, we give the value of x, the corresponding improved Euler value of y, and the true value of y.

2. 0.5, 1.3514, 1.3191
3. 0.5, 2.2949, 2.2974
4. 0.5, 0.7142, 0.7131
5. 0.5, 0.8526, 0.8513
6. 0.5, 1.5575, 1.5576
7. 0.5, 2.6405, 2.6475
8. 0.5, 0.4053, 0.4055
9. 0.5, 1.2873, 1.2874
10. 0.5, 1.3309, 1.3333

In Problems 11 through 16 we give the final value of x, the corresponding values of y with $h = 0.01$ and with $h = 0.005$, and the true value of y.

11. 1.0, -0.71824, -0.71827, -0.71828
12. 1.0, 2.99995, 2.99999, 3.00000
13. 2.0, 4.89901, 4.89899, 4.89898
14. 2.0, 3.25847, 3.25878, 3.25889
15. 3.0, 3.44445, 3.44445, 3.44444
16. 3.0, 8.84511, 8.84509, 8.84509

In Problems 17 through 24 we give the final value of x and the corresponding values of y for $h = 0.1, 0.02, 0.004$, and 0.0008.

17. 1.0, 0.35183, 0.35030, 0.35023, 0.35023
18. 2.0, 1.68043, 1.67949, 1.67946, 1.67946
19. 2.0, 6.40834, 6.41134, 6.41147, 6.41147
20. 2.0, -1.26092, -1.26003, -1.25999, -1.25999
21. 2.0, 2.87204, 2.87245, 2.87247, 2.87247
22. 2.0, 7.31578, 7.32841, 7.32916, 7.32920
23. 1.0, 1.22967, 1.23069, 1.23073, 1.23073
24. 1.0, 1.00006, 1.00000, 1.00000, 1.00000
25. With both step sizes $h = 0.01$ and $h = 0.005$ the approximate velocity after 1 second is 15.962 ft/sec (80% of the limiting velocity of 20 ft/sec); after 2 seconds it is 19.185 ft/sec (96% of the limiting velocity).
26. With both step sizes $h = 1$ and $h = 0.5$ the approximate population after 5 years is 49.391 deer (65% of the limiting population of 75 deer); after 10 seconds it is 66.113 deer (88% of the limiting population).
27. With successive step sizes $h = 0.1, 0.01, 0.001, \ldots$ the first three approximations to $y(2)$ we obtain are 1.0109, 1.0045, and 1.0045. It therefore seems likely that $y(2) \approx 1.0045$.
28. With successive step sizes $h = 0.1, 0.01, 0.001, \ldots$ the first four approximations to $y(2)$ we obtain are 1.4662, 1.4634, 1.4633, and 1.4633. It therefore seems likely that $y(2) \approx 1.4633$.
29. Impact speed approximately 43.22 m/s
30. Impact speed approximately 43.48 m/s

Section 2.6

1. $y(0.25) \approx 1.55762$; $y(0.25) = 1.55760$.
$y(0.5) \approx 1.21309$; $y(0.5) = 1.21306$.
Solution: $y = 2e^{-x}$

In Problems 2 through 10 we give the approximation to $y(0.5)$, its true value, and the solution.

2. 1.35867, 1.35914; $y = \frac{1}{2}e^{2x}$
3. 2.29740, 2.29744; $y = 2e^x - 1$
4. 0.71309, 0.71306; $y = 2e^{-x} + x - 1$
5. 0.85130, 0.85128; $y = -e^x + x + 2$
6. 1.55759, 1.55760; $u = 2\exp\left(-x^2\right)$
7. 2.64745, 2.64749; $y = 3\exp\left(-x^3\right)$
8. 0.40547, 0.40547; $y = \ln(x + 1)$
9. 1.28743, 1.28743; $y = \tan\frac{1}{4}(x + \pi)$
10. 1.33337, 1.33333; $y = (1 - x^2)^{-1}$
11. *Solution*: $y(x) = 2 - e^x$.

x	h = 0.2 y	h = 0.1 y	Exact y
0.0	1.00000	1.00000	1.00000
0.2	0.77860	0.77860	0.77860
0.4	0.50818	0.50818	0.50818
0.6	0.17789	0.17788	0.17788
0.8	-0.22552	-0.22554	-0.22554
1.0	-0.71825	-0.71828	-0.71828

In Problems 12 through 16 we give the final value of x, the corresponding Runge-Kutta approximations with $h = 0.2$ and with $h = 0.1$, the exact value of y, and the solution.

12. 1.0, 2.99996, 3.00000, 3.00000;
$y = 1 + 2/(2 - x)$
13. 2.0, 4.89900, 4.89898, 4.89898;
$y = \sqrt{8 + x^4}$
14. 2.0, 3.25795, 3.25882, 3.25889;
$y = 1/(1 - \ln x)$
15. 3.0, 3.44445, 3.44444, 3.44444;
$y = x + 4x^{-2}$
16. 3.0, 8.84515, 8.84509, 8.84509;
$y = (x^6 - 37)^{1/3}$

In Problems 17 through 24 we give the final value of x and the corresponding values of y with $h = 0.2, 0.1, 0.05$, and 0.025.

17. 1.0, 0.350258, 0.350234, 0.350232, 0.350232
18. 2.0, 1.679513, 1.679461, 1.679459, 1.679459
19. 2.0, 6.411464, 6.411474, 6.411474, 6.411474
20. 2.0, -1.259990, -1.259992, -1.259993, -1.259993
21. 2.0, 2.872467, 2.872468, 2.872468, 2.872468
22. 2.0, 7.326761, 7.328452, 7.328971, 7.329134
23. 1.0, 1.230735, 1.230731, 1.230731, 1.230731
24. 1.0, 1.000000, 1.000000, 1.000000, 1.000000
25. With both step sizes $h = 0.1$ and $h = 0.05$, the approximate velocity after 1 second is 15.962 ft/sec (80% of the limiting velocity of 20 ft/sec); after 2 seconds it is 19.185 ft/sec (96% of the limiting velocity).

26. With both step sizes $h = 6$ and $h = 3$, the approximate population after 5 years is 49.3915 deer (65% of the limiting population of 75 deer); after 10 years it is 66.1136 deer (88% of the limiting population).

27. With successive step sizes $h = 1, 0.1, 0.01, \ldots$ the first four approximations to $y(2)$ we obtain are 1.05722, 1.00447, 1.00445and 1.00445. Thus it seems likely that $y(2) \approx 1.00445$ accurate to 5 decimal places.

28. With successive step sizes $h = 1, 0.1, 0.01, \ldots$ the first four approximations to $y(2)$ we obtain are 1.48990, 1.46332, 1.46331, and 1.46331. Thus it seems likely that $y(2) \approx 1.4633$ accurate to 5 decimal places.

29. Time aloft: approximately 9.41 seconds

30. Time aloft: approximately 9.41 seconds

Chapter 3

Section 3.1

1. $y(x) = \frac{5}{2}e^x - \frac{5}{2}e^{-x}$

2. $y(x) = 2e^{3x} - 3e^{-3x}$

3. $y(x) = 3\cos 2x + 4\sin 2x$

4. $y(x) = 10\cos 5x - 2\sin 5x$

5. $y(x) = 2e^x - e^{2x}$

6. $y(x) = 4e^{2x} + 3e^{-3x}$

7. $y(x) = 6 - 8e^{-x}$

8. $y(x) = \frac{1}{3}(14 - 2e^{3x})$

9. $y(x) = 2e^{-x} + xe^{-x}$

10. $y(x) = 3e^{5x} - 2xe^{5x}$

11. $y(x) = 5e^x \sin x$

12. $y(x) = e^{-3x}(2\cos 2x + 3\sin 2x)$

13. $y(x) = 5x - 2x^2$

14. $y(x) = 3x^2 - 16/x^3$

15. $y(x) = 7x - 5x \ln x$

16. $y(x) = 2\cos(\ln x) + 3\sin(\ln x)$

21. Linearly independent

22. Linearly independent

23. Linearly independent

24. Linearly dependent

25. Linearly independent

26. Linearly independent

28. $y(x) = 1 - 2\cos x - \sin x$

29. There is no contradiction because if the given differential equation is divided by x^2 to get the form in Eq. (8), then the resulting coefficient functions $p(x) = -4/x$ and $q(x) = 6/x^2$ are not continuous at $x = 0$.

33. $y(x) = c_1 e^x + c_2 e^{2x}$

34. $y(x) = c_1 e^{-5x} + c_2 e^{3x}$

35. $y(x) = c_1 + c_2 e^{-5x}$

36. $y(x) = c_1 + c_2 e^{-3x/2}$

37. $y(x) = c_1 e^{-x/2} + c_2 e^x$

38. $y(x) = c_1 e^{-x/2} + c_2 e^{-3x/2}$

39. $y(x) = (c_1 + c_2 x)e^{-x/2}$

40. $y(x) = (c_1 + c_2 x)e^{2x/3}$

41. $y(x) = c_1 e^{-4x/3} + c_2 e^{5x/2}$

42. $y(x) = c_1 e^{-4x/7} + c_2 e^{3x/5}$

43. $y'' + 10y' = 0$

44. $y'' - 100y = 0$

45. $y'' + 20y' + 100y = 0$

46. $y'' - 110y' + 1000y = 0$

47. $y'' = 0$

48. $y'' - 2y' - y = 0$

49. The high point is $\left(\ln \frac{7}{4}, \frac{16}{7}\right)$.

50. $(-\ln 2, -2)$

52. $y(x) = c_1 x + c_2/x$

53. $y(x) = c_1 x^{-4} + c_2 x^3$

54. $y(x) = c_1 x^{-3/2} + c_2 x^{1/2}$

55. $y(x) = c_1 + c_2 \ln x$

56. $y(x) = x^2(c_1 + c_2 \ln x)$

Section 3.2

1. $15 \cdot (2x) - 16 \cdot (3x^2) - 6 \cdot (5x - 8x^2) \equiv 0$

2. $(-4)(5) + (5)(2 - 3x^2) + (1)(10 + 15x^2) \equiv 0$

3. $1 \cdot 0 + 0 \cdot \sin x + 0 \cdot e^x \equiv 0$

4. $(6)(17) + (-51)(2\sin^2 x) + (-34)(3\cos^2 x) \equiv 0$

5. $1 \cdot 17 - 34 \cdot \cos^2 x + 17 \cdot \cos 2x \equiv 0$

6. $(-1)(e^x) + (1)(\cosh x) + (1)(\sinh x) \equiv 0$

13. $y(x) = \frac{4}{3}e^x - \frac{1}{3}e^{-2x}$

14. $y(x) = \frac{1}{2}(3e^x - 6e^{2x} + 3e^{3x})$

15. $y(x) = (2 - 2x + x^2)e^x$

16. $y(x) = -12e^x + 13e^{2x} - 10xe^{2x}$

17. $y(x) = \frac{1}{9}(29 - 2\cos 3x - 3\sin 3x)$

18. $y(x) = e^x(2 - \cos x - \sin x)$

19. $y(x) = x + 2x^2 + 3x^3$

20. $y(x) = 2x - x^{-2} + x^{-2}\ln x$

21. $y(x) = 2\cos x - 5\sin x + 3x$

22. $y(x) = 4e^{2x} - e^{-2x} - 3$

23. $y(x) = e^{-x} + 4e^{3x} - 2$

24. $y(x) = e^x(3\cos x + 4\sin x) + x + 1$

38. $y_2(x) = \dfrac{1}{x^3}$

39. $y_2(x) = xe^{x/2}$

40. $y_2(x) = xe^x$

41. $y_2(x) = x + 2$

42. $y_2(x) = 1 + x^2$

Section 3.3

1. $y(x) = c_1 e^{2x} + c_2 e^{-2x}$

2. $y(x) = c_1 + c_2 e^{3x/2}$

3. $y(x) = c_1 e^{2x} + c_2 e^{-5x}$

4. $y(x) = c_1 e^{x/2} + c_2 e^{3x}$

5. $y(x) = c_1 e^{-3x} + c_2 xe^{-3x}$

6. $y(x) = e^{-5x/2}\left[c_1 \exp\left(\frac{1}{2}x\sqrt{5}\right) + c_2 \exp\left(-\frac{1}{2}x\sqrt{5}\right)\right]$

7. $y(x) = c_1 e^{3x/2} + c_2 xe^{3x/2}$

8. $y(x) = e^{3x}(c_1 \cos 2x + c_2 \sin 2x)$

9. $y(x) = e^{-4x}(c_1 \cos 3x + c_2 \sin 3x)$

10. $y(x) = c_1 + c_2 x + c_3 x^2 + c_4 e^{-3x/5}$

11. $y(x) = c_1 + c_2 x + c_3 e^{4x} + c_4 xe^{4x}$

12. $y(x) = c_1 + c_2 e^x + c_3 xe^x + c_4 x^2 e^x$

13. $y(x) = c_1 + c_2 e^{-2x/3} + c_3 xe^{-2x/3}$

14. $y(x) = c_1 e^x + c_2 e^{-x} + c_3 \cos 2x + c_4 \sin 2x$

15. $y(x) = c_1 e^{2x} + c_2 xe^{2x} + c_3 e^{-2x} + c_4 xe^{-2x}$

16. $y(x) = (c_1 + c_2 x)\cos 3x + (c_3 + c_4 x)\sin 3x$

17. $y(x) = c_1 \cos\left(x/\sqrt{2}\right) + c_2 \sin\left(x/\sqrt{2}\right) + c_3 \cos\left(2x/\sqrt{3}\right) + c_4 \sin\left(2x/\sqrt{3}\right)$

18. $y(x) = c_1 e^{2x} + c_2 e^{-2x} + c_3 \cos 2x + c_4 \sin 2x$

19. $y(x) = c_1 e^x + c_2 e^{-x} + c_3 xe^{-x}$

20. $y(x) = e^{-x/2}\left[(c_1 + c_2 x)\cos\left(\frac{1}{2}x\sqrt{3}\right) + (c_3 + c_3 x)\sin\left(\frac{1}{2}x\sqrt{3}\right)\right]$

21. $y(x) = 5e^x + 2e^{3x}$

22. $y(x) = e^{-x/3}\left[3\cos\left(x/\sqrt{3}\right) + 5\sqrt{3}\sin\left(x/\sqrt{3}\right)\right]$

23. $y(x) = e^{3x}(3\cos 4x - 2\sin 4x)$

24. $y(x) = \frac{1}{2}(-7 + e^{2x} + 8e^{-x/2})$

25. $y(x) = \frac{1}{4}(-13 + 6x + 9e^{-2x/3})$

26. $y(x) = \frac{1}{5}(24 - 9e^{-5x} - 25xe^{-5x})$

27. $y(x) = c_1 e^x + c_2 e^{-2x} + c_3 xe^{-2x}$

28. $y(x) = c_1 e^{2x} + c_2 e^{-x} + c_3 e^{-x/2}$

29. $y(x) = c_1 e^{-3x} + e^{3x/2}\left[c_2 \cos\left(\frac{3}{2}x\sqrt{3}\right) + c_3 \sin\left(\frac{3}{2}x\sqrt{3}\right)\right]$

30. $y(x) = c_1 e^{-x} + c_2 e^{2x} + c_3 \cos(x\sqrt{3}) + c_4 \sin(x\sqrt{3})$

31. $y(x) = c_1 e^x + e^{-2x}(c_2 \cos 2x + c_3 \sin 2x)$

32. $y(x) = c_1 e^{2x} + (c_2 + c_3 x + c_4 x^2)e^{-x}$

33. $y(x) = c_1 e^{3x} + e^{-3x}(c_2 \cos 3x + c_3 \sin 3x)$

34. $y(x) = c_1 e^{2x/3} + c_2 \cos 2x + c_3 \sin 2x$

35. $y(x) = c_1 e^{-x/2} + c_2 e^{-x/3} + c_3 \cos 2x + c_4 \sin 2x$

36. $y(x) = c_1 e^{7x/9} + e^{-x}(c_2 \cos x + c_3 \sin x)$

37. $y(x) = 11 + 5x + 3x^2 + 7e^x$

38. $y(x) = 2e^{5x} - 2\cos 10x$

39. $y^{(3)} - 6y'' + 12y' - 8y = 0$

40. $y^{(3)} - 2y'' + 4y' - 8y = 0$

41. $y^{(4)} - 16y = 0$

42. $y^{(6)} + 12y^{(4)} + 48y'' + 64y = 0$

44. (a) $x = i, -2i$ (b) $x = -i, 3i$

45. $y(x) = c_1 e^{-ix} + c_2 e^{3ix}$

46. $y(x) = c_1 e^{3ix} + c_2 e^{-2ix}$

47. $y(x) = c_1 \exp\left(\left[1 + i\sqrt{3}\right]x\right) + c_2 \exp\left(-\left[1 + i\sqrt{3}\right]x\right)$

48. $y(x) =$
$\frac{1}{3}\left(e^x + \exp\left[\frac{1}{2}\left(-1 + i\sqrt{3}\right)x\right] + \exp\left[\frac{1}{2}\left(-1 - i\sqrt{3}\right)x\right]\right)$

49. $y(x) = 2e^{2x} - 5e^{-x} + 3\cos x - 9\sin x$

52. $y(x) = c_1 \cos(3\ln x) + c_2 \sin(3\ln x)$

53. $y(x) = x^{-3}[c_1 \cos(4\ln x) + c_2 \sin(4\ln x)]$

54. $y(x) = c_1 + c_2 \ln x + c_3 x^{-3}$

55. $y(x) = c_1 + x^2(c_2 + c_3 \ln x)$

56. $y(x) = c_1 + c_2 \ln x + c_3(\ln x)^2$

57. $y(x) = c_1 + x^3\left(c_2 x^{-\sqrt{3}} + c_3 x^{+\sqrt{3}}\right)$

58. $y(x) = x^{-1}[c_1 + c_2 \ln x + c_3(\ln x)^2]$

Section 3.4

1. Frequency: 2 rad/s $(1/\pi$ Hz); period: π s

2. Frequency: 8 rad/sec $(4/\pi$ Hz); period: $\pi/4$ sec

3. Amplitude: 2 m; frequency: 5 rad/s; period: $2\pi/5$ s

4. (a) $x(t) = \frac{13}{12}\cos(12t - \alpha)$ with $\alpha = 2\pi - \tan^{-1}(5/12) \approx 5.8884$; (b) Amplitude: $\frac{13}{12}$ m; period: $\pi/6$ sec

6. About 7.33 mi

7. About 10450 ft

8. 29.59 in.

10. Amplitude: 100 cm; period: about 2.01 sec

11. About 3.8 in.

13. (a) $x(t) = 50(e^{-2t/5} - e^{-t/2})$; (b) 4.096 exactly

14. (a) $x(t) = 25e^{-t/5}\cos(3t - \alpha)$ with $\alpha = \tan^{-1}(3/4) \approx 0.6435$; (b) envelope curves $x = \pm 25e^{-t/5}$; pseudoperiod $2\pi/3$

15. $x(t) = 4e^{-2t} - 2e^{-4t}$, overdamped; $u(t) = 2\cos(2\sqrt{2}t)$

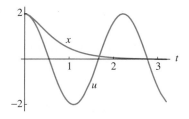

16. $x(t) = 4e^{-3t} - 2e^{-7t}$, overdamped; $u(t) \approx 2\sqrt{\frac{22}{21}}\cos(\sqrt{21}\,t - 0.2149)$

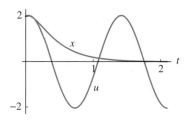

17. $x(t) = 5e^{-4t}(2t + 1)$, critically damped; $u(t) \approx \frac{5}{2}\sqrt{5}\cos(4t - 5.8195)$

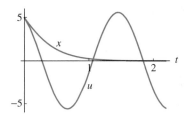

18. $x(t) = 2e^{-3t}\cos\left(4t - \frac{3\pi}{2}\right)$, underdamped; $u(t) = \frac{8}{5}\cos\left(5t - \frac{3\pi}{2}\right)$

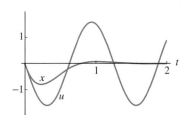

19. $x(t) \approx \frac{1}{3}\sqrt{313}\,e^{-5t/2}\cos(6t - 0.8254)$, underdamped; $u(t) \approx \frac{4}{13}\sqrt{233}\cos\left(\frac{13}{2}t - 0.5517\right)$

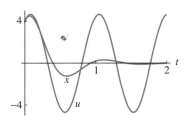

20. $x(t) \approx 13e^{-4t}\cos(2t - 1.1760)$, underdamped; $u(t) \approx \sqrt{\frac{129}{5}}\cos(2\sqrt{5}\,t - 0.1770)$

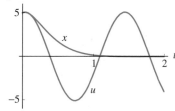

21. $x(t) \approx 10e^{-5t} \cos(10t - 0.9273)$, underdamped;
$u(t) \approx 2\sqrt{14} \cos(5\sqrt{5}\,t - 0.6405)$

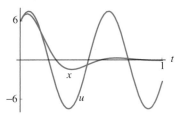

22. (b) The time-varying amplitude is $\frac{2}{3}\sqrt{3}$, the frequency is $4\sqrt{3}$ rad/s, and the phase angle is $\pi/6$.

23. (a) $k \approx 7018$ lb/ft; (b) After about 2.47 s

34. Damping constant: $c \approx 11.51$ lb/ft/s; spring constant: $k \approx 189.68$ lb/ft

Section 3.5

1. $y_p(x) = \frac{1}{25}e^{3x}$

2. $y_p(x) = -\frac{1}{4}(5 + 6x)$

3. $y_p(x) = \frac{1}{39}(\cos 3x - 5 \sin 3x)$

4. $y_p(x) = \frac{1}{9}(-4e^x + 3xe^x)$

5. $y_p(x) = \frac{1}{26}(13 + 3\cos 2x - 2\sin 2x)$

6. $y_p(x) = \frac{1}{343}(4 - 56x + 49x^2)$

7. $y_p(x) = -\frac{1}{6}(e^x - e^{-x}) = -\frac{1}{3}\sinh x$

8. $y_p(x) = \frac{1}{4}x \sinh 2x$

9. $y_p(x) = -\frac{1}{3} + \frac{1}{16}(2x^2 - x)e^x$

10. $y_p(x) = \frac{1}{6}(2x \sin 3x - 3x \cos 3x)$

11. $y_p(x) = \frac{1}{8}(3x^2 - 2x)$

12. $y_p(x) = 2x + \frac{1}{2}x \sin x$

13. $y_p(x) = \frac{1}{65}e^x(7 \sin x - 4 \cos x)$

14. $y_p(x) = \frac{1}{24}(-3x^2 e^x + x^3 e^x)$

15. $y_p(x) \equiv -17$

16. $y_p(x) = \frac{1}{81}(45 + e^{3x} - 6xe^{3x} + 9x^2 e^{3x})$

17. $y_p(x) = \frac{1}{4}(x^2 \sin x - x \cos x)$

18. $y_p(x) = -\frac{1}{144}(24xe^x - 19xe^{2x} + 6x^2 e^{2x})$

19. $y_p(x) = \frac{1}{8}(10x^2 - 4x^3 + x^4)$

20. $y_p(x) = -7 + \frac{1}{3}xe^x$

21. $y_p(x) = xe^x(A \cos x + B \sin x)$

22. $y_p(x) = Ax^3 + Bx^4 + Cx^5 + Dxe^x$

23. $y_p(x) = Ax \cos 2x + Bx \sin 2x + Cx^2 \cos 2x + Dx^2 \sin 2x$

24. $y_p(x) = Ax + Bx^2 + (Cx + Dx^3)e^{-3x}$

25. $y_p(x) = Axe^{-x} + Bx^2 e^{-x} + Cxe^{-2x} + Dx^2 e^{-2x}$

26. $y_p(x) = (Ax + Bx^2)e^{3x} \cos 2x + (Cx + Dx^2)e^{3x} \sin 2x$

27. $y_p(x) = Ax \cos x + Bx \sin x + Cx \cos 2x + Dx \sin 2x$

28. $y_p(x) = (Ax + Bx^2 + Cx^3) \cos 3x + (Dx + Ex^2 + Fx^3) \sin 3x$

29. $y_p(x) = Ax^3 e^x + Bx^4 e^x + Cxe^{2x} + Dxe^{-2x}$

30. $y_p(x) = (A + Bx + Cx^2) \cos x + (D + Ex + Fx^2) \sin x$

31. $y(x) = \cos 2x + \frac{3}{4}\sin 2x + \frac{1}{2}x$

32. $y(x) = \frac{1}{6}(15e^{-x} - 16e^{-2x} + e^x)$

33. $y(x) = \cos 3x - \frac{2}{15}\sin 3x + \frac{1}{5}\sin 2x$

34. $y(x) = \cos x - \sin x + \frac{1}{2}x \sin x$

35. $y(x) = e^x(2 \cos x - \frac{5}{2}\sin x) + \frac{1}{2}x + 1$

36. $y(x) = \frac{1}{192}(234 + 240x - 9e^{-2x} - 33e^{2x} - 12x^2 - 4x^4)$

37. $y(x) = 4 - 4e^x + 3xe^x + x - \frac{1}{2}x^2 e^x + \frac{1}{6}x^3 e^x$

38. $y(x) = \frac{1}{85}[e^{-x}(176 \cos x + 197 \sin x) - (6 \cos 3x + 7 \sin 3x)]$

39. $y(x) = -3 + 3x - \frac{1}{2}x^2 + \frac{1}{6}x^3 + 4e^{-x} + xe^{-x}$

40. $y(x) = \frac{1}{4}(5e^{-x} + 5e^x + 10 \cos x - 20)$

41. $y_p(x) = 255 - 450x + 30x^2 + 20x^3 + 10x^4 - 4x^5$

42. $y(x) = 10e^{-x} + 35e^{2x} + 210 \cos x + 390 \sin x + y_p(x)$ where $y_p(x)$ is the particular solution of Problem 41.

43. (b) $y(x) = c_1 \cos 2x + c_2 \sin 2x + \frac{1}{4}\cos x - \frac{1}{20}\cos 3x$

44. $y(x) = e^{-x/2}\left[c_1 \cos\left(\frac{1}{2}x\sqrt{3}\right) + c_2 \sin\left(\frac{1}{2}x\sqrt{3}\right)\right] + \frac{1}{26}(-3 \cos 2x + 2 \sin 2x) + \frac{1}{482}(15 \cos 4x + 4 \sin 4x)$

45. $y(x) = c_1 \cos 3x + c_2 \sin 3x + \frac{1}{24} - \frac{1}{10}\cos 2x - \frac{1}{56}\cos 4x$

46. $y(x) = c_1 \cos x + c_2 \sin x + \frac{1}{16}(3x \cos x + 3x^2 \sin x) + \frac{1}{128}(3 \sin 3x - 4x \cos 3x)$

47. $y_p(x) = \frac{2}{3}e^x$

48. $y_p(x) = -\frac{1}{12}(6x + 1)e^{-2x}$

49. $y_p(x) = x^2 e^{2x}$

50. $y_p(x) = \frac{1}{16}(4x \cosh 2x - \sinh 2x)$

51. $y_p(x) = -\frac{1}{4}(\cos 2x \cos x - \sin 2x \sin x) + \frac{1}{20}(\cos 5x \cos 2x + \sin 5x \sin 2x) = -\frac{1}{5}\cos 3x$ (!)

52. $y_p(x) = -\frac{1}{6}x \cos 3x$

53. $y_p(x) = \frac{2}{3}x \sin 3x + \frac{2}{9}(\cos 3x) \ln |\cos 3x|$

54. $y_p(x) = -1 - (\cos x) \ln |\csc x - \cot x|$

55. $y_p(x) = \frac{1}{8}(1 - x \sin 2x)$

56. $y_p(x) = -\frac{1}{9}e^x(3x + 2)$

58. $y_p(x) = x^3(\ln x - 1)$

59. $y_p(x) = \frac{1}{4}x^4$

60. $y_p(x) = -\frac{72}{5}x^{4/3}$

61. $y_p(x) = \ln x$

62. $y_p(x) = -x^2 + x \ln\left|\frac{1 + x}{1 - x}\right| + \frac{1}{2}(1 + x^2) \ln |1 - x^2|$

Section 3.6

1. $x(t) = 2 \cos 2t - 2 \cos 3t$

2. $x(t) = \frac{3}{2}\sin 2t - \sin 3t$

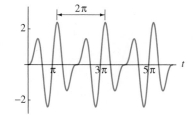

3. $x(t) = \sqrt{138388} \cos(10t - \alpha) + 5\cos(5t - \beta)$ with
$\alpha = 2\pi - \tan^{-1}(1/186) \approx 6.2778$ and
$\beta = \tan^{-1}(4/3) \approx 0.9273$.

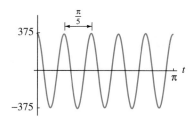

4. $x(t) = 2\sqrt{106} \cos(5t - \alpha) + 10\cos 4t$ with
$\alpha = \pi - \tan^{-1}(9/5) \approx 2.0779$

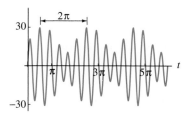

5. $x(t) = (x_0 - C) \cos \omega_0 t + C \cos \omega t$, where $C = F_0/(k - m\omega^2)$
7. $x_{sp}(t) = \frac{10}{13} \cos(3t - \alpha)$ with $\alpha = \pi - \tan^{-1}(12/5) \approx 1.9656$

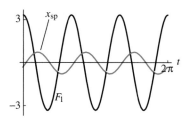

8. $x_{sp}(t) = \frac{4}{25} \cos(5t - \alpha)$ with $\alpha = 2\pi - \tan^{-1}(3/4) \approx 5.6397$

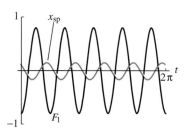

9. $x_{sp}(t) = \frac{3}{\sqrt{40001}} \cos(10t - \alpha)$ with
$\alpha = \pi + \tan^{-1}(199/20) \approx 4.6122$

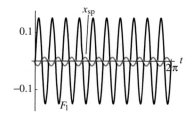

10. $x_{sp}(t) = \frac{10}{793} \sqrt{61} \cos(10t - \alpha)$ with
$\alpha = \pi + \tan^{-1}(171/478) \approx 3.4851$

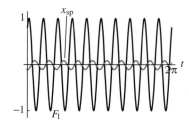

11. $x_{sp}(t) = \frac{\sqrt{10}}{4} \cos(3t - \alpha)$ with $\alpha = \pi - \tan^{-1}(3) \approx 1.8925$
$x_{tr}(t) = \frac{5}{4}\sqrt{2}\, e^{-2t} \cos(t - \beta)$ with $\beta = 2\pi - \tan^{-1}(7) \approx 4.8543$

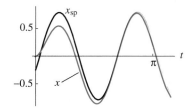

12. $x_{sp}(t) = \frac{5}{3\sqrt{29}} \cos(3t - \alpha)$ with $\alpha = \pi + \tan^{-1}(2/5) \approx 3.5221$
$x_{tr}(t) = \frac{25}{6\sqrt{29}} e^{-3t} \cos(2t - \beta)$ with $\beta = \tan^{-1}(5/2) \approx 1.1903$

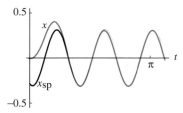

13. $x_{sp}(t) = \frac{300}{\sqrt{1469}} \cos(10t - \alpha)$ with
$\alpha = \pi - \tan^{-1}(10/37) \approx 2.9320$
$x_{tr}(t) = 2\sqrt{\frac{113314}{1469}}\, e^{-t} \cos(5t - \beta)$ with
$\beta = 2\pi - \tan^{-1}(421/12895) \approx 6.2505$

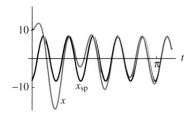

14. $x_{sp}(t) = \sqrt{485} \cos(t - \alpha)$ with $\alpha = \tan^{-1}(22) \approx 1.5254$
$x_{tr}(t) = \sqrt{3665}\, e^{-4t} \cos(3t - \beta)$ with
$\beta = \pi + \tan^{-1}(52/31) \approx 4.1748$

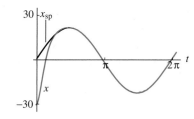

15. $C(\omega) = 2/\sqrt{4 + \omega^4}$; there is no practical resonance frequency.

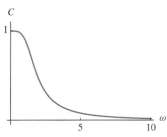

16. $C(\omega) = 10/\sqrt{25 + 6\omega^2 + \omega^4}$; there is no practical resonance frequency.

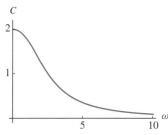

17. $C(\omega) = 50/\sqrt{2025 - 54\omega^2 + \omega^4}$; there is practical resonance at frequency $\omega = 3\sqrt{3}$.

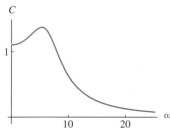

18. $C(\omega) = 100/\sqrt{422500 - 1200\omega^2 + \omega^4}$; there is practical resonance at frequency $\omega = 10\sqrt{6}$.

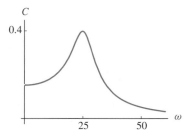

19. $\omega = \sqrt{384}$ rad/sec (approximately 3.12 Hz)
20. $\omega \approx 44.27$ rad/sec (approximately 7.05 Hz)
21. $\omega_0 = \sqrt{(g/L) + (k/m)}$
22. $\omega_0 = \sqrt{k/(m + I/a^2)}$
23. (a) Natural frequency: $\sqrt{10}$ rad/s (approximately 0.50 Hz);
(b) amplitude: approximately 10.625 in.

Section 3.7

1. $I(t) = 4e^{-5t}$
2. $I(t) = 4(1 - e^{-5t})$
3. $I(t) = \frac{4}{145}(\cos 60t + 12 \sin 60t - e^{-5t})$
4. $I(t) = 5(e^{-10t} - e^{-20t})$; $I_{max} = I(\frac{1}{10} \ln 2) = 5/4$.

5. $I(t) = \frac{5}{6}e^{-10t} \sin 60t$

6. $I_{sp}(t) = \frac{1}{37}(-21 \cos 60t + 22 \sin 60t) = (5/\sqrt{37}) \cos(60t - \alpha)$,
where $\alpha = \pi - \tan^{-1}(22/21) \approx 2.3329$.

7. (a) $Q(t) = E_0 C(1 - e^{-t/RC})$; $I(t) = (E_0/R)e^{-t/RC}$

8. (a) $Q(t) = 10te^{-5t}$; $I(t) = 10(1 - 5t)e^{-5t}$;
(b) $Q_{max} = Q(1/5) = 2e^{-1}$.

9. (a) $Q(t) = (\cos 120t + 6 \sin 120t - e^{-20t})/1480$
$I(t) = (36 \cos 120t - 6 \sin 120t + e^{-20t})/74$
(b) $I_{sp} = \frac{6}{74}(6 \cos 120t - \sin 120t) = \frac{3}{\sqrt{37}} \cos(120t - \alpha)$ with
$\alpha = 2\pi - \tan^{-1}\frac{1}{6}$.

11. $I_{sp}(t) = \frac{10}{\sqrt{37}} \sin(2t - \delta)$ with $\delta = 2\pi - \tan^{-1}(1/6) \approx 6.1180$

12. $I_{sp}(t) = \frac{2}{\sqrt{17}} \sin(10t - \delta)$ with $\delta = 2\pi - \tan^{-1}(1/4) \approx 6.0382$

13. $I_{sp}(t) = \frac{20}{\sqrt{13}} \sin(5t - \delta)$ with $\delta = 2\pi - \tan^{-1}(2/3) \approx 5.6952$

14. $I_{sp}(t) \approx 0.9990 \sin(100t - 0.8272)$

15. $I_{sp}(t) \approx 0.1591 \sin(60\pi t - 4.8576)$

16. $I_{sp}(t) \approx 1.6125 \sin(377t - 1.2282)$

17. $I(t) = -25e^{-4t} \sin 3t$

18. $I(t) = \frac{50}{171}(19e^{-10t} - 18e^{-20t} - e^{-t})$

19. $I(t) = 10e^{-20t} - 10e^{-10t} - 50te^{-10t}$

20. $I(t) = -\frac{10}{37\sqrt{11}}e^{-3t/2}(\sqrt{11} \cos t\sqrt{11}/2 + 27 \sin t\sqrt{11}/2) + \frac{10}{37}(\cos 2t + 6 \sin 2t)$

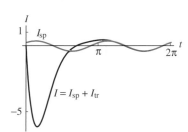

21. $I(t) = -\frac{10}{39}e^{-t}(12 \cos 3t + 47 \sin 3t) + \frac{20}{13}(2 \cos 5t + 3 \sin 5t)$

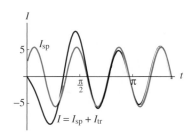

22. $I(t) \approx -e^{-25t}(0.1574 \cos 25t\sqrt{159} + 0.0262 \sin 25t\sqrt{159}) + (0.1574 \cos 60\pi t + 0.0230 \sin 60\pi t)$

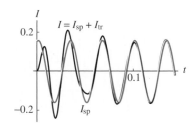

Section 3.8

1. Only positive eigenvalues $\{n^2\pi^2/4\}$ and associated eigenfunctions $\{\cos(n\pi x/2)\}$ for $n = 1, 3, 5, \ldots$.
2. Eigenvalue $\lambda_0 = 0$ with eigenfunction $y_0(x) \equiv 1$, and positive eigenvalues $\{n^2\}$ with associated eigenfunctions $\{\cos nx\}$ for $n = 1, 2, 3, \ldots$.
3. Only positive eigenvalues $\{n^2/4\}$ for $n = 1, 2, 3, \ldots$. The nth eigenfunction $y_n(x)$ is $\cos(nx/2)$ if n is odd, $\sin(nx/2)$ if n is even.
4. Eigenvalue $\lambda_0 = 0$ with eigenfunction $y_0(x) \equiv 1$, and positive eigenvalues $\{n^2/4\}$ for $n = 1, 2, 3, \ldots$. The nth eigenfunction $y_n(x)$ is $\sin(nx/2)$ if n is odd, $\cos(nx/2)$ if n is even.
5. Only positive eigenvalues $\{n^2\pi^2/64\}$ for $n = 1, 2, 3, \ldots$. The nth eigenfunction $y_n(x)$ is $\cos(n\pi x/8) + \sin(n\pi x/8)$ if n is odd, $\cos(n\pi x/8) - \sin(n\pi x/8)$ if n is even.

7–8. In the figure below, points of intersection of the curve $y = \tan z$ with the lines $y = \pm z$ are labeled with their z-coordinates. We see that α_n lies just to the right of the vertical line $z = (2n-1)\pi/2$, while β_n lies just to the left of the line $z = (2n+1)\pi/2$.

Chapter 4

Section 4.1

1. $x_1' = x_2$, $x_2' = -7x_1 - 3x_2 + t^2$
2. $x_1' = x_2$, $x_2' = x_3$, $x_3' = x_4$, $x_4' = -x_1 + 3x_2 - 6x_3 + \cos 3t$
3. $x_1' = x_2$, $t^2 x_2' = (1 - t^2)x_1 - tx_2$
4. $x_1' = x_2$, $x_2' = x_3$, $t^3 x_3' = -5x_1 - 3tx_2 + 2t^2 x_3 + \ln t$
5. $x_1' = x_2$, $x_2' = x_3$, $x_3' = x_2^2 + \cos x_1$
6. $x_1' = x_2$, $x_2' = 5x_1 - 4y_1$, $y_1' = y_2$, $y_2' = -4x_1 + 5y_1$
7. $x_1' = x_2$, $y_1' = y_2$, $x_2' = -kx_1 \cdot (x_1^2 + y_1^2)^{-3/2}$, $y_2' = -ky_1 \cdot (x_1^2 + y_1^2)^{-3/2}$
8. $x_1' = x_2$, $x_2' = -4x_1 + 2y_1 - 3x_2$ $y_1' = y_2$, $y_2' = 3x_1 - y_1 - 2y_2 + \cos t$
9. $x_1' = x_2$, $y_1' = y_2$, $z_1' = z_2$, $x_2' = 3x_1 - y_1 + 2z_1$, $y_2' = x_1 + y_1 - 4z_1$, $z_2' = 5x_1 - y_1 - z_1$
10. $x_1' = x_2$, $x_2' = x_1(1 - y_1)$ $y_1' = y_2$, $y_2' = y_1(1 - x_1)$
11. $x(t) = A \cos t + B \sin t$, $y(t) = B \cos t - A \sin t$

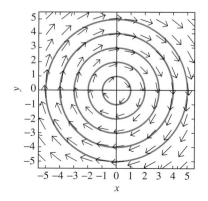

12. $x(t) = Ae^t + Be^{-t}$, $y(t) = Ae^t - Be^{-t}$

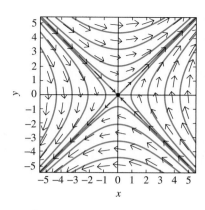

13. $x(t) = A \cos 2t + B \sin 2t$, $y(t) = -B \cos 2t + A \sin 2t$; $x(t) = \cos 2t$, $y(t) = \sin 2t$

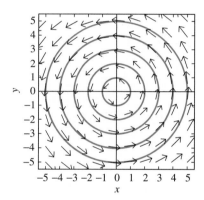

14. $x(t) = A \cos 10t + B \sin 10t$, $y(t) = B \cos 10t - A \sin 10t$; $x(t) = 3 \cos 10t + 4 \sin 10t$, $y(t) = 4 \cos 10t - 3 \sin 10t$

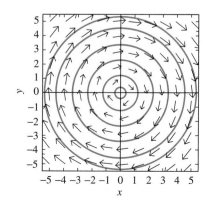

15. $x(t) = A \cos 2t + B \sin 2t$, $y(t) = 4B \cos 2t - 4A \sin 2t$

$B = -\frac{11}{3}$ in the particular solution.

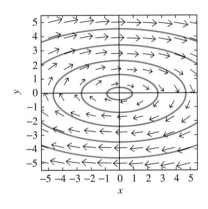

16. $x(t) = A \cos 4t + B \sin 4t$, $y(t) = \frac{1}{2}B \cos 4t - \frac{1}{2}A \sin 4t$

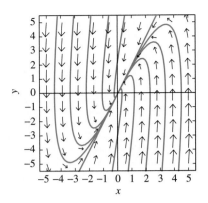

19. $x(t) = -e^{-2t} \sin 3t$, $y(t) = e^{-2t}(3 \cos 3t + 2 \sin 3t)$

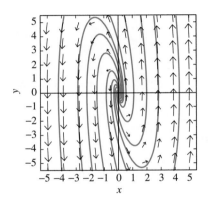

17. $x(t) = Ae^{-3t} + Be^{2t}$, $y(t) = -3Ae^{-3t} + 2Be^{2t}$; $x(t) = e^{2t}$, $y(t) = 2e^{2t}$

20. $x(t) = (A + Bt)e^{3t}$, $y(t) = (3A + B + 3Bt)e^{3t}$

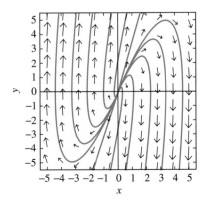

27. $2(I_1' - I_2') + 50I_1 = 100 \sin 60t$, $2(I_2' - I_1') + 25I_2 = 0$

18. $x(t) = Ae^{-2t} + Be^{-5t}$, $y(t) = 2Ae^{-2t} + 5Be^{-5t}$; $A = \frac{17}{3}$ and

28. $I_1' = -20(I_1 - I_2)$, $I_2' = 40(I_1 - I_2)$

Section 4.2

1. $x(t) = a_1 e^{-t} + a_2 e^{2t}, \ y(t) = a_2 e^{2t}$

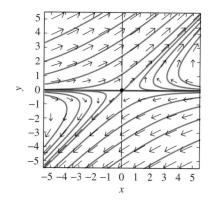

2. $x(t) = (c_1 + c_2 t)e^{-t}, \ y(t) = (c_1 - \frac{1}{2}c_2 + c_2 t)e^{-t}$

3. $x(t) = \frac{4}{5}(e^{3t} - e^{-2t}), \ y(t) = \frac{2}{5}(6e^{3t} - e^{-2t})$

4. $x(t) = \frac{1}{2}(3e^{2t} - e^{-2t}), \ y(t) = \frac{1}{2}(3e^{2t} - 5e^{-2t})$

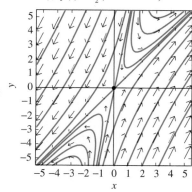

5. $x(t) = e^{-t}(a_1 \cos 2t + a_2 \sin 2t),$
$y(t) = -\frac{1}{2}e^{-t}[(a_1 + a_2)\cos 2t + (a_2 - a_1)\sin 2t]$

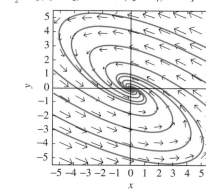

6. $x(t) = e^{-2t}(3\cos 3t + 9\sin 3t), \ y(t) = e^{-2t}(2\cos 3t - 4\sin 3t)$

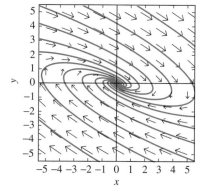

7. $x(t) = a_1 e^{2t} + a_2 e^{3t} - \frac{1}{3}t + \frac{1}{18}, \ y(t) = -2a_1 e^{2t} - a_2 e^{3t} - \frac{2}{3}t - \frac{5}{9}$
8. $x(t) = c_1 e^t + c_2 e^{3t} + e^{2t}, \ y(t) = -c_1 e^t + c_2 e^{3t}$
9. $x(t) = 3a_1 e^t + a_2 e^{-t} - \frac{1}{5}(7\cos 2t + 4\sin 2t),$
$y(t) = a_1 e^t + a_2 e^{-t} - \frac{1}{5}(2\cos 2t + 4\sin 2t)$
10. $x(t) = e^t, \ y(t) = -e^t$
11. $x(t) = a_1 \cos 3t + a_2 \sin 3t - \frac{11}{20}e^t - \frac{1}{4}e^{-t},$
$y(t) = \frac{1}{3}[(a_1 - a_2)\cos 3t + (a_1 + a_2)\sin 3t] + \frac{1}{10}e^t$
12. $x(t) = c_1 e^{2t} + c_2 e^{-2t} + c_3 e^{3t} + c_4 e^{-3t},$
$y(t) = -c_1 e^{2t} - c_2 e^{-2t} + \frac{3}{2}c_3 e^{3t} + \frac{3}{2}c_4 e^{-3t}$
13. $x(t) = a_1 \cos 2t + a_2 \sin 2t + b_1 \cos 3t + b_2 \sin 3t,$
$y(t) = \frac{1}{2}(a_1 \cos 2t + a_2 \sin 2t) - 2(b_1 \cos 3t + b_2 \sin 3t)$
14. $x(t) = c_1 \cos 2t + c_2 \sin 2t + \frac{1}{3}\sin t,$
$y(t) = c_1 \cos 2t + c_2 \sin 2t + c_3 \cos 2t\sqrt{2} +$
$c_4 \sin 2t\sqrt{2} + \frac{4}{21}\sin t$

15. $x(t) = a_1 \cos t + a_2 \sin t + b_1 \cos 2t + b_2 \sin 2t$,
$y(t) = a_2 \cos t - a_1 \sin t + b_2 \cos 2t - b_1 \sin 2t$

17. $x(t) = a_1 \cos t + a_2 \sin t + b_1 e^{2t} + b_2 e^{-2t}$,
$y(t) = 3a_2 \cos t - 3a_1 \sin t + b_1 e^{2t} - b_2 e^{-2t}$

18. $x(t) = \frac{1}{6}(4c_1 e^{3t} - 3c_2 e^{-4t})$, $y(t) = c_1 e^{3t} + c_2 e^{-4t}$,
$z(t) = \frac{1}{6}(-4c_1 e^{3t} + 3c_2 e^{-4t})$

19. $x(t) = a_1 + a_2 e^{4t} + a_3 e^{8t}$, $y(t) = 2a_1 - 2a_3 e^{8t}$,
$z(t) = 2a_1 - 2a_2 e^{4t} + 2a_3 e^{8t}$

20. $x(t) = a_1 e^{2t} + a_2 e^{-t} + \frac{2}{3} t e^{-t}$, $y(t) = a_1 e^{2t} + b_2 e^{-t} - \frac{1}{3} t e^{-t}$,
$z(t) = a_1 e^{2t} - \left(a_2 + b_2 + \frac{1}{3}\right) e^{-t} - \frac{1}{3} t e^{-t}$

23. Infinitely many solutions

24. No solution

25. Infinitely many solutions

26. Two arbitrary constants

27. No arbitrary constants

28. No solution

29. Four arbitrary constants

31. $I_1(t) = 2 + e^{-5t}\left[-2\cos\left(10t/\sqrt{6}\right) + 4\sqrt{6}\sin\left(10t/\sqrt{6}\right)\right]$,
$I_2(t) = \left(20/\sqrt{6}\right)e^{-5t}\sin\left(10t/\sqrt{6}\right)$

32. $I_1(t) = \frac{1}{1321}(120e^{-25t/3} - 120\cos 60t + 1778\sin 60t)$,
$I_2(t) = \frac{1}{1321}(-240e^{-25t/3} + 240\cos 60t + 1728\sin 60t)$

33. $I_1(t) = \frac{2}{3}(2 + e^{-60t})$, $I_2(t) = \frac{4}{3}(1 - e^{-60t})$

37. (a) $x(t) = a_1 \cos 5t + a_2 \sin 5t + b_1 \cos 5t\sqrt{3} + b_2 \sin 5t\sqrt{3}$,
$y(t) = 2a_1 \cos 5t + 2a_2 \sin 5t - 2b_1 \cos 5t\sqrt{3} - 2b_2 \sin 5t\sqrt{3}$;
(b) In the natural mode with frequency $\omega_1 = 5$, the masses
move in the same direction, whereas in the natural mode with
frequency $\omega_2 = 5\sqrt{3}$ they move in opposite directions. In each
case the amplitude of the motion of m_2 is twice that of m_1.

39. $x(t) = a_1 \cos t + a_2 \sin t + b_1 \cos 2t + b_2 \sin 2t$,
$y(t) = 2a_1 \cos t + 2a_2 \sin t - b_1 \cos 2t - b_2 \sin 2t$.
In the natural mode with frequency $\omega_1 = 1$ the masses move in
the same direction, with the amplitude of motion of the second
mass twice that of the first mass. In the natural mode with
frequency $\omega_2 = 2$ they move in opposite directions with the
same amplitude of motion.

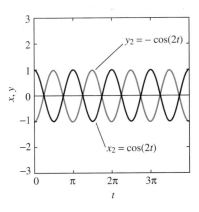

40. $x(t) = a_1 \cos 5t + a_2 \sin 5t + b_1 \cos 10t + b_2 \sin 10t$,
$y(t) = 2a_1 \cos 5t + 2a_2 \sin 5t - b_1 \cos 10t - b_2 \sin 10t$.

41. $x(t) = a_1 \cos t + a_2 \sin t + b_1 \cos 3t + b_2 \sin 3t$,
$y(t) = a_1 \cos t + a_2 \sin t - b_1 \cos 3t - b_2 \sin 3t$.
In the natural mode with frequency $\omega_1 = 1$ the masses move in
the same direction, while in the natural mode with frequency
$\omega_2 = 3$ they move in opposite directions. In each case the
amplitudes of motion of the two masses are equal.

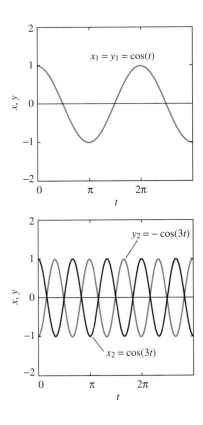

42. $x(t) = a_1 \cos t + a_2 \sin t + b_1 \cos 2t + b_2 \sin 2t$,
$y(t) = a_1 \cos t + a_2 \sin t - \frac{1}{2} b_1 \cos 2t - \frac{1}{2} b_2 \sin 2t$.

43. $x(t) = a_1 \cos t + a_2 \sin t + b_1 \cos t\sqrt{5} + b_2 \sin t\sqrt{5}$,
$y(t) = a_1 \cos t + a_2 \sin t - b_1 \cos t\sqrt{5} - b_2 \sin t\sqrt{5}$.

In the natural mode with frequency $\omega_1 = 1$ the masses move in the same direction, while in the natural mode with frequency $\omega_2 = \sqrt{5}$ they move in opposite directions. In each case the amplitudes of motion of the two masses are equal.

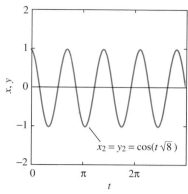

46. $x(t) = a_1 \cos 2t + a_2 \sin 2t + b_1 \cos 4t + b_2 \sin 4t$,
$y(t) = a_1 \cos 2t + a_2 \sin 2t - b_1 \cos 4t - b_2 \sin 4t$.

Section 4.3

The format for the first eight answers is this: $(x(t), y(t))$ at $t = 0.2$ by the Euler method, by the improved Euler method, by the Runge-Kutta method, and finally the actual values.

1. $(0.8800, 2.5000)$, $(0.9600, 2.6000)$, $(1.0027, 2.6401)$, $(1.0034, 2.6408)$
2. $(0.8100, -0.8100)$, $(0.8200, -0.8200)$, $(0.8187, -0.8187)$, $(0.8187, -0.8187)$
3. $(2.8100, 2.3100)$, $(3.2200, 2.6200)$, $(3.6481, 2.9407)$, $(3.6775, 2.9628)$
4. $(3.3100, -1.6200)$, $(3.8200, -2.0400)$, $(4.2274, -2.4060)$, $(4.2427, -2.4205)$
5. $(-0.5200, 2.9200)$, $(-0.8400, 2.4400)$, $(-0.5712, 2.4485)$, $(-0.5793, 2.4488)$
6. $(-1.7600, 4.6800)$, $(-1.9200, 4.5600)$, $(-1.9029, 4.4995)$, $(-1.9025, 4.4999)$
7. $(3.1200, 1.6800)$, $(3.2400, 1.7600)$, $(3.2816, 1.7899)$, $(3.2820, 1.7902)$
8. $(2.1600, -0.6300)$, $(2.5200, -0.4600)$, $(2.5320, -0.3867)$, $(2.5270, -0.3889)$
9. At $t = 1$ we obtain $(x, y) = (3.99261, 6.21770)$ $(h = 0.1)$ and $(3.99234, 6.21768)$ $(h = 0.05)$; the actual value is $(3.99232, 6.21768)$.
10. At $t = 1$ we obtain $(x, y) = (1.31498, 1.02537)$ $(h = 0.1)$ and $(1.31501, 1.02538)$ $(h = 0.05)$; the actual value is $(1.31501, 1.02538)$.
11. At $t = 1$ we obtain $(x, y) = (-0.05832, 0.56664)$ $(h = 0.1)$ and $(-0.05832, 0.56665)$ $(h = 0.05)$; the actual value is $(-0.05832, 0.56665)$.
12. We solved $x' = y$, $y' = -x + \sin t$, $x(0) = y(0) = 0$. With $h = 0.1$ and also with $h = 0.05$ we obtain the actual value $x(1.0) \approx 0.15058$.
13. Runge-Kutta, $h = 0.1$: about 1050 ft in about 7.7 s
14. Runge-Kutta, $h = 0.1$: about 1044 ft in about 7.8 s
15. Runge-Kutta, $h = 1.0$: about 83.83 mi in about 168 s
16. At $40°$: 5.0 s, 352.9 ft; at $45°$: 5.4 s, 347.2 ft; at $50°$: 5.8 s, 334.2 ft (all values approximate)
17. At $39.0°$ the range is about 352.7 ft. At $39.5°$ it is 352.8; at $40°$, 352.9; at $40.5°$, 352.6; at $41.0°$, 352.1.
18. Just under $57.5°$
19. Approximately 253 ft/s
20. Maximum height: about 1005 ft, attained in about 5.6 s; range: about 1880 ft; time aloft: about 11.6 s
21. Runge-Kutta with $h = 0.1$ yields these results:
(a) 21400 ft, 46 s, 518 ft/s; (b) 8970 ft, 17.5 s; (c) 368 ft/s (at $t \approx 23$).

44. $x(t) = a_1 \cos t\sqrt{2} + a_2 \sin t\sqrt{2} + b_1 \cos 2t + b_2 \sin 2t$,
$y(t) = a_1 \cos t\sqrt{2} + a_2 \sin t\sqrt{2} - b_1 \cos 2t - b_2 \sin 2t$.

45. $x(t) = a_1 \cos t\sqrt{2} + a_2 \sin t\sqrt{2} + b_1 \cos t\sqrt{8} + b_2 \sin t\sqrt{8}$,
$y(t) = a_1 \cos t\sqrt{2} + a_2 \sin t\sqrt{2} - \frac{1}{2}b_1 \cos t\sqrt{8} - \frac{1}{2}b_2 \sin t\sqrt{8}$.
In the natural mode with frequency $\omega_1 = \sqrt{2}$ the two masses move in the same direction with equal amplitudes of oscillation. In the natural mode with frequency $\omega_2 = \sqrt{8} = 2\sqrt{2}$ the two masses move in opposite directions with the amplitude of m_2 being half that of m_1.

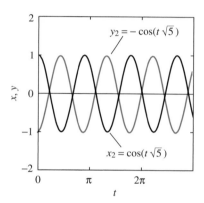

Chapter 5

Section 5.1

1. (a) $\begin{bmatrix} 13 & -18 \\ 23 & 17 \end{bmatrix}$; (b) $\begin{bmatrix} 0 & -1 \\ 2 & 19 \end{bmatrix}$;

(c) $\begin{bmatrix} -9 & -11 \\ 47 & -9 \end{bmatrix}$; (d) $\begin{bmatrix} -10 & -37 \\ 14 & -8 \end{bmatrix}$

2. $(AB)C = A(BC) = \begin{bmatrix} -33 & -7 \\ -27 & 103 \end{bmatrix}$;

$A(B+C) = AB + AC = \begin{bmatrix} -18 & -4 \\ 68 & -8 \end{bmatrix}$

3. $AB = \begin{bmatrix} -1 & 8 \\ 46 & -1 \end{bmatrix}$; $BA = \begin{bmatrix} 11 & -12 & 14 \\ -14 & 0 & 7 \\ 0 & 8 & -13 \end{bmatrix}$

4. $Ay = \begin{bmatrix} 2t^2 - \cos t \\ 3t^2 - 4\sin t + 5\cos t \end{bmatrix}$, $Bx = \begin{bmatrix} 2t + 3e^{-t} \\ -14t \\ 6t - 2e^{-t} \end{bmatrix}$

5. (a) $\begin{bmatrix} 21 & 2 & 1 \\ 4 & 44 & 9 \\ -27 & 34 & 45 \end{bmatrix}$; (b) $\begin{bmatrix} 9 & 21 & -13 \\ -5 & -8 & 24 \\ -25 & -19 & 26 \end{bmatrix}$;

(c) $\begin{bmatrix} 0 & -6 & 1 \\ 10 & 31 & -15 \\ 16 & 58 & -23 \end{bmatrix}$; (d) $\begin{bmatrix} -10 & -8 & 5 \\ 18 & 12 & -10 \\ 11 & 22 & 6 \end{bmatrix}$;

(e) $\begin{bmatrix} 3-t & 2 & -1 \\ 0 & 4-t & 3 \\ -5 & 2 & 7-t \end{bmatrix}$

7. $\det(A) = \det(B) = 0$ **8.** $\det(AB) = \det(BA) = 144$

9. $(AB)' = \begin{bmatrix} 1 - 8t + 18t^2 & 1 + 2t - 12t^2 + 32t^3 \\ 3 + 3t^2 - 4t^3 & 8t + 3t^2 + 4t^3 \end{bmatrix}$

11. $x = \begin{bmatrix} x \\ y \end{bmatrix}$, $P(t) = \begin{bmatrix} 0 & -3 \\ 3 & 0 \end{bmatrix}$, $f(t) = \begin{bmatrix} 0 \\ 0 \end{bmatrix}$

13. $x = \begin{bmatrix} x \\ y \end{bmatrix}$, $P(t) = \begin{bmatrix} 2 & 4 \\ 5 & -1 \end{bmatrix}$, $f(t) = \begin{bmatrix} 3e^t \\ -t^2 \end{bmatrix}$

15. $x = \begin{bmatrix} x \\ y \\ z \end{bmatrix}$, $P(t) = \begin{bmatrix} 0 & 1 & 1 \\ 1 & 0 & 1 \\ 1 & 1 & 0 \end{bmatrix}$, $f(t) = \begin{bmatrix} 0 \\ 0 \\ 0 \end{bmatrix}$

17. $x = \begin{bmatrix} x \\ y \\ z \end{bmatrix}$, $P(t) = \begin{bmatrix} 3 & -4 & 1 \\ 1 & 0 & -3 \\ 0 & 6 & -7 \end{bmatrix}$, $f(t) = \begin{bmatrix} t \\ t^2 \\ t^3 \end{bmatrix}$

19. $x = \begin{bmatrix} x_1 \\ x_2 \\ x_3 \\ x_4 \end{bmatrix}$, $P(t) = \begin{bmatrix} 0 & 1 & 0 & 0 \\ 0 & 0 & 2 & 0 \\ 0 & 0 & 0 & 3 \\ 4 & 0 & 0 & 0 \end{bmatrix}$, $f(t) = \begin{bmatrix} 0 \\ 0 \\ 0 \\ 0 \end{bmatrix}$

21. $W(t) = e^{3t}$; $x(t) = \begin{bmatrix} 2c_1e^t + c_2e^{2t} \\ -3c_1e^t - c_2e^{2t} \end{bmatrix}$

22. $W(t) = -5e^t$; $x(t) = \begin{bmatrix} c_1e^{3t} + 2c_2e^{-2t} \\ 3c_1e^{3t} + c_2e^{-2t} \end{bmatrix}$

23. $W(t) \equiv 4$; $x(t) = \begin{bmatrix} c_1e^{2t} + c_2e^{-2t} \\ c_1e^{2t} + 5c_2e^{-2t} \end{bmatrix}$

24. $W(t) = e^{5t}$; $x(t) = \begin{bmatrix} c_1e^{3t} + c_2e^{2t} \\ -c_1e^{3t} - 2c_2e^{2t} \end{bmatrix}$

25. $W(t) = 7e^{-3t}$; $x(t) = \begin{bmatrix} 3c_1e^{2t} + c_2e^{-5t} \\ 2c_1e^{2t} + 3c_2e^{-5t} \end{bmatrix}$

26. $W(t) = 16e^{9t}$; $x(t) = \begin{bmatrix} 2c_1e^t - 2c_2e^{3t} + 2c_3e^{5t} \\ 2c_1e^t - 2c_3e^{5t} \\ c_1e^t + c_2e^{3t} + c_3e^{5t} \end{bmatrix}$

27. $W(t) \equiv 3$; $x(t) = \begin{bmatrix} c_1e^{2t} + c_2e^{-t} \\ c_1e^{2t} + c_3e^{-t} \\ c_1e^{2t} - (c_2 + c_3)e^{-t} \end{bmatrix}$

28. $W(t) = -84e^{7t}$; $x(t) = \begin{bmatrix} c_1 + 2c_2e^{3t} - c_3e^{4t} \\ 6c_1 + 3c_2e^{3t} + 2c_3e^{4t} \\ -13c_1 - 2c_2e^{3t} + c_3e^{4t} \end{bmatrix}$

29. $W(t) = e^{2t}$; $x(t) = \begin{bmatrix} 3c_1e^{-2t} + c_2e^t + c_3e^{3t} \\ -2c_1e^{-2t} - c_2e^t - c_3e^{3t} \\ 2c_1e^{-2t} + c_2e^t \end{bmatrix}$

30. $W(t) = 1$; $x(t) = \begin{bmatrix} c_1e^{-t} + c_4e^t \\ c_3e^t \\ c_2e^{-t} + 3c_4e^t \\ c_1e^{-t} - 2c_3e^t \end{bmatrix}$

31. $x = 2x_1 - x_2$

32. $x = 7x_1 - 2x_2$

33. $x = 15x_1 - 4x_2$

34. $x = \frac{8}{7}(3x_1 - 2x_2)$

35. $x = x_1 + 2x_2 + x_3$

36. $x = 7x_1 + 3x_2 + 5x_3$

37. $x = 3x_1 - 3x_2 - 5x_3$

38. $x = -2x_1 + 15x_2 - 4x_3$

39. $x = 3x_1 + 7x_2 + x_3 - 2x_4$

40. $x = 13x_1 + 41x_2 + 3x_3 - 12x_4$

41. (a) $x_2 = tx_1$, so neither is a constant multiple of the other.
(b) $W(x_1, x_2) \equiv 0$, whereas Theorem 2 would imply that $W \neq 0$ if x_1 and x_2 were independent solutions of a system of the indicated form.

Section 5.2

1. $x_1(t) = c_1e^{-t} + c_2e^{3t}$, $x_2(t) = -c_1e^{-t} + c_2e^{3t}$

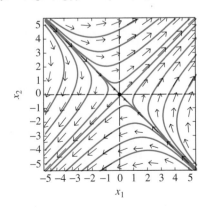

2. $x_1(t) = c_1e^{-t} + 3c_2e^{4t}$, $x_2(t) = -c_1e^{-t} + 2c_2e^{4t}$

3. General solution $x_1(t) = c_1e^{-t} + 4c_2e^{6t}$, $x_2(t) = -c_1e^{-t} + 3c_2e^{6t}$
Particular solution $x_1(t) = \frac{1}{7}(-e^{-t} + 8e^{6t})$,
$x_2(t) = \frac{1}{7}(e^{-t} + 6e^{6t})$.

4. $x_1(t) = c_1e^{-2t} + c_2e^{5t}$, $x_2(t) = -6c_1e^{-2t} + c_2e^{5t}$

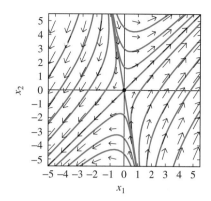

5. $x_1(t) = c_1e^{-t} + 7c_2e^{5t}$, $x_2(t) = c_1e^{-t} + c_2e^{5t}$

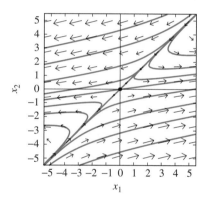

6. General solution $x_1(t) = 5c_1e^{3t} + c_2e^{4t}$, $x_2(t) = -6c_1e^{3t} - c_2e^{4t}$
Particular solution $x_1(t) = -5e^{3t} + 6e^{4t}$, $x_2(t) = 6e^{3t} - 6e^{4t}$.

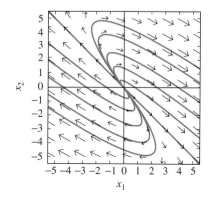

7. $x_1(t) = c_1e^{t} + 2c_2e^{-9t}$, $x_2(t) = c_1e^{t} - 3c_2e^{-9t}$

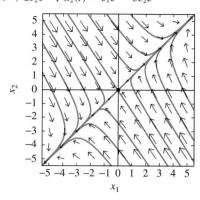

8. $x_1(t) = 5c_1\cos 2t + 5c_2\sin 2t$,
$x_2(t) = (c_1 - 2c_2)\cos 2t + (2c_1 + c_2)\sin 2t$

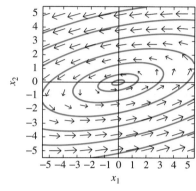

9. General solution $x_1(t) = 5c_1\cos 4t + 5c_2\sin 4t$,
$x_2(t) = c_1(2\cos 4t + 4\sin 4t) + c_2(2\sin 4t - 4\cos 4t)$.
Particular solution $x_1(t) = 2\cos 4t - \frac{11}{4}\sin 4t$,
$x_2(t) = 3\cos 4t + \frac{1}{2}\sin 4t$

10. $x_1(t) = -2c_1\cos 3t - 2c_2\sin 3t$,
$x_2(t) = (3c_1 + 3c_2)\cos 3t + (3c_2 - 3c_1)\sin 3t$

11. General solution $x_1(t) = e^{t}(c_1\cos 2t - c_2\sin 2t)$,
$x_2(t) = e^{t}(c_1\sin 2t + c_2\cos 2t)$
Particular solution $x_1(t) = -4e^{t}\sin 2t$, $x_2(t) = 4e^{t}\cos 2t$

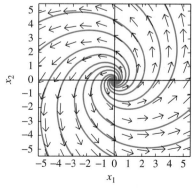

12. $x_1(t) = e^{2t}(-5c_1\cos 2t - 5c_2\sin 2t)$,
$x_2(t) = e^{2t}[(c_1 + 2c_2)\cos 2t + (-2c_1 + c_2)\sin 2t]$

13. $x_1(t) = 3e^{2t}(c_1\cos 3t - c_2\sin 3t)$,
$x_2(t) = e^{2t}[(c_1 + c_2)\cos 3t + (c_1 - c_2)\sin 3t]$

14. $x_1(t) = e^{3t}(c_1\cos 4t + c_2\sin 4t)$,
$x_2(t) = e^{3t}(c_1\sin 4t - c_2\cos 4t)$

15. $x_1(t) = 5e^{5t}(c_1 \cos 4t - c_2 \sin 4t)$,
$x_2(t) = e^{5t}[(2c_1 + 4c_2) \cos 4t + (4c_1 - 2c_2) \sin 4t]$

16. $x_1(t) = c_1 e^{-10t} + 2c_2 e^{-100t}$, $x_2(t) = 2c_1 e^{-10t} - 5c_2 e^{-100t}$

17. $x_1(t) = c_1 e^{9t} + c_2 e^{6t} + c_3$,
$x_2(t) = c_1 e^{9t} - 2c_2 e^{6t}$,
$x_3(t) = c_1 e^{9t} + c_2 e^{6t} - c_3$

18. $x_1(t) = c_1 e^{9t} + 4c_3$,
$x_2(t) = 2c_1 e^{9t} + c_2 e^{6t} - c_3$,
$x_3(t) = 2c_1 e^{9t} - c_2 e^{6t} - c_3$

19. $x_1(t) = c_1 e^{6t} + c_2 e^{3t} + c_3 e^{3t}$,
$x_2(t) = c_1 e^{6t} - 2c_2 e^{3t}$,
$x_3(t) = c_1 e^{6t} + c_2 e^{3t} - c_3 e^{3t}$

20. $x_1(t) = c_1 e^{9t} + c_2 e^{6t} + c_3 e^{2t}$,
$x_2(t) = c_1 e^{9t} - 2c_2 e^{6t}$,
$x_3(t) = c_1 e^{9t} + c_2 e^{6t} - c_3 e^{2t}$

21. $x_1(t) = 6c_1 + 3c_2 e^{t} + 2c_3 e^{-t}$,
$x_2(t) = 2c_1 + c_2 e^{t} + c_3 e^{-t}$,
$x_3(t) = 5c_1 + 2c_2 e^{t} + 2c_3 e^{-t}$

22. $x_1(t) = c_2 e^{t} + c_3 e^{3t}$,
$x_2(t) = c_1 e^{-2t} - c_2 e^{t} - c_3 e^{3t}$,
$x_3(t) = -c_1 e^{-2t} + c_3 e^{3t}$

23. $x_1(t) = c_1 e^{2t} + c_3 e^{3t}$,
$x_2(t) = -c_1 e^{2t} + c_2 e^{-2t} - c_3 e^{3t}$,
$x_3(t) = -c_2 e^{-2t} + c_3 e^{3t}$

24. $x_1(t) = c_1 e^{t} + c_2(2 \cos 2t - \sin 2t) + c_3(\cos 2t + 2 \sin 2t)$
$x_2(t) = -c_1 e^{t} - c_2(3 \cos 2t + \sin 2t) + c_3(\cos 2t - 3 \sin 2t)$
$x_3(t) = c_2(3 \cos 2t + \sin 2t) + c_3(3 \sin 2t - \cos 2t)$

25. $x_1(t) = c_1 + e^{2t}[(c_2 + c_3) \cos 3t + (-c_2 + c_3) \sin 3t]$,
$x_2(t) = -c_1 + 2e^{2t}(-c_2 \cos 3t - c_3 \sin 3t)$,
$x_3(t) = 2e^{2t}(c_2 \cos 3t + c_3 \sin 3t)$

26. $x_1(t) = 4e^{3t} - e^{-t}(4 \cos t - \sin t)$,
$x_2(t) = 9e^{3t} - e^{-t}(9 \cos t + 2 \sin t)$,
$x_3(t) = 17e^{-t} \cos t$

27. $x_1(t) = 15e^{-0.2t}$, $x_2(t) = 15(e^{-0.2t} - e^{-0.4t})$.
The maximum amount ever in tank 2 is $x_2(5 \ln 2) = 3.75$ lb.

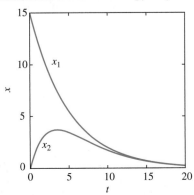

28. $x_1(t) = 15e^{-0.4t}$, $x_2(t) = 40(-e^{-0.4t} + e^{-0.25t})$.
The maximum amount ever in tank 2 is about 6.85 lb.

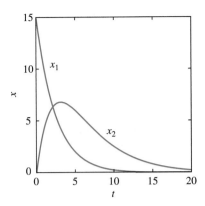

29. $x_1(t) = 10 + 5e^{-0.6t}$, $x_2(t) = 5 - 5e^{-0.6t}$

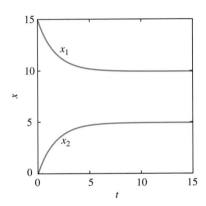

30. $x_1(t) = 5c_1 + c_2 e^{-0.65t}$, $x_2(t) = 8c_1 - c_2 e^{-0.65t}$.

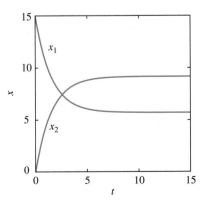

31. $x_1(t) = 27e^{-t}$,
$x_2(t) = 27e^{-t} - 27e^{-2t}$,
$x_3(t) = 27e^{-t} - 54e^{-2t} + 27e^{-3t}$.
The maximum amount of salt ever in tank 3 is $x_3(\ln 3) = 4$

pounds.

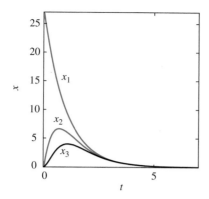

$x_3(\frac{1}{2}\ln 5) \approx 21.4663$ pounds.

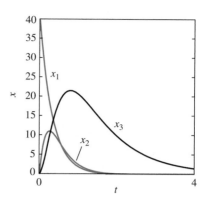

32. $x_1(t) = 45e^{-3t}$,
$x_2(t) = -135e^{-3t} + 135e^{-2t}$,
$x_3(t) = 135e^{-3t} - 270e^{-2t} + 135e^{-t}$.
The maximum amount of salt ever in tank 3 is $x_3(\ln 3) = 20$ pounds.

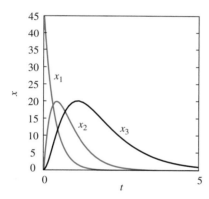

35. $x_1(t) = 10 - \frac{1}{7}\left(55e^{-18t} - 216e^{-11t}\right)$,
$x_2(t) = 3 - \frac{1}{7}\left(165e^{-18t} - 144e^{-11t}\right)$,
$x_3(t) = 20 + \frac{1}{7}\left(220e^{-18t} - 360e^{-11t}\right)$.
The limiting amounts of salt in tanks 1, 2, and 3 are 10 lb, 3 lb, and 20 lb.

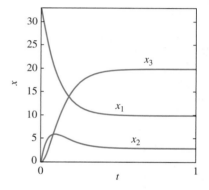

33. $x_1(t) = 45e^{-4t}$,
$x_2(t) = 90e^{-4t} - 90e^{-6t}$,
$x_3(t) = -270e^{-4t} + 135e^{-6t} + 135e^{-2t}$.
The maximum amount of salt ever in tank 3 is $x_3\left(\frac{1}{2}\ln 3\right) = 20$ pounds.

36. $x_1(t) = 4 + e^{-3t/5}[14\cos(3t/10) - 2\sin(3t/10)]$,
$x_2(t) = 10 - e^{-3t/5}[10\cos(3t/10) - 10\sin(3t/10)]$,
$x_3(t) = 4 - e^{-3t/5}[4\cos(3t/10) + 8\sin(3t/10)]$.
The limiting amounts of salt in tanks 1, 2, and 3 are 4 lb, 10 lb, and 4 lb.

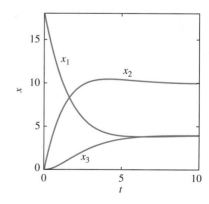

34. $x_1(t) = 40e^{-3t}$,
$x_2(t) = 60e^{-3t} - 60e^{-5t}$,
$x_3(t) = -150e^{-3t} + 75e^{-5t} + 75e^{-t}$.
The maximum amount of salt ever in tank 3 is

37. $x_1(t) = 30 + e^{-3t}[25\cos(t\sqrt{2}) + 10\sqrt{2}\sin(t\sqrt{2})]$,
$x_2(t) = 10 - e^{-3t}[10\cos(t\sqrt{2}) - \frac{25}{2}\sqrt{2}\sin(t\sqrt{2})]$,
$x_3(t) = 15 - e^{-3t}[15\cos(t\sqrt{2}) + \frac{45}{2}\sqrt{2}\sin(t\sqrt{2})]$.
The limiting amounts of salt in tanks 1, 2, and 3 are 30 lb, 10 lb,

and 15 lb.

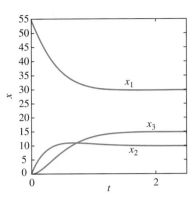

38. $x_1(t) = c_1 e^t,$
$x_2(t) = -2c_1 e^t + c_2 e^{2t},$
$x_3(t) = 3c_1 e^t - 3c_2 e^{2t} + c_3 e^{3t},$
$x_4(t) = -4c_1 e^t + 6c_2 e^{2t} - 4c_3 e^{3t} + c_4 e^{4t}$

39. $x_1(t) = 3c_1 e^t + c_4 e^{-2t},$
$x_2(t) = -2c_1 e^t + c_3 e^{2t} - c_4 e^{-2t},$
$x_3(t) = 4c_1 e^t + c_2 e^{-t},$
$x_4(t) = c_1 e^t$

40. $x_1(t) = c_1 e^{2t},$
$x_2(t) = -3c_1 e^{2t} + 3c_2 e^{-2t} - c_4 e^{-5t},$
$x_3(t) = c_3 e^{5t},$
$x_4(t) = -c_2 e^{-2t} - 3c_3 e^{5t}$

41. $x_1(t) = 2e^{10t} + e^{15t} = x_4(t), \; x_2(t) = -e^{10t} + 2e^{15t} = x_3(t)$

42. $\mathbf{x}(t) = c_1 \begin{bmatrix} 3 \\ -1 \\ 2 \end{bmatrix} + c_2 \begin{bmatrix} 1 \\ 1 \\ 1 \end{bmatrix} e^{2t} + c_3 \begin{bmatrix} 2 \\ -3 \\ 1 \end{bmatrix} e^{5t}$

43. $\mathbf{x}(t) = c_1 \begin{bmatrix} 3 \\ -1 \\ 5 \end{bmatrix} e^{-2t} + c_2 \begin{bmatrix} 1 \\ 1 \\ 1 \end{bmatrix} e^{4t} + c_3 \begin{bmatrix} 1 \\ -1 \\ 3 \end{bmatrix} e^{8t}$

44. $\mathbf{x}(t) = c_1 \begin{bmatrix} 3 \\ -2 \\ 2 \end{bmatrix} e^{-3t} + c_2 \begin{bmatrix} 7 \\ 1 \\ 5 \end{bmatrix} e^{6t} + c_3 \begin{bmatrix} 5 \\ -3 \\ 3 \end{bmatrix} e^{12t}$

45. $\mathbf{x}(t) =$
$c_1 \begin{bmatrix} 1 \\ 1 \\ 1 \\ -1 \end{bmatrix} e^{-3t} + c_2 \begin{bmatrix} 1 \\ 2 \\ -1 \\ 1 \end{bmatrix} + c_3 \begin{bmatrix} 2 \\ 1 \\ 1 \\ 1 \end{bmatrix} e^{3t} + c_4 \begin{bmatrix} 1 \\ -1 \\ 2 \\ -1 \end{bmatrix} e^{6t}$

46. $\mathbf{x}(t) =$
$c_1 \begin{bmatrix} 3 \\ 2 \\ -1 \\ 1 \end{bmatrix} e^{-4t} + c_2 \begin{bmatrix} 1 \\ 2 \\ 2 \\ -1 \end{bmatrix} e^{2t} + c_3 \begin{bmatrix} 1 \\ 1 \\ -1 \\ 1 \end{bmatrix} e^{4t} + c_4 \begin{bmatrix} 3 \\ -2 \\ 3 \\ -3 \end{bmatrix} e^{8t}$

47. $\mathbf{x}(t) =$
$c_1 \begin{bmatrix} 2 \\ 2 \\ 1 \\ -1 \end{bmatrix} e^{-3t} + c_2 \begin{bmatrix} 1 \\ 2 \\ -1 \\ 1 \end{bmatrix} e^{3t} + c_3 \begin{bmatrix} 2 \\ 1 \\ 1 \\ 1 \end{bmatrix} e^{6t} + c_4 \begin{bmatrix} 1 \\ -1 \\ 2 \\ -1 \end{bmatrix} e^{9t}$

48. $\mathbf{x}(t) =$
$c_1 \begin{bmatrix} 1 \\ 2 \\ -1 \\ 2 \end{bmatrix} e^{16t} + c_2 \begin{bmatrix} 2 \\ 5 \\ 1 \\ -1 \end{bmatrix} e^{32t} + c_3 \begin{bmatrix} 3 \\ -1 \\ 1 \\ 2 \end{bmatrix} e^{48t} + c_4 \begin{bmatrix} 1 \\ 1 \\ 2 \\ -3 \end{bmatrix} e^{64t}$

49. $\mathbf{x}(t) = c_1 \begin{bmatrix} 1 \\ 0 \\ 3 \\ 1 \\ 1 \end{bmatrix} e^{-3t} + c_2 \begin{bmatrix} 0 \\ 3 \\ 0 \\ -1 \\ 1 \end{bmatrix} + c_3 \begin{bmatrix} 1 \\ 7 \\ 1 \\ 1 \\ 1 \end{bmatrix} e^{3t} +$

$c_4 \begin{bmatrix} 0 \\ 1 \\ 0 \\ 1 \\ 1 \end{bmatrix} e^{6t} + c_5 \begin{bmatrix} 2 \\ 0 \\ 5 \\ 2 \\ 1 \end{bmatrix} e^{9t}$

50. $\mathbf{x}(t) = c_1 \begin{bmatrix} 0 \\ 1 \\ 1 \\ 1 \\ 0 \\ 1 \end{bmatrix} e^{-7t} + c_2 \begin{bmatrix} 1 \\ 0 \\ 0 \\ 0 \\ 1 \\ 1 \end{bmatrix} e^{-4t} + c_3 \begin{bmatrix} 0 \\ 1 \\ 0 \\ 1 \\ 0 \\ 1 \end{bmatrix} e^{3t} +$

$c_4 \begin{bmatrix} 0 \\ 0 \\ 0 \\ 0 \\ 1 \\ 0 \end{bmatrix} e^{5t} + c_5 \begin{bmatrix} 1 \\ 1 \\ 0 \\ 0 \\ 0 \\ 1 \end{bmatrix} e^{9t} + c_6 \begin{bmatrix} 0 \\ 0 \\ 1 \\ -1 \\ -1 \\ 0 \end{bmatrix} e^{11t}$

Section 5.3

1. The natural frequencies are $\omega_0 = 0$ and $\omega_1 = 2$. In the degenerate natural mode with "frequency" $\omega_0 = 0$ the two masses move linearly with $x_1(t) = x_2(t) = a_0 + b_0 t$. At frequency $\omega_1 = 2$ they oscillate in opposite directions with equal amplitudes.

2. The natural frequencies are $\omega_1 = 1$ and $\omega_2 = 3$. In the natural mode with frequency ω_1, the two masses m_1 and m_2 move in the same direction with equal amplitudes of oscillation. At frequency ω_2 they move in opposite directions with equal amplitudes.

3. The natural frequencies are $\omega_1 = 1$ and $\omega_2 = 2$. In the natural mode with frequency ω_1, the two masses m_1 and m_2 move in the same direction with equal amplitudes of oscillation. In the natural mode with frequency ω_2 they move in opposite directions with the amplitude of oscillation of m_1 twice that of m_2.

4. The natural frequencies are $\omega_1 = 1$ and $\omega_2 = \sqrt{5}$. In the natural mode with frequency ω_1, the two masses m_1 and m_2 move in the same direction with equal amplitudes of oscillation. At frequency ω_2 they move in opposite directions with equal amplitudes.

5. The natural frequencies are $\omega_1 = \sqrt{2}$ and $\omega_2 = 2$. In the natural mode with frequency ω_1, the two masses m_1 and m_2 move in the same direction with equal amplitudes of oscillation. At frequency ω_2 they move in opposite directions with equal amplitudes.

6. The natural frequencies are $\omega_1 = \sqrt{2}$ and $\omega_2 = \sqrt{8}$. In the natural mode with frequency ω_1, the two masses m_1 and m_2 move in the same direction with equal amplitudes of oscillation. In the natural mode with frequency ω_2 they move in opposite directions with the amplitude of oscillation of m_1 twice that of m_2.

7. The natural frequencies are $\omega_1 = 2$ and $\omega_2 = 4$. In the natural mode with frequency ω_1, the two masses m_1 and m_2 move in the same direction with equal amplitudes of oscillation. At frequency ω_2 they move in opposite directions with equal amplitudes.

8. $x_1(t) = 2 \cos t + 3 \cos 3t - 5 \cos 5t,$
$x_2(t) = 2 \cos t - 3 \cos 3t + \cos 5t.$
We have a superposition of three oscillations, in which the two masses move (1) in the same direction with frequency $\omega_1 = 1$ and equal amplitudes; (2) in opposite directions with frequency $\omega_2 = 3$ and equal amplitudes; (3) in opposite directions with frequency $\omega_3 = 5$ and with the amplitude of motion of m_1 being 5 times that of m_2.

9. $x_1(t) = 5\cos t - 8\cos 2t + 3\cos 3t$,
$x_2(t) = 5\cos t + 4\cos 2t - 9\cos 3t$.
We have a superposition of three oscillations, in which the two masses move (1) in the same direction with frequency $\omega_1 = 1$ and equal amplitudes; (2) in opposite directions with frequency $\omega_2 = 2$ and with the amplitude of motion of m_1 being twice that of m_2; (3) in opposite directions with frequency $\omega_3 = 3$ and with the amplitude of motion of m_2 being 3 times that of m_1.

10. $x_1(t) = \cos 2t - 15\cos 4t + 14\cos t$,
$x_2(t) = \cos 2t + 15\cos 4t + 16\cos t$.
We have a superposition of three oscillations, in which the two masses move (1) in the same direction with frequency $\omega_1 = 1$ and with the amplitude of motion of m_2 being 8/7 times that of m_1; (2) in the same direction with frequency $\omega_2 = 2$ and equal amplitudes; (3) in opposite directions with frequency $\omega_3 = 4$ and equal amplitudes.

11. (a) The natural frequencies are $\omega_1 = 6$ and $\omega_2 = 8$. In mode 1 the two masses oscillate in the same direction with frequency $\omega_1 = 6$ and with the amplitude of motion of m_1 being twice that of m_2. In mode 2 the two masses oscillate in opposite directions with frequency $\omega_2 = 8$ and with the amplitude of motion of m_2 being 3 times that of m_1.
(b) $x(t) = 2\sin 6t + 19\cos 7t$, $y(t) = \sin 6t + 3\cos 7t$
We have a superposition of (only two) oscillations, in which the two masses move (1) in the same direction with frequency $\omega_1 = 6$ and with the amplitude of motion of m_1 being twice that of m_2; (2) in the same direction with frequency $\omega_3 = 7$ and with the amplitude of motion of m_1 being 19/3 times that of m_2.

12. The system's three natural modes of oscillation have (1) natural frequency $\omega_1 = \sqrt{2}$ with amplitude ratios $1:0:-1$; (2) natural frequency $\omega_2 = \sqrt{2+\sqrt{2}}$ with amplitude ratios $1:-\sqrt{2}:1$; (3) natural frequency $\omega_3 = \sqrt{2-\sqrt{2}}$ with amplitude ratios $1:\sqrt{2}:1$.

13. The system's three natural modes of oscillation have (1) natural frequency $\omega_1 = 2$ with amplitude ratios $1:0:-1$; (2) natural frequency $\omega_2 = \sqrt{4+2\sqrt{2}}$ with amplitude ratios $1:-\sqrt{2}:1$; (3) natural frequency $\omega_3 = \sqrt{4-2\sqrt{2}}$ with amplitude ratios $1:\sqrt{2}:1$.

15. $x_1(t) = \frac{2}{3}\cos 5t - 2\cos 5\sqrt{3}\,t + \frac{4}{3}\cos 10t$,
$x_2(t) = \frac{4}{3}\cos 5t + 4\cos 5\sqrt{3}\,t + \frac{16}{3}\cos 10t$.
We have a superposition of two oscillations with the natural frequencies $\omega_1 = 5$ and $\omega_2 = 5\sqrt{3}$ and a forced oscillation with frequency $\omega = 10$. In each of the two natural oscillations the amplitude of motion of m_2 is twice that of m_1, while in the forced oscillation the amplitude of motion of m_2 is four times that of m_1.

20. $x_1'(t) = -v_0, x_2'(t) = 0, x_1'(t) = v_0$ for $t > \pi/2$
21. $x_1'(t) = -v_0, x_2'(t) = 0, x_1'(t) = 2v_0$ for $t > \pi/2$
22. $x_1'(t) = -2v_0, x_2'(t) = v_0, x_1'(t) = v_0$ for $t > \pi/2$
23. $x_1'(t) = 2v_0, x_2'(t) = 2v_0, x_1'(t) = 3v_0$ for $t > \pi/2$
24. (a) $\omega_1 \approx 1.0293$ Hz; $\omega_2 \approx 1.7971$ Hz.
(b) $v_1 \approx 28$ mi/h; $v_2 \approx 49$ mi/h
27. $\omega_1 = 2\sqrt{10}, v_1 \approx 40.26$ (ft/s (about 27 mi/h),
$\omega_2 = 5\sqrt{5}, v_2 \approx 71.18$ ft/s (about 49 mi/h)
28. $\omega_1 \approx 6.1311, v_1 \approx 39.03$ ft/s (about 27 mi/h)
$\omega_2 \approx 10.3155, v_2 \approx 65.67$ ft/s (about 45 mi/h)
29. $\omega_1 \approx 5.0424, v_1 \approx 32.10$ ft/s (about 22 mi/h),
$\omega_2 \approx 9.9158, v_2 \approx 63.13$ ft/s (about 43 mi/h)

Section 5.4

1. Repeated eigenvalue $\lambda = -3$, eigenvector $\mathbf{v} = \begin{bmatrix} 1 & -1 \end{bmatrix}^T$;
$x_1(t) = (c_1 + c_2 + c_2 t)e^{-3t}, x_2(t) = (-c_1 - c_2 t)e^{-3t}$

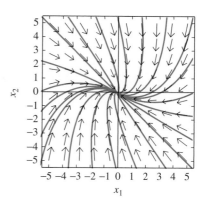

2. Repeated eigenvalue $\lambda = 2$, single eigenvector $\mathbf{v} = \begin{bmatrix} 1 & 1 \end{bmatrix}^T$;
$x_1(t) = (c_1 + c_2 + c_2 t)e^{2t}, x_2(t) = (c_1 + c_2 t)e^{2t}$

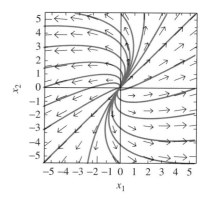

3. Repeated eigenvalue $\lambda = 3$, eigenvector $\mathbf{v} = \begin{bmatrix} -2 & 2 \end{bmatrix}^T$;
$x_1(t) = (-2c_1 + c_2 - 2c_2 t)e^{3t}, x_2(t) = (2c_1 + 2c_2 t)e^{3t}$

4. Repeated eigenvalue $\lambda = 4$, single eigenvector $\mathbf{v} = \begin{bmatrix} -1 & 1 \end{bmatrix}^T$;
$x_1(t) = (-c_1 + c_2 - c_2 t)e^{4t}, x_2(t) = (c_1 + c_2 t)e^{4t}$

5. Repeated eigenvalue $\lambda = 5$, eigenvector $\mathbf{v} = \begin{bmatrix} 2 & -4 \end{bmatrix}^T$;
$x_1(t) = (2c_1 + c_2 + 2c_2 t)e^{5t}, x_2(t) = (-4c_1 - 4c_2 t)e^{5t}$

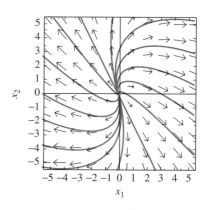

6. Repeated eigenvalue $\lambda = 5$, single eigenvector $\mathbf{v} = \begin{bmatrix} -4 & 4 \end{bmatrix}^T$;
$x_1(t) = (-4c_1 + c_2 - 4c_2 t)e^{5t}, x_2(t) = (4c_1 + 4c_2 t)e^{5t}$

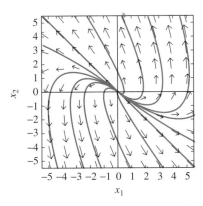

7. Eigenvalues $\lambda = 2, 2, 9$ with three linearly independent eigenvectors; $x_1(t) = c_1 e^{2t} + c_2 e^{2t}$, $x_2(t) = c_1 e^{2t} + c_3 e^{9t}$, $x_3(t) = c_2 e^{2t}$

8. Eigenvalues $\lambda = 7, 13, 13$ with three linearly independent eigenvectors; $x_1(t) = 2c_1 e^{7t} - c_3 e^{13t}$, $x_2(t) = -3c_1 e^{7t} + c_3 e^{13t}$, $x_3(t) = c_1 e^{7t} + c_2 e^{13t}$

9. Eigenvalues $\lambda = 5, 5, 9$ with three linearly independent eigenvectors; $x_1(t) = c_1 e^{5t} + 7c_2 e^{5t} + 3c_3 e^{9t}$, $x_2(t) = 2c_1 e^{5t}$, $x_3(t) = 2c_2 e^{5t} + c_3 e^{9t}$

10. Eigenvalues $\lambda = 3, 3, 7$ with three linearly independent eigenvectors; $x_1(t) = 5c_1 e^{3t} - 3c_2 e^{3t} + 2c_3 e^{7t}$, $x_2(t) = 2c_1 e^{3t} + c_3 e^{7t}$, $x_3(t) = c_2 e^{3t}$

11. Triple eigenvalue $\lambda = -1$ of defect 2; $x_1(t) = (-2c_2 + c_3 - 2c_3 t)e^{-t}$, $x_2(t) = (c_1 - c_2 + c_2 t - c_3 t + \frac{1}{2}c_3 t^2)e^{-t}$, $x_3(t) = (c_2 + c_3 t)e^{-t}$

12. Triple eigenvalue $\lambda = -1$ of defect 2; $x_1(t) = e^{-t}(c_1 + c_3 + c_2 t + \frac{1}{2}c_3 t^2)$ $x_2(t) = e^{-t}(c_1 + c_2 t + \frac{1}{2}c_3 t^2)$, $x_3(t) = e^{-t}(c_2 + c_3 t)$

13. Triple eigenvalue $\lambda = -1$ of defect 2; $x_1(t) = (c_1 + c_2 t + \frac{1}{2}c_3 t^2)e^{-t}$, $x_2(t) = (2c_2 + c_3 + 2c_3 t)e^{-t}$, $x_3(t) = (c_2 + c_2 t)e^{-t}$

14. Triple eigenvalue $\lambda = -1$ of defect 2; $x_1(t) = e^{-t}(5c_1 + c_2 + c_3 + 5c_2 t + c_3 t + \frac{5}{2}c_3 t^2)$, $x_2(t) = e^{-t}(-25c_1 - 5c_2 - 25c_2 t - 5c_3 t - \frac{25}{2}c_3 t^2)$, $x_3(t) = e^{-t}(-5c_1 + 4c_2 - 5c_2 t + 4c_3 t - \frac{5}{2}c_3 t^2)$

15. Triple eigenvalue $\lambda = 1$ of defect 1; $x_1(t) = (3c_1 + c_3 - 3c_3 t)e^t$, $x_2(t) = (-c_1 + c_3 t)e^t$, $x_3(t) = (c_2 + c_3 t)e^t$

16. Triple eigenvalue $\lambda = 1$ of defect 1; $x_1(t) = e^t(3c_1 + 3c_2 + c_3)$ $x_2(t) = e^t(-2c_1 - 2c_3 t)$, $x_3(t) = e^t(-2c_2 + 2c_3 t)$

17. Triple eigenvalue $\lambda = 1$ of defect 1; $x_1(t) = (2c_1 + c_2)e^t$, $x_2(t) = (-3c_2 + c_3 + 6c_3 t)e^t$, $x_3(t) = -9(c_1 + c_3 t)e^t$

18. Triple eigenvalue $\lambda = 1$ of defect 1; $x_1(t) = e^t(-c_1 - 2c_2 + c_3)$, $x_2(t) = e^t(c_2 + c_3 t)$, $x_3(t) = e^t(c_1 - 2c_3 t)$

19. Double eigenvalues $\lambda = -1$ and $\lambda = 1$, each with defect 1; $x_1(t) = c_1 e^{-t} + c_4 e^t$, $x_2(t) = c_3 e^t$, $x_3(t) = c_2 e^{-t} + 3c_4 e^t$, $x_4(t) = c_1 e^{-t} - 2c_3 e^t$

20. Eigenvalue $\lambda = 2$ with multiplicity 4 and defect 3; $x_1(t) = (c_1 + c_3 + c_2 t + c_4 t + \frac{1}{2}c_3 t^2 + \frac{1}{6}c_4 t^3)e^{2t}$, $x_2(t) = (c_2 + c_3 t + \frac{1}{2}c_4 t^2)e^{2t}$, $x_3(t) = (c_3 + c_4 t)e^{2t}$, $x_4(t) = c_4 e^{2t}$

21. Eigenvalue $\lambda = 1$ with multiplicity 4 and defect 2; $x_1(t) = (-2c_2 + c_3 - 2c_3 t)e^t$, $x_2(t) = (c_2 + c_3 t)e^t$, $x_3(t) = (c_2 + c_4 + c_3 t)e^t$, $x_4(t) = (c_1 + c_2 t + \frac{1}{2}c_3 t^2)e^t$

22. Eigenvalue $\lambda = 1$ with multiplicity 4 and defect 2; $x_1(t) = (c_1 + 3c_2 + c_4 + c_2 t + 3c_3 t + \frac{1}{2}c_3 t^2)e^t$, $x_2(t) = -(2c_2 - c_3 + 2c_3 t)e^t$, $x_3(t) = (c_2 + c_3 t)e^t$, $x_4(t) = -(2c_1 + 6c_2 + 2c_2 t + 6c_3 t + c_3 t^2)e^t$

23. $\mathbf{x}(t) = c_1 \mathbf{v}_1 e^{-t} + (c_2 \mathbf{v}_2 + c_3 \mathbf{v}_3)e^{3t}$ with $\mathbf{v}_1 = \begin{bmatrix} 1 & -1 & 2 \end{bmatrix}^T$, $\mathbf{v}_2 = \begin{bmatrix} 4 & 0 & 9 \end{bmatrix}^T$, $\mathbf{v}_3 = \begin{bmatrix} 0 & 2 & 1 \end{bmatrix}^T$

24. $\mathbf{x}(t) = c_1 \mathbf{v}_1 e^{-t} + (c_2 \mathbf{v}_2 + c_3 \mathbf{v}_3)e^{3t}$ with $\mathbf{v}_1 = \begin{bmatrix} 5 & 3 & -3 \end{bmatrix}^T$, $\mathbf{v}_2 = \begin{bmatrix} 4 & 0 & -1 \end{bmatrix}^T$, $\mathbf{v}_3 = \begin{bmatrix} 2 & -1 & 0 \end{bmatrix}^T$

25. $\mathbf{x}(t) = \left[c_1 \mathbf{v}_1 + c_2(\mathbf{v}_1 t + \mathbf{v}_2) + c_3 \left(\frac{1}{2}\mathbf{v}_1 t^2 + \mathbf{v}_2 t + \mathbf{v}_3 \right) \right] e^{2t}$ with $\mathbf{v}_1 = \begin{bmatrix} -1 & 0 & -1 \end{bmatrix}^T$, $\mathbf{v}_2 = \begin{bmatrix} -4 & -1 & 0 \end{bmatrix}^T$, and $\mathbf{v}_3 = \begin{bmatrix} 1 & 0 & 0 \end{bmatrix}^T$

26. $\mathbf{x}(t) = \left[c_1 \mathbf{v}_1 + c_2(\mathbf{v}_1 t + \mathbf{v}_2) + c_3 \left(\frac{1}{2}\mathbf{v}_1 t^2 + \mathbf{v}_2 t + \mathbf{v}_3 \right) \right] e^{3t}$ with $\mathbf{v}_1 = \begin{bmatrix} 0 & 2 & 2 \end{bmatrix}^T$, $\mathbf{v}_3 = \begin{bmatrix} 2 & 1 & -3 \end{bmatrix}^T$, and $\mathbf{v}_3 = \begin{bmatrix} 1 & 0 & 0 \end{bmatrix}^T$

27. $\mathbf{x}(t) = [c_1 \mathbf{v}_1 + c_2(\mathbf{v}_1 t + \mathbf{v}_2) + c_3 \mathbf{v}_3]e^{2t}$ with $\mathbf{v}_1 = \begin{bmatrix} -5 & 3 & 8 \end{bmatrix}^T$, $\mathbf{v}_2 = \begin{bmatrix} 1 & 0 & 0 \end{bmatrix}^T$, $\mathbf{v}_3 = \begin{bmatrix} 1 & 1 & 0 \end{bmatrix}^T$

28. $\mathbf{x}(t) = \left[c_1 \mathbf{v}_1 + c_2(\mathbf{v}_1 t + \mathbf{v}_2) + c_3 \left(\frac{1}{2}\mathbf{v}_1 t^2 + \mathbf{v}_2 t + \mathbf{v}_3 \right) \right] e^{2t}$ with $\mathbf{v}_1 = \begin{bmatrix} 119 & -289 & 0 \end{bmatrix}^T$, $\mathbf{v}_2 = \begin{bmatrix} -17 & 34 & 17 \end{bmatrix}^T$, and $\mathbf{v}_3 = \begin{bmatrix} 1 & 0 & 0 \end{bmatrix}^T$

29. $\mathbf{x}(t) = [c_1 \mathbf{v}_1 + c_2(\mathbf{v}_1 t + \mathbf{v}_2)]e^{-t} + [c_3 \mathbf{v}_3 + c_4(\mathbf{v}_3 t + \mathbf{v}_4)]e^{2t}$ with $\mathbf{v}_1 = \begin{bmatrix} 1 & -3 & -1 & -2 \end{bmatrix}^T$, $\mathbf{v}_2 = \begin{bmatrix} 0 & 1 & 0 & 0 \end{bmatrix}^T$, $\mathbf{v}_3 = \begin{bmatrix} 0 & -1 & 1 & 0 \end{bmatrix}^T$, $\mathbf{v}_4 = \begin{bmatrix} 0 & 0 & 2 & 1 \end{bmatrix}^T$

30. $\mathbf{x}(t) = [c_1 \mathbf{v}_1 + c_2(\mathbf{v}_1 t + \mathbf{v}_2)]e^{-t} + [c_3 \mathbf{v}_3 + c_4(\mathbf{v}_3 t + \mathbf{v}_4)]e^{2t}$, with $\mathbf{v}_1 = \begin{bmatrix} 0 & 1 & -1 & -3 \end{bmatrix}^T$, $\mathbf{v}_2 = \begin{bmatrix} 0 & 0 & 1 & 2 \end{bmatrix}^T$, $\mathbf{v}_3 = \begin{bmatrix} -1 & 0 & 0 & 0 \end{bmatrix}^T$, $\mathbf{v}_4 = \begin{bmatrix} 0 & 0 & 3 & 5 \end{bmatrix}^T$

31. $\mathbf{x}(t) = \left[c_1 \mathbf{v}_1 + c_2(\mathbf{v}_1 t + \mathbf{v}_2) + c_3 \left(\frac{1}{2}\mathbf{v}_1 t^2 + \mathbf{v}_2 t + \mathbf{v}_3 \right) + c_4 \mathbf{v}_4 \right] e^t$ with $\mathbf{v}_1 = \begin{bmatrix} 42 & 7 & -21 & -42 \end{bmatrix}^T$, $\mathbf{v}_2 = \begin{bmatrix} 34 & 22 & -10 & -27 \end{bmatrix}^T$, $\mathbf{v}_3 = \begin{bmatrix} -1 & 0 & 0 & 0 \end{bmatrix}^T$, $\mathbf{v}_4 = \begin{bmatrix} 0 & 1 & 3 & 0 \end{bmatrix}^T$

32. $\mathbf{x}(t) = (c_1 \mathbf{v}_1 + c_2 \mathbf{v}_2)e^{2t} + (c_3 \mathbf{v}_3 + c_4 \mathbf{v}_4 + c_5 \mathbf{v}_5)e^{3t}$ with $\mathbf{v}_1 = \begin{bmatrix} 8 & 0 & -3 & 1 & 0 \end{bmatrix}^T$, $\mathbf{v}_2 = \begin{bmatrix} 1 & 0 & 0 & 0 & 3 \end{bmatrix}^T$, $\mathbf{v}_3 = \begin{bmatrix} 3 & -2 & -1 & 0 & 0 \end{bmatrix}^T$, $\mathbf{v}_4 = \begin{bmatrix} 2 & -2 & 0 & -3 & 0 \end{bmatrix}^T$, $\mathbf{v}_5 = \begin{bmatrix} 1 & -1 & 0 & 0 & 3 \end{bmatrix}^T$

33. $\mathbf{x}_1(t) = \begin{bmatrix} \cos 4t & \sin 4t & 0 & 0 \end{bmatrix}^T e^{3t}$, $\mathbf{x}_2(t) = \begin{bmatrix} -\sin 4t & \cos 4t & 0 & 0 \end{bmatrix}^T e^{3t}$, $\mathbf{x}_3(t) = \begin{bmatrix} t \cos 4t & t \sin 4t & \cos 4t & \sin 4t \end{bmatrix}^T e^{3t}$, $\mathbf{x}_4(t) = \begin{bmatrix} -t \sin 4t & t \cos 4t & -\sin 4t & \cos 4t \end{bmatrix}^T e^{3t}$

34. $\mathbf{x}_1(t) = \begin{bmatrix} \sin 3t \\ 3\cos 3t - 3\sin 3t \\ 0 \\ \sin 3t \end{bmatrix} e^{2t}$,

$\mathbf{x}_2(t) = \begin{bmatrix} -\cos 3t \\ 3\sin 3t + 3\cos 3t \\ 0 \\ -\cos 3t \end{bmatrix} e^{2t}$,

$\mathbf{x}_3(t) = \begin{bmatrix} 3\cos 3t + t\sin 3t \\ (3t - 10)\cos 3t - (3t + 9)\sin 3t \\ \sin 3t \\ t\sin 3t \end{bmatrix} e^{2t}$,

$$\mathbf{x}_4(t) = \begin{bmatrix} -t\cos 3t + 3\sin 3t \\ (3t+9)\cos 3t + (3t-10)\sin 3t \\ -\cos 3t \\ -t\cos 3t \end{bmatrix} e^{2t}$$

35. $x_1(t) = x_2(t) = v_0(1 - e^{-t}); \; \lim\limits_{t\to\infty} x_1(t) = \lim\limits_{t\to\infty} x_2(t) = v_0$

36. $x_1(t) = v_0(2 - 2e^{-t} - te^{-t}),$
$x_2(t) = v_0(2 - 2e^{-t} - te^{-t} - \frac{1}{2}t^2 e^{-t});$
$\lim\limits_{t\to\infty} x_1(t) = \lim\limits_{t\to\infty} x_2(t) = 2v_0$

Section 5.5

1. $\Phi(t) = \begin{bmatrix} e^t & e^{3t} \\ -e^t & e^{3t} \end{bmatrix}, \; \mathbf{x}(t) = \frac{1}{2}\begin{bmatrix} 5e^t + e^{3t} \\ -5e^t + e^{3t} \end{bmatrix}$

2. $\Phi(t) = \begin{bmatrix} 1 & e^{4t} \\ 2 & -2e^{4t} \end{bmatrix}, \; \mathbf{x}(t) = \frac{1}{4}\begin{bmatrix} 3 + 5e^{4t} \\ 6 - 10e^{4t} \end{bmatrix}$

3. $\Phi(t) = \begin{bmatrix} 5\cos 4t & -5\sin 4t \\ 2\cos 4t + 4\sin 4t & 4\cos 4t - 2\sin 4t \end{bmatrix},$
$\mathbf{x}(t) = \frac{1}{4}\begin{bmatrix} -5\sin 4t \\ 4\cos 4t - 2\sin 4t \end{bmatrix}$

4. $\Phi(t) = e^{2t}\begin{bmatrix} 1 & 1+t \\ 1 & t \end{bmatrix}, \; \mathbf{x}(t) = e^{2t}\begin{bmatrix} 1+t \\ t \end{bmatrix}$

5. $\Phi(t) = \begin{bmatrix} 2\cos 3t & -2\sin 3t \\ -3\cos 3t + 3\sin 3t & 3\cos 3t + 3\sin 3t \end{bmatrix},$
$\mathbf{x}(t) = \frac{1}{3}\begin{bmatrix} 3\cos 3t - \sin 3t \\ -3\cos 3t + 6\sin 3t \end{bmatrix}$

6. $\Phi(t) = e^{5t}\begin{bmatrix} \cos 4t - 2\sin 4t & 2\cos 4t + 2\sin 4t \\ 2\cos 4t & 2\sin 4t \end{bmatrix},$
$\mathbf{x}(t) = 2e^{5t}\begin{bmatrix} \cos 4t + \sin 4t \\ \sin 4t \end{bmatrix}$

7. $\Phi(t) = \begin{bmatrix} 6 & 3e^t & 2e^{-t} \\ 2 & e^t & e^{-t} \\ 5 & 2e^t & 2e^{-t} \end{bmatrix}, \; \mathbf{x}(t) = \begin{bmatrix} -12 + 12e^t + 2e^{-t} \\ -4 + 4e^t + e^{-t} \\ -10 + 8e^t + 2e^{-t} \end{bmatrix}$

8. $\Phi(t) = \begin{bmatrix} 0 & e^t & e^{3t} \\ e^{-2t} & -e^t & -e^{3t} \\ -e^{-2t} & 0 & e^{3t} \end{bmatrix}, \; \mathbf{x}(t) = \begin{bmatrix} e^t \\ -e^t + e^{-2t} \\ -e^{-2t} \end{bmatrix}$

9. $e^{\mathbf{A}t} = \begin{bmatrix} 2e^{3t} - e^t & -2e^{3t} + 2e^t \\ e^{3t} - e^t & -e^{3t} + 2e^t \end{bmatrix}$

10. $e^{\mathbf{A}t} = \begin{bmatrix} -2 + 3e^{2t} & 3 - 3e^{2t} \\ -2 + 2e^{2t} & 3 - 2e^{2t} \end{bmatrix}$

11. $e^{\mathbf{A}t} = \begin{bmatrix} 3e^{3t} - 2e^{2t} & -3e^{3t} + 3e^{2t} \\ 2e^{3t} - 2e^{2t} & -2e^{3t} + 3e^{2t} \end{bmatrix}$

12. $e^{\mathbf{A}t} = \begin{bmatrix} -3e^t + 4e^{2t} & 4e^t - 4e^{2t} \\ -3e^t + 3e^{2t} & 4e^t - 3e^{2t} \end{bmatrix}$

13. $e^{\mathbf{A}t} = \begin{bmatrix} 4e^{3t} - 3e^t & -4e^{3t} + 4e^t \\ 3e^{3t} - 3e^t & -3e^{3t} + 4e^t \end{bmatrix}$

14. $e^{\mathbf{A}t} = \begin{bmatrix} -8e^t + 9e^{2t} & 6e^t - 6e^{2t} \\ -12e^t + 12e^{2t} & 9e^t - 8e^{2t} \end{bmatrix}$

15. $e^{\mathbf{A}t} = \begin{bmatrix} 5e^{2t} - 4e^t & -10e^{2t} + 10e^t \\ 2e^{2t} - 2e^t & -4e^{2t} + 5e^t \end{bmatrix}$

16. $e^{\mathbf{A}t} = \begin{bmatrix} -9e^t + 10e^{2t} & 15e^t - 15e^{2t} \\ -6e^t + 6e^{2t} & 10e^t - 9e^{2t} \end{bmatrix}$

17. $e^{\mathbf{A}t} = \frac{1}{2}\begin{bmatrix} e^{4t} + e^{2t} & e^{4t} - e^{2t} \\ e^{4t} - e^{2t} & e^{4t} + e^{2t} \end{bmatrix}$

18. $e^{\mathbf{A}t} = \frac{1}{2}\begin{bmatrix} e^{2t} + e^{6t} & -e^{2t} + e^{6t} \\ -e^{2t} + e^{6t} & e^{2t} + e^{6t} \end{bmatrix}$

19. $e^{\mathbf{A}t} = \frac{1}{5}\begin{bmatrix} 4e^{10t} + e^{5t} & 2e^{10t} - 2e^{5t} \\ 2e^{10t} - 2e^{5t} & e^{10t} + 4e^{5t} \end{bmatrix}$

20. $e^{\mathbf{A}t} = \frac{1}{5}\begin{bmatrix} e^{5t} + 4e^{15t} & -2e^{5t} + 2e^{15t} \\ -2e^{5t} + 2e^{15t} & 4e^{5t} + e^{15t} \end{bmatrix}$

21. $e^{\mathbf{A}t} = \begin{bmatrix} 1+t & -t \\ t & 1-t \end{bmatrix}$

22. $e^{\mathbf{A}t} = \begin{bmatrix} 1+6t & 4t \\ -9t & 1-6t \end{bmatrix}$

23. $e^{\mathbf{A}t} = \begin{bmatrix} 1+t & -t & -t-t^2 \\ t & 1-t & t-t^2 \\ 0 & 0 & 1 \end{bmatrix}$

24. $e^{\mathbf{A}t} = \begin{bmatrix} 1+3t & 0 & -3t \\ 5t + 18t^2 & 1 & 7t - 18t^2 \\ 3t & 0 & 1-3t \end{bmatrix}$

25. $e^{\mathbf{A}t} = \begin{bmatrix} e^{2t} & 5te^{2t} \\ 0 & e^{2t} \end{bmatrix}, \; \mathbf{x}(t) = e^{\mathbf{A}t}\begin{bmatrix} 4 \\ 7 \end{bmatrix}$

26. $e^{\mathbf{A}t} = \begin{bmatrix} e^{7t} & 0 \\ 11te^{7t} & e^{7t} \end{bmatrix}, \; \mathbf{x}(t) = e^{\mathbf{A}t}\begin{bmatrix} 5 \\ -10 \end{bmatrix}$

27. $e^{\mathbf{A}t} = \begin{bmatrix} e^t & 2te^t & (3t+2t^2)e^t \\ 0 & e^t & 2te^t \\ 0 & 0 & e^t \end{bmatrix}, \; \mathbf{x}(t) = e^{\mathbf{A}t}\begin{bmatrix} 4 \\ 5 \\ 6 \end{bmatrix}$

28. $e^{\mathbf{A}t} = \begin{bmatrix} e^{5t} & 0 & 0 \\ 10te^{5t} & e^{5t} & 0 \\ (20t+150t^2)e^{5t} & 30te^{5t} & e^{5t} \end{bmatrix}, \; \mathbf{x}(t) = e^{\mathbf{A}t}\begin{bmatrix} 40 \\ 50 \\ 60 \end{bmatrix}$

29. $e^{\mathbf{A}t} = \begin{bmatrix} 1 & 2t & 3t+6t^2 & 4t+6t^2+4t^3 \\ 0 & 1 & 6t & 3t+6t^2 \\ 0 & 0 & 1 & 2t \\ 0 & 0 & 0 & 1 \end{bmatrix} e^t,$
$\mathbf{x}(t) = e^{\mathbf{A}t}\begin{bmatrix} 1 \\ 1 \\ 1 \\ 1 \end{bmatrix}$

30. $e^{\mathbf{A}t} = e^{3t}\begin{bmatrix} 1 & 0 & 0 & 0 \\ 6t & 1 & 0 & 0 \\ 9t+18t^2 & 6t & 1 & 0 \\ 12t + 54t^2 + 36t^3 & 9t+18t^2 & 6t & 1 \end{bmatrix},$
$\mathbf{x}(t) = e^{\mathbf{A}t}\begin{bmatrix} 1 \\ 1 \\ 1 \\ 1 \end{bmatrix}$

33. $\mathbf{x}(t) = \begin{bmatrix} c_1\cosh t + c_2\sinh t \\ c_1\sinh t + c_2\cosh t \end{bmatrix}$ **35.** $e^{\mathbf{A}t} = \begin{bmatrix} e^{3t} & 4te^{3t} \\ 0 & e^{3t} \end{bmatrix}$

36. $e^{\mathbf{A}t} = e^t\begin{bmatrix} 1 & 2t & 3t+4t^2 \\ 0 & 1 & 4t \\ 0 & 0 & 1 \end{bmatrix}$

37. $e^{\mathbf{A}t} = \begin{bmatrix} e^{2t} & 3e^{2t} - 3e^t & 13e^{2t} - (13+9t)e^t \\ 0 & e^t & 3te^t \\ 0 & 0 & e^t \end{bmatrix}$

38. $e^{\mathbf{A}t} = \begin{bmatrix} e^{5t} & 4e^{10t} - 4e^{5t} & 16e^{10t} - (16+50t)e^{5t} \\ 0 & e^{10t} & 4e^{10t} - 4e^{5t} \\ 0 & 0 & e^{5t} \end{bmatrix}$

39. $e^{\mathbf{A}t} =$
$\begin{bmatrix} e^t & 3te^t & 12e^{2t} - (12+9t)e^t & (51+18t)e^t - (51-36t)e^{2t} \\ 0 & e^t & 3e^{2t} - 3e^t & 6e^t - (6-9t)e^{2t} \\ 0 & 0 & e^{2t} & 4e^{3t} - 4e^{2t} \\ 0 & 0 & 0 & e^{2t} \end{bmatrix}$

40. $e^{\mathbf{A}t} =$
$\begin{bmatrix} e^{2t} & 4te^{2t} & (4t+8t^2)e^{2t} & 100e^{3t} - (100+96t+32t^2)e^{2t} \\ 0 & e^{2t} & 4te^{2t} & 20e^{3t} - (20+16t)e^{2t} \\ 0 & 0 & e^{2t} & 4e^{3t} - 4e^{2t} \\ 0 & 0 & 0 & e^{3t} \end{bmatrix}$

Section 5.6

1. $x(t) = \frac{7}{3}$, $y(t) = -\frac{8}{3}$

2. $x(t) = \frac{1}{8}(1 + 12t)$, $y(t) = -\frac{1}{4}(5 + 4t)$

3. $x(t) = \frac{1}{756}(864e^{-t} + 4e^{6t} - 868 + 840t - 504t^2)$,
   $y(t) = \frac{1}{756}(-864e^{-t} + 3e^{6t} + 861 - 882t + 378t^2)$

4. $x(t) = \frac{1}{84}(99e^{5t} - 8e^{-2t} - 7e^t)$, $y(t) = \frac{1}{84}(99e^{5t} + 48e^{-2t} - 63e^t)$

5. $x(t) = \frac{1}{3}(-12 - e^{-t} - 7te^{-t})$, $y(t) = \frac{1}{3}(-6 - 7te^{-t})$

6. $x(t) = -\frac{1}{256}(91 + 16t)e^t$, $y(t) = \frac{1}{32}(25 + 16t)e^t$

7. $x(t) = \frac{1}{410}(369e^t + 166e^{-9t} - 125\cos t - 105\sin t)$,
   $y(t) = \frac{1}{410}(369e^t - 249e^{-9t} - 120\cos t - 150\sin t)$

8. $x(t) = \frac{1}{3}(17\cos t + 2\sin t)$, $y(t) = \frac{1}{3}(3\cos t + 5\sin t)$

9. $x(t) = \frac{1}{4}(\sin 2t + 2t\cos 2t + t\sin 2t)$, $y(t) = \frac{1}{4}t\sin 2t$

10. $x(t) = \frac{1}{13}e^t(4\cos t - 6\sin t)$, $y(t) = \frac{1}{13}e^t(3\cos t + 2\sin t)$

11. $x(t) = \frac{1}{2}(1 - 4t + e^{4t})$, $y(t) = \frac{1}{4}(-5 + 4t + e^{4t})$

12. $x(t) = t^2$, $y(t) = -t^2$

13. $x(t) = \frac{1}{2}(1 + 5t)e^t$, $y(t) = -\frac{5}{2}te^t$

14. $x(t) = \frac{1}{8}(-2 + 4t - e^{4t} + 2te^{4t})$, $y(t) = \frac{1}{2}t(-2 + e^{4t})$

15. (a) $x_1(t) = 200(1 - e^{-t/10})$, $x_2(t) = 400(1 + e^{-t/10} - 2e^{-t/20})$
    (b) $x_1(t) \to 200$ and $x_2(t) \to 400$ as $t \to +\infty$
    (c) Tank 1: about 6 min 56 s; tank 2: about 24 min 34 s

16. (a) $x_1(t) = 600(1 - e^{-t/20})$, $x_2(t) = 300(1 + e^{-t/10} - 2e^{-t/20})$
    (b) $x_1(t) \to 600$ and $x_2(t) \to 300$ as $t \to \infty$
    (c) Tank 1: about 8 min 7 sec; tank 2: about 17 min 13 sec

17. $x_1(t) = 102 - 95e^{-t} - 7e^{5t}$, $x_2(t) = 96 - 95e^{-t} - e^{5t}$

18. $x_1(t) = 68 - 110t - 75e^{-t} + 7e^{5t}$, $x_2(t) = 74 - 80t - 75e^{-t} + e^{5t}$

19. $x_1(t) = -70 - 60t + 16e^{-3t} + 54e^{2t}$,
    $x_2(t) = 5 - 60t - 32e^{-3t} + 27e^{2t}$

20. $x_1(t) = 3e^{2t} + 60te^{2t} - 3e^{-3t}$, $x_2(t) = -6e^{2t} + 30te^{2t} + 6e^{-3t}$

21. $x_1(t) = -e^{-t} - 14e^{2t} + 15e^{3t}$, $x_2(t) = -5e^{-t} - 10e^{2t} + 15e^{3t}$

22. $x_1(t) = -10e^{-t} - 7te^{-t} + 10e^{3t} - 5te^{3t}$,
    $x_2(t) = -15e^{-t} - 35te^{-t} + 15e^{3t} - 5te^{3t}$

23. $x_1(t) = 3 + 11t + 8t^2$, $x_2(t) = 5 + 17t + 24t^2$

24. $x_1(t) = 2 + t + \ln t$, $x_2(t) = 5 + 3t - \dfrac{1}{t} + 3\ln t$

25. $x_1(t) = -1 + 8t + \cos t - 8\sin t$,
    $x_2(t) = -2 + 4t + 2\cos t - 3\sin t$

26. $x_1(t) = 3\cos t - 32\sin t + 17t\cos t + 4t\sin t$,
    $x_2(t) = 5\cos t - 13\sin t + 6t\cos t + 5t\sin t$

27. $x_1(t) = 8t^3 + 6t^4$, $x_2(t) = 3t^2 - 2t^3 + 3t^4$

28. $x_1(t) = -7 + 14t - 6t^2 + 4t^2\ln t$,
    $x_2(t) = -7 + 9t - 3t^2 + \ln t - 2t\ln t + 2t^2\ln t$

29. $x_1(t) = t\cos t - (\ln\cos t)(\sin t)$,
    $x_2(t) = t\sin t + (\ln\cos t)(\cos t)$

30. $x_1(t) = \frac{1}{2}t^2\cos 2t$, $x_2(t) = \frac{1}{2}t^2\sin 2t$

31. $x_1(t) = (9t^2 + 4t^3)e^t$, $x_2(t) = 6t^2 e^t$, $x_3(t) = 6te^t$

32. $x_1(t) = (44 + 18t)e^t + (-44 + 26t)e^{2t}$,
    $x_2(t) = 6e^t + (-6 + 6t)e^{2t}$, $x_3(t) = 2te^{2t}$

33. $x_1(t) = 15t^2 + 60t^3 + 95t^4 + 12t^5$, $x_2(t) = 15t^2 + 55t^3 + 15t^4$,
    $x_3(t) = 15t^2 + 20t^3$, $x_4(t) = 15t^2$

34. $x_1(t) = 4t^3 + (4 + 16t + 8t^2)e^{2t}$,
    $x_2(t) = 3t^2 + (2 + 4t)e^{2t}$,
    $x_3(t) = (2 + 4t + 2t^2)e^{2t}$, $x_4(t) = (1 + t)e^{2t}$

Chapter 6

Section 6.1

1. 6.1.13 2. 6.1.15 3. 6.1.18 4. 6.1.12
5. 6.1.11 6. 6.1.17 7. 6.1.14 8. 6.1.16

9. Equilibrium solutions $x(t) \equiv 0$, ± 2. The critical point $(0, 0)$ in the phase plane looks like a center, whereas the points $(\pm 2, 0)$ look like saddle points.

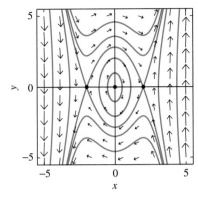

10. Equilibrium solution $x(t) \equiv 0$. The critical point $(0, 0)$ in the phase plane looks like a spiral sink.

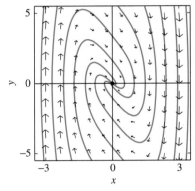

11. Equilibrium solutions $x(t) \equiv \ldots, -2\pi, -\pi, 0, \pi, 2\pi, \ldots$. The phase portrait shown in the solutions manual suggests that the critical point $(n\pi, 0)$ in the phase plane is a spiral sink if n is even, but is a saddle point if n is odd.

12. Equilibrium solution $x(t) \equiv 0$. The critical point $(0, 0)$ in the phase plane looks like a spiral source, with the solution curves emanating from this source spiraling outward toward a closed curve trajectory.

13. Solution $x(t) = x_0 e^{-2t}$, $y(t) = y_0 e^{-2t}$. The origin is a stable proper node similar to the one illustrated in Fig. 6.1.4.

14. Solution $x(t) = x_0 e^{2t}$, $y(t) = y_0 e^{-2t}$. The origin is an unstable saddle point.

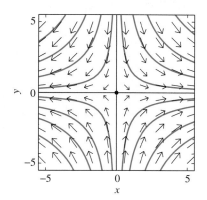

15. Solution $x(t) = x_0 e^{-2t}$, $y(t) = y_0 e^{-t}$. The origin is a stable node.

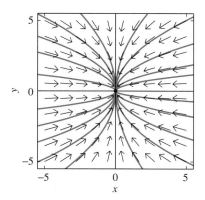

16. Solution $x(t) = x_0 e^{t}$, $y(t) = y_0 e^{3t}$. The origin is an unstable improper node.

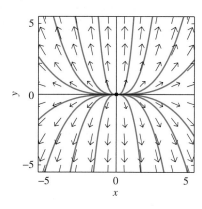

17. Solution $x(t) = A \cos t + B \sin t$, $y(t) = B \cos t - A \sin t$. The

origin is a stable center.

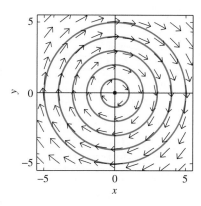

18. Solution $x(t) = A \cos 2t + B \sin 2t$, $y(t) = -2B \cos 2t + 2A \sin 2t$. The origin is a stable center.

19. Solution $x(t) = A \cos 2t + B \sin 2t$, $y(t) = B \cos 2t - A \sin 2t$. The origin is a stable center.

20. Solution $x(t) = e^{-2t}(A \cos t + B \sin t)$, $y(t) = e^{-2t}[(-2A + B) \cos t - (A + 2B) \sin t]$. The origin is a stable spiral point.

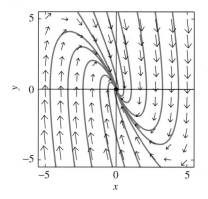

23. The origin and the circles $x^2 + y^2 = C > 0$; the origin is a stable center.

24. The origin and the hyperbolas $y^2 - x^2 = C$; the origin is an unstable saddle point.

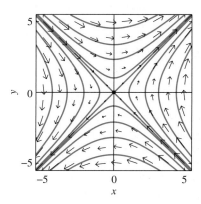

25. The origin and the ellipses $x^2 + 4y^2 = C > 0$; the origin is a stable center.

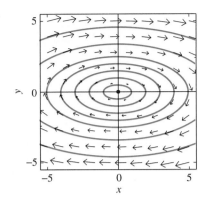

26. The origin and the ovals of the form $x^4 + y^4 = C > 0$; the origin is a stable center.

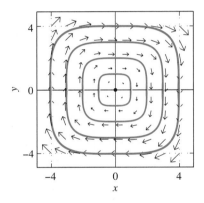

Section 6.2

1. Asymptotically stable node

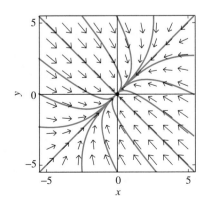

2. Unstable improper node

3. Unstable saddle point

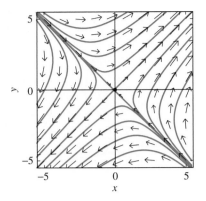

4. Unstable saddle point

5. Asymptotically stable node

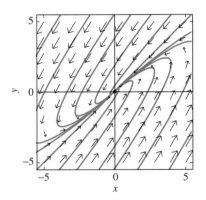

6. Unstable node

7. Unstable spiral point

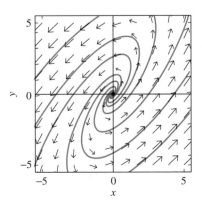

8. Asymptotically stable spiral point

9. Stable, but not asymptotically stable, center

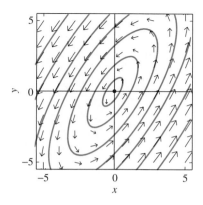

10. Stable, but not asymptotically stable, center

11. Asymptotically stable node: (2, 1)

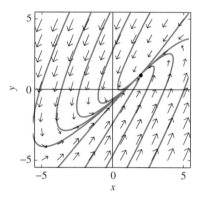

12. Unstable improper node: (2, −3)

13. Unstable saddle point: (2, 2)

14. Unstable saddle point: (3, 4)

15. Asymptotically stable spiral point: (1, 1)

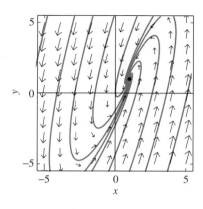

16. Unstable spiral point: (3, 2)

17. Stable center: $\left(\frac{5}{2}, -\frac{1}{2}\right)$

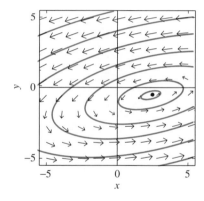

18. Stable, but not asymptotically stable, center: (−2, −1)

19. (0, 0) is a stable node. Also, there is a saddle point at (0.67, 0.40).

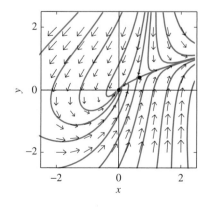

20. (0, 0) is an unstable node. Also, there is a saddle point at

$(-1, -1)$ and a spiral sink at $(-2.30, -1.70)$.

$(-1.08, -0.68)$.

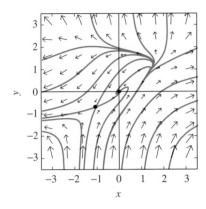

21. $(0, 0)$ is an unstable saddle point. Also, there is a spiral sink at $(-0.51, -2.12)$.

24. $(0, 0)$ is an spiral source. No other critical points are visible.

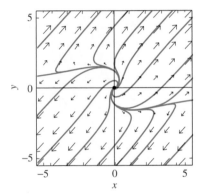

22. $(0, 0)$ is an unstable saddle point. Also, there are nodal sinks at $(\pm 0.82, \pm 5.06)$ and nodal sources at $(\pm 3.65, \mp 0.59)$.

25. Theorem 2 implies only that $(0, 0)$ is a stable sink—either a node or a spiral point. The phase portrait for $-5 \le x, y \le 5$ shows also a saddle point at $(0.74, -3.28)$ and spiral sink at $(2.47, -0.46)$. The origin looks like nodal sink in a second phase portrait for $-0.2 \le x, y \le 0.2$, which also reveals a second saddle point at $(0.12, 0.07)$.

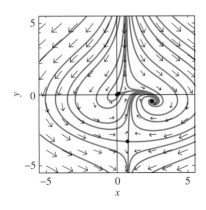

23. $(0, 0)$ is a spiral sink. Also, there is a saddle point at

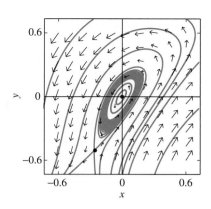

26. Theorem 2 implies only that $(0, 0)$ is an unstable source. The phase portrait for $-3 \leq x, y \leq 3$ shows also saddle points at $(0.20, 0.25)$ and $(-0.23, -1.50)$, as well as a nodal sink at $(2.36, 0.58)$.

28. Theorem 2 implies only that $(0, 0)$ is a center or a spiral point, but does not establish its stability (though in the phase portrait it looks like a likely center). The phase portrait for $-0.25 \leq x \leq 0.25, -1 \leq y \leq 1$ also shows saddle points at $(0.13, 0.63)$ and $(-0.12, -0.47)$.

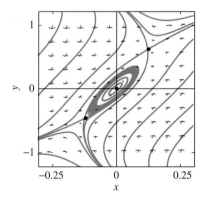

27. Theorem 2 implies only that $(0, 0)$ is a center or a spiral point, but does not establish its stability. The phase portrait for $-2 \leq x, y \leq 2$ shows also saddle points at $(-0.25, -0.51)$ and $(-1.56, 1.64)$, plus a nodal sink at $(-1.07, -1.20)$. The origin looks like a likely center in a second phase portrait for $-0.6 \leq x, y \leq 0.6$.

29. There is a saddle point at $(0, 0)$. The other critical point $(1, 1)$ is indeterminate, but looks like a center in the phase portrait.

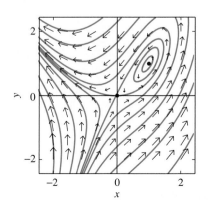

30. There is a saddle point at $(1, 1)$ and a spiral sink at $(-1, 1)$.

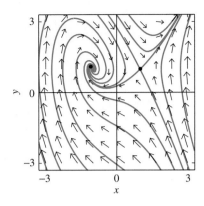

31. There is a saddle point at $(1, 1)$ and a spiral sink at $(-1, -1)$.

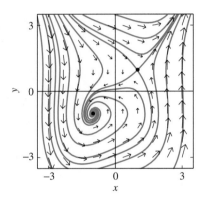

32. There is a saddle point at $(2, 1)$ and a spiral sink at $(-2, -1)$.

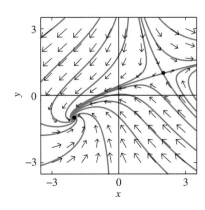

37. Note that the differential equation is homogeneous.

Section 6.3

1. Linearization at $(0, 0)$: $x' = 200x$, $y' = -150y$; phase plane portrait:

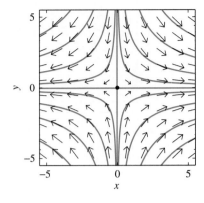

Linearization at $(75, 50)$: $u' = -300v$, $v' = 100u$; phase plane portrait:

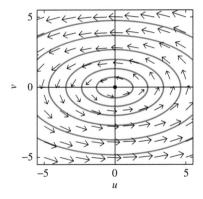

5. The characteristic equation is $\lambda^2 + 45\lambda + 126 = 0$.

7. The characteristic equation is $(-24 - \lambda)^2 - 2 \cdot (18)^2 = 0$. Phase plane portrait:

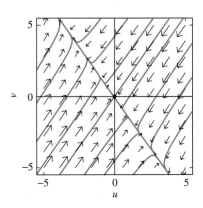

Phase plane portrait for the nonlinear system in Problems 4–7:

portrait:

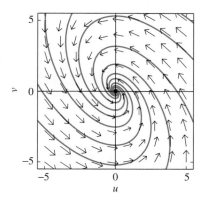

9. The characteristic equation is $\lambda^2 + 58\lambda - 120 = 0$.

10. The characteristic equation is $(\lambda + 36)(\lambda + 18) - 576 = 0$.
Phase plane portrait:

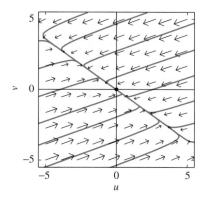

Phase plane portrait for the nonlinear system in Problems 8–10:

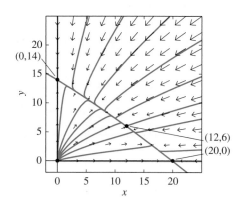

12. The characteristic equation is $\lambda^2 + 2\lambda - 15 = 0$.

13. The characteristic equation is $\lambda^2 + 2\lambda + 6 = 0$. Phase plane

15. The characteristic equation is $\lambda^2 + 2\lambda - 24 = 0$.

17. The characteristic equation is $\lambda^2 - 4\lambda + 6 = 0$. Phase plane
portrait:

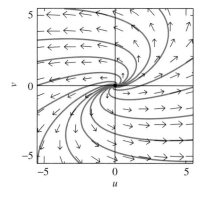

19. The characteristic equation is $\lambda^2 + 10 = 0$. Phase plane portrait:

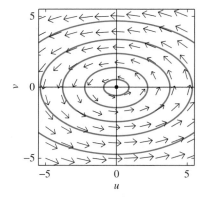

21. The characteristic equation is $\lambda^2 - \lambda - 6 = 0$.

22. The characteristic equation is $\lambda^2 - 5\lambda + 10 = 0$. Phase plane portrait:

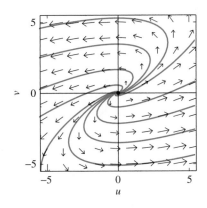

24. The characteristic equation is $\lambda^2 + 5\lambda - 14 = 0$.

25. The characteristic equation is $\lambda^2 + 5\lambda + 10 = 0$. Phase plane portrait:

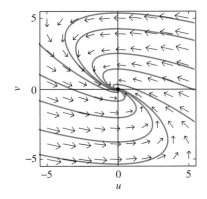

26. Naturally growing populations in competition
Critical points: nodal source $(0, 0)$ and saddle point $(3, 2)$
Nonzero coexisting populations $x(t) \equiv 3, y(t) \equiv 2$

27. Naturally declining populations in cooperation
Critical points: nodal sink $(0, 0)$ and saddle point $(3, 2)$
Nonzero coexisting populations $x(t) \equiv 3, y(t) \equiv 2$

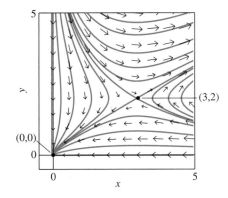

28. Naturally declining predator, naturally growing prey population
Critical points: saddle point $(0, 0)$ and apparent stable center $(4, 8)$

Nonzero coexisting populations $x(t) \equiv 4, y(t) \equiv 8$

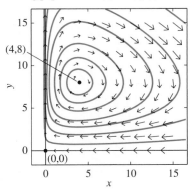

29. Logistic and naturally growing populations in competition
Critical points: nodal source $(0, 0)$, nodal sink $(3, 0)$, and saddle point $(2, 2)$
Nonzero coexisting populations $x(t) \equiv 2, y(t) \equiv 2$

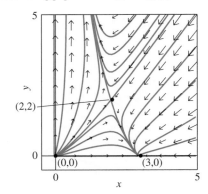

30. Logistic and naturally declining populations in cooperation
Critical points: saddle point $(0, 0)$, nodal sink $(3, 0)$, and saddle point $(5, 4)$
Nonzero coexisting populations $x(t) \equiv 5, y(t) \equiv 4$

31. Logistic prey, naturally declining predator population
Critical points: saddle points $(0, 0)$ and $(3, 0)$, spiral sink $(2, 4)$
Nonzero coexisting populations $x(t) \equiv 2, y(t) \equiv 4$

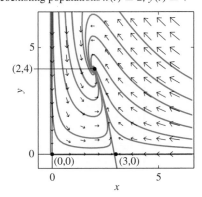

32. Logistic populations in cooperation
Critical points: nodal source $(0, 0)$, saddle points $(10, 0)$ and $(0, 20)$, nodal sink $(30, 60)$
Nonzero coexisting populations $x(t) \equiv 30, y(t) \equiv 60$

33. Logistic prey and predator populations
Critical points: nodal source $(0, 0)$, saddle points $(30, 0)$ and $(0, 20)$, nodal sink $(4, 22)$

Nonzero coexisting populations $x(t) \equiv 4$, $y(t) \equiv 22$

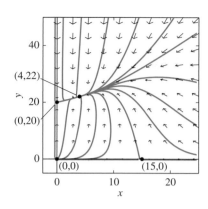

34. Logistic prey and predator populations
Critical points: nodal source $(0, 0)$, saddle points $(15, 0)$ and
$(0, 5)$, spiral sink $(10, 10)$
Nonzero coexisting populations $x(t) \equiv 10$, $y(t) \equiv 10$

Section 6.4

1. Eigenvalues: -2, -3; stable node

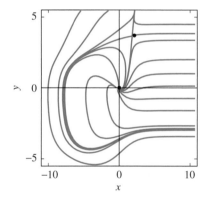

2. Eigenvalues: 1, 3; unstable node

3. Eigenvalues: -3, 5; unstable saddle point

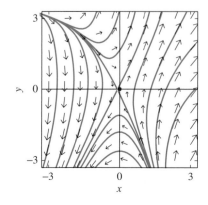

4. Eigenvalues: $-1 \pm 2i$; stable spiral point

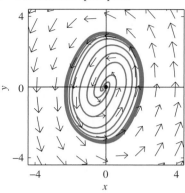

5. Critical points: $(0, n\pi)$ where n is an integer; an unstable saddle
point if n is even, a stable spiral point if n is odd

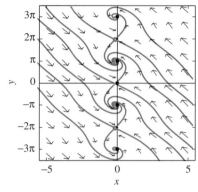

6. Critical points: $(n, 0)$ where n is an integer; an unstable saddle
point if n is even, a stable spiral point if n is odd

7. Critical points: $(n\pi, n\pi)$ where n is an integer; an unstable
saddle point if n is even, a stable spiral point if n is odd

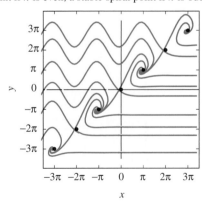

8. Critical points: $(n\pi, 0)$ where n is an integer; an unstable node if
n is even, an unstable saddle point if n is odd

9. If n is odd then $(n\pi, 0)$ is an unstable saddle point.

10. If n is odd then $(n\pi, 0)$ is a stable node.

11. $(n\pi, 0)$ is a stable spiral point.

12. Unstable saddle points at $(2, 0)$ and $(-2, 0)$, a stable center at
$(0, 0)$

13. Unstable saddle points at $(2, 0)$ and $(-2, 0)$, a stable spiral point
at $(0, 0)$

14. Stable centers at $(2, 0)$ and $(-2, 0)$, an unstable saddle point at
$(0, 0)$

15. A stable center at $(0, 0)$ and an unstable saddle point at $(4, 0)$

16. Stable centers at $(2, 0)$, $(0, 0)$, and $(-2, 0)$, unstable saddle points at $(1, 0)$ and $(-1, 0)$

17. $(0, 0)$ is a spiral sink.

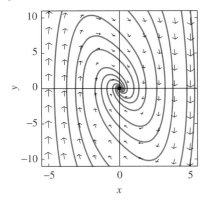

18. $(0, 0)$ is a spiral sink; the points $(\pm 2, 0)$ are saddle points.

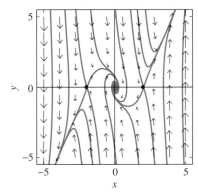

19. $(0, 0)$ is a spiral sink.

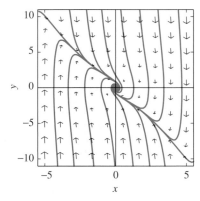

20. $(n\pi, 0)$ is a spiral sink if n is even, a saddle point if n is odd.

Chapter 7

Section 7.1

1. $1/s^2$, $s > 0$
2. $2/s^3$, $s > 0$
3. $e/(s - 3)$, $s > 3$
4. $s/(s^2 + 1)$, $s > 0$
5. $1/(s^2 - 1)$, $s > 1$
6. $\frac{1}{2}[1/s - s/(s^2 + 4)]$, $s > 0$
7. $(1 - e^{-s})/s$, $s > 0$

8. $(e^{-s} - e^{-2s})/s$, $s > 0$
9. $(1 - e^{-s} - se^{-s})/s^2$, $s > 0$
10. $(s - 1 + e^{-s})/s^2$, $s > 0$
11. $\frac{1}{2}\sqrt{\pi} s^{-3/2} + 3s^{-2}$, $s > 0$
12. $(45\pi - 192s^{3/2})/(8s^{7/2})$, $s > 0$
13. $s^{-2} - 2(s - 3)^{-1}$, $s > 3$
14. $3\sqrt{\pi}/(4s^{5/2}) + 1/(s + 10)$, $s > 0$
15. $s^{-1} + s(s^2 - 25)^{-1}$, $s > 5$ **16.** $(s + 2)/(s^2 + 4)$, $s > 0$
17. $\cos^2 2t = \frac{1}{2}(1 + \cos 4t)$; $\frac{1}{2}[s^{-1} + s/(s^2 + 16)]$, $s > 0$
18. $3/(s^2 + 36)$, $s > 0$
19. $s^{-1} + 3s^{-2} + 6s^{-3} + 6s^{-4}$, $s > 0$
20. $1/(s - 1)^2$, $s > 1$
21. $(s^2 - 4)/(s^2 + 4)^2$, $s > 0$
22. $\frac{1}{2}[s/(s^2 - 36) - s^{-1}]$
23. $\frac{1}{2}t^3$
24. $2\sqrt{t/\pi}$
25. $1 - \frac{8}{3}t^{3/2}\pi^{-1/2}$
26. e^{-5t}
27. $3e^{4t}$
28. $3\cos 2t + \frac{1}{2}\sin 2t$
29. $\frac{5}{3}\sin 3t - 3\cos 3t$
30. $-\cosh 2t - \frac{9}{2}\sinh 2t$
31. $\frac{3}{5}\sinh 5t - 10\cosh 5t$
32. $2u(t - 3)$
37. $f(t) = 1 - u(t - a)$. Your figure should indicate that the graph of f contains the point $(a, 0)$, but not the point $(a, 1)$.
38. $f(t) = u(t - a) - u(t - b)$. Your figure should indicate that the graph of f contains the points $(a, 1)$ and $(b, 0)$, but not the points $(a, 0)$ and $(b, 1)$.
39. Figure 7.2.8 shows the graph of the unit staircase function.

Section 7.2

1. $x(t) = 5\cos 2t$
2. $x(t) = 3\cos 3t + \frac{4}{3}\sin 3t$
3. $x(t) = \frac{2}{3}(e^{2t} - e^{-t})$
4. $x(t) = \frac{1}{2}(7e^{-3t} - 3e^{-5t})$
5. $x(t) = \frac{1}{3}(2\sin t - \sin 2t)$
6. $x(t) = \frac{1}{3}(\cos t - \cos 2t)$
7. $x(t) = \frac{1}{8}(9\cos t - \cos 3t)$
8. $x(t) = \frac{1}{9}(1 - \cos 3t)$
9. $x(t) = \frac{1}{6}(2 - 3e^{-t} + e^{-3t})$
10. $x(t) = \frac{1}{4}(2t - 3 + 12e^{-t} - 9e^{-2t})$
11. $x(t) = 1$, $y(t) = -2$
12. $x(t) = \frac{2}{9}(e^{2t} - e^{-t} - 3te^{-t})$, $y(t) = \frac{1}{9}(e^{2t} - e^{-t} + 6te^{-t})$
13. $x(t) = -\left(2/\sqrt{3}\right)\sinh\left(t/\sqrt{3}\right)$,
$y(t) = \cosh\left(t/\sqrt{3}\right) + \left(1/\sqrt{3}\right)\sinh\left(t/\sqrt{3}\right)$
14. $x(t) = \frac{1}{4}(2t - 3\sin 2t)$, $y(t) = -\frac{1}{8}(2t + 3\sin 2t)$
15. $x(t) = \frac{1}{3}\left(2 + e^{-3t/2}[\cos(rt/2) + r\sin(rt/2)]\right)$,
$y(t) = \frac{1}{21}\left(28 - 9e^t + 2e^{-3t/2}[\cos(rt/2) + 4r\sin(rt/2)]\right)$ where $r = \sqrt{3}$
16. $x(t) = \cos t + \sin t$, $y(t) = e^t - \cos t$, $z(t) = -2\sin t$
17. $f(t) = \frac{1}{3}(e^{3t} - 1)$
18. $f(t) = \frac{3}{5}(1 - e^{-5t})$
19. $f(t) = \frac{1}{4}(1 - \cos 2t) = \frac{1}{2}\sin^2 t$
20. $f(t) = \frac{1}{9}(6\sin 3t - \cos 3t + 1)$
21. $f(t) = t - \sin t$
22. $f(t) = \frac{1}{9}(-1 + \cosh 3t)$
23. $f(t) = -t + \sinh t$
24. $f(t) = \frac{1}{2}(e^{-2t} - 2e^{-t} + 1)$

Section 7.3

1. $24/(s-\pi)^5$

2. $\frac{3}{4}\sqrt{\pi}\,(s+4)^{-5/2}$

3. $3\pi/[(s+2)^2+9\pi^2]$

4. $\sqrt{2}\,(2s+5)/(4s^2+4s+17)$

5. $\frac{3}{2}e^{2t}$

6. $(t-t^2)e^{-t}$

7. te^{-2t}

8. $e^{-2t}\cos t$

9. $e^{3t}\left(3\cos 4t+\frac{7}{2}\sin 4t\right)$

10. $\frac{1}{36}e^{2t/3}\left(8\cos\frac{4}{3}t-5\sin\frac{4}{3}t\right)$

11. $\frac{1}{2}\sinh 2t$

12. $2+3e^{3t}$

13. $3e^{-2t}-5e^{-5t}$

14. $2+e^{2t}-3e^{-t}$

15. $\frac{1}{25}(e^{5t}-1-5t)$

16. $\frac{1}{125}[e^{2t}(5t-2)+e^{-3t}(5t+2)]$

17. $\frac{1}{16}(\sinh 2t-\sin 2t)$

18. $e^{4t}\left(1+12t+24t^2+\frac{32}{3}t^3\right)$

19. $\frac{1}{3}(2\cos 2t+2\sin 2t-2\cos t-\sin t)$

20. $\frac{1}{32}[e^{2t}(2t-1)+e^{-2t}(2t+1)]$

21. $\frac{1}{2}e^{-t}(5\sin t-3t\cos t-2t\sin t)$

22. $\frac{1}{64}e^{t/2}[(4t+8)\cos t+(4-3t)\sin t]$

27. $\frac{1}{4}e^{-3t}(8\cos 4t+9\sin 4t)$

28. $\frac{1}{4}(1-2e^{2t}+e^{4t})$

29. $\frac{1}{8}(-6t+3\sinh 2t)$

30. $\frac{1}{10}[2e^{-t}-e^{-2t}(2\cos 2t+\sin 2t)]$

31. $\frac{1}{15}(6e^{2t}-5-e^{-3t})$

32. $\frac{1}{2}(\cosh t+\cos t)$

33. $x(t)=r(\cosh rt\sin rt-\sinh rt\cos rt)$ where $r=1/\sqrt{2}$

34. $\frac{1}{2}\sin 2t+\frac{1}{3}\sin 3t$

35. $\frac{1}{16}(\sin 2t-2t\cos 2t)$

36. $\frac{1}{50}[2e^{2t}+(10t-2)\cos t-(5t+14)\sin t]$

37. $\frac{1}{50}[(5t-1)e^{-t}+e^{-2t}(\cos 3t+32\sin 3t)]$

38. $\frac{1}{510}e^{-3t}(489\cos 3t+307\sin 3t)+\frac{1}{170}(7\cos 2t+6\sin 2t)$

39.

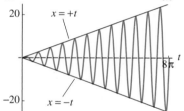

Section 7.4

1. $\frac{1}{2}t^2$

2. $(e^{at}-at-1)/a^2$

3. $\frac{1}{2}(\sin t-t\cos t)$

4. $2(t-\sin t)$

5. te^{at}

6. $(e^{at}-e^{bt})/(a-b)$

7. $\frac{1}{3}(e^{3t}-1)$

8. $\frac{1}{4}(1-\cos 2t)$

9. $\frac{1}{54}(\sin 3t-3t\cos 3t)$

10. $(kt-\sin kt)/k^3$

11. $\frac{1}{4}(\sin 2t+2t\cos 2t)$

12. $\frac{1}{5}[1-e^{-2t}(\cos t+2\sin t)]$

13. $\frac{1}{10}(3e^{3t}-3\cos t+\sin t)$

14. $\frac{1}{3}(\cos t-\cos 2t)$

15. $6s/(s^2+9)^2,\ s>0$

16. $(2s^3-24s)/(s^2+4)^3,\ s>0$

17. $(s^2-4s-5)/(s^2-4s+13)^2,\ s>0$

18. $\dfrac{2(3s^2+6s+7)}{(s+1)^2(s^2+2s+5)^2},\ s>0$

19. $\frac{1}{2}\pi-\arctan s=\arctan(1/s),\ s>0$

20. $\frac{1}{2}\ln(s^2+4)-\ln s,\ s>0$

21. $\ln s-\ln(s-3),\ s>3$

22. $\ln(s+1)-\ln(s-1),\ s>1$

23. $-(2\sinh 2t)/t$

24. $2(\cos 2t-\cos t)/t$

25. $e^{-2t}+e^{3t}-2\cos t)/t$

26. $(e^{-2t}\sin 3t)/t$

27. $2(1-\cos t)/t$

28. $\frac{1}{8}(t\sin t-t^2\cos t)$

29. $(s+1)X'(s)+4X(s)=0;\ x(t)=Ct^3e^{-t},\ C\neq 0$

30. $X(s)=A/(s+3)^3;\ x(t)=Ct^2e^{-3t},\ C\neq 0$

31. $(s-2)X'(s)+3X(s)=0;\ x(t)=Ct^2e^{2t},\ C\neq 0$

32. $(s^2+2s)X'(s)+(4s+4)X(s)=0;$
$x(t)=C(1-t-e^{-2t}-te^{-2t}),\ C\neq 0$

33. $(s^2+1)X'(s)+4sX(s)=0;\ x(t)=C(\sin t-t\cos t),\ C\neq 0$

34. $x(t)=Ce^{-2t}(\sin 3t-3t\cos 3t),\ C\neq 0$

Section 7.5

1. $f(t)=u(t-3)\cdot(t-3)$

2. $f(t)=(t-1)u(t-1)-(t-3)u(t-3)$

3. $f(t)=u(t-1)\cdot e^{-2(t-1)}$

4. $f(t)=e^{t-1}u(t-1)-e^2e^{t-2}u(t-2)$

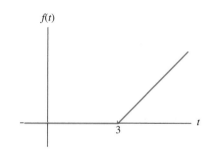

5. $f(t) = u(t - \pi) \cdot \sin(t - \pi) = -u(t - \pi) \sin t$

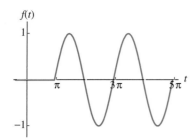

6. $f(t) = u(t - 1) \cdot \cos \pi(t - 1) = -u(t - 1) \cos \pi t$

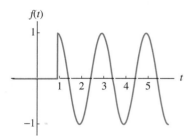

7. $f(t) = \sin t - u(t - 2\pi) \sin(t - 2\pi) = [1 - u(t - 2\pi)] \sin t$

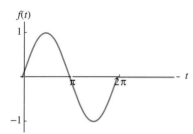

8. $f(t) = \cos \pi t - u(t - 2) \cos \pi(t - 2) = [1 - u(t - 2)] \cos \pi t$

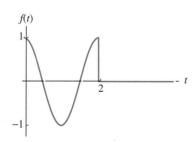

9. $f(t) = \cos \pi t + u(t - 3) \cos \pi(t - 3) = [1 - u(t - 3)] \cos \pi t$

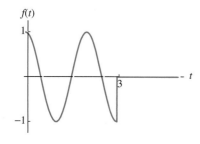

10. $f(t) = 2u(t - \pi) \cos 2(t - \pi) - 2u(t - 2\pi) \cos 2(t - 2\pi)$
$= 2[u(t - \pi) - u(t - 2\pi)] \cos 2t$

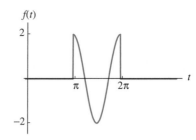

11. $f(t) = 2[1 - u_3(t)]$; $F(s) = 2(1 - e^{-3s})/s$
12. $F(s) = (e^{-s} - e^{-4s})/s$
13. $F(s) = (1 - e^{-2\pi s})/(s^2 + 1)$
14. $F(s) = s(1 - e^{-2s})/(s^2 + \pi^2)$
15. $F(s) = (1 + e^{-3\pi s})/(s^2 + 1)$
16. $F(s) = 2(e^{-\pi s} - e^{-2\pi s})/(s^2 + 4)$
17. $F(s) = \pi(e^{-2s} + e^{-3s})/(s^2 + \pi^2)$
18. $F(s) = 2\pi(e^{-3s} + e^{-5s})/(4s^2 + \pi^2)$
19. $F(s) = e^{-s}(s^{-1} + s^{-2})$
20. $F(s) = (1 - e^{-s})/s^2$
21. $F(s) = (1 - 2e^{-s} + e^{-2s})/s^2$
28. $F(s) = (1 - e^{-as} - ase^{-as})/[s^2(1 - e^{-2as})]$
31. $x(t) = \frac{1}{2}[1 - u(t - \pi)] \sin^2 t$

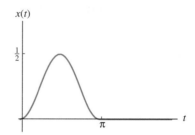

32. $x(t) = g(t) - u(t - 2)g(t - 2)$ where
$g(t) = \frac{1}{12}(3 - 4e^{-t} + e^{-4t})$.

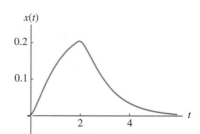

33. $x(t) = \frac{1}{8}[1 - u(t - 2\pi)] \left(\sin t - \frac{1}{3} \sin 3t\right)$

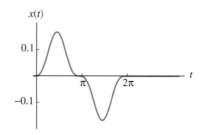

34. $x(t) = g(t) - u(t-1)[g(t-1) + h(t-1)]$ where
$g(t) = t - \sin t$ and $h(t) = 1 - \cos t$.

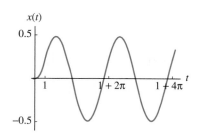

35. $x(t) = \frac{1}{4}\{-1 + t + (t+1)e^{-2t} + u(t-2)\left[1 - t + (3t-5)e^{-2(t-2)}\right]\}$

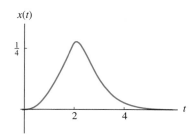

36. $i(t) = e^{-10t} - u(t-1)e^{-10(t-1)}$

37. $i(t) = [1 - u(t-2\pi)]\sin 100t$

38. $i(t) = \frac{10}{99}[1 - (u-\pi)](\cos 10t - \cos 100t)$

39. $i(t) = \frac{1}{50}\left[(1 - e^{-50t})^2 - u(t-1)(1 + 98e^{-50(t-1)} - 99e^{-100(t-1)})\right]$

40. $i(t) = \frac{1}{50}\left[(1 - e^{-50t} - 50te^{-50t}) - u(t-1)(1 - e^{-50(t-1)} + 2450te^{-50(t-1)})\right]$

41. $x(t) = 2|\sin t|\sin t$

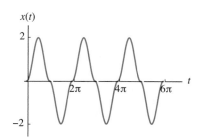

42. $x(t) = g(t) + 2\sum_{n=1}^{\infty}(-1)^n u(t - n\pi)g(t - n\pi)$ where
$g(t) = 1 - \frac{1}{3}e^{-t}(3\cos 3t + \sin 3t)$

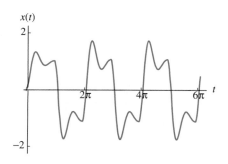

Section 7.6

1. $x(t) = \frac{1}{2}\sin 2t$

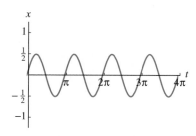

2. $x(t) = \frac{1}{2}[1 + u(t - \pi)]\sin 2t$

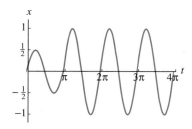

3. $x(t) = \frac{1}{4}[1 - e^{-2t} - 2te^{-2t}] + u(t-2)(t-2)e^{-2(t-2)}$

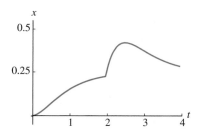

4. $x(t) = -2 + t + 2e^{-t} + 3te^{-t}$

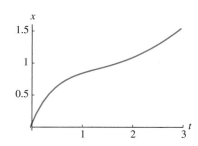

5. $x(t) = 2u(t - \pi)e^{-(t-\pi)}\sin(t - \pi)$

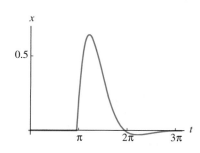

6. $x(t) = \frac{1}{6}(t - 2u(t - 3\pi)) \sin 3t$

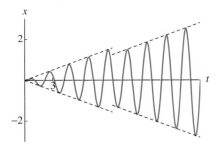

7. $x(t) = \left[2 - e^{2\pi} u(t - \pi) + e^{4\pi} u(t - 2\pi)\right] e^{-2t} \sin t$

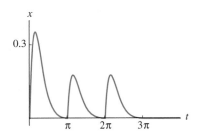

8. $x(t) = (2 + 5t)e^{-t} - u(t - 2)(t - 2)e^{-(t-2)}$

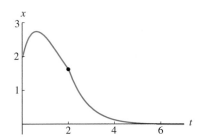

9. $x(t) = \int_0^t \frac{1}{2}(\sin 2\tau) f(t - \tau)\, d\tau$

10. $x(t) = \int_0^t \tau e^{-3\tau} f(t - \tau)\, d\tau$

11. $x(t) = \int_0^t (e^{-3\tau} \sinh \tau) f(t - \tau)\, d\tau$

12. $x(t) = \frac{1}{2} \int_0^t (e^{-2\tau} \sin 2\tau) f(t - \tau)\, d\tau$

13. (a) $mx_\epsilon(t) = p[t^2 - u_\epsilon(t)(t - \epsilon)^2]/(2\epsilon)$;
   (b) If $t > \epsilon$, then $mx_\epsilon(t) = p(2\epsilon t - \epsilon^2)/(2\epsilon)$, and hence
   $mx_\epsilon(t) \to pt$ as $\epsilon \to 0$;
   (c) $mv = (mx)' = (pt)' = 0$.

15. The transform of each of the two given initial value problems is
   $(ms^2 + k)X(s) = mv_0 = p_0$.

17. (b) $i(t) = e^{-100(t-1)} u_1(t) - e^{-100(t-2)} u_2(t)$.
   If $t > 2$, then $i(t) = -(e^{100} - 1)e^{100(1-t)} < 0$.

18. $i(t) = [1 - u(t - \pi)] \sin 10t$

19. $i(t) = \sum_{n=0}^{\infty} u(t - n\pi/10) \sin 10t$

20. $i(t) = \sum_{n=0}^{\infty} (-1)^n u(t - n\pi/5) \sin 10t$

21. $i(t) = \sum_{n=0}^{\infty} u(t - n\pi/10)e^{3n\pi} e^{-30t} \sin t$

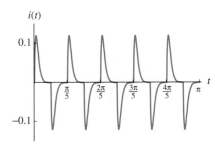

22. $x(t) = \sum_{n=0}^{\infty} u(t - 2n\pi) \sin t$

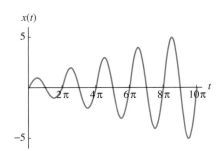

Chapter 8

Section 8.1

1. $y(x) = c_0 \left(1 + x + \dfrac{x^2}{2} + \dfrac{x^3}{3!} + \cdots\right) = c_0 e^x$; $\rho = +\infty$

2. $y(x) = c_0 \left(1 + \dfrac{4x}{1!} + \dfrac{4^2 x^2}{2!} + \dfrac{4^3 x^3}{3!} + \dfrac{4^4 x^4}{4!} + \cdots\right) = c_0 e^{4x}$;
   $\rho = \infty$

3. $y(x) = c_0 \left(1 - \dfrac{3x}{2} + \dfrac{(3x)^2}{2!2^2} - \dfrac{(3x)^3}{3!2^3} + \dfrac{(3x)^4}{4!2^4} - \cdots\right) =$
   $c_0 e^{-3x/2}$; $\rho = +\infty$

4. $y(x) = c_0 \left(1 - \dfrac{x^2}{1!} + \dfrac{x^4}{2!} - \dfrac{x^6}{3!} + \cdots\right) = c_0 e^{-x^2}$; $\rho = \infty$

5. $y(x) = c_0 \left(1 + \dfrac{x^3}{3} + \dfrac{x^6}{2!3^2} + \dfrac{x^9}{3!3^3} + \cdots\right) = c_0 \exp\left(\frac{1}{3}x^3\right)$;
   $\rho = +\infty$

6. $y(x) = c_0 \left(1 + \dfrac{x}{2} + \dfrac{x^2}{4} + \dfrac{x^3}{8} + \dfrac{x^4}{16} + \cdots\right) = \dfrac{2c_0}{2 - x}$; $\rho = 2$

7. $y(x) = c_0(1 + 2x + 4x^2 + 8x^3 + \cdots) = \dfrac{c_0}{1 - 2x}$; $\rho = \frac{1}{2}$

8. $y(x) = c_0 \left(1 + \dfrac{x}{2} - \dfrac{x^2}{8} + \dfrac{x^3}{16} - \dfrac{5x^4}{128} + \cdots\right) = c_0 \sqrt{1 + x}$;
   $\rho = 1$

9. $y(x) = c_0(1 + 2x + 3x^2 + 4x^3 + \cdots) = \dfrac{c_0}{(1 - x)^2}$; $\rho = 1$

10. $y(x) = c_0 \left(1 - \dfrac{3x}{2} + \dfrac{3x^2}{8} + \dfrac{x^3}{16} + \dfrac{3x^4}{128} + \cdots\right) = c_0(1 - x)^{3/2}$;
   $\rho = 1$

11. $y(x) = c_0 \left(1 + \dfrac{x^2}{2!} + \dfrac{x^4}{4!} + \dfrac{x^6}{6!} + \cdots\right) +$
   $c_1 \left(x + \dfrac{x^3}{3!} + \dfrac{x^5}{5!} + \dfrac{x^7}{7!} + \cdots\right)$
   $= c_0 \cosh x + c_1 \sinh x$; $\rho = +\infty$

12. $y(x) = c_0 \left(1 + \dfrac{(2x)^2}{2!} + \dfrac{(2x)^4}{4!} + \dfrac{(2x)^6}{6!} + \cdots \right) +$
$\dfrac{c_1}{2} \left((2x) + \dfrac{(2x)^3}{3!} + \dfrac{(2x)^5}{5!} + \dfrac{(2x)^7}{7!} + \cdots \right) =$
$c_0 \cosh 2x + \dfrac{c_1}{2} \sinh 2x; \rho = \infty$

13. $y(x) = c_0 \left(1 - \dfrac{(3x)^2}{2!} + \dfrac{(3x)^4}{4!} - \dfrac{(3x)^6}{6!} + \cdots \right) +$
$\dfrac{c_1}{3} \left(3x - \dfrac{(3x)^3}{3!} + \dfrac{(3x)^5}{5!} - \dfrac{(3x)^7}{7!} + \cdots \right)$
$= c_0 \cos 3x + \frac{1}{3} c_1 \sin 3x; \rho = +\infty$

14. $y(x) = x + c_0 \left(1 - \dfrac{x^2}{2!} + \dfrac{x^4}{4!} - \dfrac{x^6}{6!} + \cdots \right)$
$+ (c_1 - 1) \left(x - \dfrac{x^3}{3!} + \dfrac{x^5}{5!} - \dfrac{x^7}{7!} + \cdots \right)$
$= x + c_0 \cos x + (c_1 - 1) \sin x; \rho = \infty$

15. $(n+1)c_n = 0$ for all $n \geq 0$, so $c_n = 0$ for all $n \geq 0$.

16. $2nc_n = c_n$ for all $n \geq 0$, so $c_n = 0$ for all $n \geq 0$.

17. $c_0 = c_1 = 0$ and $c_{n+1} = -nc_n$ for $n \geq 1$, thus $c_n = 0$ for all $n \geq 0$.

18. $c_n = 0$ for all $n \geq 0$

19. $(n+1)(n+2)c_{n+2} = -4c_n$;
$y(x) = \dfrac{3}{2} \left[(2x) - \dfrac{(2x)^3}{3!} + \dfrac{(2x)^5}{5!} - \dfrac{(2x)^7}{7!} + \cdots \right] = \dfrac{3}{2} \sin 2x$

20. $(n+1)(n+2)c_{n+2} = 4c_n$;
$y(x) = 2 \left[1 + \dfrac{(2x)^2}{2!} + \dfrac{(2x)^4}{4!} + \dfrac{(2x)^6}{6!} + \cdots \right] = 2 \cosh 2x$

21. $n(n+1)c_{n+1} = 2nc_n - c_{n-1}$;
$y(x) = x + x^2 + \dfrac{x^3}{2!} + \dfrac{x^4}{3!} + \dfrac{x^5}{4!} + \cdots = xe^x$

22. $n(n+1)c_{n+1} = -nc_n + 2c_{n-1}; y = e^{-2x}$

23. As $c_0 = c_1 = 0$ and $(n^2 - n + 1)c_n + (n-1)c_{n-1} = 0$ for $n \geq 2$, $c_n = 0$ for all $n \geq 0$

Section 8.2

1. $c_{n+2} = c_n; y(x) = c_0 \displaystyle\sum_{n=0}^{\infty} x^{2n} + c_1 \displaystyle\sum_{n=0}^{\infty} x^{2n+1} = \dfrac{c_0 + c_1 x}{1 - x^2}; \rho = 1$

2. $c_{n+2} = -\frac{1}{2} c_n; \rho = 2;$
$y(x) = c_0 \displaystyle\sum_{n=0}^{\infty} \dfrac{(-1)^n x^{2n}}{2^n} + c_1 \displaystyle\sum_{n=0}^{\infty} \dfrac{(-1)^n x^{2n+1}}{2^n}$

3. $(n+2)c_{n+2} = -c_n;$
$y(x) = c_0 \displaystyle\sum_{n=0}^{\infty} \dfrac{(-1)^n x^{2n}}{n! 2^n} + c_1 \displaystyle\sum_{n=0}^{\infty} \dfrac{(-1)^n x^{2n+1}}{(2n+1)!!}; \rho = +\infty$

4. $(n+2)c_{n+2} = -(n+4)c_n; \rho = 1;$
$y(x) = c_0 \displaystyle\sum_{n=0}^{\infty} (-1)^n (n+1) x^{2n} + \frac{1}{3} c_1 \displaystyle\sum_{n=0}^{\infty} (-1)^n (2n+3) x^{2n+1}$

5. $3(n+2)c_{n+2} = nc_n; \rho = \sqrt{3}; y(x) = c_0 + c_1 \displaystyle\sum_{n=0}^{\infty} \dfrac{x^{2n+1}}{(2n+1)3^n}$

6. $(n+1)(n+2)c_{n+2} = (n-3)(n-4)c_n; \rho = \infty;$
$y(x) = c_0(1 + 6x^2 + x^4) + c_1(x + x^3)$

7. $3(n+1)(n+2)c_{n+2} = -(n-4)^2 c_n;$
$y(x) = c_0 \left(1 - \dfrac{8x^2}{3} + \dfrac{8x^4}{27} \right) +$
$c_1 \left(x - \dfrac{x^3}{2} + \dfrac{x^5}{120} + 9 \displaystyle\sum_{n=3}^{\infty} \dfrac{(-1)^n (2n-5)!! x^{2n+1}}{(2n+1)!3^n} \right)$

8. $2(n+1)(n+2)c_{n+2} = (n-4)(n+4)c_n; y(x) = c_0(1 - 4x^2 +$
$2x^4) + c_1 \left(x - \dfrac{5x^3}{4} + \dfrac{7x^5}{32} + \displaystyle\sum_{n=3}^{\infty} \dfrac{(2n-5)!!(2n+3)!! x^{2n+1}}{(2n+1)!2^n} \right)$

9. $(n+1)(n+2)c_{n+2} = (n+3)(n+4)c_n; \rho = 1;$
$y(x) = c_0 \displaystyle\sum_{n=0}^{\infty} (n+1)(2n+1)x^{2n} + \dfrac{c_1}{3} \displaystyle\sum_{n=0}^{\infty} (n+1)(2n+3)x^{2n+1}$

10. $3(n+1)(n+2)c_{n+2} = -(n-4)c_n;$
$y(x) = c_0 \left(1 + \dfrac{2x^2}{3} + \dfrac{x^4}{27} \right) +$
$c_1 \left(x + \dfrac{x^3}{6} + \dfrac{x^5}{360} + 3 \displaystyle\sum_{n=3}^{\infty} \dfrac{(-1)^n (2n-5)!! x^{2n+1}}{(2n+1)!3^n} \right)$

11. $5(n+1)(n+2)c_{n+2} = 2(n-5)c_n;$
$y(x) = c_1 \left(x - \dfrac{4x^3}{15} + \dfrac{4x^5}{375} \right) +$
$c_0 \left(1 - x^2 + \dfrac{x^4}{10} + \dfrac{x^6}{750} + 15 \displaystyle\sum_{n=4}^{\infty} \dfrac{(2n-7)!! \, 2^n x^{2n}}{(2n)!5^n} \right)$

12. $c_2 = 0; (n+2)c_{n+3} = c_n;$
$y(x) = c_0 \left(1 + \displaystyle\sum_{n=1}^{\infty} \dfrac{x^{3n}}{2 \cdot 5 \cdots (3n-1)} \right) + c_1 \displaystyle\sum_{n=0}^{\infty} \dfrac{x^{3n+1}}{n! 3^n}$

13. $c_2 = 0; (n+3)c_{n+3} = -c_n;$
$y(x) = c_0 \displaystyle\sum_{n=0}^{\infty} \dfrac{(-1)^n x^{3n}}{n! 3^n} + c_1 \displaystyle\sum_{n=0}^{\infty} \dfrac{(-1)^n x^{3n+1}}{1 \cdot 4 \cdots (3n+1)}$

14. $c_2 = 0; (n+2)(n+3)c_{n+3} = -c_n;$
$y(x) = c_0 \left(1 + \displaystyle\sum_{n=1}^{\infty} \dfrac{(-1)^n x^{3n}}{3^n \cdot n! \cdot 2 \cdot 5 \cdots (3n-1)} \right) +$
$c_1 \displaystyle\sum_{n=0}^{\infty} \dfrac{(-1)^n x^{3n+1}}{3^n \cdot n! \cdot 1 \cdot 4 \cdots (3n+1)}$

15. $c_2 = c_3 = 0; (n+3)(n+4)c_{n+4} = -c_n;$
$y(x) = c_0 \left(1 + \displaystyle\sum_{n=1}^{\infty} \dfrac{(-1)^n x^{4n}}{4^n \cdot n! \cdot 3 \cdot 7 \cdots (4n-1)} \right) +$
$c_1 \displaystyle\sum_{n=0}^{\infty} \dfrac{(-1)^n x^{4n+1}}{4^n \cdot n! \cdot 5 \cdot 9 \cdots (4n+1)}$

16. $y(x) = x$

17. $y(x) = 1 + x^2$

18. $y(x) = 2 \displaystyle\sum_{n=0}^{\infty} \dfrac{(-1)^n (x-1)^{2n}}{n! 2^n}$; converges for all x

19. $y(x) = \frac{1}{3} \displaystyle\sum_{n=0}^{\infty} (2n+3)(x-1)^{2n+1}$; converges if $0 < x < 2$

20. $y(x) = 2 - 6(x-3)^2$; converges for all x

21. $y(x) = 1 + 4(x+2)^2$; converges for all x

22. $y(x) = 2x + 6$

23. $2c_2 + c_0 = 0; (n+1)(n+2)c_{n+2} + c_n + c_{n-1} = 0$ for $n \geq 1;$
$y_1(x) = 1 - \dfrac{x^2}{2} - \dfrac{x^3}{6} + \cdots; y_2(x) = x - \dfrac{x^3}{6} - \dfrac{x^4}{12} + \cdots$

24. $y_1(x) = 1 + \dfrac{x^3}{3} + \dfrac{x^5}{5} + \dfrac{x^6}{45} + \cdots;$
$y_2(x) = x + \dfrac{x^3}{3} + \dfrac{x^4}{6} + \dfrac{x^5}{5} + \cdots$

25. $c_2 = c_3 = 0, (n+3)(n+4)c_{n+4} + (n+1)c_{n+1} + c_n = 0$ for $n \geq 0; y_1(x) = 1 - \dfrac{x^4}{12} + \dfrac{x^7}{126} + \cdots;$
$y_2(x) = x - \dfrac{x^4}{12} - \dfrac{x^5}{20} + \cdots$

26. $y(x) = c_0 \left(1 - \dfrac{x^6}{30} + \dfrac{x^9}{72} + \cdots\right) + c_1 \left(x - \dfrac{x^7}{42} + \dfrac{x^{10}}{90} + \cdots\right)$

27. $y(x) = 1 - x - \dfrac{x^2}{2} + \dfrac{x^3}{3} - \dfrac{x^4}{24} + \dfrac{x^5}{30} + \dfrac{29x^6}{720} + \dfrac{13x^7}{630} - \dfrac{143x^8}{40320} + \cdots;$

$y(0.5) \approx 0.4156$

28. $y(x) = c_0 \left(1 - \dfrac{x^2}{2} + \dfrac{x^3}{6} + \cdots\right) + c_1 \left(x - \dfrac{x^3}{6} + \dfrac{x^4}{12} + \cdots\right)$

29. $y_1(x) = 1 - \dfrac{1}{2}x^2 + \dfrac{1}{720}x^6 + \cdots;$

$y_2(x) = x - \dfrac{1}{6}x^3 - \dfrac{1}{60}x^5 + \cdots$

30. $y(x) = c_0 \left(1 - \dfrac{x^2}{2} + \dfrac{x^3}{6} + \cdots\right) + c_1 \left(x - \dfrac{x^2}{2} + \dfrac{x^4}{18} + \cdots\right)$

33. The following figure shows the interlaced zeros of the 4th and 5th Hermite polynomials.

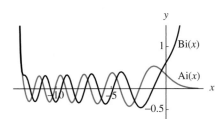

34. The figure below results when we use $n = 40$ terms in each summation. But with $n = 50$ we get the same picture as Fig. 8.2.3 in the text.

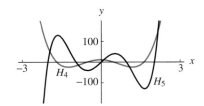

Section 8.3

1. Ordinary point
2. Ordinary point
3. Irregular singular point
4. Irregular singular point
5. Regular singular point; $r_1 = 0, r_2 = -1$
6. Regular singular point; $r_1 = 1, r_2 = -2$
7. Regular singular point; $r = -3, -3$
8. Regular singular point; $r = \frac{1}{2}, -3$
9. Regular singular point $x = 1$
10. Regular singular point $x = 1$
11. Regular singular points $x = 1, -1$
12. Irregular singular point $x = 2$
13. Regular singular points $x = 2, -2$
14. Irregular singular points $x = 3, -3$
15. Regular singular point $x = 2$
16. Irregular singular point $x = 0$, regular singular point $x = 1$
17. $y_1(x) = \cos\sqrt{x},\ y_2(x) = \sin\sqrt{x}$
18. $y_1(x) = \displaystyle\sum_{n=0}^{\infty} \dfrac{x^n}{n!(2n+1)!!},\ y_2(x) = x^{-1/2} \displaystyle\sum_{n=0}^{\infty} \dfrac{x^n}{n!(2n-1)!!}$

19. $y_1(x) = x^{3/2}\left(1 + 3\displaystyle\sum_{n=1}^{\infty} \dfrac{x^n}{n!(2n+3)!!}\right),$

$y_2(x) = 1 - x - \displaystyle\sum_{n=2}^{\infty} \dfrac{x^n}{n!(2n-3)!!}$

20. $y_1(x) = x^{1/3}\displaystyle\sum_{n=0}^{\infty} \dfrac{(-1)^n 2^n x^n}{n! \cdot 4 \cdot 7 \cdots (3n+1)},$

$y_2(x) = \displaystyle\sum_{n=0}^{\infty} \dfrac{(-1)^n 2^n x^n}{n! \cdot 2 \cdot 5 \cdots (3n-1)}$

21. $y_1(x) = x\left(1 + \displaystyle\sum_{n=1}^{\infty} \dfrac{x^{2n}}{n! \cdot 7 \cdot 11 \cdots (4n+3)}\right),$

$y_2(x) = x^{-1/2}\left(1 + \displaystyle\sum_{n=1}^{\infty} \dfrac{x^{2n}}{n! \cdot 1 \cdot 5 \cdots (4n-3)}\right)$

22. $y_1(x) = x^{3/2}\left(1 + \displaystyle\sum_{n=1}^{\infty} \dfrac{(-1)^n x^{2n}}{n! \cdot 9 \cdot 13 \cdots (4n+5)}\right),$

$y_2(x) = x^{-1}\left(1 + \displaystyle\sum_{n=1}^{\infty} \dfrac{(-1)^{n-1} x^{2n}}{n! \cdot 3 \cdot 7 \cdots (4n-1)}\right)$

23. $y_1(x) = x^{1/2}\left(1 + \displaystyle\sum_{n=1}^{\infty} \dfrac{x^{2n}}{2^n \cdot n! \cdot 19 \cdot 31 \cdots (12n+7)}\right),$

$y_2(x) = x^{-2/3}\left(1 + \displaystyle\sum_{n=1}^{\infty} \dfrac{x^{2n}}{2^n \cdot n! \cdot 5 \cdot 17 \cdots (12n-7)}\right)$

24. $y_1(x) = x^{1/3}\left(1 + \displaystyle\sum_{n=1}^{\infty} \dfrac{(-1)^n x^{2n}}{2^n \cdot n! \cdot 7 \cdot 13 \cdots (6n+1)}\right),$

$y_2(x) = 1 + \displaystyle\sum_{n=1}^{\infty} \dfrac{(-1)^n x^{2n}}{2^n \cdot n! \cdot 5 \cdot 11 \cdots (6n-1)}$

25. $y_1(x) = x^{1/2}\displaystyle\sum_{n=0}^{\infty} \dfrac{(-1)^n x^n}{n! \cdot 2^n} = x^{1/2}e^{-x/2},$

$y_2(x) = 1 + \displaystyle\sum_{n=1}^{\infty} \dfrac{(-1)^n x^n}{(2n-1)!!}$

26. $y_1(x) = x^{1/2}\displaystyle\sum_{n=0}^{\infty} \dfrac{x^{2n}}{n! \cdot 2^n} = x^{1/2}\exp\left(\tfrac{1}{2}x^2\right),$

$y_2(x) = 1 + \displaystyle\sum_{n=1}^{\infty} \dfrac{2^n x^{2n}}{3 \cdot 7 \cdots (4n-1)}$

27. $y_1(x) = \dfrac{1}{x}\cos 3x,\ y_2(x) = \dfrac{1}{x}\sin 3x$

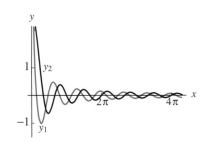

28. $y_1(x) = \dfrac{1}{x}\cosh 2x$, $y_2(x) = \dfrac{1}{x}\sinh 2x$

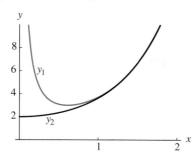

29. $y_1(x) = \dfrac{1}{x}\cos\dfrac{x}{2}$, $y_2(x) = \dfrac{1}{x}\sin\dfrac{x}{2}$

30. $y_1(x) = \cos x^2$, $y_2(x) = \sin x^2$

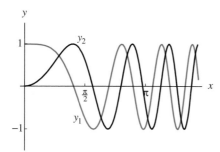

31. $y_1(x) = x^{1/2}\cosh x$, $y_2(x) = x^{1/2}\sinh x$

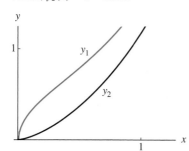

32. $y_1(x) = x + \dfrac{x^2}{5}$,

$y_2(x) = x^{-1/2}\left(1 - \dfrac{5x}{2} - \dfrac{15x^2}{8} - \dfrac{5x^3}{48} + \cdots\right)$

33. $y_1(x) = x^{-1}\left(1 + 10x + 5x^2 + \dfrac{10x^3}{9} + \cdots\right)$,

$y_2(x) = x^{1/2}\left(1 + \dfrac{11x}{20} - \dfrac{11x^2}{224} + \dfrac{671x^3}{24192} + \cdots\right)$

34. $y_1(x) = x\left(1 - \dfrac{x^2}{42} + \dfrac{x^4}{1320} + \cdots\right)$,

$y_2(x) = x^{-1/2}\left(1 - \dfrac{7x^2}{24} + \dfrac{19x^4}{3200} + \cdots\right)$

Section 8.4

1. $y_1(x) = \dfrac{1+x}{x^2}$, $y_2(x) = 1 + 2\displaystyle\sum_{n=1}^{\infty}\dfrac{x^n}{(n+2)!}$

2. $y_1(x) = \dfrac{1}{x^2}\left(1 + x + \dfrac{x^2}{2} + \dfrac{x^3}{6}\right)$, $y_2(x) = 1 + 24\displaystyle\sum_{n=1}^{\infty}\dfrac{x^n}{(n+4)!}$

3. $y_1(x) = \dfrac{1}{x^4}\left(1 - 3x + \dfrac{9x^2}{2} - \dfrac{9x^3}{2}\right)$,

$y_2(x) = 1 + 24\displaystyle\sum_{n=1}^{\infty}\dfrac{(-1)^n 3^n x^n}{(n+4)!}$

4. $y_1(x) = \dfrac{1}{x^5}\left(1 - \dfrac{3x}{5} + \dfrac{9x^2}{50} - \dfrac{9x^3}{250} + \dfrac{27x^4}{5000}\right)$,

$y_2(x) = 1 + 120\displaystyle\sum_{n=1}^{\infty}\dfrac{(-1)^n 3^n x^n}{(n5)!\cdot 5^n}$

5. $y_1(x) = 1 + \dfrac{3x}{4} + \dfrac{x^2}{4} + \dfrac{x^3}{24}$,

$y_2(x) = x^5\left(1 + 120\displaystyle\sum_{n=1}^{\infty}\dfrac{(n+1)x^n}{(n+5)!}\right)$

6. $y_1(x) = x^4\left(1 + \dfrac{8}{5}\displaystyle\sum_{n=1}^{\infty}\dfrac{(2n+5)!!x^n}{n!\,(n+4)!2^n}\right)$

7. $y_1(x) = \dfrac{1}{x^2}(2 - 6x + 9x^2)$, $y_2(x) = \displaystyle\sum_{n=1}^{\infty}\dfrac{(-1)^{n-1}3^n x^n}{(n+2)!}$

8. $y_1(x) = 3 + 2x + x^2$, $y_2(x) = \dfrac{x^4}{(1-x)^2}$

9. $y_1(x) = 1 + \dfrac{x^2}{2^2} + \dfrac{x^4}{2^2\cdot 4^2} + \dfrac{x^6}{x^2\cdot 4^2\cdot 6^2} + \cdots$,

$y_2(x) = y_1(x)\cdot\left(\ln x - \dfrac{x^2}{4} + \dfrac{5x^4}{128} - \dfrac{23x^6}{3456} + \cdots\right)$

10. $y_1(x) = x\left(1 - \dfrac{x^2}{2^2} + \dfrac{x^4}{2^2\cdot 4^2} - \dfrac{x^6}{2^2\cdot 4^2\cdot 6^2} + \cdots\right)$,

$y_2(x) = y_1(x)\cdot\left(\ln x + \dfrac{x^2}{4} + \dfrac{5x^4}{128} + \dfrac{23x^6}{3456} + \cdots\right)$

11. $y_1(x) = x^2\left(1 - 2x + \dfrac{3x^2}{2} - \dfrac{2x^3}{3} + \cdots\right)$,

$y_2(x) = y_1(x)\cdot\left(\ln x + 3x + \dfrac{11x^2}{4} + \dfrac{49x^3}{18} + \cdots\right)$

12. $y_1(x) = x^2\left(1 - \dfrac{x}{2} + \dfrac{3x^2}{20} - \dfrac{x^3}{30} + \dfrac{x^4}{168} - \cdots\right)$,

$y_2(x) = y_1(x)\cdot\left(-\dfrac{1}{3x^3} + \dfrac{1}{20x} + \dfrac{x}{700} + \cdots\right)$

13. $y_1(x) = x^3\left(1 - 2x + 2x^2 - \dfrac{4x^3}{3} + \cdots\right)$,

$y_2(x) = y_1(x)\cdot\left(2\ln x - \dfrac{1}{2x^2} - \dfrac{2}{x} + \dfrac{4x}{3} + \cdots\right)$

14. $y_1(x) = x^2\left(1 - \dfrac{2x}{5} + \dfrac{x^2}{10} - \dfrac{2x^3}{105} + \dfrac{x^4}{336} - \cdots\right)$,

$y_2(x) = y_1(x)\cdot\left(-\dfrac{1}{4x^4} + \dfrac{1}{15x^3} + \dfrac{1}{100x^2} - \dfrac{13}{1750x} + \cdots\right)$;

$y_2(x)$ contains no logarithmic term.

16. $y_1(x) = x^{3/2}\left(1 + \displaystyle\sum_{n=1}^{\infty}\dfrac{(-1)^n x^{2n}}{2^n\cdot n!\cdot 5\cdot 7\cdots(2n+3)}\right)$,

$y_2(x) = x^{-3/2}\left(1 + \displaystyle\sum_{n=1}^{\infty}\dfrac{(-1)^n x^{2n}}{2^n\cdot n!\cdot (-1)\cdot 1\cdot 3\cdots(2n-3)}\right)$

Section 8.5

2.

4.

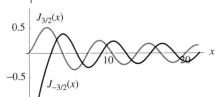

5. $J_4(x) = \dfrac{1}{x^2}(x^2 - 24)J_0(x) + \dfrac{8}{x^3}(6 - x^2)J_1(x)$

12. The following figure corroborates the calculated value $y(0) = 3$.

13. $x^2 J_1(x) + x J_1(x) - \displaystyle\int J_0(x)\,dx + C$

14. $(x^3 - 4x)J_1(x) + 2x^2 J_0(x) + C$

15. $(x^4 - 9x^2)J_1(x) + (3x^3 - 9x)J_0(x) + 9\displaystyle\int J_0(x)\,dx + C$

16. $-x J_1(x) + \displaystyle\int J_0(x)\,dx + C$

17. $2x J_1(x) - x^2 J_0(x) + C$

18. $3x^2 J_1(x) + (3x - x^3)J_0(x) - 3\displaystyle\int J_0(x)\,dx + C$

19. $(4x^3 - 16x)J_1(x) + (8x^2 - x^4)J_0(x) + C$

20. $-2J_1(x) + \displaystyle\int J_0(x)\,dx + C$

21. $J_0(x) - \dfrac{4}{x}J_1(x) + C$

26.

Section 8.6

1. $y(x) = x\,[c_1 J_0(x) + c_2 Y_0(x)]$

2. $y(x) = \dfrac{1}{x}\,[c_1 J_1(x) + c_2 Y_1(x)]$

3. $y(x) = x\,[c_1 J_{1/2}(3x^2) + c_2 J_{-1/2}(3x^2)]$

4. $y(x) = x^3\,[c_1 J_2(2x^{1/2}) + c_2 Y_2(2x^{1/2})]$

5. $y(x) = x^{-1/3}\,[c_1 J_{1/3}\left(\tfrac{1}{3}x^{3/2}\right) + c_2 J_{-1/3}\left(\tfrac{1}{3}x^{3/2}\right)]$

6. $y(x) = x^{-1/4}\,[c_1 J_0(2x^{3/2}) + c_2 Y_0(2x^{3/2})]$

7. $y(x) = x^{-1}\,[c_1 J_0(x) + c_2 Y_0(x)]$

8. $y(x) = x^2\,[c_1 J_1(4x^{1/2}) + c_2 Y_1(4x^{1/2})]$

9. $y(x) = x^{1/2}\,[c_1 J_{1/2}(2x^{3/2}) + c_2 J_{-1/2}(2x^{3/2})]$

10. $y(x) = x^{-1/4}\,[c_1 J_{3/2}\left(\tfrac{2}{5}x^{5/2}\right) + c_2 J_{-3/2}\left(\tfrac{2}{5}x^{5/2}\right)]$

11. $y(x) = x^{1/2}\,[c_1 J_{1/6}\left(\tfrac{1}{3}x^3\right) + c_2 J_{-1/6}\left(\tfrac{1}{3}x^3\right)]$

12. $y(x) = x^{1/2}\,[c_1 J_{1/5}\left(\tfrac{4}{5}x^{5/2}\right) + c_2 J_{-1/5}\left(\tfrac{4}{5}x^{5/2}\right)]$

Chapter 9

Section 9.1

1. $\tfrac{2}{3}\pi$

2. 1

3. $\tfrac{4}{3}\pi$

4. 6

5. π

6. $\tfrac{1}{2}$

7. Not periodic

8. Not periodic

9. π

10. $\frac{1}{3}\pi$

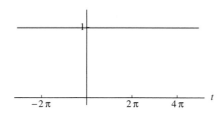

11. $a_0 = 2$; $a_n = b_n = 0$ for $n \geq 1$

12. $-\dfrac{12}{\pi}\left(\sin t + \dfrac{1}{3}\sin 3t + \dfrac{1}{5}\sin 5t + \cdots\right)$

13. $\dfrac{1}{2} + \dfrac{2}{\pi}\left(\sin t + \dfrac{1}{3}\sin 3t + \dfrac{1}{5}\sin 5t + \cdots\right)$

14. $\dfrac{1}{2} - \dfrac{10}{\pi}\left(\sin t + \dfrac{1}{3}\sin 3t + \dfrac{1}{5}\sin 5t + \cdots\right)$

15. $2\left(\sin t - \dfrac{1}{2}\sin 2t + \dfrac{1}{3}\sin 3t - \cdots\right)$

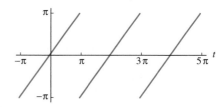

16. $\pi - 2\left(\sin t + \dfrac{1}{2}\sin 2t + \dfrac{1}{3}\sin 3t + \cdots\right)$

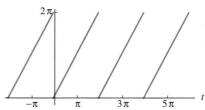

17. $\dfrac{\pi}{2} - \dfrac{4}{\pi}\left(\cos t + \dfrac{1}{9}\cos 3t + \dfrac{1}{25}\cos 5t + \cdots\right)$

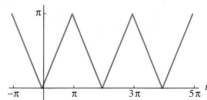

18. $\dfrac{\pi}{2} + \dfrac{4}{\pi}\left(\cos t + \dfrac{1}{9}\cos 3t + \dfrac{1}{25}\cos 5t + \cdots\right)$

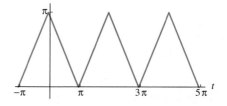

19. $a_0 = \dfrac{\pi}{4}$; $a_n = \dfrac{1 - (-1)^n}{n^2 \pi}$ for $n \geq 1$; $b_n = -\dfrac{1}{n}$ for $n \geq 1$.

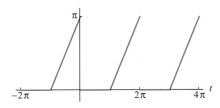

20. $\dfrac{1}{2} + \dfrac{2}{\pi}\left(\cos t - \dfrac{1}{3}\cos 3t + \dfrac{1}{5}\cos 5t - \cdots\right)$

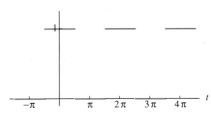

21. $\dfrac{1}{3}\pi^2 - 4\left(\cos t - \dfrac{1}{4}\cos 2t + \dfrac{1}{9}\cos 3t - \cdots\right)$

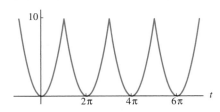

22. $a_0 = \dfrac{8}{3}\pi^2$; $a_n = \dfrac{4}{n}$ for $n \geq 1$; $b_n = -\dfrac{4\pi}{n}$ for $n \geq 1$.

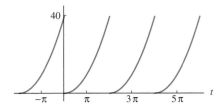

23. $a_0 = \dfrac{1}{3}\pi^2$; $a_n = \dfrac{2 \cdot (-1)^n}{n^2}$ for $n \geq 1$;

$b_n = 2 \cdot \dfrac{(-1)^n - 1}{\pi n^3} - \pi \cdot \dfrac{(-1)^n}{n}$ for $n \geq 1$

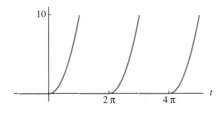

24. $b_n = 0$ for $n \geq 1$; $a_n = 0$ if n is odd;

$a_n = -\dfrac{4}{\pi(n^2 - 1)}$ for $n = 0, 2, 4, \ldots$.

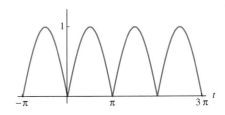

25. $a_0 = 1$, $a_4 = \dfrac{1}{2}$, and all other coefficients are zero.

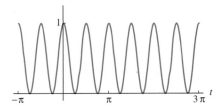

26. $\dfrac{1}{2}\sin t + \dfrac{1}{\pi} -$
$\dfrac{2}{\pi}\left(\dfrac{1}{1 \cdot 3}\cos 2t + \dfrac{1}{3 \cdot 5}\cos 4t + \dfrac{1}{5 \cdot 7}\cos 6t + \cdots\right)$

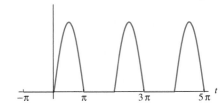

Section 9.2

1. $\dfrac{8}{\pi}\left(\sin\dfrac{\pi t}{3} + \dfrac{1}{3}\sin\dfrac{3\pi t}{3} + \dfrac{1}{5}\sin\dfrac{5\pi t}{3} + \cdots\right)$

2. $\dfrac{1}{2} + \dfrac{2}{\pi}\left(\sin\dfrac{\pi t}{5} + \dfrac{1}{3}\sin\dfrac{3\pi t}{5} + \dfrac{1}{5}\sin\dfrac{5\pi t}{5} + \cdots\right)$

3. $\dfrac{1}{2} - \dfrac{6}{\pi}\left(\sin\dfrac{t}{2} + \dfrac{1}{3}\sin\dfrac{3t}{2} + \dfrac{1}{5}\sin\dfrac{5t}{2} + \cdots\right)$

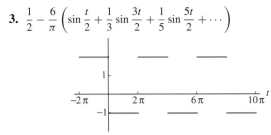

4. $\dfrac{4}{\pi}\left(\sin\dfrac{\pi t}{2} - \dfrac{1}{2}\sin\dfrac{2\pi t}{2} + \dfrac{1}{3}\sin\dfrac{3\pi t}{2} - \cdots\right)$

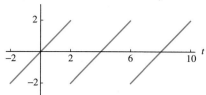

5. $4\left(\sin\dfrac{t}{2} - \dfrac{1}{2}\sin\dfrac{2t}{2} + \dfrac{1}{3}\sin\dfrac{3t}{2} - \cdots\right)$

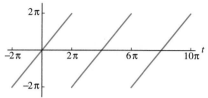

6. $\dfrac{3}{2} - \dfrac{3}{\pi}\left(\sin\dfrac{2\pi t}{3} + \dfrac{1}{2}\sin\dfrac{4\pi t}{3} + \dfrac{1}{3}\sin\dfrac{6\pi t}{3} + \cdots\right)$

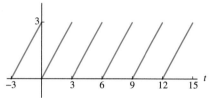

7. $\dfrac{1}{2} - \dfrac{4}{\pi^2}\left(\cos\pi t + \dfrac{1}{9}\cos 3\pi t + \dfrac{1}{25}\cos 5\pi t + \cdots\right)$

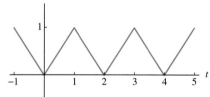

8. $\dfrac{1}{3} - \dfrac{\sqrt{3}}{\pi}\Bigl(\cos\dfrac{2\pi t}{3} - \dfrac{1}{2}\cos\dfrac{4\pi t}{3}$
$\quad + \dfrac{1}{4}\cos\dfrac{8\pi t}{3} - \dfrac{1}{5}\cos\dfrac{10\pi t}{3} + \cdots\Bigr)$

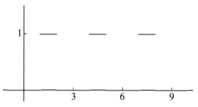

9. $\dfrac{1}{3} - \dfrac{4}{\pi^2}\left(\cos\pi t - \tfrac{1}{4}\cos 2\pi t + \tfrac{1}{9}\cos 3\pi t - \cdots\right)$

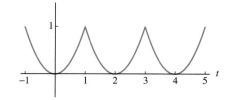

10. $\dfrac{2}{3} - \dfrac{8}{\pi^2}\left(\cos\dfrac{\pi t}{2} - \dfrac{1}{4}\cos\dfrac{2\pi t}{2} + \dfrac{1}{9}\cos\dfrac{3\pi t}{2} - \cdots\right) +$
$\quad \dfrac{4}{\pi}\left(\sin\dfrac{\pi t}{2} - \dfrac{1}{2}\sin\dfrac{2\pi t}{2} + \dfrac{1}{3}\sin\dfrac{3\pi t}{2} - \cdots\right) -$
$\quad \dfrac{16}{\pi^3}\left(\sin\dfrac{\pi t}{2} + \dfrac{1}{27}\sin\dfrac{3\pi t}{2} + \dfrac{1}{125}\sin\dfrac{5\pi t}{2} + \cdots\right)$

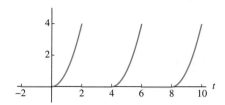

11. $a_0 = \dfrac{4}{\pi}$; $a_n = \dfrac{4\cdot(-1)^{n+1}}{\pi(4n^2-1)}$; $b_n = 0$ for all $n \geq 1$.

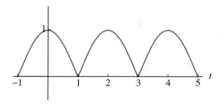

12. $L = \dfrac{1}{2}$; $a_0 = \dfrac{4}{\pi}$; $a_n = -\dfrac{4}{\pi(4n^2-1)}$ for $n \geq 1$;
$\quad b_n = 0$ for all $n \geq 1$.

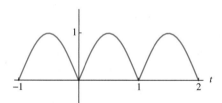

13. $a_0 = \dfrac{2}{\pi}$; $a_1 = 0$; $a_n = -\dfrac{1+(-1)^n}{\pi(n^2-1)}$ for $n \geq 2$;
$\quad b_1 = \tfrac{1}{2}$; $b_n = 0$ if $n \geq 2$.

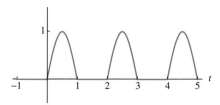

14. $\dfrac{1}{2}\sin t + \dfrac{4}{\pi}\left(\dfrac{1}{3}\cos\dfrac{t}{2} - \dfrac{1}{5}\cos\dfrac{3t}{2} - \dfrac{1}{21}\cos\dfrac{5t}{2} - \cdots\right)$

15.

16.

17.

18.

19.

20.

21.

24.

25.

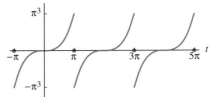

Section 9.3

1. Cosine series: $f(t) = 1$

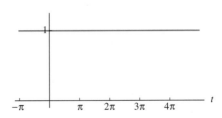

Sine series:
$$f(t) = \frac{4}{\pi}\left(\sin t + \frac{1}{3}\sin 3t + \frac{1}{5}\sin 5t + \frac{1}{7}\sin 7t + \cdots\right)$$

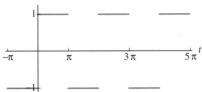

2. Cosine series: $f(t) =$
$$\frac{1}{2} + \frac{4}{\pi^2}\left(\cos \pi t + \frac{\cos 3\pi t}{3^2} + \frac{\cos 5\pi t}{5^2} + \frac{\cos 7\pi t}{7^2} + \cdots\right)$$

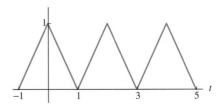

Sine series:
$$f(t) = \frac{2}{\pi}\left(\sin \pi t + \frac{\sin 2\pi t}{2} + \frac{\sin 3\pi t}{3} + \frac{\sin 4\pi t}{4} + \cdots\right)$$

3. Cosine series: $f(t) =$
$$\frac{8}{\pi^2}\left(\cos\frac{\pi t}{2} + \frac{1}{3^2}\cos\frac{3\pi t}{2} + \frac{1}{5^2}\cos\frac{5\pi t}{2} + \frac{1}{7^2}\cos\frac{7\pi t}{2} + \cdots\right)$$

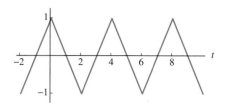

Sine series:
$$f(t) = \frac{4}{\pi}\left(\frac{\sin\pi t}{2} + \frac{\sin 2\pi t}{4} + \frac{\sin 3\pi t}{6} + \frac{\sin 4\pi t}{8} + \cdots\right)$$

4. Cosine series: $f(t) =$
$$1 - \frac{16}{\pi^2}\left(\frac{\cos\pi t}{2^2} + \frac{\cos 3\pi t}{6^2} + \frac{\cos 5\pi t}{10^2} + \frac{\cos 7\pi t}{14^2} + \cdots\right)$$

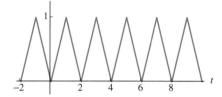

Sine series: $f(t) =$
$$\frac{8}{\pi^2}\left(\sin\frac{\pi t}{2} - \frac{1}{3^2}\sin\frac{3\pi t}{2} + \frac{1}{5^2}\sin\frac{5\pi t}{2} - \frac{1}{7^2}\sin\frac{7\pi t}{2} + \cdots\right)$$

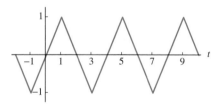

5. Cosine series: $f(t) = \frac{1}{3} - \frac{2\sqrt{3}}{\pi}\left(\frac{1}{2}\cos\frac{2\pi t}{3} - \frac{1}{4}\cos\frac{4\pi t}{3} + \right.$
$$\left.\frac{1}{8}\cos\frac{8\pi t}{3} - \frac{1}{10}\cos\frac{10\pi t}{3} + \cdots\right)$$

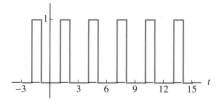

Sine series:
$$f(t) = \frac{2}{\pi}\left(\sin\frac{\pi t}{3} - \frac{2}{3}\sin\frac{3\pi t}{3} + \frac{1}{5}\sin\frac{5\pi t}{3} + \frac{1}{7}\sin\frac{7\pi t}{3} - \right.$$

$$\left.\frac{2}{9}\sin\frac{9\pi t}{3} + \frac{1}{11}\sin\frac{11\pi t}{3} + \cdots\right)$$

6. Cosine series: $f(t) =$
$$\frac{\pi^2}{3} - 4\left(\cos t - \frac{1}{2^2}\cos 2t + \frac{1}{3^2}\cos 3t + \frac{1}{4^2}\cos 4t + \cdots\right)$$

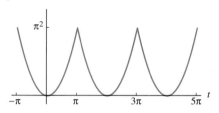

Sine series:
$$f(t) = 2\pi\left(\sin t - \frac{1}{2}\sin 2t + \frac{1}{3}\sin 3t - \frac{1}{4}\sin 4t + \cdots\right) -$$
$$\frac{8}{\pi}\left(\sin t + \frac{1}{3^2}\sin 3t + \frac{1}{5^3}\sin 5t + \frac{1}{7^3}\sin 7t + \cdots\right)$$

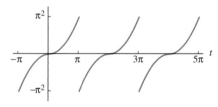

7. Cosine series:
$$f(t) = \frac{\pi^2}{6} - 4\left(\frac{\cos 2t}{2^2} + \frac{\cos 4t}{4^2} + \frac{\cos 6t}{6^2} + \frac{\cos 8t}{8^2} + \cdots\right)$$

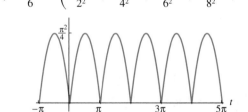

Sine series: $f(t) = \frac{8}{\pi}\left(\sin t + \frac{\sin 3t}{3^3} + \frac{\sin 5t}{5^3} + \frac{\sin 7t}{7^3} + \cdots\right)$

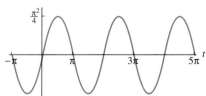

8. Cosine series: $f(t) =$
$$\frac{1}{6} - \frac{4}{\pi^2}\left(\frac{\cos 2\pi t}{2^2} + \frac{\cos 4\pi t}{4^2} + \frac{\cos 6\pi t}{6^2} + \frac{\cos 8\pi t}{8^2} + \cdots\right)$$
Sine series:
$$f(t) = \frac{8}{\pi^3}\left(\sin\pi t + \frac{\sin 3\pi t}{3^3} + \frac{\sin 5\pi t}{5^3} + \frac{\sin 7\pi t}{7^3} + \cdots\right)$$

The graphs of these two series look precisely the same as those in Problem 7, except with a scale of -1 to 5 (rather than $-\pi$ to 5π) on the t-axis, and with arches of height $1/4$ (rather than $\pi^2/4$).

9. Cosine series:
$$f(t) = \frac{2}{\pi} - \frac{4}{\pi^2}\left(\frac{\cos 2t}{3} + \frac{\cos 4t}{15} + \frac{\cos 6t}{35} + \frac{\cos 8t}{63} + \cdots\right)$$
Sine series: $f(t) = \sin t$
The graphs of these two series look essentially the same as those in Problem 7, except with sine arches rather than quadratic arches.

10. Cosine series:
$$f(t) = \frac{1}{\pi} - \frac{4}{\pi}\left(-\frac{1}{3}\cos\frac{t}{2} + \frac{1}{5}\cos\frac{3t}{2} + \frac{2}{12}\cos\frac{4t}{2} + \right.$$
$$\left. \frac{1}{21}\cos\frac{5t}{2} + \frac{1}{45}\cos\frac{7t}{2} + \frac{2}{60}\cos\frac{8t}{2} + \cdots\right)$$

Sine series:
$$f(t) = \frac{1}{2}\sin t - \frac{4}{\pi}\left(\frac{1}{3}\sin\frac{t}{2} + \frac{1}{5}\sin\frac{3t}{2} - \frac{1}{21}\sin\frac{5t}{2} + \right.$$
$$\left. \frac{1}{45}\sin\frac{7t}{2} - \frac{1}{77}\sin\frac{9t}{2} + \cdots\right)$$

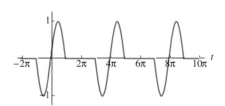

11. $x(t) = \dfrac{4}{\pi}\displaystyle\sum_{n\text{ odd}}\dfrac{\sin nt}{n(2 - n^2)} =$
$$\frac{4}{\pi}\left(\sin t - \frac{\sin 3t}{21} - \frac{\sin 5t}{115} - \frac{\sin 7t}{329} - \cdots\right)$$

12. $x(t) = -\dfrac{4}{\pi}\left(\dfrac{\sin t}{5} + \dfrac{\sin 3t}{39} + \dfrac{\sin 5t}{145} + \dfrac{\sin 7t}{371} + \cdots\right)$

13. $x(t) = \dfrac{2}{\pi}\displaystyle\sum_{n=1}^{\infty}\dfrac{(-1)^n\sin n\pi t}{n(n^2\pi^2 - 1)}$

14. $x(t) = \dfrac{16}{\pi}\displaystyle\sum_{n=1}^{\infty}\dfrac{(-1)^n\sin(n\pi t/2)}{n(n^2\pi^2 - 8)}$

15. $x(t) = \dfrac{\pi}{4} + \dfrac{4}{\pi}\displaystyle\sum_{n\text{ odd}}\dfrac{\cos nt}{n^2(n^2 - 2)} =$
$$\frac{\pi}{4} + \frac{4}{\pi}\left(-\cos t + \frac{\cos 3t}{63} + \frac{\cos 5t}{575} + \frac{\cos 7t}{2303} + \cdots\right)$$

17. *Suggestion:* Substitute $u = -t$ in the left-hand integral.

Section 9.4

1. $x_{\text{sp}}(t) = \dfrac{12}{\pi}\displaystyle\sum_{n\text{ odd}}\dfrac{\sin nt}{n(5 - n^2)} =$
$$\frac{12}{\pi}\left(\frac{\sin t}{4} - \frac{\sin 3t}{12} - \frac{\sin 5t}{100} - \frac{\sin 7t}{308} - \cdots\right).$$

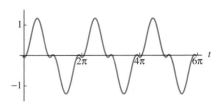

2. $x_{\text{sp}}(t) = \dfrac{48}{\pi}\displaystyle\sum_{n\text{ odd}}\dfrac{(-1)^{(n-1)/2}}{n(40 - \pi^2 n^2)}\cos\dfrac{n\pi t}{2}.$

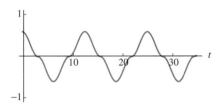

3. $x_{\text{sp}}(t) = 4\displaystyle\sum_{n=1}^{\infty}\dfrac{(-1)^{n-1}\sin nt}{n(3 - n^2)} =$
$$4\left(\frac{\sin t}{2} + \frac{\sin 2t}{2} - \frac{\sin 3t}{18} + \frac{\sin 4t}{52} - \cdots\right).$$

4. $x_{\text{sp}} = \dfrac{1}{2} - \dfrac{64}{\pi^2}\displaystyle\sum_{n\text{ odd}}\dfrac{\cos n\pi t/2}{\pi^2 n^2(16 - \pi^2 n^2)}.$

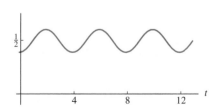

5. $x_{\text{sp}}(t) = \dfrac{8}{\pi^3}\displaystyle\sum_{n\text{ odd}}\dfrac{\sin n\pi t}{n^3(10 - n^2\pi^2)}$

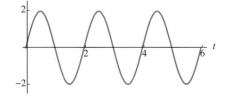

6. $x_{sp} = \dfrac{4}{\pi} - \dfrac{4}{\pi} \displaystyle\sum_{n \text{ even}} \dfrac{\cos nt}{(n^2 - 1)(n^2 - 2)}$

$= \dfrac{4}{\pi} \left(1 - \dfrac{\cos 2t}{6} - \dfrac{\cos 4t}{210} - \dfrac{\cos 6t}{1190} - \cdots \right).$

7. The Fourier series $F(t) = \dfrac{4}{\pi} \displaystyle\sum_{n \text{ odd}} \dfrac{\sin nt}{n}$ contains a sin 3t term, so resonance does occur.

8. No resonance occurs.

9. The Fourier series $F(t) = \dfrac{4}{\pi} \displaystyle\sum_{n \text{ odd}} \dfrac{\sin nt}{n}$ contains no sin 2t term, so no resonance occurs.

10. Resonance does occur.

11. The Fourier series $F(t) = \dfrac{\pi}{2} - \dfrac{4}{\pi} \displaystyle\sum_{n \text{ odd}} \dfrac{\cos nt}{n^2}$ contains no cos 4t term, so no resonance occurs.

12. Resonance does occur.

13. $x_{sp}(t) \approx (1.2725) \sin(t - 0.0333) + (0.2542) \sin(3t - 3.0817) + (0.0364) \sin(5t - 3.1178) + \cdots$

14. $x_{sp}(t) \approx (0.2500) \sin(t - 0.0063) - (0.2000) \sin(2t - 0.0200) + (4.444) \sin(3t - 1.5708) - (0.0714) \sin(4t - 3.1130) + \cdots$

15. $x_{sp}(t) \approx (0.08150) \sin(\pi t - 1.44692) + (0.00004) \sin(3\pi t - 3.10176) + \cdots$

16. $x_{sp}(t) \approx 0.5000 + 1.0577 \cos(\pi t/2 - 0.0103) - 0.0099 \cos(3\pi t/2 - 3.1390) - 0.0011 \cos(5\pi t/2 - 3.1402) \cdots$

17. (a) $x_{sp}(t) \approx (0.5687) \sin(\pi t - 0.0562) + (0.4721) \sin(3\pi t - 0.3891) + (0.01396) \sin(5\pi t - 2.7899) + (0.0318) \sin(7\pi t - 2.9874) + \cdots$

18. $x_{sp}(t) \approx 0.0531 \sin(t - 0.0004) - 0.0088 \sin(3t - 0.0019) + 1.0186 \sin(5t - 1.5708) - 0.0011 \sin(7t - 3.1387) + \cdots$

Section 9.5

1. $u(x, t) = 4e^{-12t} \sin 2x$

2. $u(x, t) \equiv 7$

3. $u(x, y) = 5 \exp(-2\pi^2 t) \sin \pi x - \frac{1}{5} \exp(-18\pi^2 t) \sin 3\pi x$

4. $u(x, t) = 2e^{-4t} \sin 2x + 2e^{-36t} \sin 6x$

5. $u(x, t) = 4 \exp\left(-\dfrac{8\pi^2 t}{9}\right) \cos\left(\dfrac{2\pi x}{3}\right) - 2 \exp\left(-\dfrac{32\pi^2 t}{9}\right) \cos\left(\dfrac{4\pi x}{3}\right)$

6. $u(x, t) = \exp(-2\pi^2 t) \sin 2\pi x + \frac{1}{2} \exp(-8\pi^2 t) \sin 4\pi x$

7. $u(x, t) = \dfrac{1}{2} + \dfrac{1}{2} \exp\left(-\dfrac{16\pi^2 t}{3}\right) \cos 4\pi x$

8. $u(x, t) = 5 \exp(-4\pi^2 t) \cos 2\pi x + 5 \exp(-16\pi^2 t) \cos 4\pi x$

9. $u(x, t) = \dfrac{100}{\pi} \displaystyle\sum_{n \text{ odd}} \dfrac{1}{n} \exp\left(-\dfrac{n^2\pi^2 t}{250}\right) \sin \dfrac{n\pi x}{5}$

10. $u(x, t) = \dfrac{80}{\pi} \displaystyle\sum_{n=1}^{\infty} \dfrac{(-1)^{n+1}}{n} \exp\left(-\dfrac{n^2\pi^2 t}{500}\right) \sin \dfrac{n\pi x}{10}$

11. $u(x, t) = 20 - \dfrac{160}{\pi^2} \displaystyle\sum_{n \text{ odd}} \dfrac{1}{n^2} \exp\left(-\dfrac{n^2\pi^2 t}{500}\right) \cos \dfrac{n\pi x}{10}$

12. $u(x, t) = \dfrac{80000}{\pi^3} \displaystyle\sum_{n \text{ odd}} \dfrac{1}{n^3} \exp\left(-\dfrac{n^2\pi^2 t}{10000}\right) \sin \dfrac{n\pi x}{100}$

13. (a) $u(x, t) = \dfrac{400}{\pi} \displaystyle\sum_{n \text{ odd}} \dfrac{1}{n} \exp\left(-\dfrac{n^2\pi^2 kt}{1600}\right) \sin \dfrac{n\pi x}{40}$;

(b) with $k = 1.15$, $u(20, 300) \approx 15.16°C$;

(c) about 19 h 16 min

14. (b) $u(10, 60) \approx 25.15°C$; (c) 6 min 54.3 s

16. (b) 15 h

Section 9.6

1. $y(x, t) = \frac{1}{10} \cos 4t \sin 2x$

2. $y(x, t) = \frac{1}{10} \cos \pi t \sin \pi x - \frac{1}{20} \cos 3\pi t \sin 3\pi x$

3. $y(x, t) = \dfrac{1}{10} \left(\cos \dfrac{t}{2} + 2 \sin \dfrac{t}{2} \right) \sin x$

4. $y(x, y) = \frac{1}{10} \cos \pi t \sin 2\pi x$

5. $y(x, t) = \dfrac{1}{4} \cos 5\pi t \sin \pi x + \dfrac{1}{\pi} \sin 10\pi t \sin 2\pi x$

6. $y(x, t) = \displaystyle\sum_{n \text{ odd}} \dfrac{8}{\pi n^3} \cos 10nt \sin nx$

7. $y(x, t) = \displaystyle\sum_{n=1}^{\infty} \dfrac{(-1)^{n+1}}{5\pi^2 n^2} \sin 10n\pi t \sin n\pi x$

8. $y(x, t) = \cos 2t \sin x + \dfrac{4}{\pi} \displaystyle\sum_{n \text{ odd}} \dfrac{\sin 2nt \sin nx}{n}$.

9. $y(x, t) = \dfrac{4}{\pi^4} \displaystyle\sum_{n \text{ odd}} \dfrac{\sin 2n\pi t \sin n\pi x}{n^4}$.

10. $y(x, t) = \dfrac{8}{5\pi} \displaystyle\sum_{n \text{ odd}} \dfrac{(5n \cos 5nt + \sin 5nt)}{n^2(4 - n^2)}$.

11. Fundamental frequency: 256 Hz; velocity: 1024 ft/s

Section 9.7

1. $u(x, y) = \displaystyle\sum_{n=1}^{\infty} c_n \sinh \dfrac{n\pi x}{b} \sin \dfrac{n\pi y}{b}$ where

$c_n = \dfrac{2}{b \sinh(n\pi a/b)} \displaystyle\int_0^b g(y) \sin \dfrac{n\pi y}{b} \, dy$

2. $u(x, y) = \displaystyle\sum_{n=1}^{\infty} c_n \sinh \dfrac{n\pi(a - x)}{b} \sin \dfrac{n\pi y}{b}$ where

$c_n = \dfrac{2}{b \sinh(n\pi a/b)} \displaystyle\int_0^b g(y) \sin \dfrac{n\pi y}{b} \, dy$

3. $u(x, y) = \displaystyle\sum_{n=1}^{\infty} c_n \sin \dfrac{n\pi x}{a} \sinh \dfrac{n\pi y}{a}$ where

$c_n = \dfrac{2}{a \sinh(n\pi b/a)} \displaystyle\int_0^a f(x) \sin \dfrac{n\pi x}{a} \, dx$

4. $u(x, y) = b_0 y + \displaystyle\sum_{n=1}^{\infty} b_n \cos \dfrac{n\pi x}{a} \sinh \dfrac{n\pi y}{a}$ where $b_0 = a_0/2b$,

$b_n = a_n/(\sinh n\pi b/a)$ and $\{a_n\}_0^\infty$ are the Fourier cosine coefficients of $f(x)$ on the interval $0 \leq x \leq a$.

5. $u(x, y) = \dfrac{a_0}{2a}(a - x) + \displaystyle\sum_{n=1}^{\infty} a_n \dfrac{\sinh(n\pi[a - x]/b)}{\sinh(n\pi a/b)} \cos \dfrac{n\pi y}{b}$,

where $a_n = \dfrac{2}{b} \displaystyle\int_0^b g(y) \cos \dfrac{n\pi y}{b} \, dy$

6. $u(x, y) = A_0 + \displaystyle\sum_{n=1}^{\infty} A_n \cos \dfrac{n\pi x}{a} \cosh \dfrac{n\pi y}{a}$ where $A_0 = a_0/2$,

$A_n = a_n/(\cosh n\pi b/a)$ and $\{a_n\}_0^\infty$ are the Fourier cosine coefficients of $f(x)$ on the interval $0 \leq x \leq a$.

7. $u(x, y) = \sum_{n=1}^{\infty} b_n \exp\left(-\dfrac{n\pi y}{a}\right) \sin \dfrac{n\pi x}{a}$

where $b_n = \dfrac{2}{a} \displaystyle\int_0^a f(x) \sin \dfrac{n\pi x}{a}\, dx$

8. $u(x, y) = \dfrac{a_0}{2} + \sum_{n=1}^{\infty} a_n e^{-n\pi y/a} \cos \dfrac{n\pi x}{a}$ where $\{a_n\}_0^{\infty}$ are the

Fourier cosine coefficients of $f(x)$ on the interval $0 \le x \le a$.

9. $u(0, 5) \approx 41.53$; $u(5, 5) = 50$; $u(10, 5) \approx 58.47$

11. $u(x, y) = \sum_{n\,odd} c_n \sinh \dfrac{n\pi(a - x)}{2b} \cos \dfrac{n\pi y}{2b}$ where

$c_n = \dfrac{2}{b \sinh(n\pi a/(2b))} \displaystyle\int_0^b g(y) \cos \dfrac{n\pi y}{2b}\, dy$

13. $c_n = \dfrac{2}{\pi a^n} \displaystyle\int_0^{\pi} f(\theta) \sin n\theta\, d\theta$

14. $c_n = \dfrac{2}{\pi a^n} \displaystyle\int_0^{\pi} f(\theta) \cos n\theta\, d\theta$

15. $c_n = \dfrac{2}{\pi a^{n/2}} \displaystyle\int_0^{\pi} f(\theta) \sin \dfrac{n\theta}{2}\, d\theta$

Chapter 10

Section 10.1

7. $1 = 2hL \sum_{n=1}^{\infty} \dfrac{1 - \cos \beta_n}{\beta_n(hL + \cos^2 \beta_n)} \sin \dfrac{\beta_n}{L}, \; 0 < x < L$

8. $1 = \sum_{n=1}^{\infty} \dfrac{4 \sin \beta_n}{2\beta_n + \sin 2\beta_n} \cos \dfrac{\beta_n x}{L}, 0 < x < L$

9. $x = 2h(1 + h) \sum_{n=1}^{\infty} \dfrac{\sin \beta_n \sin \beta_n x}{\beta_n^2(h + \cos^2 \beta_n)}, 0 < x < 1$

10. $x = \sum_{n=1}^{\infty} \dfrac{4(\beta_n \sin \beta_n + \cos \beta_n - 1)}{\beta_n(2\beta_n + \sin 2\beta_n)} \cos \beta_n x, 0 < x < 1$

Section 10.2

2. $u(x, y) = \sum_{n=1}^{\infty} c_n \sin \dfrac{\beta_n x}{L} \sinh \dfrac{\beta_n(L - y)}{L}$, where $\{\beta_n\}_1^{\infty}$ are the

positive roots of the equation $\tan x = -x/hL$, and

$c_n = \dfrac{4\beta_n}{L(\sinh \beta_n)(2\beta_n - \sin 2\beta_n)} \displaystyle\int_0^L f(x) \cos \dfrac{\beta_n x}{L}\, dx$.

3. $u(x, y) = \sum_{n=1}^{\infty} c_n \sinh \dfrac{\beta_n(L - x)}{L} \cos \dfrac{\beta_n y}{L}$, where $\{\beta_n\}_1^{\infty}$ are the

positive roots of the equation $\tan x = x/hL$, and

$c_n = \dfrac{2h}{(\sinh \beta_n)(hL + \sin^2 \beta_n)} \displaystyle\int_0^L g(y) \cos \dfrac{\beta_n y}{L}\, dy$.

4. $u(x, y) = \sum_{n=1}^{\infty} c_n \sin \dfrac{\beta_n x}{L} \exp\left(-\dfrac{\beta_n y}{L}\right)$, where $\{\beta_n\}_1^{\infty}$ are the

positive roots of the equation $\tan x = -x/hL$, and

$c_n = \dfrac{4\beta_n}{L(2\beta_n - \sin 2\beta_n)} \displaystyle\int_0^L f(x) \cos \dfrac{\beta_n x}{L}\, dx$.

5. $u(x, t) = \sum_{n=1}^{\infty} c_n \exp\left(-\dfrac{\beta_n^2 kt}{L^2}\right) X_n(x)$, where

$X_n(x) = \beta_n \cos \dfrac{\beta_n x}{L} + hL \sin \dfrac{\beta_n x}{L}$, $\{\beta_n\}_1^{\infty}$ are the positive roots

of the equation $\tan x = -x/hL$, and

$c_n = \left(\displaystyle\int_0^L f(x)X_n(x)\, dx\right) \bigg/ \displaystyle\int_0^L X_n(x)^2\, dx$.

6. $u(x, t) = \sum_{n=1}^{\infty} c_n \exp\left(-\dfrac{\beta_n^2 kt}{L^2}\right) X_n(x)$, where

$X_n(x) = \beta_n \cos \dfrac{\beta_n x}{L} + hL \sin \dfrac{\beta_n x}{L}$, $\{\beta_n\}_1^{\infty}$ are the positive roots

of the equation $\tan x = 2hLx/(x^2 - h^2 L^2)$, and

$c_n = \left(\displaystyle\int_0^L f(x)X_n(x)\, dx\right) \bigg/ \displaystyle\int_0^L X_n(x)^2\, dx$.

7. $u(1, 1) \approx 30.8755 + 0.4737 + 0.0074 + 0.0002 + 0.0000 + \cdots$
$\approx 31.4°$

10. (a) $a \approx 5.08 \times 10^5$ cm/sec ≈ 11364 mph.
(b) $a \approx 1.50 \times 10^5$ cm/sec ≈ 3355 mph.

15. $\displaystyle\int_0^L \sin \dfrac{\beta_m x}{L} \sin \dfrac{\beta_n x}{L}\, dx = -\dfrac{LM \cos \beta_m \cos \beta_n}{m\beta_m \beta_n} \ne 0$

20. (b) $\omega_1 \approx 1578$ rad/sec ≈ 251 cycles/sec. Thus we hear middle C (approximately).

Section 10.3

In Problems 1–6, ω_n denotes the nth natural frequency of vibration.

1. $\omega_n = \dfrac{n\pi}{L} \sqrt{\dfrac{E}{\delta}}$

2. $\omega_n = \dfrac{n\pi}{L} \sqrt{\dfrac{E}{\delta}}$

3. $\omega_n = \dfrac{(2n - 1)\pi}{2L} \sqrt{\dfrac{E}{\delta}}$

4. $\omega_n = \dfrac{\beta_n}{L} \sqrt{\dfrac{E}{\delta}}$, where β_n is the nth positive root of the equation

$\tan x = \dfrac{M/m}{x}$.

5. $\omega_n = \dfrac{\beta_n}{L} \sqrt{\dfrac{E}{\delta}}$, where β_n is the nth positive root of the equation

$AE\beta \tan \beta = kL$.

6. $\omega_n = \dfrac{\beta_n}{L} \sqrt{\dfrac{E}{\delta}}$, where β_n is the nth positive root of the equation

$(m_0 m_1 z^2 - M^2) \sin z = M(m_0 + m_1)z \cos z$.

15. 1.03 Hz

Section 10.4

3. (a) $u(r, t) = \sum_{n=1}^{\infty} c_n J_0\left(\dfrac{\gamma_n r}{c}\right) \sin \dfrac{\gamma_n at}{c}$ where

$c_n = \dfrac{2a P_0}{\pi c\rho a^2 \gamma_n J_1(\gamma_n)^2} \cdot \dfrac{J_1(\gamma_n \epsilon/c)}{\gamma_n \epsilon/c}$.

(b) How do you know that $J_1(x)/x \to 1/2$ as $x \to 0$?

4. (a) $u(r, t) = \sum_{n=1}^{\infty} c_n \exp\left(-\dfrac{\gamma_n^2 kt}{c^2}\right) J_0\left(\dfrac{\gamma_n r}{c}\right)$ where

$c_n = \dfrac{2q_0}{s\pi c^2 J_1(\gamma_n)^2} \cdot \dfrac{J_1(\gamma_n \epsilon/c)}{\gamma_n \epsilon/c}$.

11. $u(r, t) = \dfrac{F_0}{\omega^2 J_0(\omega b/a)}\left[J_0\left(\dfrac{\omega r}{a}\right) - J_0\left(\dfrac{\omega b}{a}\right)\right] \sin \omega t$, where b

is the radius of the circular membrane.

Appendix

1. $y_0 = 3$, $y_1 = 3 + 3x$, $y_2 = 3 + 3x + \frac{3}{2}x^2$,
$y_3 = 3 + 3x + \frac{3}{2}x^2 + \frac{1}{2}x^3$,
$y_4 = 3 + 3x + \frac{3}{2}x^2 + \frac{1}{2}x^3 + \frac{1}{8}x^4$; $y(x) = 3e^x$

3. $y_0 = 1$, $y_1 = 1 - x^2$, $y_2 = 1 - x^2 + \frac{1}{2}x^4$,
$y_3 = 1 - x^2 + \frac{1}{2}x^4 - \frac{1}{6}x^6$,
$y_4 = 1 - x^2 + \frac{1}{2}x^4 - \frac{1}{6}x^6 + \frac{1}{24}x^8$; $y(x) = \exp\left(-x^2\right)$

5. $y_0 = 0$, $y_1 = 2x$, $y_2 = 2x + 2x^2$,
$y_3 = 2x + 2x^2 + \frac{4}{3}x^3$,
$y_4 = 2x + 2x^2 + \frac{4}{3}x^3 + \frac{2}{3}x^4$; $y(x) = e^{2x} - 1$

7. $y_0 = 0$, $y_1 = x^2$, $y_2 = x^2 + \frac{1}{2}x^4$, $y_3 = x^2 + \frac{1}{2}x^4 + \frac{1}{6}x^6$,
$y_4 = x^2 + \frac{1}{2}x^4 + \frac{1}{6}x^6 + \frac{1}{24}x^8$; $y(x) = \exp(x^2) - 1$

9. $y_0 = 1$, $y_1 = (1+x) + \frac{1}{2}x^2$, $y_2 = (1+x+x^2) + \frac{1}{6}x^3$,
$y_3 = \left(1 + x + x^2 + \frac{1}{3}x^3\right) + \frac{1}{24}x^4$;
$y(x) = 2e^x - 1 - x = 1 + x + x^2 + \frac{1}{3}x^3 + \cdots$

11. $y_0 = 1$, $y_1 = 1 + x$, $y_2 = (1 + x + x^2) + \frac{1}{3}x^3$,
$y_3 = (1 + x + x^2 + x^3) + \frac{2}{3}x^4 + \frac{1}{3}x^5 + \frac{1}{9}x^6 + \frac{1}{63}x^7$;
$y(x) = \dfrac{1}{1-x} = 1 + x + x^2 + x^3 + x^4 + x^5 + \cdots$

12. $y_0 = 1$, $y_1 = 1 + \frac{1}{2}x$, $y_2 = 1 + \frac{1}{2}x + \frac{3}{8}x^3 + \frac{1}{8}x^3 + \frac{1}{64}x^4$,

$y_3 = 1 + \frac{1}{2}x + \frac{3}{8}x^2 + \frac{5}{16}x^3 + \frac{13}{64}x^4 + \cdots$; $y(x) = (1-x)^{-1/2}$

13. $\begin{bmatrix} x_0 \\ y_0 \end{bmatrix} = \begin{bmatrix} 1 \\ -1 \end{bmatrix}$, $\begin{bmatrix} x_1 \\ y_1 \end{bmatrix} = \begin{bmatrix} 1 + 3t \\ -1 + 3t \end{bmatrix}$,

$\begin{bmatrix} x_2 \\ y_2 \end{bmatrix} = \begin{bmatrix} 1 + 3t + \frac{1}{2}t^2 \\ -1 + 5t - \frac{1}{2}t^2 \end{bmatrix}$,

$\begin{bmatrix} x_3 \\ y_3 \end{bmatrix} = \begin{bmatrix} 1 + 3t + \frac{1}{2}t^2 + \frac{1}{3}t^3 \\ -1 + 5t - \frac{1}{2}t^2 + \frac{5}{6}t^3 \end{bmatrix}$

14. $\mathbf{x}(t) = \begin{bmatrix} e^t + te^t \\ e^t \end{bmatrix}$ **16.** $y_3(1) \approx 0.350185$

INDEX

Boldface page numbers indicate where terms are defined.

Table of Integrals (cont.)

30. $\displaystyle \int \cos au \, \cos bu \, du = \frac{\sin(a-b)u}{2(a-b)} + \frac{\sin(a+b)u}{2(a+b)} + C \quad \text{if } a^2 \neq b^2$

31. $\displaystyle \int \sin au \, \cos bu \, du = -\frac{\cos(a-b)u}{2(a-b)} - \frac{\cos(a+b)u}{2(a+b)} + C \quad \text{if } a^2 \neq b^2$

32. $\displaystyle \int \sin^n u \, du = -\frac{1}{n} \sin^{n-1} u \, \cos u + \frac{n-1}{n} \int \sin^{n-2} u \, du$

33. $\displaystyle \int \cos^n u \, du = \frac{1}{n} \cos^{n-1} u \, \sin u + \frac{n-1}{n} \int \cos^{n-2} u \, du$

34. $\displaystyle \int \tan^n u \, du = \frac{1}{n-1} \tan^{n-1} u - \int \tan^{n-2} u \, du \quad \text{if } n \neq 1$

35. $\displaystyle \int \cot^n u \, du = -\frac{1}{n-1} \cot^{n-1} u - \int \cot^{n-2} u \, du \quad \text{if } n \neq 1$

36. $\displaystyle \int \sec^n u \, du = \frac{1}{n-1} \sec^{n-2} u \, \tan u + \frac{n-2}{n-1} \int \sec^{n-2} u \, du \quad \text{if } n \neq 1$

37. $\displaystyle \int \csc^n u \, du = -\frac{1}{n-1} \csc^{n-2} u \, \cot u + \frac{n-2}{n-1} \int \csc^{n-2} u \, du \quad \text{if } n \neq 1$

38. $\displaystyle \int u \sin u \, du = \sin u - u \cos u + C$

39. $\displaystyle \int u \cos u \, du = \cos u + u \sin u + C$

40. $\displaystyle \int u^n \sin u \, du = -u^n \cos u + n \int u^{n-1} \cos u \, du$

41. $\displaystyle \int u^n \cos u \, du = u^n \sin u - n \int u^{n-1} \sin u \, du$

FORMS INVOLVING $\sqrt{u^2 \pm a^2}$

42. $\displaystyle \int \sqrt{u^2 \pm a^2} \, du = \frac{u}{2} \sqrt{u^2 \pm a^2} \pm \frac{a^2}{2} \ln \left| u + \sqrt{u^2 \pm a^2} \right| + C$

43. $\displaystyle \int \frac{du}{\sqrt{u^2 \pm a^2}} = \ln \left| u + \sqrt{u^2 \pm a^2} \right| + C$

FORMS INVOLVING $\sqrt{a^2 - u^2}$

$\displaystyle = \frac{u}{2} \sqrt{a^2 - u^2} + \frac{a^2}{2} \sin^{-1} \frac{u}{a} + C$

$\displaystyle = \sqrt{a^2 - u^2} - a \ln \left| \frac{a + \sqrt{a^2 - u^2}}{u} \right| + C$